THE
BIG
BOOK
OF
ANSWERS

"We kill for the
idea of each other,
+ ideas are dangerous
Things to love" Atticus

REVISED AND UPDATED

THE
BIG
BOOK
— OF —
ANSWERS

EDITED BY KEVIN S. HILE

VISIBLE
INK
PRESS

Detroit

THE
BIG BOOK
OF
ANSWERS

Copyright © 2017 by Visible Ink Press. Portions previously published in *The Handy Anatomy Answer Book*, *The Handy Art History Answer Book*, *The Handy Astronomy Answer Book*, *The Handy Biology Answer Book*, *The Handy California Answer Book*, *The Handy Geography Answer Book*, *The Handy History Answer Book*, *The Handy Islam Answer Book*, *The Handy Physics Answer Book*, *The Handy Technology Answer Book*; and *The Handy Science Answer Book*, 4th edition, copyright © 2011 by The Carnegie Library of Pittsburgh.

This publication is a creative work fully protected by all applicable copyright laws, as well as by misappropriation, trade secret, unfair competition, and other applicable laws.

No part of this book may be reproduced in any form without permission in writing from the publisher, except by a reviewer who wishes to quote brief passages in connection with a review written for inclusion in a magazine, newspaper, or website.

All rights to this publication will be vigorously defended.

Visible Ink Press®
43311 Joy Rd., #414
Canton, MI 48187–2075

Visible Ink Press is a registered trademark of Visible Ink Press LLC.

Most Visible Ink Press books are available at special quantity discounts when purchased in bulk by corporations, organizations, or groups. Customized printings, special imprints, messages, and excerpts can be produced to meet your needs. For more information, contact Special Markets Director, Visible Ink Press, www.visibleink.com or 734–667–3211.

Managing Editor: Kevin S. Hile
Page design: Mary Claire Krzewinsk
Jacket art © Andy McClelland
Jacket design: Igor Satanovsky
Typesetting: Marco DiVita
Indexer: Larry Baker

Printed in the United States of America

10 9 8 7 6 5 4 3 2 1

Contents

Photo Sources

Bruce Blaus (Wikicommons): p. 613 (top).

Electronic Illustrators Group: pp. 375, 523.

Mikhail Evstafiev: p. 159.

Henry McRae Prod./Universal Pictures: p. 274.

Michael Hicks: p. 355.

Library of Congress: pp. 73, 127, 250, 266, 280.

NASA: pp. 408, 423, 435, 483, 485.

NASA, ESA, CFHT, CXO, M.J. Jee (University of California, Davis), and A. Mahdavi (San Francisco State University): p. 400.

NASA/JPL-Caltech/A. Kashlinsky: p. 399.

NASA/JPL-Caltech/Space Science Institute: p. 418.

NASA/JPL-Caltech/T. Pyle: p. 410.

NASA/WMAP Science Team: p. 398.

National Archives and Records Administration: pp. 50, 62, 95, 192, 460.

New York World-Telegram and the Sun: p. 91.

Nova: p. 543.

OpenStax College: p. 65.

Revista Argentina: p. 139.

Runner1616 (Wikicommons): p. 347.

San Francisco State University: p. 400.

Shutterstock: pp. 4, 7, 10, 14, 26, 36, 38, 42, 46, 53, 68, 70, 83, 101, 105, 114, 118, 123, 164, 168, 174, 185, 187, 190, 196, 199, 208, 210, 212, 217, 224, 248, 255, 259, 268, 271, 278, 281, 283, 284, 285, 314, 316, 343 (top), 346, 348, 349, 353, 359, 370, 377, 383, 406, 413, 416, 417, 419, 420, 430, 450, 452, 453, 456, 457, 459, 482, 488, 492, 493, 495, 512, 518, 521, 544, 548, 551, 552, 579, 582, 589, 591, 594, 601, 603, 604, 607, 609, 611, 612, 613 (bottom), 615, 616, 617, 618, 624, 625, 627, 628, 630, 635, 636, 639, 641, 644, 646, 671, 673, 674, 675, 677.

Smithsonian Institution: pp. 87, 343 (bottom).

U.S. government and other public domain sources: pp. 18, 57, 66, 80, 113, 132, 142, 149, 156, 206, 207, 213, 227, 230, 232, 244, 245, 257, 263, 292, 293, 296, 298, 301, 303, 314, 315, 318, 319, 340, 342, 372, 379, 382, 386, 388, 432, 433, 440, 442, 498, 503, 517, 524, 525, 528, 536, 539, 546, 563, 642.

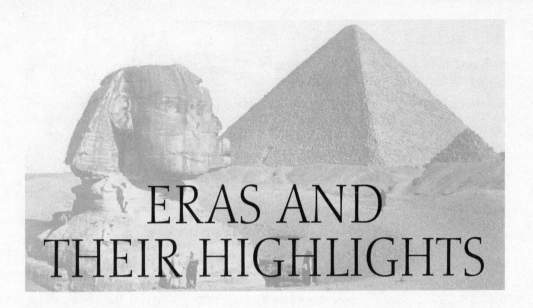

ERAS AND THEIR HIGHLIGHTS

When did history begin?

History began when human beings were able to document events in writing; anything prior to the advent of writing is commonly referred to as prehistoric. Humans began to write approximately 3,500 years before Christ, and the Classical Age, which began with the rise of Greek civilization around 2000 B.C.E.

What is the Prehistoric era?

The term Prehistoric era refers to the time before written history began, so it encompasses the Stone Age, the Bronze Age, and the Iron Age. The Prehistoric era spans the time from about 2,000,000 B.C.E. to roughly 2000 B.C.E., when the Classical Age began with the rise of the Greek and Roman empires.

What is the Paleolithic Age?

Paleolithic literally means "Old Stone Age." Coined by archeologist John Lubbock (1834–1913) in 1865, it refers to the vast time period when humans used stone tools. It precedes the Mesolithic and Neolithic Ages. All three of these time periods—Paleolithic, Mesolithic, and Neolithic—are considered part of the Stone Age.

Who came up with the system of classifying older human history into the three ages?

Danish archeologist Christian Jürgensen Thomson (1788–1865) receives credit for categorizing early world history into three ages based on the principal tools used by humans. These three periods are the Stone Age, the Bronze Age, and the Iron Age.

When did humankind first walk on the face of Earth?

For decades after the discovery of "Lucy" (in the 1970s), it was thought that humankind first walked the Earth about three million years ago. But fossil finds in the mid-1990s pushed the evolutionary starting-point for humans to more than four million years ago. Further astonishing finds in the early 2000s led researchers to conclude that human ancestors first walked the Earth nearly six million years ago.

In November 1974, American Donald C. Johanson (1943–) made one of paleoanthropology's most widely publicized finds when he discovered a partial skeleton at Hadar, Ethiopia. More than three million years old, the female skeleton was the most complete hominid fossil ever found, but the skull was not recovered. The creature stood three and a half feet tall and, although apelike, had definitely walked upright. When Johanson officially announced his find in 1979, "Lucy" (named for the Beatles song "Lucy in the Sky with Diamonds," which was popular in the camp at the time the fossil was found) became known as the mother of all humankind. (Her sex was confirmed by the pelvic bones.) Since she was an erect-walker, the finding gave certainty to theories that hominids walked erect at three million years B.C.E.

After the discovery of Lucy, older hominid fossils were unearthed by researchers in the field. In 1994 anthropologist Meave Leakey (1942–) and her associates found fossils of a 4.1-million-year-old bipedal species near Lake Turkana, Kenya. These were designated Australopithecus anamensis. Fossils discovered between 1997 and 2001 in the Middle Awash region of Ethiopia were determined to be nearly six million years old. In 2001 Yohannes Haile-Selassie (Cleveland Museum) and coauthors Tim White and Gen Suwa (University of Tokyo Museum) reported the monumental findings in the journal *Nature*: The hominid, named *Ardipithecus kadabba*, was thought to "represent the first species on the human branch of the family tree just after the evolutionary split [from chimpanzees]."

What is the Stone Age?

What people commonly refer to as the Stone Age is actually two ages: The Old Stone Age (about 2,000,000 B.C.E. to about 10,000 B.C.E.) and the New Stone Age (c. 10,000 to c. 3300 B.C.E.). It was during these periods that humans used stone tools.

During the Old Stone Age, man was evolving from his apelike ancestors into modern-looking hunter-gatherers. Early modern man's progress continued to the end of the Old Stone Age, around 10,000 B.C.E. Then, as the Earth warmed, the hunter-gatherers again revolutionized their way of life. They opted for a more settled existence in which they could exercise greater control over their food supplies. With the coming of the New Stone Age, or Neolithic Age, humans turned to agriculture.

The New Stone Age brought profound changes in the development of humans. Neolithic man learned to produce food rather than collect it. People were no longer dependent on hunting, fishing, and gathering wild fruit and nuts for subsistence. They learned to cultivate crops, domesticate animals, make pottery, weave textiles from fiber and hair, and produce more sophisticated tools and weapons by hammering, grinding, and polishing granite, jasper, and other hard stone. More substantial houses and communities, even fortified villages, came into being, laying the foundation for the great civilizations that would follow.

Near the end of the New Stone Age, craftsmen in the Middle East learned to make tools and weapons from metal. The world's earliest known manmade copper objects—beads, pins, and awls—were fabricated in Turkey and Iran around 8000 B.C.E. Archeological evidence points to copper mining in the Balkans around 5000 B.C.E. From there the technology probably spread west, reaching the Alps about a thousand years later and marking the beginning of the Copper Age (c. 4000 to 2200 B.C.E.).

What is the Bronze Age?

The Bronze Age (c. 3300 to 2500 B.C.E.) is the period of human culture when man began using bronze metal to make objects—principally, tools. The Neolithic Age slowly came to an end as various cultures in Eurasia that had depended on wood, stone, and bone for tools began to develop the techniques for metallurgy. Bronze proved to be an excellent material for making tools and weapons. People in the Middle East learned to produce bronze by mixing tin and copper (hence, the transition years between the Neolithic Age and the Bronze Age are sometimes referred to as the Copper Age). Bronze had considerable hardness, strength, and density, and it proved more reliable and durable than the stone, wood, and bone tools that had been in use. The Bronze Age lasted until the beginning of the Iron Age.

When did the Iron Age begin?

The real advent of the Iron Age came not with the discovery of metal (in about 2500 B.C.E.), but with the invention of the process of casing or steeling it, probably about 1500 B.C.E. This happened when it was learned that by repeatedly reheating wrought iron in a charcoal fire and then hammering it, it not only became harder than bronze but kept its hardness after long use. (Wrought iron was discovered accidentally when smiths found that by hammering the small beadlike pieces of iron left as a residue after smelting copper they could form the iron particles into a mass. This kind of wrought iron, however, was good only for decorative purposes, and for more than a thousand years after 2500 B.C.E., iron remained a precious ornamental metal. Bronze, which was harder and capable of being sharpened to a fine cutting edge, continued to be the metal for tools and weapons.)

The next technological improvement, which again meant a further hardening of the metal, was the process of quenching it, which involved repeatedly plunging the hot iron into cold water. It was only after this series of discoveries and inventions that the significant impact of iron on culture and civilization was appreciably felt.

Because bronze was scarce, it was also costly. Consequently, it was not until iron came into use that humans extended their control over nature. For this reason, iron has been called the "democratic metal." Widespread use of iron tools meant a general increase in living standards. For example, the use of iron axes brought about the clearing of forests, and therefore new land came under cultivation. Other significant developments included the application of iron tools to sheep shearing and cloth cutting, and the invention of the lathe, the most fundamental machine tool.

The Iron Age lasted until the beginning of the Classical Age (c. 2000 B.C.E.).

What were the hallmarks of ancient Egypt?

One of the world's oldest civilizations, ancient Egypt developed about 3000 B.C.E., or 5,000 years ago, in the Nile River valley; it lasted until 332 B.C.E., when it was conquered by Alexander the Great (356–323 B.C.E.). In that time, Egypt was ruled by thirty dynasties. Most of those dynasties fall into three kingdoms: Old Kingdom (during the third millennium B.C.E.), Middle Kingdom (early second millennium B.C.E.), and New Kingdom (mid-second millennium B.C.E.); the kingdoms were followed by intermediate periods, which were times of weakened government or foreign domination.

The First Dynasty was founded by Menes in 3110 B.C.E., after he united the rival kingdoms of Upper and Lower Egypt under his rule and established the capital at Memphis (the present-day village of Mit Rahina, fourteen miles south of Cairo, in northern Egypt). During the Old Kingdom commerce prospered and the arts flourished, as evidenced by the Great Pyramids at Giza (including the Great Sphinx), which were begun during the Fourth Dynasty (c. 2500 B.C.E.). The Old Kingdom was followed by a 258-year (intermediate) period of weak rulers and anarchy, which was ended when Amenemhet I rose to power in 1991 B.C.E., reunifying Egypt and beginning the Middle Kingdom. During the Middle Kingdom, Egypt launched imperialistic campaigns, expanding its territory and conquering Palestine and Syria in the east. About 1720 B.C.E., Semitic nomads entered Egypt and wrested power from the pharaohs, establishing the fifteenth through the seventeenth dynasties—a peaceful and prosperous period. But the Egyptians expelled this foreign influence (c. 1570 B.C.E.) to establish the New Kingdom: the 200 years that followed were the height of Egyptian civilization, with the cities of Thebes and Memphis regarded as the political, commercial, and cultural centers of the known world.

Ancient Egyptians invented a calendar, created a form of hieroglyphic writing, and developed papyrus (paper made from the papyrus plant). Situated along the Nile and south of the Mediterranean Sea, Egyptians also produced early seagoing vessels. But it is their buildings for which this ancient group is renowned: In addition to the Great Pyramids at Giza, the impressive relics that have been discovered include those at Abu Simbel, where King Ramses II (1303–1213 B.C.E.) had two temples built out of rock during his reign (c. 1279–1213 B.C.E.); numerous ruins and tombs at Abydos; a complex of temples and shrines at Karnak (part of the site of ancient Thebes); and temples and other buildings at Luxor (also part of ancient Thebes).

During the last 700 years of ancient Egypt (c. 1085–332 B.C.E.), the kingdom increasingly came under foreign domination, which weakened it to the point that Alexander the Great was able to claim it without struggle in 332 B.C.E.

The Abu Simbel Temple of King Ramses II.

THE CLASSICAL AGE:
2000 B.C.E. TO 500 C.E.

What is the Classical Age?

The Classical Age refers to the ancient Roman and Greek worlds, roughly 2000 B.C.E. to 500 C.E. The Classical Age followed the Prehistoric era and preceded the Middle Ages. During this period, the ancient Greeks and Romans made contributions to literature, philosophy, science, the arts, and letters that are still relevant today.

How did Greek civilization begin?

Ancient Greek civilization began with the Minoans. Europe's first advanced civilization, the Minoans were a prosperous and peaceful people who flourished on the Mediterranean island of Crete from about 3000 to 1450 B.C.E. The Minoans built structures from stone, plaster, and timbers; painted walls with brilliant frescoes; made pottery; wove and dyed cloth; cultivated the land (they are believed to be the first people to produce an agricultural surplus, which they exported); constructed stone roads and bridges; and built highly advanced drainage systems and aqueducts. (At Knossos, the royal family had a system for showers and even had toilets that could be flushed.) The Minoans were a sophisticated people who loved music and dance, games and entertainment.

What is the Mycenaean Age?

The Minoans were either conquered by or succeeded by the Mycenaeans, who were mainland Greeks: In about 1450 B.C.E., Crete was struck by a 200-foot tsunami (or seismic wave), which is thought to either have completely destroyed the island or to have weakened it to a point that it could be overtaken. The Mycenaeans flourished from about 1650 B.C.E. to 1200 B.C.E., a time known as the Mycenaean Age, carrying forth the culture and skills they had learned from the Minoans (who had been their neighbors). The Mycenaeans were skilled horsemen, charioteers, and accomplished sailors who ruled the Aegean Sea. Mycenaean culture revolved around its fortified palaces, called acropolises (top cities). Its cities included Argos, Corinth, Sparta, and the then-small cities of Athens and Thebes.

In about 1200 B.C.E. the Mycenaeans attacked the city of Troy, which was considered the key to the profitable Black Sea trade, thus launching the Trojan War. After ten years of fighting (a period that is recounted by Greek poet Homer [c. 850–? B.C.E.] in the *Iliad*), the Mycenaeans were victorious. But soon their period of triumph ended as the Dorian peoples (from the northwestern part of the Greek mainland) overran most of the Peloponnesus (the southern peninsula of Greece). The Dorians, aided by the superiority of the iron sword, flooded southward, where they sacked and burned the great Mycenaean cities and conquered the wealthy sea traders, throwing Greece into the period known as the Dark Ages, or Archaic Period, which lasted from 1100 to about 800 B.C.E.

What were the Dark Ages of ancient Greece?

After the Dorians conquered the Mycenaeans in 1100 B.C.E., these nomadic peoples thrust Greece into a period of decline that lasted more than 300 years. The Dorians rejected the life of the great Mycenaean cities in favor of their nomadic shepherding and hunting life. A tribal people, they possessed a harsh sense of justice, and the period was marked by feuds between clans. Men typically carried weapons—now made of iron (it was the Dorians who brought the new, more durable metal from the north, ending the Bronze Age in Greece).

During this Dark Age, there is little evidence of Greek civilization; the script used by the Mycenaeans disappeared, and art, which had prospered during the Mycenaean Age, declined. Under Dorian rule numerous Mycenaean cities were abandoned, and many regions and islands seem to have been depopulated. There is no evidence of trade with other countries. Poverty had overtaken the Greeks.

As the Dorians took possession of the Greek mainland, a few Mycenaean communities survived in remote areas. Many Mycenaeans fled eastward to Athens, which became a haven for those who hoped for a return to the former civilization. Other Mycenaeans crossed the Aegean and settled on the coast of Asia Minor. Most of these refugees spoke Ionian Greek.

A lasting legacy of the Dark Ages of Greece is its mythology. As Ionian Greeks attempted to hold on to the refined civilization of the Bronze Age, they commemorated the greatness of the past in song and verse, including Greek poet Homer's (c. 850–? B.C.E.) *Iliad* and *Odyssey*. These epics were combined with eighth-century poet Hesiod's *Theogony,* an account of the creation of the universe and the generations of the gods, to give rise to a new Greek religion based on the god Zeus and eleven other gods, who were believed to reside on Mount Olympus in northeastern Greece. The Greek gods were later adopted by the Romans and given different names.

What was the Golden Age of ancient Greece?

It is the period of classical Greek civilization that followed the so-called Dark Ages of Greece, which came to an end about 800 B.C.E. Over time the Dorians had become more settled, and they gradually revived trade and culture on mainland Greece. The self-governing city-state (polis) evolved, including the military center of Sparta, and Athens, which became a center for the arts, education, and democracy. This was the beginning of the great Hellenic period

Who was Pericles?

Pericles (495 B.C.E.–429 B.C.E.) was a leading Greek statesman who led Athens during the height of its powers. Called "the first citizen of Athens," Pericles led his country at the beginning of the Peloponnesian War. He fostered democracy and encouraged the growth of various forms of art and architecture.

His father, Xanthippus, was an important politician, and his mother, Agariste, came from a prestigious political family, too. He obtained an excellent education and later was a friend to several important Greek philosophers of the day, including Protagoras and Zeno of Elea.

of classical Greek civilization. Greek civilization reached its height in Athens during the mid-400s B.C.E., a period of outstanding achievement known as the Golden Age.

What are the hallmarks of classical Greek civilization?

The classical Greeks, who called themselves the Hellenes and their land Hellas, influenced western civilization more than any other people. Their contributions to every field of endeavor remain with us today, more than 2,000 years later.

Greek thought shaped science, medicine, philosophy, art, literature, architecture and engineering, mathematics, music, drama, language, and politics. The classical Greeks believed in individual freedom, reasoning, and truth, and that everything should be done in moderation. They also held that people should find time for both work and play and should balance the life of the mind with the exercise of the body.

The knowledge that became the Greek legacy had its beginnings in the settlements established in Asia Minor (the peninsula between the Black Sea and the Mediterranean, and which today is occupied by Turkey) after the Dorians invaded the Greek mainland. The Phoenician alphabet, an early alphabet developed by Semitic peoples in the ancient maritime country of Phoenicia (present-day western Syria and Lebanon), was acquired by the Greeks, who adapted it to their language. They began using it to record Greek poet Homer's (c. 850–? B.C.E.) oral epics (*Iliad* and *Odyssey*) and the works of other Greek poets and historians.

Among the great Greek philosophers are Socrates, Plato, and Aristotle. Greek literature includes the epic poetry of Homer as well as the passionate love poems of Sappho. The Greeks gave humankind the tragedies of Aeschylus, Sophocles, and Euripides, which continue to be studied by students today, along with the comedies of Aristophanes and Menander. The classical Greeks loved to speak, and oratory is considered by some to be their highest form of prose. Orators known to the modern world are Antiphon, Lysias, Isocrates, and Demosthenes.

Herodotus, called the "father of history," left the modern world with an account of the Persian Wars (500–449 B.C.E.), a conflict between the Greek city-states and the Persian Empire. The Greeks also gave humankind the "father of medicine" in physician Hippocrates, who taught that doctors should use reason to determine the cause of illness and should study the patient's appearance, behavior, and lifestyle to diagnose and treat illnesses and injuries. (The "Hippocratic Oath," versions of which are still sworn by medical students

The Greek physician Hippocrates is considered the "father of medicine."

graduating today, is attributed to Hippocrates.) Greek scientists include Thales and Pythagoras; scientist-philosophers include Leucippus and Democritus. And of course, the Greeks gave modern culture the Olympic Games.

Did the Roman Republic precede the Roman Empire?

Yes, the Roman Republic, which for centuries afterward was considered the model form of a balanced government, was established in 509 B.C.E. The Roman Empire was not established until 27 B.C.E. when Augustus (also known as Octavian; 63 B.C.E.– 14 C.E.) became its first ruler. In brief, the development of ancient Rome is as follows.

In 753 B.C.E. the city of Rome was established. (Legend has it the city was founded by Romulus.) Situated on wooded hills above the Tiber River, about fifteen miles from the sea, Rome enjoyed the advantages of access to trade routes while having natural protection from aggressors. The city was defensible. Agriculture prospered in the area, as did other economic endeavors, including manufacturing and mining.

In 509 B.C.E. the Republic was established by noblemen. The government was headed by two elected officials who were called consuls. Since they shared power, a certain measure of balance was ensured in that either one could veto the actions of the other. And the posts were brief: each elected official served for only one year. These heads of state were guided by the Roman Senate, which was made up of senior statesmen. There were also assemblies in which the people had a voice.

In 390 B.C.E. Rome was captured and sacked by the Gauls (a Celtic people from western Europe), who were able to hold it for a short time. About 300 B.C.E. the Romans came into contact with the Greeks, adopting not only some of their ideas, but their mythology as well. The Greek gods and goddesses were soon given Roman names.

By 275 B.C.E. Rome controlled most of the Italian peninsula. Their homeland stable, the Romans set their sights on overseas expansion, and between 264 and 146 B.C.E. fought the Punic Wars in order to gain territory. They conquered the Mediterranean islands of Sicily, Sardinia, and Corsica; part of Gaul; much of Spain; and Carthage (in northern Africa).

In the last century B.C.E. Rome entered a period that is considered the height of their civilization. But about the middle of that century, the Republic was torn by civil wars. After twenty years of fighting, the Roman Empire was formed in 27 B.C.E. when Augustus (Octavian) became the first emperor. While vestiges of the Republic were maintained, the emperor held supreme authority, nominating the consuls and appointing senators, controlling the provinces, and heading the army. The civilian assemblies were still in place, but had for the most part lost their voice in government.

The Roman Empire lasted nearly 500 years. By the third century C.E. Roman armies had conquered so many peoples that the empire stretched across Europe and included the entire Mediterranean coast of Africa as well as parts of the Middle East. During this time of power and expansion, trade thrived over a vast network of roads and sea routes, which extended to China, India, and Africa. Coins, made of gold, silver, copper, and bronze, were issued and controlled by the Roman government.

In 395, upon the death of emperor Theodosius the Great (347–395), the Roman Empire was divided into two: East and West. In 476, after suffering a series of attacks from nomadic Germanic tribes, Rome fell.

What was the Pax Romana?

The Pax Romana was the height of the Roman Empire, a period of peace, prosperity, and stability that lasted from 27 B.C.E. to 180 C.E., roughly two centuries. Pax Romana, or the Peace of Rome, stretched from the time of Augustus Caesar through the reign of Marcus Aurelius. Throughout this time period, Roman legions ensured that order and security were maintained in various provinces and areas of the vast empire. Marcus Aurelius, a follower of the Stoic philosophy, is regarded as perhaps the greatest of Roman emperors (alongside Caesar Augustus) and the height of the empire was achieved during his reign. During this time, no other country or force was strong enough to challenge the Roman Empire, so citizens turned their attention to commerce, learning, the arts, and literature, all of which flourished.

The Pax Romana ended during the reign of Marcus Aurelius' successor and son, Commodus, whose erratic behavior contributed to the end of the Pax Romana.

What is the legacy of ancient Rome?

Since the Romans borrowed and adapted the ideas of the Greeks, with whom they had come into contact about 300 B.C.E. and later conquered (in 146 B.C.E.), the culture of ancient Rome is sometimes called Greco-Roman. Over the course of centuries, Romans spread their ideas throughout their vast empire.

They also developed a legal code, which outlined basic principles while remaining flexible enough that lawyers and judges could interpret the laws, taking into consideration local customs and practices. *The Justinian Code* of 529 C.E. later became the model for legal systems in Europe and in Latin America. Further, Roman armies built a network of roads, aqueducts, and tunnels, putting in place an infrastructure that outlasted the empire itself. Latin, the Roman language, remained the language of educated Europeans for more than 1,000 years, while the Latin-based (or Romance) languages of Italian, French, and Spanish took over everyday communication. The economic system put in place during the height of the Roman Empire, with a centrally controlled money supply, also had lasting effect.

Though the empire had crumbled by 476 C.E., its cultural, social, and economic establishments continued to have validity well into the Middle Ages (500 to 1350).

Who were Julius and Augustus Caesar?

Julius Caesar was a decorated general known for leading Roman soldiers to victory and conquest in Gaul. He later became the ruler of Rome, serving as dictator from 49 to 44 B.C.E. Several senators, including a few of Caesar's friends, stabbed him to death in the Forum. His grandnephew, Gaius Octavius, served as Roman emperor from 31 B.C.E. to 14 C.E. He took the name of Augustus, which translates into "revered one."

What is the difference between the Roman Empire and the Holy Roman Empire?

Roughly four and a half centuries separated the two empires, both of which were comprised of vast regions of western and central Europe. The Roman Empire was established in 27

B.C.E., when Augustus (also known as Octavian; 63 B.C.E.–14 C.E.), the grandnephew, adopted son, and chosen heir of Julius Caesar (100–44 B.C.E.), became emperor. His empire lasted until 476 C.E., when Rome fell to Germanic tribes.

The Holy Roman Empire (H.R.E.) began in the mid-900s C.E., when Otto I (912–973) of Germany gained control of most of northern and central Italy. Pope John XII (c. 937–964) crowned Otto emperor in 962. In the 1200s this area of power officially became known as the Holy Roman Empire. The H.R.E. was dismantled on July 12, 1806, in the Confederation of the Rhine, which brought most of the German states under French domination—the result of the Napoleonic wars. But even after Napoleon Bonaparte (1769–1821) was permanently ousted as head of France in 1815, there were no attempts to reinstate the Holy Roman Empire.

What happened to the Celts during the Roman Empire?

The Celts were an Indo-European people who by 500 B.C.E. had spread across what is now France, Italy, Portugal, Spain, and the British Isles, and by 200 B.C.E. had expanded as far as present-day Bulgaria and Greece. When the Romans conquered much of Europe (about 300 B.C.E.), many Celts were absorbed into the Roman Empire. However, those Celts living in Ireland, Scotland, Wales, southwest England, and Brittany (in northwestern France) were able to maintain their cultures, and it is in these regions that people of Celtic origin still live today.

What is known about the Celts prior to the Roman Empire?

Before Europe was conquered by Rome, Celts, who were themselves divided into smaller tribes, had become rather advanced in many ways. Their society was divided among three classes: commoners, the educated, and aristocrats. They formed loose federations of tribes, raised crops

An Irish hut in the style of ancient Celtic construction.

10

and livestock, used the Greek alphabet to write their own language, and were among the first peoples in northern Europe to make iron. They also developed a form of metalwork that most people today recognize as Celtic, called La Tène. They never formed one united nation, however, so that when Roman armies swept across Europe, the Celtic tribes were overrun.

THE MIDDLE AGES: 500 TO 1350

What are the characteristics of medieval times?

Although the Middle Ages were shadowed by poverty, ignorance, economic chaos, bad government, and the plague, it was also a period of cultural and artistic achievement. For example, the university originated in medieval Europe (the first university was established in 1158 in Bologna, Italy). The period was marked by the belief, based on the Christian faith, that the universe is an ordered world, ruled by an infinite and all-knowing God. This belief persisted even through the turmoil of wars and social upheavals, and it is evident in the soaring Gothic architecture (such as the Cathedral of Chartres, France), the poetry of Dante Alighieri (1265–1321), the philosophy of St. Thomas Aquinas (1225–1274), the Gregorian chant, and the music of such composers as Guillaume de Machaut (c. 1300–1377).

The Elizabethan "Chain of Being"

Who were the Huns?

The Huns were a nomadic central Asian people, who in the middle of the fourth century C.E. moved westward. They first defeated the Alani (a group in the Caucasus Mountain region, between the Black and the Caspian Seas), and then conquered and drove out the Goths. Unified by the ruler Attila in 434, the Huns gained control of a large part of central and eastern Europe by about 450. The Italian countryside was ravaged in the process, and many people sought refuge on the numerous islands in the Lagoon of Venice; the settlement later became the city of Venice.

With the death of Attila in 453, the subjects of the Huns revolted and defeated them. The Huns were later absorbed into the various peoples of Europe.

Who were the barbarians?

The term is used to refer to any of the Germanic tribes that, during the middle of the first millennium C.E. (beginning about 400), repeatedly attacked Rome, eventually conquering it and dividing the territories of the West Roman Empire into many kingdoms (while what was the East Roman Empire survived as the Byzantine Empire). The Germanic tribes included the Goths, the Vandals, the Franks, and the Lombards.

Who were the Goths?

The Goths were a group of Germanic tribes who originated in what is now Scandinavia. As early as the third century C.E., the Goths invaded the eastern provinces of the Roman Empire. During the following century, they divided into two groups: a western group known as the Visigoths, who predominated north of the lower Danube River, in central Europe; and an eastern group known as the Ostrogoths, who were situated north of the Black Sea, between Europe and Asia. Along with other tribal Germanic peoples, the Goths brought the downfall of the Roman Empire.

What happened to the Ostrogoths?

The eastern division of the Goths, the Ostrogoths were overrun and absorbed by the Huns in 370. When the powerful Hun leader, Attila, died in 453, subjects of the Huns revolted and the Ostrogoths regained their freedom. Theodoric (c. 454–526) became the ruler of the Ostrogoths in 493, and it was under his leadership that the group invaded northern Italy, where they remained. In the middle of the following century, they were overthrown by the armies of the Byzantine Empire. Like other Germanic tribes, the Ostrogoths were absorbed into the various groups of Europe.

What happened to the Visigoths?

When both the Visigoths and Ostrogoths were attacked by the Huns in 370, the Visigoths fared better, many of them fleeing into a Roman province. In 378 the Visigoths rebelled against the Roman authorities. On horseback, they fought the battle of Adrianople (in present-day Turkey), destroying a Roman army and killing Rome's eastern emperor, Valens (c. 328–378). The Visigoths' introduction of the cavalry (troops trained to fight on horseback) as part of warfare determined European military, social, and political development for the next thousand years.

After the battle of Adrianople, the Visigoths moved into Italy, and under the leadership of their ruler, Alaric (c. 370–410), sacked Rome in 410, an event that signaled the beginning of the decline of the Roman Empire. After the success of the Visigoths, one tribe after another invaded the empire.

The Visigoths continued westward into Gaul, and there set up a monarchy that consisted of much of France and Spain and was centered in Toulouse. But in 507 they were driven out by the Franks, and the Visigoths withdrew into the Iberian Peninsula (present-day Spain and Portugal). Toledo was established as the capital of the Visigoth kingdom in 534. Roderick (or Rodrigo), the last of the Visigoth kings in Spain, was defeated and killed in 711 during a battle with the Muslims (Moors), who invaded from northern Africa. The Muslims went on to rule most of the Iberian Peninsula until the mid-1400s.

Who were the Vandals?

Like the Goths, the Vandals were a Germanic people who originated in an area south of the Baltic Sea in what is now Scandinavia. By 100 C.E. they had moved into the southern region

Who was Reccared I?

Reccared I (559–601) was a Visigoth king who ruled from 586 to 601. He converted to Catholicism in 587, marking a significant shift in policy. Previously, many Visigoths were members of Arian Christians, a Christian faction that believed Christ to be created by and subordinate to God the Father (based on the teachings of Arius; 250–336).

of (present-day) Poland. But there they eventually found themselves threatened by the Huns, and so they began moving westward late in the fourth century. Early in the fifth century, the Vandals overran Gaul (in western Europe), Spain, and northern Africa, where they eventually settled. Between 428 and 477 the Vandals were ruled by the powerful King Genseric. Under his reign, they ravaged Rome (in 455). Their pillage was so thorough that the word vandal is used to describe anyone who willfully destroys property that is not theirs. In 533 and 534, like the Ostrogoths, the Vandals were defeated by armies of the Byzantine Empire.

Who were the Franks?

The Franks were another Germanic people who divided into two branches: the Salians, who settled near the lower Rhine River, near the North Sea; and the Ripuarians, who moved into what is now Germany, along the middle Rhine River.

In 359 the Franks entered into the Roman Empire as allies, but in 481 Clovis (c. 466–511) gained the Salerian Frank kingship. By 486 he had begun a campaign of aggression, conquering Romans, Gauls, Visigoths, and other groups. Under this cruel and cunning king, the Franks soon controlled all of Europe—from the Mediterranean to the English Channel, and from the Pyrenees Mountains to the Rhine River. Even after Clovis's death, the Franks maintained their stronghold in the region, which is how France eventually got its name.

Though Clovis was a powerful ruler, he was succeeded as king of the Franks by the even more powerful Charlemagne (also called Charles the Great; 742–814), who ruled from 771 to 814, creating a vast empire. In 800 Pope Leo III (c. 750–816) crowned him Emperor of the West, thus initiating the Holy Roman Empire. It was after Charlemagne that the empire of the Franks began to break up, becoming the kingdoms of France, Germany, and Italy.

How were the Gauls related to the Celts?

The ancient Gauls were a Celtic people who spoke forms of the Celtic language. They occupied the ancient country of Gaul, a region west of the Rhine River and north of the Pyrenees Mountains (an area that today consists of France, Belgium, Luxembourg, part of Germany, and part of the Netherlands). The Gauls were led by priests, who were called Druids. By 390 B.C.E. the Gauls had moved southward, across the Alps and into Italy.

In the third century B.C.E., they battled the powerful Romans and were briefly successful. Ultimately, however, they were defeated, becoming subjects of Rome. Later, under Julius Caesar, the Romans conquered all of Gaul, so that by 50 B.C.E. the region became part of the Roman Empire. Five centuries later, Gaul was overrun by the Franks, for whom the region was named. Thus, French people today are descendants of the Gauls. Also, the Galatians (one of the Christian peoples to whom the Apostle Paul wrote while he was in jail) were descendants of the Gauls who settled in Macedonia and Asia Minor (the peninsula between the Black Sea and the Mediterranean, which today is occupied by Turkey).

Who were the Lombards?

The Lombards, too, were a Germanic tribe; they are believed to have originated on an island in the Baltic Sea. In the last century B.C.E., the Lombards moved into Germany and gradually continued southward so that by 500 C.E., they were settled in present-day Austria. From

568 to the mid-700s, they controlled much of Italy, posing such a serious threat to the papal supremacy that in 754, Pope Stephen II (d. 757) appealed to the powerful Franks for help. By this time the Franks were ruled by Pepin III (called Pepin the Short; c. 714–768), who was able to defeat the Lombards. The northern region of Italy, Lombardy, is named for them.

Who were the Saxons?

Saxons were a Germanic people who in the second century lived in southern Jutland, in the area of present-day Denmark and northwestern Germany. During the next two centuries the Saxons raided the coastal areas of the North Sea. By about 400, they had reached northern Gaul, the ancient country that occupied the area west and south of the Rhine River, west of the Alps, and north of the Pyrenees Mountains (roughly modern-day France, Belgium, Luxembourg, part of Germany, and part of the Netherlands). By about 450, as Roman rule was declining, the Saxons had reached England, where they merged with the Angles and began setting up Anglo-Saxon kingdoms. The Anglo-Saxons dominated England until it was conquered by Danish Vikings (under the leadership of Canute) in 1016.

Who were the Angles?

The Angles were yet another Germanic tribe; they originated in Schleswig in northwestern Germany. Like other Germanic peoples, they were on the move by the fifth century. Arriving in England, the Angles joined the Saxons (also a Germanic-speaking people), after which time they together became known as Anglo-Saxons, a term referring to any non-Celtic settler of Britain.

The ruins of the twelfth-century Wolvesey Castle in Winchester, Hampshire, England, is an excellent example of an Anglo-Saxon fortification.

Who were the Vikings?

The Vikings, also called Norsemen, were fierce, seafaring warriors who originated in Scandinavia. Beginning in the late 700s they raided England, France, Germany, Ireland, Scotland, Italy, Russia, and Spain. Great shipbuilders, the Vikings also reached Greenland, Iceland, and probably even North America long before the Europeans. (Ruins of a Norse settlement were found on the northeastern coast of Newfoundland, Canada.) The Vikings were converted to Christianity during the tenth and eleventh centuries, about the same time that the kingdoms of Norway, Denmark, and Sweden were established. Under the Danish leader Canute, Vikings conquered England in 1016 and ruled it as part of Denmark until 1042.

Who were the Danes?

The Danes are the Scandinavian people of Denmark. Their origins date as far back as 100,000 years. Beginning at about the time of Christ (c. 30 C.E.), the Danes were organized into communities that were governed by local chieftains. During the sixth and seventh centuries they participated in the Viking (pirate) raids of England, France, the Netherlands, Belgium, and Luxembourg (these last three are sometimes referred to as the Low Countries). In about 950 Denmark was united by King Harold II (also called Harald Bluetooth; c. 910–c. 985), who ten years later was converted to Christianity and thereafter fostered its spread. The Vikings gained control of England in 1016, and the Dane warrior Canute became king of England (and of Denmark). The Danes ruled England until 1042.

Who were the Normans?

The Normans, like the Danes, originated in Scandinavia and were Vikings. In the mid-800s they invaded northern France, ousting the Franks who had conquered the region 400 years earlier. There they stayed, in the region that came to be known as Normandy (or Normandie). In 1066 the Norman duke William (the Conqueror; 1027–1087) sailed across the channel and claimed the English throne, uniting Normandy with the English kingdom. This arrangement lasted until 1204 when French King Philip Augustus (1165–1223) reclaimed the territory. England took it back during the fifteenth century, but in 1450 Normandy was permanently restored to France, becoming a province. Norman descendants still live there today, and their influence is also evident across the English Channel, where the Norman nobility intermixed with the Anglo-Saxons.

What were lords?

Lords (or seigniors) were wealthy landowners during the Middle Ages (500 to 1350). By about the ninth century, much of western Europe was divided into huge estates, called manors. These were self-sufficient estates that were held by a lord (members of the clergy could also be lords). The lord would lease land to peasants who would farm it; in return, the peasants would pay the lord in taxes, in services, or in kind (with crops or goods). In addition to farmland, a manor would typically have meadow, woodland, and a small village. The lord presided over the entire manor and all the people living there. As the administrator of the land, he collected taxes and presided over legal matters. But the manors were not military entities; in other words, the lord did not promise protection to the peasants living on his land. As such, the manors were purely socioeconomic (as opposed to fiefs, which were social, economical, and political units).

What were fiefs?

A fief was an estate that was owned, governed, and protected by a lord. A fief consisted of several manors (each of which might have had its own lord) and their villages, along with all buildings on the land as well as the peasants (serfs) who worked the land, served at court, or took up arms on behalf of the lord. The lord of the fief, called a feudal lord, would secure the allegiance of the manorial lords (sometimes called seigniors), who would in turn secure the allegiance of the peasants. In short, land was exchanged for loyalty; this was feudalism, the political and economic system of the Middle Ages (500 to 1350). The word "feud" is of Germanic origin and means "fee"; in repayment for the land they lived on and for the protection they received from the lord, serfs were expected to pay the lord fees—in the form of money (taxes), services, or goods.

The feudal system arose in the seventh century. It was suspended during the Carolingian Empire, which began in 751 when a series of powerful kings (including Charlemagne, or Charles the Great: 742–814) united much of western Europe. But after Charlemagne died in 814, his grandsons fought each other and later divided the vast kingdom among themselves. Each of their territories later came under attack, dissolving Carolingian rule. By the ninth century feudalism had replaced the Carolingian Empire as the political and economic entity governing medieval life. Feudalism lasted into the fifteenth century.

What were serfs?

Serfs were the peasants who lived on either a manor or a fief, the two organizing entities of the Middle Ages (500 to 1350). They performed labor and were bound to the lord of the property where they lived and worked. A serf was somewhere between a free person and a slave: Though the word serf is derived from the Latin word *servus*, meaning "slave," the serfs had certain rights, which were governed not by law but by custom. One such custom was that a serf who could escape his lord for one year and a day was then considered free. A free peasant was called a villein, a village commoner.

What were vassals?

In the Middle Ages (500 to 1350) a vassal was anyone who was under the protection of another and therefore owed and avowed not only allegiance but a payment of some sort to their protector. Peasants (serfs and village commoners) were always vassals to a lord—whether it was the lord of the manor or the lord of the fief. But the lord of the manor was himself a vassal—to the lord of the fief. As kingdoms were created, with many fiefs within their jurisdiction, the feudal lords became the vassals of the kings.

What were knights?

In the Middle Ages (500 to 1350) knights were armed and mounted warriors who were also landholders; in other words, they were noblemen who took up arms. A knight might have been the lord of a manor who vowed to fight for the feudal lord (the lord of the fief where the manor was situated).

During the Carolingian Age (during the eighth and ninth centuries), when a monarchy was established in western Europe, a feudal lord might also have been a knight in service to the king. In times of war, any man who pledged loyalty to his lord and took up arms on his

What was a papal state?

A papal state was a manor or fief where the lord was a member of the clergy. In 754 Carolingian king Pepin the Short (c. 714–768) (the father of Charlemagne) granted extensive lands to the pope. These territories, which included much of what is now the Mediterranean coast of France as well as most of central Italy, were organized by the Roman Catholic Church into states. These states played an important role in medieval life. Like the fiefs, the papal states collected taxes and maintained courts of law. Also, like their secular counterparts, they were prone to war and invasion. Thus members of the Roman Catholic Church were temporal as well as spiritual leaders during the Middle Ages (500 to 1350). The last of the territories held by the church was in central Italy and included Rome. After 1871 these lands were claimed by Italy. The resulting land dispute (sometimes referred to as the Roman Question) was settled by the Lateran Treaty (1929), which created the sovereign state known as Vatican City.

behalf would become a knight, who later might receive lands from the lord or king as repayment. During the Crusades (1096–1291) knights were made of men who were not landowners—they were instead designated by primogeniture (the eldest son would bear the honor of becoming a knight). Knighthood was traditionally conferred by a blow on the shoulder with the flat side of a sword. Feudal knighthood ended by the sixteenth century. Today, the only vestige of this tradition is found in Britain, where knighthood is an honorific designation conferred by the king or queen on a noble or commoner for extraordinary achievement.

What was the Church's role during the Middle Ages?

Though the Roman Catholic Church became increasingly involved in secular concerns during the Middle Ages (500 to 1350), it played a much larger part in medieval European life. Missionaries converted many of the Germanic tribes; thus, the church was influential in civilizing these so-called barbarians. Further, churches throughout Europe housed travelers and served as hospitals for the sick. Monasteries and cathedrals became centers of learning.

What was the Holy Roman Empire?

The Holy Roman Empire (sometimes abbreviated H.R.E.) was a loose federation of German and Italian states, originally formed on Christmas of 800 C.E., when Charlemagne, or Charles the Great (742–814), was crowned emperor of the Romans by Pope Leo III (c. 750–816). But after Charlemagne's death, the empire lapsed and was not fully reinstated until Otto I (912–973) was crowned emperor. Though the empire was strongly associated with the Roman Catholic Church, disputes between emperors and popes began in the mid-1100s. In 1250 Pope Innocent IV (d. 1254) was successful in gaining independence from the empire for the Italian city-states.

Later in the history of the Holy Roman Empire, the House of Habsburg rose to power. But after the 1648 signing of the Peace of Westphalia, which recognized the sovereignty of all the states of the empire, the title of Holy Roman Emperor was for the most part an honorific one. With the exception of a five-year period (1740–45), the family continued to hold power until 1806, when Emperor Francis II (1768–1835) declared the end of the Holy Roman Empire.

Why was Otto I crowned emperor?

Pope John XII crowned Otto emperor of the Holy Roman Empire in 962 because Otto had defended the church in several disputes in Europe and northern Italy. The Pope gave Otto the revered title of Augustus. This action resulted in the beginning of a more than 840-year reign of the Holy Roman Empire as a major force in world affairs.

THE RENAISSANCE: 1350 TO c.1600

Why is the Renaissance considered a time of rebirth?

The term renaissance is from the French word for "rebirth," and the period from 1350 to 1600 c.e. in Europe was marked by the resurrection of classical Greek and Roman ideals; the flourishing of art, literature, and philosophy; and the beginning of modern science.

Holy Roman Emperor Otto I (912–973).

Italians in particular believed themselves to be the true heirs to Roman achievement. For this reason, it was natural that the Renaissance began in Italy, where the ruins of ancient civilization provided a constant reminder of their classical past and where subsequent artistic movements (such as Gothic) had never taken firm hold.

How did the Renaissance begin?

Social and political developments in the late Middle Ages gave rise to the spirit of the Renaissance. The Crusades (1096 to 1291)—the military expeditions undertaken by Christian powers to win the holy land from the Muslims—brought Europeans into contact with other cultures and most importantly with Byzantine civilization. The remnant of the East Roman Empire, Byzantium had preserved the knowledge of ancient times. In addition, many texts thought to have been destroyed during the tribal ransacking of the West Roman Empire (in the fifth century c.e.) remained preserved in various translations throughout the Middle East. So it was during the Crusades that some of these were brought back to Europe, where classical scholars undertook the task of deciphering the West's cultural past.

In northern Italy, a series of city-states developed independent of the larger empires to the north and south of them. These small states—Florence, Rome, Venice, and Milan, among others—gained prosperity through trade and banking, and as a result, a wealthy class of businessmen emerged. These community leaders admired and encouraged creativity, patronizing artists who might glorify their commercial achievement with great buildings, paintings, and sculptures. The most influential patrons of the arts were the Medicis, a wealthy banking family in Florence. Members of the Medici family supported many important artists, including Botticelli and Michelangelo. Guided by the Medici patronage, Florence became the most magnificent city of the period.

One way patrons encouraged art was to sponsor competitions in order to spur artists on to more significant achievement. In many cases, the losers of these contests went on to greater fame than the winners. After his defeat in the competition to create the bronze doors of the Baptistery of Florence Cathedral, architect Filippo Brunelleschi (1377–1446) made several trips to take measurements of the ruined buildings of ancient Rome. When he returned to Florence, he created the immense il duomo (dome) of the Santa Maria del Fiore Cathedral, a classically influenced structure that became the first great monument of the Renaissance.

Which artists and thinkers are considered the greatest minds of the Renaissance?

The great writers of the Renaissance include the Italian poet Petrarch (1304–1374), who became the first great writer of the Renaissance and was one of the first proponents of the concept that a "rebirth" was in progress; Florentine historian Niccolò Machiavelli (1469–1527), who wrote the highly influential work *The Prince* (1513); English dramatist and poet William Shakespeare (1564–1616), whose works many view as the culmination of Renaissance writing; Spain's Miguel de Cervantes (1547–1616), who penned Don Quixote (1605), the epic masterpiece that gave birth to the modern novel; and Frenchman François Rabelais (c. 1483–1553), who is best known for writing the five-volume novel *Gargantua and Pantagruel.*

The great artists of the Renaissance include the Italian painters/sculptors Sandro Botticelli (1445–1510), whose works include *The Birth of Venus*; Leonardo da Vinci (1452–1519), whose *Mona Lisa* and *The Last Supper* are among the most widely studied works of art; Michelangelo Buonarroti (1475–1564), whose sculpture *David* became the symbol of the new Florence; and Raphael Sanzio (1483–1520), whose *School of Athens* is considered by art historians to be the complete statement of the High Renaissance.

When did European colonialism begin?

Seeking out colonies for economic benefit is a practice which dates back to ancient times: Even the Romans ruled colonies in Europe, the Middle East, and Africa. But colonialism took hold during the Renaissance, between 1400 and 1600, when powerful European countries sent explorers to find new lands and forge new trade routes.

What controversial Pope during the Renaissance period was known for his political skill?

Pope Alexander VI (1431–1503), also known as Rodrigo Borgia, was a controversial pope who was trained in law and gifted in political diplomacy. Of Spanish origin, Borgia left law and pursued a career in the divinity. An influential cardinal, he succeeded Pope Innocent VIII. Some suspected him of rising to the papacy through less than democratic and holy means—by rank bribery.

Portugal and Spain sought sea routes to India and the Far East. In the process, the Portuguese gained control of what is now Brazil; they also established trading posts in West Africa, India, and Southeast Asia. Spain gained control of most of Latin America and vast regions of what is now the United States. However, the Dutch, English, and French also had influence in these areas. And of course, the English eventually established thirteen colonies in North America. The English also became a strong influence in India and Africa, while the Dutch gained control of the Indonesian islands (which became the Dutch East Indies).

The results of colonialism were many. While trade was expanded and there was an enormous exchange of raw goods, the colonies were also rife with conflict: Indigenous peoples were killed or forcibly displaced from their lands, and foreign powers fought with each other for control of the same areas (the British and French fought four wars in North America between 1689 and 1763 alone). Further, Europeans brought to these new lands their own languages, religions, and systems of government, imposing their culture, beliefs, and ideologies on native peoples.

THE ENLIGHTENMENT AND THE SCIENTIFIC REVOLUTION: 1600s TO 1700s

What was the Enlightenment?

The Enlightenment, which is also referred to as the Age of Reason (or alternately, as the Age of Rationalism), was a period when European philosophers emphasized the use of reason as the best method for learning the truth. Beginning in the 1600s and lasting through the 1700s, philosophers such as Jean-Jacques Rousseau (1712–1778), Voltaire (1694–1778), and John Locke (1632–1704) explored issues in education, law, and politics. They published their thoughts, issuing attacks on social injustice, religious superstition, and ignorance. Their ideas fanned the fires of the American and French revolutions in the late 1700s.

Hallmarks of the Age of Reason include the idea of the universal truth (two plus two always equals four, for example); the belief that nature is vast and complex but well ordered; the belief that humankind possesses the ability to understand the universe; the philosophy of Deism, which holds that God created the world and then left it alone; and the concept of the rational will, which posits that humans make their own choices and plans, and therefore, do not have a fate thrust upon them.

While the Age of Reason proved to be a flurry of intellectual activity that resulted in the publication of several encyclopedias of knowledge, toward the end of the eighteenth century a shift occurred. During this time Europeans began to value passion over reason, giving rise to the romantic movement and ending the Age of Reason. (This change in outlook is evident in English novelist Jane Austen's [1775–1817] *Sense and Sensibility*.)

Nevertheless, the philosophies put forth during the Age of Reason were critical to the development of Western thought. The celebration of individual reason during this era was perhaps best expressed by René Descartes (1596–1650), who refused to believe anything unless it could be proved. His statement, "I think, therefore I am," sums up the feelings of skeptical and rational inquiry that characterized intellectual thought during this era.

Which Enlightenment thinker particularly influenced the American founders?

John Locke's writings greatly influenced several of the Founding Fathers, most notably Thomas Jefferson. Locke wrote *Essay Concerning Human Understanding and Two Treatises of Government*. His explanation of natural law and the social contract are key progenitors of Jefferson's ideas reflected in the *Declaration of Independence*. Locke believed that the government should protect the rights of the people. Jefferson identified this in the *Declaration of the Independence* by declaring that people have certain "inalienable rights" including "Life, Liberty and the pursuit of Happiness."

Are the Enlightenment and the scientific revolution the same?

The two terms describe interrelated and sequential European intellectual movements that took place from the 1500s to the 1800s. Together, the movements shaped an era that would lay the foundations of modern western civilization, foundations that required the use of reason, or rational thought, to understand the universe, nature, and human relations. During this period, many of the greatest minds in Europe developed new scientific, mathematical, philosophical, and social theories.

Scientists came to believe that observation and experimentation would allow them to discover the laws of nature. Thus, the scientific method emerged, which required tools. Soon the microscope, thermometer, sextant, slide rule, and other instruments were invented. Scientists working during this time included Sir Isaac Newton (1642–1727), Joseph Priestley (1733–1804), and René Descartes (1596–1650). The era witnessed key discoveries and saw rapid advances in astronomy, anatomy, mathematics, and physics. The advances had an impact on education: Universities introduced science courses to the curricula, and elementary and secondary schools followed suit. As people became trained in science, new technologies emerged; complicated farm machinery and new equipment for textile manufacturing and transportation was developed, paving the way for the Industrial Revolution.

THE INDUSTRIAL REVOLUTION:
1700s TO 1800s

When did the Industrial Revolution begin?

The Industrial Revolution began in Great Britain during the 1700s, and by the early 1800s it had spread to western Europe and the United States. It was brought about by the introduction of steam-power-driven machinery to manufacturing. By the close of the 1800s most finished goods, which had once been made by hand or by simple machines, were produced in quantity by technologically advanced machinery.

What were the effects of the Industrial Revolution?

The dawn of the Industrial Revolution spelled the end of home- or workshop-based production. Factories were built to house the new machines, causing a population shift from rural to developing urban areas by the mid-1800s, as people went where the work was. Factory owners turned to child labor, and in the United States, to the steady influx of immigrants to run the machinery in their plants. As industry grew, it required financial institutions that could provide money for expansion, thus giving birth to a new breed of wealthy business leaders—including the extraordinarily prosperous "robber barons," the industrial and financial tycoons of the late nineteenth century.

But as industry evolved, government and policy changes did not keep pace: Serious social, political, and economic problems resulted, including poor and often dangerous working conditions, exploitation of workers (including child laborers), overcrowded housing, pollution, corruption, industry monopolies, and a widening gap between the rich and the poor. Change was slow to come, but social activism and government reforms in the late 1800s and during the Progressive Era of the early 1900s, much of which centered around trade unions, alleviated these problems. The rapid development of industry caused sweeping social changes: The Western world, which had long been agriculturally based, became an industrial society, where goods and services were the primary focus.

THE TWENTIETH CENTURY

What was the world like between the World Wars?

Before World War II began in 1939, World War I (1914–1918) was referred to as the Great War, and understandably so given its enormous impact. The price of the conflict was paid in human casualties: More than ten million soldiers died and another twenty million were wounded. Civilian deaths were equally devastating, many of which resulted from widespread hunger and flu epidemics (this was in the days preceding the advent of penicillin to treat complications from influenza).

During the 1920s, with the death toll of the Great War a recent memory, the civilized world enjoyed a period of relative peace. In the United States, the decade was known as the Roaring Twenties—ten years of prosperity and even frivolity, despite ratification of the Eighteenth Amendment to the U.S. Constitution (1919), which prohibited the sale and consumption of "intoxicating liquors."

At the close of the Great War, the League of Nations had been established to handle disputes among countries and avoid another major conflict. This was followed in 1928 by the Kellogg-Briand Pact (also called the Pact of Paris), in which fifteen nations agreed to settle conflicts by diplomacy rather than military might; eventually sixty-two nations ratified the agreement.

Meanwhile, in Germany an extreme sense of nationalism was taking hold: The Treaty of Versailles, which had ended the Great War, seriously weakened the nation, allowing the rise of the Nazi Party, led by Adolf Hitler (1889–1945). Nazis were determined to see their beloved homeland rise to power once again, and they found a ready following among the German people.

In 1929 a general downturn began in the world economy, triggered by the U.S. stock market crash of late October. As the United States fell into the severe and sustained economic crisis known as the Great Depression, other industrialized nations—including Germany—also felt the impact. Unemployment jumped to record levels in many countries, and a lack of social welfare programs resulted in the destitution of numerous families. Politicians and economists alike searched for solutions to the crisis, many turning to anti–free trade or isolationist policies to "protect their own."

Meanwhile, postwar efforts to keep peace were proving ineffective: Japan invaded Manchuria (China) in 1931; Italy conquered Ethiopia in 1936; civil war raged in Spain (1936–39); India became the site of a bitter struggle between British rulers and Indian nationalists; and the Sino–Japanese War (which began in 1937 and would be absorbed by the outbreak of World War II) was fought in Asia. A dangerous alliance was forged when Germany, Italy, and Japan formed the Axis powers in 1936. Also, by 1933, Germany had become a totalitarian state known as the Third Reich. In 1938 Nazi armies took their first steps toward gaining supremacy when they marched into Austria and claimed it, setting the stage for World War II (1939–1945).

When did the Cold War begin?

In the years following the conclusion of World War II (1939–1945), the nations of Western Europe and the United States became alarmed by Soviet advances into Eastern Europe, and many Europeans and Americans voiced concerns that Communists, led by the Soviet Union, were plotting to take over the world. Political leaders in England, the United States, and elsewhere referred to this new menace in grim terms. In March 1946 former British Prime Minister Winston Churchill (1874–1965) warned of an "Iron Curtain" of Soviet totalitarianism that had divided the European continent, and in 1947 U.S. president Harry S. Truman (1884–1972) announced a policy of containment of Communist incursion into other countries. This policy came to be known as the Truman Doctrine, and it remained an integral part of American foreign policy for the next forty years, ultimately leading to the nation's involvement in the Korean War (1950–1953) and the Vietnam War (1954–1975).

The eroding relationship between the Western powers and the Soviet-led countries of Eastern Europe was largely brought on by disagreements over Germany. At the close of World War II, marked differences of opinion on what to do with Germany had resulted in a plan for joint government of the nation by the Allies—the Soviet Union, the United States, Britain, and France. But the arrangement quickly proved unworkable. By 1948 Germany was in serious economic straits, and the United States, Britain, and France began to discuss uniting their zones. The Soviets responded by ordering a blockade of land and water traffic into Berlin, control of which had been divided between the Allies after the war (the Soviets controlled East Berlin, while the other Allies controlled West Berlin). To counter the blockade, Great Britain and the United States ordered an airlift operation to provide food and other supplies to the people of West Berlin, alleviating the effects of the eleven-month Soviet blockade. In 1949 the East-West differences resulted in the formal division of Germany into two countries: West Germany, formed by the zones occupied by the United States, Great Britain, and France, was allowed to form a democratic government, and it became officially known as the Federal Republic of Germany. The same year, East Germany (also known as the German Democratic Republic) was formed out of the Soviet zones and was folded into the "Eastern bloc" countries.

By 1949, the year that the Soviet Union exploded its first nuclear bomb, the world had been roughly divided into two camps: the United States and its democratic allies, which included the nations of Western Europe and other anticommunist governments; and the Eastern bloc, the Soviet Union and its satellite countries. These camps were soon girded by formal political alliances. In 1949 a military alliance known as the North Atlantic Treaty Organization (NATO) was formed by twelve nations (the United States, Great Britain, France, Italy, Norway, Portugal, Iceland, Denmark, Canada, Belgium, Luxembourg, and the Netherlands). By 1955 three more countries—Greece, Turkey, and West Germany—joined the alliance. The Soviet Union responded by creating the Council for Mutual Economic Assistance (COMECON) in 1949 and the Warsaw Pact in 1955. COMECON was an effort to coordinate economic and industrial activities among Communist nations, while the Warsaw Pact was a military agreement between the Soviets and the Communist governments of Eastern Europe. The Cold War was on.

What were the hallmarks of the Cold War era?

At home, the hysteria of the Cold War era reached its height with the so-called McCarthyism of the 1950s; historian Doris Kearns Goodwin described it as "one of the most destructive chapters in American political history." In early 1950, Republican senator Joseph McCarthy (1908–1957) of Wisconsin claimed to possess a list of more than two hundred known communists in the U.S. State Department. The startling accusation launched congressional inquiries conducted by the senator's subcommittee and the House Committee on Un-American Activities. Suspicions of communist subversion ran high—even in Hollywood, where a "blacklist" named those who were believed to have been involved in the Communist Party. McCarthy never produced his laundry list of offenders in the State Department, and the sorry chapter was closed when, on live television, the senator's bitter attacks went too far: In televised hearings in 1954, the senator took on the U.S. Army, determined to ferret out what he believed was a conspiracy to cover up a known communist in the ranks. Faced with McCarthy's slanderous line of questioning, Army counsel Joseph Welch (1890–1960) delivered a reply that finally disarmed McCarthy, saying "Have you no sense of decency, sir? If there is a God in heaven, your attacks will do neither you nor your cause any good." The retort was met with applause in the courtroom, heralding the end of the Communist-in-our-midst hysteria.

But the Cold War deepened during the course of the 1950s, as distrust on both sides was increased by the shadow of possible nuclear destruction. Both the United States and the Soviet Union funneled vast resources into the development of weapons systems, as each side believed deterrence would determine the victor in the Cold War: It would be won by the nation able to create weapons so powerful that the other nation would be deterred from attacking. The military build-up became an all-out arms race, and the doctrine of mutually assured destruction (MAD) came into play.

Competition between the Eastern bloc and the West spilled over into athletics, the arts, and the sciences. In 1957 the Soviets beat the West into space with the launch of the first artificial satellite, *Sputnik*, which they followed in 1961 by completing the first successful manned space launch. The United States responded by stepping up its space program and vowing to put a man on the moon.

Events in the early 1960s heightened tensions between the two sides, causing many to fear the war would turn hot: When an American U-2 spy plane was shot down over the Soviet Union and its pilot was captured in 1960, the United States was forced to admit to conducting a program of aerial reconnaissance; in 1961, the U.S.-backed invasion of Cuba, known as the Bay of Pigs, failed, revealing American involvement in the plot; also that year, the Berlin Wall was built to stop the flow of emigrants out of East Germany, and became a visible symbol of the division between East and West; and in 1962 U.S. President John Kennedy (1917–1963) and Soviet Premier Nikita Khrushchev (1894–1971) squared off in the Cuban Missile Crisis (a full-scale conflict was averted through diplomacy).

Later in the decade and into the 1970s, tensions relaxed and both sides began agreeing to limit the arms race, signing the Nuclear Non-Proliferation Treaty in 1968 and the Strategic Arms Limitation Treaty (SALT I) in 1972, and agreeing to the Helsinki Accords in 1975. But East and West remained suspicious and watchful of each other into the 1980s. Most observers agree the Cold War did not come to an end until the fall of communism in Eastern Europe (c. 1990).

What led to the decline of communism in Eastern Europe?

Anticommunist sentiment among Eastern Europeans was bolstered by the actions and policies of Soviet leader Mikhail Gorbachev (1931–). When Gorbachev took office in 1985, the Soviet economy was in decline. In order to reverse the trend, he advocated dramatic reforms to move the economy away from the government-controlled (communist) system and toward a decentralized system, similar to those of Western democracies. Gorbachev's efforts to modernize the Soviet Union were not limited to the economy; he further proposed a reduction in the power of the Communist Party, which had controlled the country since 1917. Gorbachev's programs for reform were termed *perestroika* (meaning "restructuring"). In the meantime, Gorbachev opened up relations with the West, which included visits with U.S. president Ronald Reagan (1911–2004), who strongly supported the Soviet leader's programs. Gorbachev referred to his policy of openness as *glasnost*. Both Russian terms quickly caught on around the world. While the economic reforms produced a slow and painful change for the Soviet people and Gorbachev had many detractors (including government officials), he also had many supporters—both inside and outside the Soviet Union.

People in other Eastern European countries watched with interest the Soviet move toward a more democratic system. Strikes in Poland had begun as early as 1980, where workers formed a free labor union called Solidarity. But the following year, the Communist leaders of the Soviet Union pressured the Polish government to put an end to the movement—which it did. After Gorbachev became head of the Soviet Union and initiated sweeping changes, the reform movements in other countries soon realized that the Soviets under Gorbachev would no longer take hard-handed tactics toward anticommunist efforts in other countries. In 1989 the Polish government ceased to prohibit Solidarity, and the Communist party there lost influence. The same was true in Hungary, East Germany, and Czechoslovakia. By the end of the decade, most of the Eastern European Communist governments were overthrown in favor of democratic-oriented governments. The transition was effected differently in each country: the "overthrow" in Czechoslovakia was so peaceful that it was called the Velvet Revolution; while in Romania, a bloody revolt ensued, and hard-line communist dictator Nicolae Ceausescu (1918–1989), and his wife, were executed.

In 1990 multiparty elections were held in Romania, Czechoslovakia, Hungary, East Germany, and Bulgaria. The noncommunist party that was put in power in East Germany agreed to unification with West Germany, again creating one Germany on October 3, 1990. That same year Gorbachev received the Nobel Peace Prize for his contributions to world peace.

Sections of the Berlin Wall still remain after the end of the Cold War.

When was the Berlin Wall dismantled?

The barrier wall surrounding West Berlin began coming down in November 1989, as a wave of democratization swept Europe. The concrete, electrically fortified wall was first built in 1961 as a barbed wire and cinder block structure. Communist East German leader Walter Ulbricht (1893–1973) convinced Soviet premier Nikita Khrushchev (1894–1971) that the wall was needed to prevent people from fleeing communist Eastern Europe. (Before the wall was erected, an estimated 2.5 million people had fled to the free world through West Berlin; after its completion, perhaps 5,000 managed to escape. Hundreds died trying.) When the wall was complete, it had an average height of twelve feet and ran more than one hundred miles, along which there were posts where armed East German guards stood sentinel, preventing their countrymen from escaping to the West. The wall completely surrounded West Berlin and divided the German capital between East and West, communism and the free world.

The wall was a symbol of communism's oppression and of the Cold War. On June 26, 1963, President John F. Kennedy delivered his memorable "I am a Berliner" speech in its shadows, saying, "There are some who say communism is the wave of the future…Let them come to Berlin." He went on to say that the wall was "a vivid demonstration of the failure of the communist system," and that though democracy is not perfect, democratic nations had "never had to put up a wall to keep our people in." On June 12, 1987, President Ronald Reagan (1911–2004) addressed West Berliners at the wall's Brandenburg Gate; his now-famous speech was audible on the East Berlin side of the wall as well. There, Reagan issued a challenge to Soviet leader Mikhail Gorbachev (1931–), saying "if you seek peace, if you seek prosperity for the Soviet Union and Eastern Europe, if you seek liberalization…[c]ome here to this wall…Mr. Gorbachev, tear down this wall!"

East Germany's communist government was finally toppled in October 1989. On November 9 restrictions between the two Berlins were lifted, and the wall was opened. The resulting celebration brought the wall down, with gleeful Berliners chipping away at the barrier; it was gradually dismantled. By 2005 only a few sections of the wall and some watch towers still existed—the capital no longer divided, the country a unified, democratic Germany.

EARLY TWENTY–FIRST CENTURY

How is the current era characterized?

Ask the question of most any observer, and the answer would include catchphrases like "global marketplace," "global village," or "globalization." Modern communications and transportation connect people as never before—businesses enjoy broader markets for their goods and services, manufacturing facilities and jobs are located far from the offices of the companies that market them, and people of many nationalities, races, and religions have more and more contact with one another every day, for both business and pleasure. Some observers worry that this contact will blur rich cultural differences, diluting diversity; others say that globalization will bring tolerance and increase understanding. Whatever the case, we are living our lives on a global stage: The things we buy and use are as likely to carry "Made in China" or "Made in Mexico" labels as they are any other country; people continents away talk to each other not just over the telephone, but via instant messaging, e-mail, Internet chat rooms, and social networking sites; we have an international forum—the Internet—for buying, selling, and publishing; and we can get almost anywhere in the world with all due haste. Everything travels faster today, including ideas.

The upsides are many. Modern communications and transportation made it possible, for example, for the world to mobilize aid to victims of the Southeast Asian tsunami of December 2004. But there are downsides as well. Critics say globalization is fueling the exploitation of workers in developing nations, contributing to a modern slave trade, rapidly depleting resources, and wiping out environmental diversity. These are some of the reasons protesters have demonstrated outside meetings of the World Trade Organization, why some people opposed the North American Free Trade Agreement (NAFTA) and CAFTA (Central American Free Trade Agreement), and why many people dislike that American popular culture is marketed around the world. The problem could be distilled to this: diversity versus homogeneity. And the resulting culture clashes are not restricted to the realm of scholarly thought; they are making headline news. The enemy is no longer the strong-armed, nuclear-fortified, absolutist government of the Cold War era (though, as of mid-2005, North Korea remained a serious concern); the enemy, as the U.S. State Department reminds us, is any group of individuals with extreme views.

Who is the enemy of the day?

Terrorists. News stories reinforce that this catch-all term does not only include the 9/11 hijackers and their al Qaeda associates, the Madrid and London train bombers, and suicide bombers in Gaza, but antigovernment extremists who blew up a federal building in Oklahoma City, a still-unknown distributor of deadly anthrax, and animal rights activists who routinely damage property to make a point. Terrorism is a decades (some might argue, centuries) old problem. Remember Birmingham, Alabama's Sixteenth Street Baptist Church, bombed in 1963 by white supremacists during Sunday services. Remember the 1972 summer Olympics in Munich, when the Arab terrorist group Black September killed eleven Israeli athletes held captive in the Olympic village. Remember the October 1985 hijacking of the *Achille Lauro* cruise ship by members of the Palestinian Liberation Front, who killed a wheel-chair-bound American Jew. Remember the December 1988 bombing of Pan Am Flight 103, which came down in Lockerbie, Scotland, claiming 270 lives. The list is long and growing.

The shocking events of September 11, 2001, centered the world's attention on the problem of well-financed terrorist networks that can turn the freedoms of democracy against civilians—and who are feared to have in their possession (or access to) powerful weapons of mass destruction (WMD). The events of that day launched what the U.S. government calls the Global War on Terrorism, a long battle that even the president acknowledged may not be winnable in a traditional sense. This is a new kind of war, fought not against a nation, but against anarchists halfway around the world, and in our midst. Globalization and terrorism are the twin concerns of the modern era.

GOVERNMENT AND POLITICS

What was the first national government?

It is believed to have been that of the first Egyptian king, Menes, who united Upper and Lower Egypt in 3110 B.C.E. and founded a central government at Memphis (near present-day Cairo). Ruling for sixty-two years, Menes established the first of what would eventually number thirty dynasties that ruled ancient Egypt for nearly 3,000 years—until 332 B.C.E.

By the time the Third Dynasty began around 2700 B.C.E., the central government was well established and strong—subjects believed their kings and queens to be half-human and half-god. The pharaohs lived in magnificent luxury: Palaces and temples were built for them and were filled with exotic goods from other lands. These treasures were even buried with the pharaohs in order to be enjoyed in the afterworld. It was during the Third Dynasty that the 500-year period known as the Old Kingdom or the Pyramid Age began; it would become the period that saw the building of gigantic pyramids for Egypt's kings.

EMPIRES, ROYALTY, AND DYNASTIES

Was King Tut the greatest ruler of ancient Egypt?

No, in fact, King Tut's reign was relatively unimportant in the vast history of ancient Egypt. A ruler of the Eighteenth Dynasty, Tutankhamen (c. 1370–1352 B.C.E.) was in power from age nine (1361 B.C.E.) until his death at the age of eighteen—a nine-year period that would be of little significance were it not for the November 1922 discovery of his tomb in the Valley of the Kings near ancient Thebes (present-day Luxor). Of the twenty-seven pharaohs buried near Thebes, only the tomb of the minor king, Tutankhamen, was spared looting through the ages. Having not been opened since ancient times, the tomb still contained its treasures.

In the antechamber English archeologist Howard Carter (1873–1939) found more than 600 artifacts, including funerary bouquets, sandals, robes, cups and jars, a painted casket, life-size wooden statues of Tutankhamen, animal-sided couches, remnants of chariots, and a golden throne. In the burial chambers a team of archeologists discovered four golden shrines and the golden coffin containing the royal mummy of Tutankhamen—complete with a golden mask covering his head and shoulders.

Earlier in his career, Carter had discovered the tombs of King Tut's predecessors, Queen Hatshepsut (c. 1520–c. 1468 B.C.E.) and King Thutmose IV (d. 1417 B.C.E.), both of whom were also rulers during Egypt's Eighteenth Dynasty.

Who was arguably the greatest ruler of ancient Egypt?

Ramesses II (1303 B.C.E.–1213 B.C.E.)—also known as Ramesses the Great—may be the greatest of all ancient Egyptian pharaohs, or rulers. Many referred to him as the "Great One" or the "Great Ancestor." He took command of the empire as a teenager and ruled for more than sixty years. Many famous temples and monuments were completed during his reign—a testament to his power and influence. He lived until he was ninety years old. Numerous other pharaohs took the name Ramesses, but none could match his accomplishments or power.

THE MAYA EMPIRE

Was the Maya Empire the most advanced early civilization?

In some regards, the Maya were more advanced than other civilizations. Their development preceded that of the other agrarian civilizations in North and South America, principally the Aztec and the Inca.

The Maya were an agricultural people who in about 1000 B.C.E. settled in southern Mexico and Central America. Their territory covered Mexico's Yucatan Peninsula, Belize, much of Guatemala, and parts of Honduras and El Salvador. They developed a civilization that was highly advanced: Not only did the Maya produce remarkable architecture (including flat-topped pyramids, temples, and towers that are still visited by tourists today) and art (including sculpture, painting, and murals), but they developed their own writing system—probably the first in the Western Hemisphere.

They used this system to record time, astronomical events, their history, and religion (they believed in more than 160 gods). They also developed an advanced mathematics as well as a 365-day calendar believed by some to be even more accurate than the Gregorian calendar in use today.

At its peak, the Maya population numbered some fourteen million. Their history is divided into three periods. The Pre-Classic period began about the time they originated (roughly 1000 B.C.E.) and extended into 300 C.E.; this was the group's formative period. During the Classic period, 300 to 900, Maya culture spread throughout the area and city-centers were developed at Copán (Honduras), Palenque, Uxmal, and Chichén Itzá (Mexico), and Piedras Negras, Uaxactún, and Tikal (Guatemala). Scholars believe that Tikal was home to some 50,000 people and was not only a center for government, education, economics, and science, but was also a spiritual mecca for the Maya.

It was in the second half of the Classic period that the Maya made their greatest accomplishments in art and science: Europe would not produce a superior system of mathematics for centuries to come. During the Post-Classic period (900 to1546), they were invaded by the Toltecs. However, the Maya absorbed these people rather than being conquered by them. Nevertheless, by the time the Spaniards arrived in the mid-1500s, the Maya civilization was in decline. Some historians attribute this to widespread famine or disease while others believe the decline was due to a rebellion of the people against the harsh government. Though they were conquered by the Spaniards and became assimilated into the larger culture that developed in the region, Maya Indians still survive in Mexico and Central America today.

AZTEC EMPIRE

How did the Aztec and Inca Empires compare with the Maya?

While all were advanced civilizations that were eventually conquered by Spaniards, the Inca and Aztec cultures reached their peaks in the fifteenth century—just before the arrival of the Europeans in the New World. The Maya civilization reached its zenith about 500 years earlier and was already in decline by the time of European incursion. Each group also occupied a different region of the Americas, where each carved out its own stronghold and flourished: The Aztecs settled in central Mexico, the Incas in western South America (primarily Peru), and the Maya in the Yucatan Peninsula and Central America. There is evidence that they traded with each other as well as with American Indians to the north.

The Aztecs founded their central city of Tenochtitlán (the site of Mexico City) about 1325. A poor nomadic people before their arrival in Mexico's central region, the Aztecs believed the Lake Texcoco marsh was a prophetic place to settle. Before they built it into a great city, they first had to fill in the swampy area, which they did by creating artificial islands. In the 1500s, when the Spanish first saw the remarkable city—with its system of causeways, canals, bridges, and aqueducts—they called it the Venice of the New World. In addition to constructing the impressive trade and cultural center of Tenochtitán, the Aztecs were farmers, astronomers, mathematicians, and historians who recorded the events of their civilization. Their religion was pantheistic, meaning they worshiped many gods. Given that, it's not surprising that when the Spanish conquistadors arrived, at first the Aztecs believed they were gods (or at least, the heavenly hosts of their long-awaited god Quetzalcoatl), and even welcomed them with gifts. Later, the Aztec rose up against the Europeans, but under the leadership of Hernán Cortés (1485–1547), the Spaniards conquered the group, claiming Mexico in August 1521.

The Incas developed one of the most extensive empires in all the Americas. During the hundred years before the arrival of the Europeans, the Incas expanded their territory along the western coast of South America to include parts of present-day Peru, Ecuador, Colombia, Bolivia, Chile, and Argentina. Though it was a vast region, it was nevertheless a closely knit state ruled by a powerful emperor. The government was subdivided down to the local level, but because the emperor required total obedience from his subjects, local rulers were kept in check.

Like the Aztecs in Mexico, the Inca developed an infrastructure that included a network of roads, bridges, and ferries as well as irrigation systems. They, too, built impressive edifices, demonstrating their abilities as engineers. The magnificent city of Machu Picchu was modeled in clay before construction began. The Inca were also skilled craftspeople, working with

Who was Montezuma?

Montezuma I (1398–1469) was a leading Aztec ruler who expanded the empire and consolidated power in a skillful manner. During his nearly thirty-year reign, the empire achieved several conquests of neighboring lands and generally prospered.

Montezuma II (1466–1520) was a later Aztec emperor who also accomplished great things during his reign. In fact, many historical sources say that the Aztec Empire was at its zenith in terms of size during his reign. However, Montezuma and the Aztec Empire fell victim to the Spanish conquistador Hernán Cortés, who conquered the empire and plundered its vast riches for the Spanish Crown.

gold, silver, and textiles. Like the Aztecs, the Incas worshiped many gods. And when the Spanish explorer Francisco Pizarro (c. 1475–1541) arrived in the region in 1532, he was welcomed as a god at first. However, by 1537 the Inca were brought under Spanish control.

THE ROMAN REPUBLIC

What was the government structure of the Roman Republic?

The Roman Republic, which began around 509 B.C.E., was a reaction to the Roman monarchy and the perceived excesses of too much power in one ruler. The Roman Republic, in order to avoid the prospects of tyranny, dispersed power into two elected consuls. Originally, the consuls served one-year terms but later ruled for longer terms. Power was also dispersed by having a senate that officially served as advisors to the consul. But, the Senate had more power than a mere advisory body.

Why was Julius Caesar murdered?

The Roman general and statesman Julius Caesar (100–44 B.C.E.) was stabbed to death in the senate house by a group of men, including some of his former friends, who viewed him as an ambitious tyrant and a threat to the Roman Republic. The date of the assassination, March 15, fell into relatively common usage thanks to William Shakespeare's tragedy, *Julius Caesar* (written in the late 1590s), which has a soothsayer warning the Roman general to "Beware the ides of March." After Caesar's death in 44 B.C.E., a triumvirate was formed to rule Rome, with Lepidus, Octavian (who would in 27 B.C.E. become Augustus, the Roman Empire's first ruler), and Mark Antony sharing power. It was Mark Antony (c. 83–30 B.C.E.), of "Antony and Cleopatra" fame, who aroused the mobs against Caesar's conspirators, driving them out of Rome.

The events illustrate the controversy about Julius Caesar: While some clearly viewed him as a demagogue who forced his way into power, others considered the patrician-born Caesar a man of noble character who defended the rights of the people in an oligarchic state—where the government was controlled by a few people who had only their own interests in mind. This divided opinion has followed Caesar throughout history.

While opinion is still divided on what kind of a ruler Caesar was, there can be no denying his contributions—both to Rome (which would soon emerge as the Roman Empire) and to modern civilization. In his battles, Caesar brought the provinces of Italy under his control and defeated his former co-ruler, Pompey the Great (who had, along with Caesar and Crassus, formed the first triumvirate, from 106 to 48 B.C.E.), effectively ending the oligarchy that had ruled Rome. In so doing, he had succeeded in ending the disorder that had plagued Rome for decades and laid the groundwork for the formation of the empire under his grand-nephew Augustus, in 27 B.C.E. While Caesar was in office, he planned and carried out several reforms, not the least of which was the implementation of the Julian calendar, which he introduced in 46 B.C.E. The Gregorian calendar we use today evolved from it.

Caesar also left a legacy of literature: He penned a total of ten books on his battles in Gaul (c. 58–50 B.C.E.) and on the civil war, which he had more or less started in 49 B.C.E. These clear commentaries are still considered masterpieces of military history.

THE ROMAN EMPIRE

Who were the most important rulers of the Roman Empire?

The 500 years of the Roman Empire (27 B.C.E. to. 476 C.E.) gave history some of its most noteworthy—and most diabolical—leaders. The major emperors are names that are familiar to most every student of Western civilization: Augustus, Tiberius, Caligula, Claudius, Nero, Trajan, Marcus Aurelius, Diocletian, and Constantine I (called "the Great").

Augustus, Tiberius, Caligula, Claudius, and Nero were the first five emperors, a succession covering seventy-five years of Roman rule. Octavian (63 B.C.E.–14 C.E.), later known as Augustus, became Roman emperor when, after the assassination of his great-uncle, Julius Caesar, a power struggle ensued and he defeated Mark Antony and Cleopatra to take the throne. Under Augustus's rule from 27 B.C.E. to 14 C.E. began the 200 years of the Pax Romana, a period of relative peace. During this time no power emerged that was strong enough to sustain conflict with the Roman army. Consequently, Rome was able to turn its attention to the arts, literature, education, and trade.

As second emperor of Rome, Tiberius (42 B.C.E.–37 C.E.) came under the influence of Roman politician and conspirator Sejanus (d. 31 C.E.). Tiberius was the adopted son of Emperor Augustus, and though he had been carefully schooled and groomed to take on the leadership role, ultimately he became a tyrannical ruler; the final years of his reign were marked by viciousness and cruelty. Upon Tiberius's death, his nephew Caligula (12–41 C.E.) ascended the throne. Born Gaius Caesar, he was nicknamed Caligula, meaning "Little Boots," since he was brought up in military camps and at an early age had been dressed as a soldier. For a short time Caligula ruled with moderation. But not long after he came to power he fell ill, and thereafter exhibited the erratic behavior for which he is well known. Most scholars agree that Caligula must have been crazy. He was murdered in 41 C.E., and Claudius (also a nephew to Tiberius) was then proclaimed emperor.

Claudius (10 B.C.E.–54 C.E.) renewed the expansion of Rome, waging battle with Germany, Syria, and Mauritania (present-day Algeria and Morocco), and conquering half of

33

Britain. Though his administration was reportedly well run, he had his enemies; among them was his niece, Agrippina the Younger (15?–59 C.E.), who is believed to have murdered him in 54, after securing her son, Nero, as successor to the throne.

In Nero (37–68 C.E.) the early Roman Empire had perhaps its most despotic ruler: Though his early years in power were marked by the efficient conduct of public affairs, in 59 he had his mother assassinated (she reportedly had tried to rule through her son), and Nero's legacy from that point forward is one of ruthless behavior. He was involved in murder plots, ordered the deaths of many Romans, instituted the persecution of Christians, and led an extravagant lifestyle that emptied the public coffers. He was declared a public enemy by the Roman Senate and in the year 68 took his own life.

With the exception of Augustus, the first century C.E. of the Roman Empire was marked by extreme rulers. The second century C.E. was marked by the leadership of soldiers and statesmen. Trajan (53–117), who ruled from the year 98 until his death nineteen years later, is best known for his military campaigns, which expanded Rome's territory. He was also a builder—constructing bridges, roads, and many buildings. When Marcus Aurelius (121–180) ascended to emperor in 161, he had already been in public office for more than twenty years. A man of great experience, he was reportedly both learned and of gentle character. His generals put down revolting tribes, and in addition to winning victories along the Danube River, his troops also fought barbarians in the north. Diocletian (245?–313?) had served as an army commander before becoming emperor in 284. In an effort to effectively rule the expansive territory, he divided it into four regions, each with its own ruler, though he himself remained the acknowledged chief. Two years before he abdicated the throne (305), he began the persecution of Christians—a surprising move, since he had long been friendly toward them. Unlike his predecessors who died in office, Diocletian had a retirement, which he reportedly spent gardening.

Constantine the Great (who ruled from 306 until his death in 337) is notable for reuniting the regions that Diocletian had created, bringing them all under his rule by 324. He was also the first Roman emperor to convert to Christianity. Theodosius I (347–395), also called "the Great," is known to many since he was the last to rule the united Roman Empire (from 379 to 395).

THE BYZANTINE EMPIRE

Why was Constantine I called "the Great"?

Roman emperor Constantine the Great (c. 275–337) is credited with no less than beginning a new era in history. His father, Constantius, was ruler of the Roman Empire when he died in 306. Though Constantine was named emperor by Roman soldiers, a power struggle ensued. During a battle near Rome in 312, Constantine, who had always been sympathetic toward Christians, reportedly saw a vision of a flaming cross. He emerged from the conflict both converted and victorious. For the next twelve years, Constantine ruled the West Roman Empire while Licinius (also tolerant to Christians) ruled the East. But a struggle between the two emperors ended in death for Licinius and, beginning in 325, Constantine ruled as sole emperor.

During Constantine's reign, Christians regained freedom of worship and the Christian Church became legal. In 325 he convened the Council of Nicaea (from whence came the Nicene Creed so familiar to Christians today). In moving the capital of the Roman Empire to Byzantium (in 330), Constantine shifted the empire's focus from west to east and in so doing laid the foundation for the Byzantine Empire. The Eastern Orthodox Church regards Constantine as a saint.

How was the Byzantine Empire formed?

The Byzantine Empire was a continuation of the Roman Empire—its citizens even called themselves Romans. Two dates are given for the formation of the Byzantine Empire, which, though boundaries shifted constantly, was centered in Asia Minor and the Balkan Peninsula: In 395 C.E., upon the death of emperor Theodosius the Great, the Roman Empire was divided into two: East and West. In the years that followed, the West Roman Empire was subject to repeated attacks from nomadic barbarian groups, and Rome finally fell in 476. The East Roman Empire survived as the Byzantine Empire, which after the fall of Rome laid claim to much of the lands in the west.

However, many historians date the beginning of the Byzantine Empire earlier—at 330 C.E., when Roman emperor Constantine the Great moved the capital of the then united Roman Empire from Rome to Byzantium (present-day Istanbul, Turkey—subsequently known as Constantinople). By this definition of the empire, Constantine the Great was its first ruler. He was succeeded by nearly one hundred rulers over the course of more than 1,000 years of Byzantine rule. At its height, during the sixth century reign of Justinian I from 483 to 565, the empire included parts of southern and eastern Europe, northern Africa, and the Middle East. The Byzantine Empire ended when the Ottoman Turks conquered Constantinople in 1453.

THE OTTOMAN EMPIRE

What was the Ottoman Empire?

It was a vast Turkish state founded in the thirteenth century by the Osmani Turks, who were led by descendants of Osman I (1258–c. 1326). By the middle of the next century, the Ottoman Empire consisted roughly of modern-day Turkey (the terms "Turkey" and "Ottoman Empire" are used interchangeably). The empire was expanded further by conquests during the 1400s, including the conquest of the Byzantine Empire in 1453. At its height, the Ottoman Empire extended over an area that included the Balkan Peninsula (present-day Slovenia, Croatia, Bosnia and Herzegovina, Macedonia, Yugoslavia, Romania, Bulgaria, Albania, Greece, and Turkey), Syria, Egypt, Iraq, the northern coast of Africa, Palestine, and parts of Arabia, Russia, and Hungary. The capital was placed at Constantinople (present-day Istanbul, Turkey). Thus the Turks established a Muslim empire that would remain a formidable force and influence in the region and in Europe for the next three centuries.

During the 1500s and 1600s the Ottoman Empire was the most powerful in the world. It reached its most glorious heights during the reign of Süleyman the Magnificent (1494–1566), who ruled from 1520 to 1566: It was he who added parts of Hungary to the Ottoman territory. He also tried to take Vienna, but failed. He did succeed in strengthening the

35

Ottoman navy, which dominated the Mediterranean Sea. Süleyman was not only an expansionist, but a patron of the arts and a builder. He ordered the construction of mosques (to spread the Islamic religion throughout the empire), bridges, and other public works.

But by the time World War I began in 1914, the Ottoman Empire had been in decline for some 300 years and only consisted of Asia Minor, parts of southwestern Asia, and part of the Balkan Peninsula. As one of the losing Central powers, the Ottoman Empire was dissolved in 1922 by the peace treaties that ended the war.

Yeni Camii Mosque in Istanbul, Turkey.

CHINA

THE TANG DYNASTY

What was the Tang dynasty?

The Tang (617 to 907) was the sixth-to-last Chinese dynasty. It's well known since the period saw great achievements not only in government and business, but in letters and the arts—principally lyrical poetry, formal prose, painting, sculpture, and porcelain pottery. The first published book, the *Diamond Sutra,* was produced during this time (in 868). Considered a golden age of Chinese civilization, the Tang was also an age of great expansion. At its height, the empire stretched from Turkmenistan in the west to Korea (which was a vassal state) in the east, and from Manchuria to northern India. As a result, trade prospered, with Chinese jade, porcelain, silk, rice, spices, and teas exported to India, the Middle East, and Europe. One historian called the Tang "the consummate Chinese dynasty…formidable, influential, and innovative."

One of the Tang's innovations was the balance of administrative power. Government was separated into three main branches: the Imperial Secretariat (which organized the emperor's directives into policies), the Imperial Chancellery (which reviewed the policies and monitored bureaucracy), and the Department of States Affairs (which carried out the policies through the administration of six ministries). Add to this triumvirate a Board of Censors, which ensured that corruption was kept to a minimum. This form of government outlasted the Tang dynasty: Subsequent monarchies perpetuated the system into the twentieth century.

Yet another example of the forward thinking of the Tang dynasty was in civil service. Candidates for public service were trained in the Confucian principles before they took an exam that would qualify them for official duty.

THE SONG DYNASTY

Who began the Song dynasty?

After the Tang dynasty collapsed, China fell into the hands of rival warlords, none of whom could unify the country. However, a general named Chao K'uang, also known as Zhao Khuangyin, unified the country and began what became known as the Song dynasty. He became known as Emperor Taizu. Upon his death, his younger brother, Zhao Kuangyi, succeeded him (instead of either of his two sons).

The Song dynasty never controlled as much of China as did the Tang dynasty. But, it was still successful in many respects. Under the Song dynasty, industry and trade blossomed, the government issued paper currency, and the Song dynasty became a real maritime power. The Song dynasty lasted for more than three hundred years, ending in 1279 with a successful Mongol invasion.

THE MING DYNASTY

What were the highlights of the Ming dynasty?

The focus on Chinese culture that was the hallmark of the Ming dynasty (1368 to 1644) was both its strength and its weakness. After the foreign Mongols (whose dynasty had been established by Kublai Khan in 1260) were overthrown as rulers of China in 1368, the Ming emperors returned their—and their subjects'—attention to those things that are distinctly Chinese. The focus on Chinese culture produced a flowering in the arts, evidenced by the name Ming itself, meaning "bright" or "brilliant." Architects working during this period produced the splendor of Beijing's Forbidden City. Ming porcelain, bronze, and lacquer-ware are coveted collectors' items today. Additionally, the novel and drama flourished.

And though the Ming rulers promoted this artistic renaissance and reinstated Confucianism and the program of civil service suspended by the Mongols, the rulers' myopia prevented them from seeing the threat of the nomadic Manchu people on the horizon. In 1644 the Manchus invaded from the north and conquered China, setting up the last dynastic period in Chinese history (it lasted until 1912). Nevertheless, it was the Ming, and not the Manchu, who formed the last great and truly Chinese dynasty.

EUROPE

CAROLINGIAN EMPIRE

What was the Carolingian Empire?

The empire, which united most of western Europe under a single leader from about 734 until 987, was named for the Carolingians, a family of Frankish kings.

After the decline of the Roman Empire (in 476), various Germanic tribes (including the Goths, the Vandals, the Franks, and the Anglo-Saxons) dominated western Europe—fight-

Why is Charlemagne so well known?

Charlemagne's popularity with history students is due not only to the ruler's great accomplishments during his lifetime, but also to the fact that these accomplishments were documented: His biography, titled *Vita Caroli Magni* (*The Life of Charlemagne*) was written by a fellow named Einhard (c. 770–840), who was his adviser.

Charlemagne (742–814), or Charles the Great, became king of the western Franks when his father, Pepin the Short (c. 714–768) died in 768. Upon the death of his brother, Carloman, in 771, Charles became king of all the Franks. He then went on to conquer much of western Europe, including Saxony, Lombardy, northeastern Spain, and Bavaria. He sometimes employed brutal tactics in bringing people and regions under control: During the last two decades of the eighth century, he used mass executions to subdue Saxon rebellions. Charlemagne succeeded in uniting all of these areas under one empire, and on Christmas Day 800, he had Pope Leo III (c. 750–816) crown him Emperor of the West, thus initiating the Holy Roman Empire.

As a patron of the arts, literature, and science, Charlemagne revived western Europe, which had been in decline since the fall of the West Roman Empire (in 476). He is credited with laying the foundation for the Holy Roman Empire and the European civilization that developed later in the Middle Ages. He ruled until his death in 814.

ing each other as well as the advancing Muslims to protect and expand their territories. In 719 Charles Martel (c. 688–741) united the lands of all the Franks under his rule. (The Franks were the descendants of Germanic tribes who settled in the Rhine River region of western Europe.) He then went on to protect France from Arab incursion and campaigned against the Burgundians and the Frisians, eventually bringing them under his control. Upon his death in 741, Charles Martel was succeeded by his son, Pepin III (known better perhaps as Pepin the Short; c. 714–768). It was Pepin who established the Carolingian Empire and brought the Lombards into the empire. Upon his death, he was succeeded by his son Charlemagne, or Charles the Great (742–814).

THE HOLY ROMAN EMPIRE

Who were the Habsburgs?

The Habsburgs were Europe's most powerful royal family. Even if one chose to argue the point of power, there can be no arguing the longevity of the house of Habsburg: They supplied Europe with a nearly uninterrupted stream of rulers for more than 600 years.

Also spelled Hapsburg (which is closer to the pronunciation, HAPS-berg), the name came from the castle of Habichtsburg (meaning "Hawk's Castle"), built during the early eleventh century in Switzerland. The first member of the family to bear the name was Count

Werner I (who died in 1096). It was Werner's descendant, Rudolf I (1218–1291), who was elected king of Germany and the Holy Roman Empire in 1273. When Rudolf conquered Austria three years later, he established that country as the family's new home. Austria, Bohemia, Germany, Hungary, and Spain were among the European states ruled by the house of Habsburg. With only one exception, the Habsburg family also ruled the Holy Roman Empire from 1438 (when Albert II was elected) until 1806.

It was the reign of Emperor Charles V during the sixteenth century that the Habsburg influence reached its high-water mark. When in 1496 Spain's Philip I (called Philip the Handsome; 1478–1506) married Joan of Castile (1479–1555), it assured that their son Charles V (1500–1558) would inherit the crown of Spain, which he did in 1516. (Charles was grandson to Spain's King Ferdinand and Queen Isabella.) He also inherited the rest of what by then was a vast empire, and he ruled as Holy Roman Emperor from 1519 until 1556.

Charles V is considered the greatest of all the Habsburgs, though he did face problems. Chief among these were the Protestant Reformation; opposition from his lifelong rival, Francis I (1494–1547), king of France; and the Ottoman Turks, who were at the height of their power during his reign. Nevertheless, he was a successful ruler and his accomplishments included Spain's conquest of lands in the New World—Mexico (at the hands of Hernán Cortés, 1485–1547) and Peru (by Francisco Pizarro; c. 1475–1541).

In 1867 the Habsburg Empire was reorganized as the Austro-Hungarian monarchy. That monarchy was dissolved in 1918, after World War I, with the Treaty of Versailles establishing new boundaries for the successor states.

FERDINAND AND ISABELLA

Why were Spain's King Ferdinand and Queen Isabella so powerful?

The 1469 marriage of Ferdinand (1452–1516) and Isabella (1451–1504) brought previously separate Spanish kingdoms (Aragon and Castile) under joint control. Together the monarchs went on to rule Spain and expand their realm of influence until Isabella's death in 1504. (Ferdinand ruled without his wife thereafter.) Theirs was a reign that seemed to have religion on its side: In 1496 Pope Alexander VI conferred upon each of them the title "Catholic," as in, "Ferdinand the Catholic" and "Isabella the Catholic." And for good reason, because the king's and queen's most well-known acts seemed to have been motivated by their beliefs.

It was Ferdinand and Isabella who in 1478 established the infamous Spanish Inquisition, a court that imprisoned or killed Catholics who were suspected of not following religious teachings. While the Inquisition was aimed at discovering and punishing Muslims and Jews who had converted to Catholicism but who were thought to be insincere, soon all Spaniards came to fear its power. In 1482 the monarchs undertook a war with the (Muslim) Moors, conquering the last Moorish stronghold at Granada in 1492, and forcing them back to Africa after four centuries of occupation—and influence—in the Iberian Peninsula (Spain and Portugal). The recovery of Iberia had been motivated by religion; when the king and queen expelled the Moors, they also believed they were expelling Islam from their kingdom.

That year, 1492, was a fateful one for the Spanish: Not only were the Moors driven out, but Ferdinand and Isabella also turned their attention to the Jewish "threat," expelling them, too.

(Those who remained went underground with their faith; those Iberian Jews who migrated spread their division of Judaism, called Sephardim, to North Africa and the Middle East.)

Most students of history know 1492 best as the year that explorer Christopher Columbus (1451–1506) sailed to the New World. It was Ferdinand and Isabella who sponsored his voyage, believing that the conquered lands would not only add to their authority but would provide new territory for the spread of Catholicism. The Spaniards soon emerged as a formidable sea power in the Atlantic.

THE ROMANOV DYNASTY

Who were the Romanovs?

The Romanov family ruled Russia from 1613 until 1917, when Nicholas II (1868–1918) was overthrown by the Russian Revolution (1905–17). The dynasty was established by Michael Romanov, grandnephew to Ivan the Terrible, who ruled from 1533 to 1584. There were eighteen Romanov rulers, including the much-studied Peter the Great, who ruled from 1682 to 1725, and Catherine the Great, who ruled from 1762 to 1796.

As the last tsar of Russia, Nicholas II, who ruled from 1894 to 1917, likely suffered not only the recrimination that was due him, but the public hostility that had accumulated over centuries of ruthless Romanov leadership. Nicholas's difficulties came to a head when he got Russia involved in World War I (1914–1918), which produced serious hardships for the Russian people and for which there was little public support. Once Tsar Nicholas was overthrown (and later killed) in the Russian Revolution (1905–17), Bolshevik leader Vladimir Lenin (1870–1924) set about extracting Russia from the conflict by agreeing to sever concessions to Germany. Oddly enough, the Romanov family had, in the fourteenth century, originated with a German nobleman, Andrew Kobyla, who had immigrated to Russia.

Why were tsars Peter and Catherine known as "the Great"?

The epithet "the Great" can be misleading: While Romanov tsars Peter the Great, who ruled from 1682 to 1725, and Catherine the Great, who ruled from 1762 to 1796, are among the best-known of the Romanov dynasty and both had many accomplishments during their reigns, they are also known for having increased their power at the expense of others.

Peter is recognized for introducing western European civilization to Russia and for elevating Russia to the status of a great European power. But he also relied on the serfs (the peasants who were little more than indentured servants to the lords) not only to provide the bulk of the funding he needed to fight almost continuous wars, but for the manpower as well: Most soldiers were serfs. The man responsible for establishing schools (including the Academy of Sciences), reforming the calendar, and simplifying the alphabet also carried out ruthless reforms. Peter's most vainglorious act was, perhaps, to move the capital from Moscow to the city he had built for himself on the swampy lands ceded by Sweden: St. Petersburg (known as Petrograd from 1914 to 1924, and as Leningrad from 1924 to 1991). As his "window on Europe," Peter succeeded in making the city into a brilliant cultural center.

For her part, Catherine the Great may well be acknowledged as a patron of the arts and literature (one who corresponded with the likes of French writer Voltaire; 1694–1778), but she, too, increased the privileges of the nobility while making the lives of the serfs even more miserable. Her true colors were shown by how she ascended to power in the first place. In 1744 she married Peter (III), who became tsar of Russia in 1762. That same year, Catherine conspired with her husband's enemies to depose him. He was later killed. And so Catherine came to power, proclaiming herself tsarina. She began her reign by attempting reforms, but a peasant uprising (1773–74) and the French Revolution (which began in 1789) prompted her only to strengthen and protect her absolute authority. Like Peter the Great, she, too, extended the frontiers of the empire through a series of conquests. By the end of her reign, in 1796, Catherine had reduced even the free peasants to the level of serfdom.

GREAT BRITAIN

What are England's royal "houses"?

England's royal houses are simply families, including ancestors, descendants, and kin. Since 1066 England's rulers have come from a series of ten royal houses: Normandy (ruled 1066 to 1135), Blois (1135 to 1154), Plantagenet (1154 to 1399), Lancaster (1399 to 1471), York (1471 to 1485), Tudor (1485 to 1603), Stuart (1603 to 1649, restored 1660 to 1714), Hanover (1714 to 1901), Saxe-Coborg (1901 to 1910), and Windsor (1910 to present).

Prior to the establishment of the House of Normandy, England had been ruled by Saxons and Danes since 802. The first king of the House of Normandy was William I (also known as William the Conqueror [c. 1028–1087]), who was the son of the French Duke of Normandy. William invaded England in 1066, on the death of Edward the Confessor and the ascension of Harold II (c. 1022–1066). Ousting Harold, William was coronated at Westminster Abbey on Christmas Day. William's grandson, Stephen, was all that consisted of the short-lived reign of the House of Blois (named such since Stephen was the Count of Blois and Chartres, though he was raised in the court of his uncle, King Henry I, whom he succeeded).

The House of Plantagenet, also called the House of Anjou, included the ten-year reign (1189 to 1199) of Richard I, or Richard the Lionheart (1157–1099), who fought his father, Henry II (1068–1135), and his brothers for control of the throne. Richard's military prowess made him the hero of romantic legends. Thereafter, two contending branches of the House of Plantagenet—the houses of Lancaster and York—vied for the crown in the infamous War of the Roses (1455–85). The struggle finally ended when Henry VII (a Lancaster) ascended the throne and married into the House of York, reuniting the two sides of the family under the newly minted House of Tudor.

The Tudors were a famous lot, remembered for the reigns of Henry VIII (1509 to 1547) and his daughters, Mary I (1553 to 1558) and Elizabeth I (1558 to 1603). The Tudors were followed by the Stuarts, whose reign was interrupted by the establishment of the Commonwealth and Protectorate under Oliver Cromwell (1599–1658). The house was restored to power, giving history the eight-year period known as the Restoration, in 1660. It was King William III (1650–1702), a Stuart, and Queen Mary II (1662–1694), who began in 1689 to rule England in a more modern fashion—through Parliament.

41

A Stuart descendant, George I (1660–1727), established the House of Hanover, which originated in Germany. Queen Victoria (1819–1901), who presided over the Victorian Age (1837–1901), was of the House of Hanover. She was succeeded by her son, Edward VII (1841–1910), who established the House of Saxe-Coburg. Technically, this is the royal house still at the helm today—the name was changed to Windsor during World War I (1914–1918).

THE TUDORS

How did the House of Tudor originate?

The name of a royal family that ruled England for well over a century, from 1485 to 1603, came from a Welshman, Owen Tudor, who sometime after 1422 married Catherine of Valois (1401–1437), the widow of Henry V, who ruled from 1413 to 1422. The family did not come to power until Henry VII (1457–1509) ascended the throne. Ruling from 1485 until his death in 1509, Henry VII ended the bitter, thirty-year War of the Roses—during which two noble families, the houses of Lancaster and York, had struggled against each other for control of the throne. (The conflict earned its name since the badge of each house depicted a rose, one red and the other white.) In taking power, Henry VII became the head of the House of Lancaster, and in 1486 he married into the House of York, thus uniting the two former enemies and founding his own Tudor dynasty. (He's known as Henry Tudor.)

Why is Henry VIII so famous (or infamous)?

The reign of Henry VIII, from 1509 to 1547, is perhaps the most well-known Tudor monarchy. It was marked by papal conflicts and England's subsequent break with the Roman Catholic Church. When Henry's wife, Catherine of Aragon (1485–1536), failed to produce a male heir, he appealed to the pope to grant him a divorce. The request was of course denied. Though Henry went on to have his marriage to Catherine declared invalid (on the grounds that she was his brother's widow) and he secretly married Anne Boleyn (c. 1507–1536) in 1533, his troubles with the church continued. In 1534 he set up the Church of England, declaring the monarch as its head. He went to extreme measures to ensure the act was upheld— even executing his appointed chancellor, Sir Thomas More (1478–1535), for his refusal to acknowledge royal supremacy.

Henry VIII was eventually successful in procuring a male heir to the throne—but it

Henry VIII

required a third marriage, to Jane Seymour (c. 1509–1537): His son, Edward VI (1537–53), succeeded him in 1547. Nevertheless, it was Henry VIII's daughters who went on to make history. Mary I, who ruled England and Ireland from 1553 to 1558, was the daughter of Henry and his first wife, Catherine of Aragon. In 1554 Mary wed Spain's Philip II (1527–1598), forming a temporary alliance between the two powers. The following year she realigned England with the Catholic Church, undertaking the persecution of Protestants and earning herself the name "Bloody Mary."

Why did Queen Elizabeth I have an entire age named after her?

Ascending the throne in 1558, Queen Elizabeth (1533–1603) remained in power until 1603, a forty-five-year period during which England dominated the seas to become a European power; colonization began, with Sir Walter Raleigh (1554–1618) and others establishing British settlements in North America; culture flourished, with the likes of William Shakespeare (1564–1616), Christopher Marlowe (1564–1593), and Sir Edmund Spenser (1552–1599) producing literary masterpieces; and industry and commerce boomed. This was the Elizabethan Age, one of England's most prosperous times.

One of the most well-known events of Elizabeth's reign was England's defeat of the Spanish Armada in July–August 1588. This event has an interesting twist. The only child of Henry VIII (1491–1547) and his second wife, Anne Boleyn (c. 1507–1536), Elizabeth had succeeded her half-sister Mary Tudor (1516–1558) as queen. In the summer of 1588, the "invincible" Spanish fleet, which was headed to invade England, had been dispatched by none other than Spain's Philip II (1527–1598), Mary Tudor's former husband. Though the English were severely outnumbered (having only 34 ships to Spain's 132), they were aided by weather and defeated the Spanish Armada on August 8. This victory at sea opened the world to English trade and colonization.

Queen Elizabeth was the last of the Tudor rulers, who are credited with strengthening the monarchy in England. They were succeeded by the House of Stuart in 1603, when James I (1566–1625), who ruled from 1603 to 1625, ascended the throne. It is that James who gave the world the King James Version of the Bible. He is also notable for having been the son of Mary, Queen of Scots (1542–1587), whom Elizabeth I had reluctantly put to death.

HOUSE OF STUART

Who was Mary, Queen of Scots?

Mary Stuart was born in 1542 to James V of Scotland, who ruled from 1513 to 1542, and his wife, Mary of Guise. When Mary was just six days old, her father died, making the infant a queen. Her mother ruled the country as a regent until 1561, when Mary officially took on her duties. She was, by all reports, a beautiful and charming young woman whose courage and mettle would be tested by time. When she ascended the throne, she inherited her mother's struggle with the Protestants, who were led by John Knox (1513–1572), a former Catholic priest who was involved in the Reformation. As a Roman Catholic, Mary was subject to harsh verbal attacks issued by Knox, who denounced the pope's authority and the practices of the church. But this was not the worst of her troubles: In 1565 Mary wed her

English cousin, Lord Darnley (1545–1567), in an attempt to secure her claim to the English throne as successor to Elizabeth I (1533–1603), also her cousin.

But Mary's ambitions would be her undoing. She quickly grew to dislike her husband, who became aligned with her Protestant opponents and successfully carried out a plot to murder—in her presence—Mary's adviser, David Rizzio (c. 1533–1566). Surprisingly, Mary and Darnley reconciled shortly thereafter (a politically savvy move on her part), and she conceived a child, James, who was born in 1566. Darnley had enemies of his own, and one year later he was murdered. Mary promptly married the Earl of Bothwell (1536–1578), with whom she had fallen in love well before becoming a widow. Bothwell was accused of Darnley's murder, and though he was acquitted, his marriage to the queen shocked Scotland. The people took up arms, forcing Mary to abdicate the throne in 1567. She was twenty-five years old.

Fleeing to England, Mary, Queen of Scots, was given refuge by Elizabeth I (1533–1603). Though she was technically a prisoner, Mary nevertheless was able to conspire with Elizabeth's enemies—including English Catholics and the Spanish—in attempts to kill her. When one such plot was discovered in 1586, Mary was charged for her involvement in it and was put on trial. Found guilty, she was put to death in 1587, though Elizabeth hesitated to take such action.

THE WINDSORS

How did the House of Windsor originate?

The origins of Windsor, the family name of the royal house of Great Britain, can be traced to the 1840 marriage of Queen Victoria (who ruled from 1837 to 1901) to her first cousin Albert, the son of the Duke of Saxe-Coburg-Gotha (in present-day Germany). As a foreigner, Prince Albert had to overcome the distrust of the British public, which he did by proving himself to be a devoted husband to Queen Victoria and by demonstrating his genuine concern in Britain's national affairs. Victoria and Albert had nine children. Their oldest son, Albert Edward (1841–1910), became King Edward VII upon Victoria's death in 1901. But Edward's reign lasted only until 1910, when he died and his son, George V (1865–1936), ascended the throne. George was king during World War I (1914–1918), and, in 1917, with Britain and Germany bitter enemies, he denounced his ties and claims to Germany, superseding his grandfather's (Prince Albert's) family name of Wettin and establishing the House of Windsor.

Thus, George V was the first ruling member of the House of Windsor. The others were Edward VIII (1894–1972), who abdicated the throne in 1936 so that he could marry American socialite Wallis Simpson (1896–1986); George VI (1895–1952), who became king upon his brother Edward's abdication and who would work tirelessly during World War II (1939–1945) to keep up the morale of the British people; and Elizabeth II (1926–), George VI's elder daughter, who still reigns as Queen of England as of this printing. Elizabeth, who ascended the throne in 1952, proclaimed that she and all her descendants who bear the title prince or princess are to be known as Windsor.

Which British monarch has ruled the longest?

Queen Victoria (1819–1901) claims the distinction of having remained on the throne of England the longest—a whopping sixty-four years. She became queen in June 1837 upon the death of her uncle, King William IV (1765–1837). Since she was but a teenager at the time, during the early years of her reign she relied on the guidance of the prime minister, the tactful Lord Melbourne (William Lamb; 1779–1848), whom she counted as a friend. After marrying Prince Albert (1819–1861) in 1840, she also sought out advice from him and his adviser. But by 1850 she had grown confident in her abilities, and she managed the country's affairs with authority. Later in her reign, Prime Ministers Benjamin Disraeli (1804–1881) and William Gladstone (1809–1898) gradually secured increased authority for that office—without alienating the queen. It is for this reason that she is often seen as the first modern monarch, of which she remains a lasting symbol. Queen Victoria celebrated her Diamond Jubilee in 1897 amidst an outpouring of public support. She remained on the throne four more years, until her death in 1901.

During her sixty-four-year reign, Victoria presided over the rise of industrialization in Great Britain as well as British imperialism abroad. Architecture, art, and literature flourished, in part due to the influence and interests of Prince Albert. It was the prince who, in 1851, sponsored the forward-looking Great Exhibition at London's Crystal Palace. It was the first international exposition—a world fair. The grand Crystal Palace remained a symbol of the Victorian Age until it was destroyed by fire in 1936.

On September 9, 2015, Queen Elizabeth II broke Queen Victoria's record for longest-reigning British monarch.

Why is the Magna Carta important?

The Magna Carta, arguably the most famous document in British history, has had many interpreters since it was signed by King John (1167–1216), who was under pressure to do so, on June 15, 1215, "in the meadow which is called Runnymede, between Windsor and Staines," in Surrey, England. Drawn up by English barons who were angered by the king's encroachment on their rights, the charter has been credited with no less than insuring personal liberty and putting forth the rights of the individual, which include the guarantee of a trial by jury: "No freeman shall be arrested and imprisoned, or dispossessed, or outlawed, or banished, or in any way molested; nor will be set forth against him, nor send against him, unless by the lawful judgment of his peers, and by the law of the land."

The document, to which John was forced to put his seal, asserted the rights of the barons, churchmen, and townspeople, and provided for the king's assurance that he would not encroach on their privileges. In short, the Magna Carta stipulated that the king, too, was subject to the laws of the land.

In that the Magna Carta made a provision for a Great Council, to be comprised of nobles and clergy who would approve the actions of the king vis-a-vis his subjects and ensure the tenets set forth in the charter were upheld, it is credited with laying the foundation for a parliamentary government in England.

After signing it, John immediately appealed to Pope Innocent III (1160 or 1161–1216), who issued an annulment of the charter. Nevertheless, John died before he could fight it, and the Magna Carta (which means "Great Charter") was later upheld as the basis of English feudal justice. It is still considered by many to be the cornerstone of constitutional government.

THE BIRTH OF MODERN
GOVERNMENT: BRITAIN

How old is the British parliament?

The legislative assembly of Great Britain has roots dating back to the Middle Ages (500 to 1350) when a great council, known as the Curia Regis, advised the king. This body was made up of nobility and clergy. The body evolved over time and progressively gained more power to govern.

Today Parliament consists of the House of Commons, a democratically elected body (roughly equivalent to the U.S. House of Representatives); the House of Lords, which consists of noblemen (dukes, marquesses, earls, viscounts, and barons) as well as high-ranking Anglican clergy (bishops and abbots); and the monarch (king or queen). Since 1911 the power of the House of Lords has been negligible, with the House of Commons charged with electing the prime minister (who must be a member of Commons). The prime minister—not the monarch—is the executive head of government.

Why was Oliver Cromwell important to British history?

English soldier and statesman Oliver Cromwell (1599–1658) was a key player in a chain of events that shaped modern British government. The events began when Charles I (1600–1649), House of Stuart, ascended the throne in 1625 and shortly thereafter married a French Catholic princess, immediately raising the ire of his Protestant subjects. This was not the end of England's problems with King Charles: After repeated struggles with the primarily Puritan Parliament, Charles dismissed the legislative body in 1629 and went on to rule without it for eleven years. During this period, religious and civil liberties were seriously diminished, and political and religious strife prevailed. Fearing the king's growing power, Parliament moved to raise an army, and soon civil war broke out (1642–48). Like the French Revolution (1789–99), fought 150 years later, the struggle in England was largely one between a king who claimed to rule by divine right and a government body (in this case Parliament) that claimed the right to govern the nation on behalf of the people.

Enter military leader Oliver Cromwell: After two years of indecisive battles in the English civil war, Cromwell led his parliamentary army troops to victories at Marston Moor (1644) and Naseby (1645), which re-

Oliver Cromwell

sulted in Charles' surrender. But when Charles escaped his captors in 1647, the fighting was briefly renewed. It was ended once and for all in 1648. When the king was tried the following year, Cromwell was among those leading the charge to have Charles executed. The king's opponents had their way and, having abolished the monarchy, soon established the Commonwealth of England, installing Oliver Cromwell as "Lord Protector."

Though Cromwell endeavored to bring religious tolerance to England and was somewhat successful in setting up a quasi-democratic government (he declined to take the title of king in 1657), his leadership was constantly challenged by those who wished to restore the Stuart monarchy. When Cromwell died in 1658, he was succeeded by his son, Richard (1626–1712), whose talents were not up to the challenges put to the Lord Protector. The movement to restore the monarchy—particularly the Stuart line—gained impetus, and Richard Cromwell was soon dismissed and went to live outside of England for the next twenty years.

Charles II (1630–1685), the son of Charles I, ascended the throne in 1660, beginning the eight-year period known as the Restoration. Both Charles and his brother, James II (1633–1701), who succeeded him in 1685, worked to reassert the absolutism of the Stuart monarchy. But both kings butted heads with Parliament, particularly when it came to financial matters.

Finally in 1688, James II was deposed in the so-called Glorious Revolution. William III (1650–1702), grandson of Charles I, and his wife, Queen Mary II (1662–1694), daughter of James II, were placed on the throne the following year. Though the House of Stuart remained in power, there was an important hitch: Parliament compelled William and Mary to accept the Bill of Rights (of 1689), which asserted that the Crown no longer had absolute power in England and that it must rule responsibly through the nation's representatives sitting in Parliament. Thus, the English civil war (also called the Protestant Revolution) and the influence of Oliver Cromwell and other parliamentarians laid the foundation for England's constitutional monarchy.

What was the Bill of Rights of 1689?

The English bill, accepted by King William III (1650–1702), who ruled jointly with his Protestant wife Queen Mary II (1662–1694), seriously limited royal power. After a struggle between the Stuart kings and Parliament, and the subsequent ousting of King James II (1633–1701), Parliament presented the Bill of Rights to King William and Queen Mary as a condition of their ascension: The document not only described certain civil and political rights and liberties as "true, ancient, and indubitable," but it also ironed out how the throne would be succeeded. This point was of critical importance to the future of England—the article stipulated that no Roman Catholic would rule the country. Since the Bill of Rights served to assert the role of Parliament in the government of England, it is considered one of the seminal documents of British constitutional law. It also is considered a key precursor to the U.S. Bill of Rights.

FRANCE

Did Marie Antoinette really say, "Let them eat cake"?

No, the widely quoted phrase was incorrectly attributed to her, and the entire story was probably made up. Nevertheless, the legend is not far from fact: As the daughter of a Holy Roman

47

What were the Rights of Man?

In 1789 the French assembly made the Declaration of the Rights of Man and of the Citizen, meant to flesh out the revolutionary cry of "liberty, equality, and fraternity." Influenced by the U.S. Declaration of Independence (1776) as well as the ideas of the Enlightenment, the document guaranteed religious freedom, the freedom of speech and the press, and personal security. It proclaimed that man has natural and inalienable rights, which include "liberty, property, personal security, and resistance to oppression.... " The declaration further stipulated that "No one may be accused, imprisoned, or held under arrest except in such cases and in such a way as is prescribed by law" and that "Every man is presumed innocent until he is proved guilty.... " The declaration was subsequently written into the preamble of the French constitution (1791). However, the Code Napoleon superseded many of the ideas it set forth.

Emperor (Francis I), the beautiful Marie Antoinette (1755–1793) was accustomed to a life of luxury. Unhappy in her marriage to Louis XVI (1754–1793), king of France, she pursued her own pleasurable interests with abandon. Despite the economic problems that plagued France at the time, she lived an extravagant lifestyle, which included grand balls, a "small" palace at Versailles, theater, gambling, and other frivolities. She was completely disinterested in the affairs of the nation. Many French people blamed her for corruption in the court. In short, she did much to earn herself the terrible reputation that has followed her through history.

Unpopular in her own day, one of the stories that circulated about her had Marie Antoinette asking an official why the Parisians were angry. When he explained to the queen that it was because the people had no bread, she replied, "Then let them eat cake." The French Revolution, which began in 1789, soon put an end to Marie Antoinette's excesses. Along with her husband, she was put to death by guillotine in 1793.

What were Napoleon's Hundred Days?

The term refers to Napoleon Bonaparte's last one hundred days as ruler of France. Having been defeated by his enemies—a coalition of European powers Britain, Sweden, Austria, and Prussia, who aligned themselves against Napoleon's domination—the emperor abdicated the throne in the spring of 1814, and was exiled to the island of Elba in the Mediterranean Sea. There he heard of the confusion and discontent that came after he had descended the throne. He left Elba, and with more than 1,000 men, arrived on the French coast at Cannes and marched inland to Paris. Hearing of his arrival, the new Bourbon king, Louis XVIII (1755–1824), fled. On March 20 Napoleon began a new reign, but it was only to last until the European allies defeated him again, at the Battle of Waterloo, June 12 through 18. After that battle, the so-called Little Corporal (for his diminutive stature) was permanently exiled to the British island of St. Helena, where he remained until his death in 1821.

Why is Napoleon still controversial?

Even history has not been able to sort out the widely disparate opinions of the diminutive French ruler. And both the detractors and the champions (or some would say, the apologists) continue to publish their arguments and supporting research. The most obvious point on which most scholars differ, centers on the fact that first and foremost Napoleon Bonaparte (1769–1821) was a military man. Here opinion divides quite naturally. Not long after Napoleon assumed power (in the coup of 1799), he proceeded to keep France—and the rest of Europe—at war for more than ten years. From the French perspective, Napoleon was a great man, a brilliant strategist who could not only muster his troops but could keep them motivated to fight one campaign after another. The targets of these campaigns—England, Russia, Austria, Germany, Spain, and Portugal among them—view Napoleon in quite a different light, as would be expected. Researchers from these countries have seen and rendered Napoleon's dark side, calling him a megalomaniac and a psychopath, and even seeing him as a forerunner of Adolf Hitler (1889–1945).

To further complicate the matter of how history views Napoleon, before he declared himself emperor for life (in 1804) and launched his military conquests throughout the continent and beyond (1805), Napoleon enjoyed a brief period in which many Europeans—not just the French —believed him to be a hero. After all, he assumed leadership of France after the hideous period of Robespierre's Terror and the ineffectual government of the Directory, and then he proceeded to make peace with the Americans, the Russians, and the British. Many believed Napoleon was just the man to bring order to the chaos France had known since the storming of the Bastille, and he extended an olive branch to France's longtime enemies. It looked like he would restore order at home and abroad. Of course this honeymoon did not last: By 1805 the leader many had looked to in hopes he would end the turmoil only became the cause of more turmoil. His "compulsive war-making," as one writer put it, soon swept over the continent, ultimately uniting various countries in an effort to rid Europe of the scourge that was Napoleon and his Grand Army.

Thus, students and readers are left to sort through the diverging accounts of this controversial figure. Napoleon has been called the "Emperor of Kings," credited for his vision, insight, courage, and even with the development of the modern liberal democracy; he has also been described as a compulsive tyrant who had an insatiable appetite for battle, a man whose own ambitions left millions dead. But on a few descriptions both sides can agree: He was a brave soldier, an inspired military leader, and, at least for a time, a charismatic ruler.

AMERICAN DEMOCRACY

What were the Intolerable Acts?

The so-called Intolerable Acts, also known as the Coercive Acts, were five laws passed by the British parliament early in 1774. Intended to assert British authority in the Massachusetts colony, the measures were seen as punishment for the Boston Tea Party (December 1773). In brief, the laws enacted the following: closure of the port of Boston; an English trial for any British officer or soldier who was charged with murder in the colonies; the change of the charter of Massachusetts such that the council had to be appointed by the British and that town meetings could not be held without the (British-appointed) governor's permission; the requirement that the colonists house and feed British soldiers; and the extension of the province of Quebec southward to the Ohio River.

An illustration of the Boston Tea Party.

While the British intention was to bring the Massachusetts colony under control (and actually the fifth act was not intended to have any punitive effect on the colony), the result was instead to unite all the colonies in opposition to British rule. In this regard, the acts are seen as a precursor to the American Revolution (1775–83).

Why were there two Continental Congresses?

Both meetings were called in reaction to British Parliament's attempts to assert its control in the American colonies. When colonial delegates to the First Continental Congress met, they developed a plan but were obviously prepared for it not to work, since even before dismissal they agreed to reconvene if it were necessary to do so. In short, the first Congress developed Plan A; the second resorted to Plan B (which was one last appeal to the king) and then to Plan C (finally declaring independence from Britain).

The First Continental Congress convened on September 5, 1774, in Philadelphia, Pennsylvania. The meeting was largely a reaction to the so-called Intolerable Acts (or the Coercive Acts), which British Parliament had passed in an effort to control Massachusetts after the rebellion of the Boston Tea Party (December 1773). Sentiment grew among the colonists that they would need to band together in order to challenge British authority. Soon twelve colonies dispatched fifty-six delegates to a meeting in Philadelphia. (The thirteenth colony, Georgia, declined to send representatives but agreed to go along with whatever plan was developed.) Delegates included Samuel Adams (1722–1803), George Washington (1732–1799), Patrick Henry (1736–1799), John Adams (1735–1826), and John Jay (1745–1829). Each colony had one vote, and when the meeting ended on October 26, the outcome was this: The Congress petitioned the king, declaring that the British parliament had no authority over the American colonies, that each colony could regulate its own affairs, and that the colonies would not trade with Britain until Parliament rescinded its trade and taxation policies. The petition stopped short of proclaiming independence from Great Britain, but the delegates agreed to meet again the following May—if necessary.

But King George III (1738–1820) was determined that the British Empire be preserved at all costs; he believed that if the empire lost the American colonies, then there may be a domino effect, with other British possessions encouraged to also demand independence. He feared these losses would render Great Britain a minor state, rather than the power it was. With Britain unwilling to lose control in America, in April 1775 fighting broke out between the redcoats and patriots at Lexington and Concord, Massachusetts. So, as agreed, the colonies again sent representatives to Philadelphia, convening the Second Continental Congress on May 10. Delegates—including George Washington, John Hancock (1737–1793), Thomas Jefferson (1743–1826), and Benjamin Franklin (1706–1790)—organized and prepared for the fight, creating the Continental army and naming Washington as its commander in chief. With armed conflict already under way, the Congress nevertheless moved slowly toward proclaiming independence from Britain: On July 10, two days after issuing a declaration to take up arms, Congress made another appeal to King George III, hoping to settle the matter without further conflict. The attempt failed, and the following summer the Second Continental Congress approved the Declaration of Independence, breaking off all ties with the mother country.

What does the Declaration of Independence say?

The Declaration of Independence, adopted July 4, 1776, has long been regarded as history's most eloquent statement of the rights of the people. In it, not only did the thirteen American colonies declare their freedom from Britain, they also addressed the reasons for the proclamation (naming the "causes which impel them to the separation") and cited the British government's violations of individual rights, saying "the history of the present King 'George III' of Great Britain is a history of repeated injuries and usurpations," which aimed to establish "an absolute Tyranny over these States."

Who are considered the Founding Fathers of the United States?

The term is used to refer to a number of American statesmen who were influential during the revolutionary period of the late 1700s. Though definitions vary, most include the authors of the Declaration of Independence and the signers of the U.S. Constitution among the nation's Founding Fathers.

Of the fifty-six members of the Continental Congress who signed the Declaration of Independence (July 4, 1776), the most well-known are John Adams (1735–1826) and Samuel Adams (1722–1803) of Massachusetts, Benjamin Franklin (1706–1790) of Pennsylvania, John Hancock (1737–1793) of Massachusetts, and Thomas Jefferson (1743–1826) of Virginia.

The thirty-nine men who signed the U.S. Constitution on September 17, 1787, include notable figures such as George Washington (1732–1799), who would go on, of course, to become the first president of the United States; Alexander Hamilton (1755–1804), who, as a former military aid to George Washington, went on to become the first U.S. secretary of the treasury; and James Madison (1751–1836), who is called the "father of the constitution" for his role as negotiator and recorder of debates between the delegates. At eighty-one years of age, Benjamin Franklin was the oldest signer of the Constitution and was among the six statesmen who could claim the distinction of signing both it and the Declaration of Independence; the others were George Clymer (1739–1813), Robert Morris (1734–1806), George Read (1733–1798), Roger Sherman (1721–1793), and James Wilson (1742–1798).

Patriots and politicians conspicuous by their absence from the Constitutional Convention of 1787 were John Adams and Thomas Jefferson, who were performing other government duties at the time and would each go on to become U.S. president; Samuel Adams and John Jay (1745–1829), who were not appointed as state delegates but who continued in public life, holding various federal and state government offices (including governor of their states); and Patrick Henry (1736–1799) of Virginia, who saw no need to go beyond the Articles of Confederation (1777) to grant more power to the central government. Henry's view on this issue foreshadows the discontent that crested nearly one hundred years later when twelve southern states (including Virginia) seceded from the Union, causing the Civil War (1861–1865) to break out.

Adams, Franklin, Hancock, Jefferson, Washington, Hamilton, Madison, Jay, and Henry: These are the names that come to mind when the words "Founding Fathers" are uttered. Each of them had a profound impact in the political life of the United States—even beyond their starring roles as patriots and leaders during the American revolutionary era. However, it's important to note that in many texts and to many Americans, the term Founding Fathers refers only to the men who drafted the U.S. Constitution, since it is that document that continues—more than 200 years after its signing—to provide the solid foundation for American democratic government.

What were the Articles of Confederation?

This American document was the forerunner to the U.S. Constitution (1788). Drafted by the Continental Congress at York, Pennsylvania, on November 15, 1777, the Articles of Confederation went into effect on March 1, 1781, when the last state (Maryland) ratified them. The articles had shortcomings that were later corrected by the Constitution: They provided the states with more power than the central government, stipulating that Congress rely on the states both to collect taxes and to carry out the acts of Congress.

It is largely thanks to Alexander Hamilton (1755–1804) that the articles were thrown out: Realizing they made for a weak national government, Hamilton led the charge to strengthen the central government—even at the expense of the states. Eventually, he won

Why did John Hancock go down in history as the notable signer of the Declaration of Independence?

Most Americans know that when they're putting their "John Hancock" on something, it means they're signing a document. It's because of the fifty-six men who signed their names to the historic document, it was Hancock (1737–1793) who, as president of the Second Continental Congress, signed the declaration first. Hancock also had the largest signature of the fifty-six who signed the famous document.

the backing of George Washington (1732–1799), James Madison (1751–1836), John Jay (1745–1829), and others, which led to the convening of the Philadelphia Constitutional Convention, where the ineffectual Articles of Confederation were thrown out and the Constitution was drafted.

One lasting provision of the Articles of Confederation was the ordinance of 1787. Signed in an era of westward expansion, the ordinance set the guidelines for how a territory could become a state: A legislature would be elected as soon as the population had reached 5,000 voting citizens (which were men only), and the territory would be eligible for statehood once its population had reached 60,000.

Which states were the original thirteen?

In order of admission they are Delaware, Pennsylvania, New Jersey, Georgia, Connecticut, Massachusetts, Maryland, South Carolina, New Hampshire, Virginia, New York, North Carolina, and Rhode Island. Vermont was fourteenth and the first free state (the first state without slavery).

THE U.S. CONSTITUTION

Who wrote the U.S. Constitution?

In spirit the U.S. Constitution was created by all of the fifty-five delegates to the meeting that convened on May 25, 1787, in Philadelphia's Independence Hall. Thomas Jefferson (1743–1826) called the Constitutional Convention "an assembly of demi-gods," and with good cause: The delegates were the young nation's brightest and best. Even in such stellar company, the document did have to be written. While many had a hand in this process, it was New York lawyer and future American politician and diplomat Gouverneur Morris (1752–1816) who actually took on the task of penning the Constitution, putting into prose the resolutions reached by the convention. Morris had the considerable help of the records that James Madison (1751–1836) of Virginia had kept as he managed the debates among the delegates and suggested compromises. In that capacity, and in that he designed the system of checks and balances among the legislative (Congress), the executive (the president of the United States), and the judicial (Supreme Court), Madison had considerable influence on the document's language, quite rightfully earning him the designation "father of the constitution."

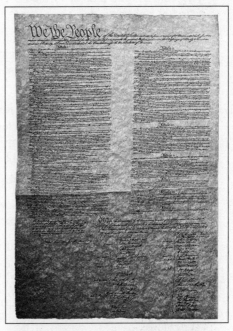

The United States Constitution is housed in the National Archives Building in Washington, D.C.

The original document, drafted by Morris, is preserved in the National Archives Building in Washington, D.C. While the Constitution has been amended by Congress, the tenets set forth therein have remained with Americans for more than two centuries, and they have provided proof to the countries of the world that a constitution outlining the principles and purposes of its government is necessary to good government.

When was the U.S. Constitution ratified?

The Constitution was ratified by the required nine states by June 21, 1788. It went into effect the following year, superseding the Articles of Confederation (1781).

What rights are protected in the Bill of Rights?

The first ten amendments to the U.S. Constitution are collectively called the Bill of Rights, which became law on December 15, 1791, and are meant to guarantee individual liberties.

- The First Amendment, which is perhaps most often cited by Americans, guarantees five freedoms: religion, speech, press, assembly, and petition. The U.S. Supreme Court later interpreted the First Amendment to also protect freedom of association.

- The Second Amendment guarantees the right to keep and bear arms (stating that "a well regulated militia being necessary to the security of a free State").

- The Third Amendment forbids peacetime quartering of soldiers in private dwellings without consent of the owner.

- The Fourth Amendment forbids the government from engaging in "unreasonable searches and seizures."

- The Fifth Amendment provides many protections for those charged with crimes. The longest amendment, the Fifth Amendment contains the following freedoms: right to a grand jury, freedom from double jeopardy, right to be free from self-incrimination, due process, and just compensation.

- The Sixth Amendment also contains numerous freedoms for those charged with crimes. Collectively, these are sometimes referred to as fair-trial rights. They include the following: speedy trial, public trial, impartial jury, right of confrontation, right of compulsory process, and the assistance of counsel.

- The Seventh Amendment guarantees trial by jury in civil cases.

- The Eighth Amendment prohibits excessive bail, excessive fines, and cruel and unusual punishment.

- The Ninth Amendment affirms that the Bill of Rights provides protection for unenumerated rights. It states that simply because a right is not enumerated, or listed, in the Constitution, it does not mean that the people do not retain that right.

- The Tenth Amendment relinquishes to the state governments those powers the Constitution did not expressly grant the federal government or deny the states. In other words, it limits the power of the federal government to that which is granted in the Constitution.

How are amendments made to the U.S. Constitution?

There are two paths that proposed amendments can take to become law. The first path is this: An amendment is proposed in Congress; two-thirds of both houses must then approve it (if they do not, then the proposal ends here); if approved in both houses of the U.S. Congress, the proposed amendment is sent to the legislatures (or conventions) of each state of the union; three-fourths of all the state legislatures must then approve it (by whatever rules each state legislature uses); once three-fourths of the states approve it, the amendment is made (if three-fourths of the states do not approve it, the amendment fails to become law).

The second path is this: The legislatures of two-thirds of the states ask for an amendment to be made to the U.S. Constitution; Congress then calls a convention to propose it; then the proposed amendment becomes a law when it is ratified by the legislatures in three-fourths of the states. While this path has never been taken, it's an important provision nonetheless since it allows for a popular, state-based proposal to be considered.

How many amendments have been made to the U.S. Constitution?

There have been twenty-seven amendments to date. The following list gives brief summaries and the year each became part of the U.S. Constitution.

- First Amendment through the Tenth Amendment (1791): Comprise the Bill of Rights.

- Eleventh Amendment (1798): Declares that U.S. federal courts cannot try any case brought against a state by a citizen of another state or country.

- Twelfth Amendment (1804): Revised the presidential and vice presidential election rules such that members of the electoral college, called electors, vote for one person as president and for another as vice president. Prior to the passage of this amendment, the electors simply voted for two men—the one receiving more votes became president and the other became vice president.

- Thirteenth Amendment (1865): Prohibits slavery. Along with amendments fourteen and fifteen, these are sometimes called the Civil War amendments, or the Reconstruction Amendments.

- Fourteenth Amendment (1868): Defines U.S. citizenship and gives all citizens equal protection under the law. (This amendment made former slaves citizens of both the United States and the state where they lived. It further forbade states to deny equal rights to any person.)

- Fifteenth Amendment (1870): States that the right of U.S. citizens to vote shall not be denied or abridged by the United States or by any state on account of race, color, or previous condition of servitude. (This amendment was meant to extend suffrage to black men.)

- Sixteenth Amendment (1913): Authorizes a federal income tax.

- Seventeenth Amendment (1913): Provides for the direct election of senators. Before this passed, state legislatures elected senators to represent them; this amendment gave that power to the people of each state.

- Eighteenth Amendment (1919): Made prohibition legal. (In other words, the manufacture and distribution of alcohol became illegal.)

- Nineteenth Amendment (1920): Granted women the right to vote.

- Twentieth Amendment (1933): Also called the "lame duck amendment," it changed congressional terms of office and the dates of the presidential inauguration so that newly elected officials take office closer to election time.

- Twenty-first Amendment (1933): Repealed Amendment Eighteen to end prohibition.

- Twenty-second Amendment (1951): Limits presidential tenure to two terms in office. (A president can hold office for no more than ten years—two years as an unelected president, and two terms as an elected president.)

- Twenty-third Amendment (1961): Grants residents of Washington, D.C., the right to vote in presidential elections.

- Twenty-fourth Amendment (1964): Outlaws the poll tax in all federal elections and primaries. (Some states had used poll taxes as a way of keeping certain populations of voters from casting their ballots; the practice had served to disenfranchise blacks and poor people.)

- Twenty-fifth Amendment (1967): Provides for procedures to fill the vice presidency and further clarifies presidential succession rules. (Upon removal, resignation, or death of the president, the vice president assumes the presidency; if a vice president is removed, resigns, or dies while in office, the president nominates a vice president who takes office upon confirmation by a majority vote of both houses of Congress.)

- Twenty-sixth Amendment (1971): Lowers the voting age for federal and state elections to eighteen.

- Twenty-seventh Amendment (1992): Prevents Congress from passing immediate salary increases for itself; it requires that salary changes passed by Congress cannot take effect until after the next congressional election. (This amendment had been passed by Congress in 1788 and was then sent to the states for ratification. Since the amendment had no time limit for ratification, it became part of the Constitution in 1992, after Michigan became the thirty-eighth state to ratify it.)

THE AMERICAN PARTY SYSTEM

What were the first political parties in the United States?

The first political parties were the Federalists and the Democratic-Republicans. The Federalists favored a strong central government, favored the mercantile and banking interests, and often took a pro-Great Britain position (at least compared to their opponents).

The Democratic-Republicans favored a less powerful central government, retention of power by the states, favored the interests of farmers along with those of the lower and middle class, and often took a foreign policy stance more in alignment with France.

Earlier, there were political leaders known as Anti-federalists, but the Federalists and the Democratic-Republicans were the first political parties after the U.S. Constitution was signed.

Who were the Whigs?

They were members of political parties in Scotland, England, and the United States. The name is derived from whiggamor (meaning "cattle driver"), which was a derogatory term used in the seventeenth century to refer to Scottish Presbyterians who opposed King Charles I of England (1600–1649). Charles, who ruled from 1625 to 1649, was deposed in a civil war and subsequently tried in court, convicted of treason, and beheaded. The British Whigs, who were mostly merchants and landed gentry, supported a strong Parliament. They were opposed by the aristocratic Tories who upheld the power of the king. For a short period during the eighteenth century, the Whigs dominated political life in England. After 1832 they became part of the Liberal Party.

At about the same time, the Whig Party in the United States emerged as one of the two major American political parties. The other was the Democratic Party (that Americans still know today), which supported President Andrew Jackson (1767–1845) for re-election in 1832. Though Jackson's first term of office had proved to be somewhat controversial, the Whigs were unable to elect their candidate (Henry Clay [1777–1852] of the so-called Southern "Cotton" Whigs), and Jackson, called "Old Hickory," went on to a second term. In the election of 1840 the Whigs, whose leadership had succeeded in uniting the party, were finally successful in putting their candidate in the White House. But William Henry Harrison (1773–1841) died after only thirty-two days in office, and his successor, John Tyler (1790–1862), alienated the Whig leaders in Congress, and they ousted him from the party. In 1848 the Whigs put Zachary Taylor (nicknamed "Old Rough and Ready;" 1784–1850) in the White House, but two years later he, too, died in office. His successor, Millard Fillmore (1800–1874), remained loyal to the Whigs, but there were problems within the party. The last Whig presidential candidate was General Winfield Scott ("Old Fuss and Feathers;" 1786–1866) in 1852, but he was defeated by Franklin Pierce (1804–1869). Shortly thereafter the Whig party broke up over the slavery issue; most of the Northern Whigs joined the Republican Party, while most of the Southern "Cotton" Whigs joined the Democratic Party.

Henry Clay

How did the Republican Party begin?

The Republican Party, one of the two principal political parties of the United States today, was founded in 1854 by those opposing the extension of slavery into new territories. The party mustered enough support to elect their candidate in 1860, Abraham Lincoln (1809–1865). During the 1880s party members nicknamed themselves the Grand Old Party; the vestige of this nickname is still around today, as the GOP. There have been seventeen Republican presidents.

How did the Democratic Party begin?

The other—and older—principal party in the United States today, the Democratic Party was founded around electing Thomas Jefferson (1743–1826) to office in 1800 (against Alexander Hamilton's Federalist Party). The party's platform favored personal liberty and the limitation of federal government. Installing Jefferson in office, the party—then called the Democratic-Republicans—went on to get its candidates into the White House for the next twenty-five years. In 1828 they became known simply as Democrats, dropping the suffix. Depending on how one counts, there have been either eighteen or nineteen Democratic presidents; Andrew Johnson (1808–1875) is problematic since he was a Democrat before joining the National Union Party ticket as the vice presidential candidate in 1864. (Some sources list both party affiliations, as in Democratic/National Union.)

How were the Southern states brought back into the Union?

Even before the Civil War had ended, Washington, D.C., considered the difficult problem of how to rejoin the seceding states with the North. Some lawmakers felt the Southern states should be treated as if they were territories that were gained through war. Others, including both Abraham Lincoln (1809–1865) and Andrew Johnson (1808–1875), reasoned that since secession was illegal, the South belonged—and always had—to the Union, and therefore the states ought to be brought back into their "proper relationship" with the federal government. They favored punishing the Southern leaders—but not the states themselves.

President Abraham Lincoln developed his 10 percent plan: As soon as 10 percent of a state's population had taken an oath of loyalty to the United States, the state would be allowed to set up a new government. But Congress opposed it, proclaiming the policy too mild, and responded by passing the Wade-Davis Bill (June 1864), making the requirements for statehood more rigid. Instead of Lincoln's 10 percent, Congress required that a majority of voters in each state would need to swear their loyalty, in an "ironclad oath," before statehood could be restored. Further, the bill stipulated that the constitution of each state had to abolish slavery and that Confederate military leaders were to be prohibited from holding political office and otherwise disenfranchised. Lincoln opposed the bill and neither signed nor returned it before Congress was dismissed, and so the Wade-Davis measure failed to become law.

When Lincoln was assassinated the following April, the matter remained unsettled. His successor, President Andrew Johnson, soon put forth a plan to readmit the states. He called for each state constitution to abolish slavery and repudiate the Confederate war debt; further, a majority of voters in each state needed to vow allegiance to the Union. Once a state had reorganized itself under this plan, Johnson required the state legislature to approve the Thirteenth Amendment (abolishing slavery in the United States). When Congress reconvened in December 1865 for the first time since Lincoln's assassination, all former Confederate states except Texas had complied with the president's specifications for statehood. But these new states had also set up Black Codes, severely restricting the rights of blacks. Further, there was violence against blacks who were the victims of attacks by white Southerners—including members of the newly formed Ku Klux Klan, a secret white organization that spread terror across the South.

Congress became determined to fight the readmission of the Southern states by Johnson's lenient standards, and it refused to seat any representatives from the South. The move angered President Johnson, and political volleying between the legislature and the executive office began. Ultimately, it was Congress that determined the process by which the Southern states were readmitted.

By the summer of 1868 the legislatures of seven (of eleven) Southern states had approved the Fourteenth Amendment. The remaining four states—Georgia, Mississippi, Texas, and Virginia—complied with the requirements for statehood by 1870, at which time the Union was restored and Congressional representatives from the South were again welcomed in Washington.

In the intervening period (between Congress's rejection of President Johnson's plan for statehood and the ratification of the Fourteenth and Fifteenth Amendments), the South was governed by military administrators who protected people and property and oversaw the reorganization of government in each state.

THE AMERICAN PRESIDENCY

Why does the president of the United States give a State of the Union Address?

The U.S. Constitution requires the president to annually present a joint session of Congress (attended by representatives and senators) with a status report on the nation. Presidents George Washington (1732–1799) and John Adams (1735–1826), the first and second presidents, delivered their messages in person. Thereafter the State of the Union was sent as a written message, which was read in Congress. But President Woodrow Wilson (1856–1924) delivered his messages in person, including that of January 1918, when he delivered the Fourteen Points—his formulation of a peace program for Europe once World War I (1914–1918) had ended. Since Franklin D. Roosevelt (1882–1945) held office (beginning in 1933), all U.S. presidents have made formal addresses to Congress.

What was the Kitchen Cabinet?

It was the name given to President Andrew Jackson's unofficial group of advisers, who reportedly met with him in the White House kitchen. The group included the then secretary of state Martin Van Buren (1782–1862), who went on to become vice president (during Jackson's second term) and president from 1837 to 1841; F. P. Blair (1791–1876), editor of the *Wash-*

Which U.S. president held the first press conference?

President Woodrow Wilson (1856–1924) was the first president to routinely assemble the press to answer questions for the public. On March 15, 1913, shortly after his inauguration, he called the first presidential press conference. More than one hundred news reporters attended the event. Decades later, President John F. Kennedy (1917–1963) became known for his frequent use of the televised press conference to directly communicate with Americans.

ington Post, who was active in American politics and later helped get Abraham Lincoln elected to office (1860); and Amos Kendall (1789–1869), a journalist who was also a speech writer for Jackson and went on to become U.S. postmaster general. The Kitchen Cabinet was influential in formulating policy during Jackson's first term (1829–33), many believe because the president's real cabinet, which he convened infrequently, had proved ineffective. But Jackson, the seventh president of the United States, drew harsh criticism for relying on his cronies in this way. When he reorganized the cabinet in 1831, the Kitchen Cabinet disbanded.

Jackson's favoritism to his circle of friends did not end with the Kitchen Cabinet, however. During his presidency the "spoils system" was in full force: Jackson gave public offices as rewards to many of his loyal supporters. Though the term spoils system was popularized during Jackson's terms in office (it was his friend, Senator William Marcy, who coined the phrase when he stated, "to the victor belong the spoils of the enemy"), Jackson was not the first president to grant political powers to his party's members. And the practice continued through the nineteenth century. However, beginning in 1883 laws were passed that gradually put an end to, or at least limited, the spoils system.

What was Teapot Dome?

Teapot Dome was a notorious political scandal that was on a level with Watergate (1972). While the early 1920s abuses of power affected President Warren G. Harding (1865–1923), it was not Harding who was implicated in the crimes. Albert Bacon Fall (1861–1944), Harding's secretary of the interior, secretly transferred government oil lands at Elk Hills, California, and Teapot Dome, Wyoming, to private use, and he did so without a formal bidding process. Fall leased the Elk Hills naval oil reserves to American businessman Edward L. Doheny (1856–1935) in exchange for an interest-free "loan" of $100,000. Fall made a similar arrangement with another businessman, Harry F. Sinclair (1876–1956) of Sinclair Oil Corporation—leasing the Teapot Dome reserves in exchange for $300,000 in cash, bonds, and livestock.

The scandal was revealed in 1922, and committees of the U.S. Senate and a special commission spent the next six years sorting it all out. By the time the hearings and investigations were concluded in 1928, Harding had died; Fall had resigned from office and taken a job working for Sinclair; all three players—Doheny, Sinclair, and Fall—had faced charges; and the government had successfully sued the oil companies for the return of the lands. The punishments were light considering the serious nature of the charges: Fall was convicted of accepting a bribe, fined $100,000, and sentenced to a year in prison, while Doheny and Sinclair were both indicted but later acquitted of the charges against them, which included conspiracy and bribery.

How were Theodore and Franklin Roosevelt related?

The two men, among America's most well-known presidents, were distant cousins. Theodore Roosevelt (1858–1919) was born in New York City, and after a career in public service that included organizing the first volunteer cavalry regiment that was known as the Rough Riders, the ardent outdoors enthusiast became vice president in 1901. When President William McKinley (1843–1901) died in office later that year (on September 14), "Teddy" Roosevelt succeeded him as president. He was elected in his own right in 1904 and went on to serve until 1909, spending nearly two full terms in the White House.

Teddy Roosevelt was president of the United States when he walked his niece, Eleanor Roosevelt (1884–1962), down the aisle on March 17, 1905. The young woman was marrying her distant cousin Franklin Delano Roosevelt (1882–1945), who had been courting her since he entered college at Harvard in 1900.

Franklin D. Roosevelt was born in Hyde Park, New York. Like his fifth cousin Theodore, Franklin went on to a life of public service, which bore some remarkable similarities to that of his cousin: Both Theodore and Franklin served as assistant secretary of the U.S. Navy (1897–1898 and 1913–1920, respectively) and both were governors of New York (1899–1900 and 1929–1933, respectively). As presidents, both served the nation for more than one term—but Franklin Roosevelt made history for being the only president to be elected for third and fourth terms. (In 1951, the U.S. Congress voted in favor of the Twenty-second Amendment, limiting presidential tenure to just two terms.) Both served the country in times of conflict: For Theodore it was the Russo–Japanese War (1904–05)—which he was instrumental in ending with the Treaty of Portsmouth (New Hampshire) on September 5, 1905, and for which he was awarded the Nobel Peace Prize the following year. Franklin Roosevelt was one of the so-called Big Three leaders: Along with Britain's Sir Winston Churchill (1874–1965) and the Soviet Union's Joseph Stalin (1879–1953), he coordinated the Allied nations' effort against Nazi Germany and Japan during World War II (1939–1945). He, too, was a champion of peace, having been central in laying plans for the United Nations.

It's an interesting note, however, that when Teddy Roosevelt ran for president in 1912, he was opposed by his young Democratic cousin Franklin, then a state senator in New York, who supported Woodrow Wilson (1856–1924) in the presidential race. After Wilson was elected, he appointed Franklin Roosevelt assistant secretary of the navy—a post that delighted him for combining his vocation (politics) with his avocation (ships), and one that certainly furthered his political career. By the end of World War I (1914–1918), Franklin Roosevelt was a well-known national figure.

Theodore and Franklin also shared an interest in outdoor activities. But Franklin's participation in sports was curtailed when he was stricken with polio in August 1921. The thirty-nine-year-old Roosevelt was paralyzed for a time, and though he later regained movement and was able to walk with braces, he never fully recovered. Through fierce determination he

FDR's long tenure as president led to what constitutional amendment?

Franklin Delano Roosevelt (1882–1945) was elected to the office of the presidency an unprecedented four times. At that time, there was no official limit on how many terms a president could serve. President George Washington likely could have served at least a third consecutive term but opted not to run a third time. This established a tradition.

But, it was a tradition that FDR did not follow, winning four elections. He died shortly into his fourth term. In 1951, Congress passed the Twenty-second Amendment, which begins: "No person shall be elected to the office of the President more than twice...."

continued his life of public service, becoming president in 1933. He saw the country through two of its most trying periods: the Great Depression (1929–1939) and World War II (1939–1945). He died suddenly of a brain hemorrhage in April 1945.

Why was Eleanor Roosevelt called "the people's First Lady"?

While several First Ladies before her had also been active in the nation's life, Eleanor Roosevelt (1884–1962), wife of thirty-second President of the United States Franklin D. Roosevelt (1882–1945), stands out as one of the country's most active first ladies and as a woman of enormous accomplishment in her own right. During her husband's adminis-

President Franklin Roosevelt and First Lady Eleanor Roosevelt

tration, which began in the dark days of the Great Depression (1929–1941) and continued as the world again went to war, Eleanor Roosevelt acted not only as an adviser to the president, but as the president's eyes and ears on the nation—traveling in a way that his physical condition prevented him from doing.

From the start, Eleanor Roosevelt remained in constant communication with the American people: She was known for her weekly press conferences, numbering some 350 by the end of the Roosevelt presidency, that were open only to women reporters. In 1934 she began a radio program, which became so popular that she was soon dubbed "the First Lady of Radio." Beginning in 1936 she authored a daily column called "My Day," which was syndicated to newspapers around the country. These forums gave the First Lady an unprecedented voice in American life and gave Americans a clear understanding of their First Lady and her concerns.

Concerned about the effects of the Great Depression on American children, she was instrumental in creating the National Youth Administration, which helped high school and university students complete their studies before joining the workforce. She was a champion of minority groups, declaring that the right to work "should know no color lines" and resigning from the Daughters of the American Revolution when the group refused to allow black singer Marian Anderson (1897–1993) to perform at Constitution Hall.

Eleanor Roosevelt was known for getting out among the people; she lectured frequently and made other public appearances in which she met and spoke face-to-face with the American people. A famous cartoon depicted a coal miner pausing in his work to exclaim, "For gosh sakes, here comes Mrs. Roosevelt." During World War II (1939–1945) she made a remarkable 23,000-mile trip across the South Pacific, where she untiringly visited American GIs in field hospitals and on the lines.

Mrs. Roosevelt was an advocate for the people, and it just so happened that she lived in the White House. A beloved First Lady who actively supported liberal causes and humanitarian concerns, she has been a model to subsequent First Ladies, women politicians, and activists.

How many U.S. presidents have been assassinated?

Four American presidents have been assassinated in office: Abraham Lincoln, James Garfield, William McKinley, and John F. Kennedy.

Abraham Lincoln (1809–1865) was shot on the evening of April 14, 1865, as he sat in the presidential box of Ford's Theatre in Washington, D.C., watching a performance of "Our American Cousin." The man who fired the shot was actor John Wilkes Booth (1838–1865), who then jumped onto the stage, fell (breaking a leg), and limped away, calling out, "Sic semper tyrannis" (a Latin phrase meaning "Thus always to tyrants"). The president lived through the night, attended by family. He died just after 7:00 A.M. on April 15. He was succeeded in office by Vice President Andrew Johnson (1808–1875). On April 26 a search party found Booth in a Virginia barn, where he was fatally shot.

James Garfield (1831–1881) was en route to a class reunion at Williams College (Williamstown, Massachusetts), on July 2, 1881, when his assailant fired two shots at him in a Washington, D.C., train station. The shooter was Charles J. Guiteau (1841–1882), who held a grudge against the president. One of Guiteau's bullets had only grazed the president; the other was fixed in his back, and doctors were unable to locate it. Today the president's life might well have been spared, but the medical treatment of the late 1800s, which lacked both the X ray machine and antiseptics, could not save him. He lived eighty days more, dying at a cottage on the New Jersey shore on September 19. He was succeeded in office by Vice President Chester Arthur (1830–1886). Guiteau's trial lawyer would later claim that Garfield's assassin was insane, but it was an unsuccessful plea for his life: In 1882 he was convicted and hung.

On September 6, 1901, President William McKinley (1843–1901) was attending a reception in Buffalo, New York, where the previous day he had delivered a speech. As he approached a man to shake his hand, the fellow fired two shots at McKinley. One bullet delivered only a minor flesh wound, but the other lodged in his stomach. Surgeons operated, but gangrene and infection set in, claiming the president's life the morning of September 14. He was succeeded in office by Vice President Theodore Roosevelt (1858–1919). The shooter was identified as avowed anarchist Leon F. Czolgosz (1873–1901); he was tried, convicted, and put to death in 1901.

President John F. Kennedy (1917–1963), accompanied by his wife, Jacqueline Bouvier Kennedy (1929–1994), was assassinated while travelling in a motorcade through the streets of Dallas, Texas, on November 22, 1963. They were en route to the Dallas Trade Mart, where the president was scheduled to make a lunchtime speech. At 12:30 P.M., shots rang out; the president, who was riding in the back seat of a convertible, was hit in the neck and head. He was rushed to a nearby hospital, where he died at 1:00 P.M. The nation's loss was immediately felt, as television and radio stations broadcast the message live that Kennedy had been shot and killed. He was succeeded by Vice President Lyndon Baines Johnson (1908–1973), who took the oath of office aboard an airplane just after 2:30 P.M. Lee Harvey Oswald (1939–1963) was arrested for Kennedy's murder, but would not live long enough to be tried. Oswald was shot and killed by nightclub owner Jack Ruby (1911–1967) while being transferred to jail. Although conspiracy theories regarding Kennedy's assassination have run rampant since the day he died, a ten-month investigation by the Warren Commission concluded that Oswald acted alone.

Additionally there were assassination attempts on the lives of Presidents Andrew Jackson (April 14, 1835), Theodore Roosevelt (October 14, 1912), Franklin D. Roosevelt (February 15, 1933), Harry S. Truman (November 1, 1950), Gerald R. Ford (two attempts, both in September 1975), and Ronald Reagan (March 30, 1981). Theodore Roosevelt and Ronald Reagan recovered from their injuries; the others were not injured in the attempts.

What happened at Watergate?

Watergate is a complex of upscale apartment and office buildings in Washington, D.C. In July 1972 five men were caught breaking into the Democratic Party's national headquarters there. Among these men was James McCord Jr. (1924–), the security coordinator of the Committee for the Re-election of the President (CRP). McCord was among those working to get President Richard Nixon (1913–1994), a Republican, elected to a second term in office.

All five men who were caught in the break-in were indicted on charges of burglary and wiretapping, as were CRP aide G. Gordon Liddy (1930–) and White House consultant E. Howard Hunt (1918–2007). Five of the men pleaded guilty to the charges. McCord and Liddy were tried and found guilty.

In February 1972—five months before the break-in at Watergate—President Nixon had traveled to China, becoming the first U.S. president to visit that country. In May he traveled to Moscow, where he signed the Strategic Arms Limitation Treaty (SALT-1 treaty), the first such treaty between the United States and the U.S.S.R. When the election was held in November, Nixon won in a landslide victory over the Democratic candidate George McGovern (1922–1998).

But early in Nixon's second term, which began in 1973, the Watergate affair became a full-blown political scandal when convicted burglar James McCord wrote a letter to District Court Judge John Sirica (1904–1992), charging a massive cover-up in the Watergate break-in. A special Senate committee began televised investigations into the affair. Before it was all over, about forty people, including high-level government officials, had been charged with crimes including burglary, wiretapping of citizens, violating campaign finance laws by accepting contributions in exchange for political favors, the use of government agencies to harm political opponents, and sabotage.

Among those prosecuted were John Dean (1938–), former White House counsel, and Attorney General John Mitchell (1913–1988). It was revealed that members of the Nixon administration had known about the Watergate burglary. It was also discovered that the president had taped conversations in the Oval Office. When Dean and Mitchell were convicted, public confidence in President Nixon plummeted. In July 1974 the Judiciary Committee of the House of Representatives was preparing articles of impeachment (including one that charged the president with obstruction of justice) against the president. The impeachment proceedings would not make it as far as the Senate: Nixon chose to resign on August 9, 1974. He was the first, and, so far, only U.S. president to resign from office.

Shortly after taking office, Nixon's successor, Gerald R. Ford (1913–2006), pardoned Nixon. But Watergate remains a dark chapter in the nation's history.

What was the Iran-Contra affair?

It was a series of actions on the part of U.S. federal government officials, which came to light in November 1986. The discoveries had the immediate effect of hurting President Ronald

Reagan (1911–2004), whose policy of antiterrorism had been undermined by activities initiated from his own executive office. Following in-depth hearings and investigations into "who knew what, when," special prosecutor Lawrence Walsh (1912–) submitted his report on January 18, 1994, stating that the dealings with Iran and with the contra rebels in Nicaragua had "violated United States policy and law."

The tangled string of events involved Reagan's national security advisers Robert McFarlane (1937–) and Admiral John Poindexter (1936–), Lieutenant Colonel Oliver North (1943–), Poindexter's military aide, the Iranian government, and Nicaraguan rebels.

The U.S. officials evidently had begun their dealings with both the Iranian government and the Nicaraguan rebels with the goal of freeing seven Americans who were held hostage by Iranian-backed rebels in Lebanon. President Reagan had met with the families of the captives and was naturally concerned about the hostage situation. Under pressure to work to free the hostages, McFarlane, Poindexter, and North arranged to sell an estimated $30 million in spare parts and antiaircraft missiles to Iran (then at war with neighboring Iraq). In return, the Iranian government would put pressure on the terrorist groups to release the Americans.

Profits from the arms sale to Iran were then diverted by Lieutenant North to the contras in Central America who were fighting the dictatorial Nicaraguan government. Congress had already passed laws that prohibited U.S. government aid to the Nicaraguan rebels; the diversion of funds certainly appeared to violate those laws.

The Iran-Contra affair led to North's dismissal and to Poindexter's resignation. Both men were prosecuted. Though the hostages were freed, Reagan's public image was seriously damaged by how the release had been achieved.

During the Iran-Contra hearings in 1987, National Security Commission officials revealed that they had been willing to take the risk of providing arms to Iran in exchange for the safe release of the hostages because they all remembered the U.S. government's failed attempt in 1980 to rescue hostages held at the American Embassy in Tehran, Iran.

Nevertheless, the deal with Iran had supplied a hostile country with American arms that could then be used against the United States. In 1987 Iran did launch an offensive when it attacked Kuwaiti oil-tankers that were registered as American and laid mines in the Persian Gulf. The United States responded by sending in the navy, which attacked Iranian patrol boats. During this military initiative, the U.S. Navy accidentally shot down a civilian passenger jet, killing everyone on board.

Why was President Clinton impeached?

Some believe the proceedings were nothing more than a "vast right-wing conspiracy," a term coined by First Lady Hillary Rodham Clinton (1947–) early in 1998. Still, others—including enough members of the U.S. House of Representatives to bring eleven counts of impeachment against President Clinton in December 1998—felt the nation's chief had perjured himself and obstructed justice. Many also believed he had jeopardized the authority of the U.S. presidency. Accused of having an affair with White House intern Monica Lewinsky, President Clinton vehemently denied it. Upon continued investigation, conducted by Special Prosecutor Kenneth Starr's office, the allegations proved to be true. Since the president had been so adamant in his statements to the contrary, evidence began to accumulate that he had lied about his relationship with the young woman and that he had tried to cover up the matter.

Many believed the charges against Clinton did not constitute the high crimes and misdemeanors called for by the U.S. Constitution to remove a president from office. Nevertheless, in January 1999 the U.S. Senate organized itself to hear the charges against the president. When the trial concluded in February, Clinton was acquitted of both perjury and obstruction of justice. He served out his second term and left office with high approval ratings, despite being the subject of the longest criminal investigation of a president in history.

The Clinton impeachment was the first time the federal legislature had convened itself as a court in more than 130 years—since the impeachment hearings of President Andrew Johnson (1808–1875) in 1868.

Photo caption here.

Are the Bushes the first father-son presidents?

No, the nation's forty-first (George H. W. Bush; 1924–) and forty-third (George W. Bush; 1946–) presidents were preceded as father-son presidents by John Adams (1735–1826), the second president of the United States, and John Quincy Adams (1767–1848), the sixth.

There have been other presidents whose relatives held the office before them: Benjamin Harrison, the twenty-third president, was the grandson of the nation's ninth, William Henry Harrison. Zachary Taylor, the twelfth president, and James Madison, the fourth, were second cousins. Franklin Delano Roosevelt was preceded in the office by his distant cousin, Teddy Roosevelt. Genealogists determined that FDR had ties to ten other presidents as well, four of them were blood relatives and six were relatives by marriage: John Adams, John Quincy Adams, Ulysses S. Grant, William Henry Harrison, Benjamin Harrison, James Madison, William Howard Taft, Zachary Taylor, Martin Van Buren, and George Washington.

THE POSTWAR ERA

How was the United Nations formed?

Officially, the United Nations (UN) was not formed until October 1945. However, events during World War II (1939–1945) had paved the way for the founding of the international peacekeeping organization that today is so familiar to people around the globe.

Fervent German nationalist Adolf Hitler (1889–1945) and his troops invaded Poland in 1939, and soon Nazi Germany had conquered much of Europe. Leaders of nine nations—Belgium, Czechoslovakia, France, Greece, Luxembourg, the Netherlands, Norway, Poland, and Yugoslavia—met with Britain and its Commonwealth states in London. There, on June 12, 1941, the countries signed the Inter-Allied Declaration, vowing to work together for a free world. Two months later, on August 14, U.S. president Franklin Delano Roosevelt (1882–1945) and British Prime Minister Winston Churchill (1874–1965) signed the Atlantic Charter. In it the two leaders outlined their aims for peace.

On January 1, 1942, the "declaration by the United Nations" was signed by twenty-six countries who pledged to work together to fight the Axis powers (Germany, Italy, and Japan), and they agreed not to make peace separately. The term United Nations, otherwise known as the UN, is believed to have originated with Roosevelt.

In late November and early December 1943, the Big Three—Roosevelt, Churchill, and Soviet premier Joseph Stalin (1879–1953)—met in Tehran, Iran, for the first time during the war. There these Allied nations leaders cited the responsibility of a United Nations organization in keeping the peace once the war was over. Though ending the war was first and foremost in the minds of these leaders, all had seen two world wars fought in close succession and were determined that the nations of the world could work together to prevent such an event from happening again.

In August 1944, at the Dumbarton Oaks Conference in Washington, D.C., representatives of Britain, the United States, the Soviet Union, and China met to make plans for the peacekeeping organization that had been envisioned. The outcome of that meeting, which lasted into October, was the basic concept for the UN Security Council as we know it—with the world's (five) major powers having permanent seats on the council and a limited and rotating membership beyond that.

When the Big Three met again at the Yalta Conference (in the Soviet Union) in February 1945, they discussed matters that were central to ending the fighting with Germany and with Japan. But Roosevelt, Churchill, and Stalin also announced that a conference of the United Nations would open in San Francisco on April 25 of that year.

Having directed the United States' massive war effort, Roosevelt did not live to see the end of World War II or the creation of the international peacekeeping body. Roosevelt died suddenly on April 12, 1945. The war in Europe ended May 7. And during the closing days of World War II, the UN was chartered—the representatives of the Allied nations met as promised in San Francisco. On June 26, 1945, the governing treaty was signed by the delegates. On October 24, 1945, shortly after the war ended with Japan, the United Nations officially came into existence when the required number of nations approved the charter. Fifty-one nations were members of the UN at the outset; as of 2012 the membership numbered 193.

What does the United Nations do?

Representatives of member countries work to keep peace and ensure security for people around the globe. Over the decades, the UN has expanded its role as a provider of humanitarian aid and stepped up its efforts in the area of human rights. When disputes arise, the UN works toward diplomatic resolution. Though not always successful in its role as peacekeeper or peace negotiator, the organization has provided a forum for debate, which has prevented some disputes from developing into major wars. And through its various agencies, the UN provides assistance to developing nations, promotes humanitarian causes, and sends relief to war-torn areas.

However, critics have charged the international organization with arbitrarily defining borders between countries, saying that these drawn boundaries divide ethnic groups and result in conflicts (such as in the Middle East and Africa).

How many nations are members of the United Nations today?

In 2012 the United Nations (UN) membership stood at 193 nations, with the most recent additions having been Montenegro (2006) and South Sudan (2011).

What are the bodies and agencies of the United Nations?

The UN's charter established six main bodies and explains their duties and operating methods. The General Assembly is the major forum: all member nations are represented there, and the assembly can discuss any issue that is deemed relevant and important to the UN; the Security Council has the major responsibility for preserving peace; the Economic and Social Council investigates economic questions and works to improve living standards; the Secretariat is the UN's administrative body, helping all organs do their work; the Trusteeship Council assists non-self-governing territories; and the International Court of Justice hears disputes between member nations. Except for the last one, all bodies convene in the UN headquarters in New York City. The International Court of Justice meets in The Hague. The Trusteeship Council was suspended in 1994, when the last UN trust territory, Palau, gained independence.

Since the charter was written in 1945, the United Nations has established numerous agencies, committees, and commissions to help carry out its work around the world. Among

The Hague, Netherlands

those that are most well known to the public are the United Nations Educational, Scientific, and Cultural Organization (UNESCO), which encourages the exchange of ideas among nations; the United Nations International Children's Emergency Fund (UNICEF), which assists children and adolescents worldwide, particularly those in devastated areas or developing countries; the World Health Organization (WHO), which promotes high health standards around the globe; the International Labor Organization (ILO), which works to improve labor conditions and protect workers; and the International Monetary Fund (IMF), which addresses currency and trade issues.

Who are the members of the United Nations Security Council?

According to the UN charter, the Security Council has fifteen members: five permanent and ten that are elected by the General Assembly for two-year terms. The permanent members are China, France, the Russian Federation, the United Kingdom, and the United States. The ten temporary slots are elected annually, five nations at a time. In 2012, the ten non-permanent members were Azerbaijan, India, South Africa, Columbia, Morocco, Togo, Germany, Pakistan, Guatemala, and Portugal.

What is the G-8?

It is the Group of Eight, an annual meeting of the world's leading industrial democracies: Canada, France, Germany, Italy, Japan, Russia, the United Kingdom, and the United States. It began as the Group of Six, with a 1975 conference in France, where representatives of six nations (France, Germany, Italy, Japan, the United Kingdom, and the United States) met to discuss international economic and political issues. The goal of the meeting was to shore up cooperation on matters of concern to the member nations. Canada joined the group in 1976 and Russia in 1994 (though the nation did not participate fully in the sessions until 1998). Hosting responsibilities rotate among the eight member countries. In 2004 the United States hosted the 30th meeting, on an island off the coast of Georgia. Among the agenda items were the training of international peacekeepers, setting up a global initiative to develop a human immunodeficiency virus (HIV) vaccine, and developing a plan to end famine in the Horn of Africa (easternmost Africa, including Somalia, Ethiopia, and Djibouti) by 2009. The leaders and representatives of non-G-8 countries were invited to participate in discussions relevant to them. The thirty-seventh meeting was held in the French commune of Deauville, in 2011.

INDIA

Why was Mohandas Gandhi called "Mahatma"?

Mohandas Gandhi (1869–1948) was called "Mahatma" (meaning "great-souled") by the common people, who viewed him as India's national and spiritual leader. He is considered the father of his country. He was born in India on October 2, 1869. As a young man, Gandhi studied law in Britain. Practicing briefly in India, he then traveled to British-controlled South Africa on business. Observing oppressive treatment of Indian immigrants there, he held his first campaign of passive resistance. Gandhi would later become very well known for this method of protest, called satyagraha (meaning "firmness in truth").

Back in India as of 1915, Gandhi organized a movement of the people against the British government there: Britain had taken control of India during the 1700s and remained in power. After World War I (1914–1918), Indian nationalists fought what would be a long and sometimes bitter struggle for political independence. While Gandhi's protests took the form of nonviolent campaigns of civil disobedience, such as boycotts and fasts (hunger strikes), he was more than once arrested by the authorities for causing disorder, as his actions inspired more extreme measures on the part of his followers, whose protests took the form of rioting.

Mohandas Gandhi

As a member and, later, the president of India's chief political party, the Indian National Congress, Gandhi led a fight to rid the country of its rigid caste system, which organizes Indian society into distinct classes and groups. In Gandhi's time, not only were there four varna, or social classes, but there was a fifth group of "untouchables" who ranked even below the lowest class of peasants and laborers. Improving the lot of the untouchables was of tantamount importance to the leader, who by this time had abandoned Western ways in favor of a life of simplicity.

Beginning in 1937 Gandhi became less active in government, giving up his official roles, but he continued to be regarded as a leader of the independence movement. During World War II (1939–1945), he was arrested for demanding British withdrawal from the conflict. Released from prison in 1944, Gandhi was central to the postwar negotiations that in 1947 resulted in an independent India. A believer in the unity of humankind under one God, he remained tolerant to Christian and Muslim beliefs. Amidst an outbreak of violence between Hindus and Muslims, Gandhi was on a prayer vigil in New Delhi when a Hindu fanatic fatally shot him in 1948.

Was Indira Gandhi related to Mohandas Gandhi?

No, the two were not related, except by events. After India achieved independence in 1947, the country's first prime minister was Jawaharlal Nehru (1889–1964), who had been a follower of Mohandas Gandhi (1869–1948), the great leader of India's long struggle for autonomy from Great Britain. During his entire tenure (1947 to 1964) as leader of India, Nehru was assisted by his only child, Indira (1917–1984), who in 1942 married a man named Feroze Gandhi—of no relation to Mohandas Gandhi. Indira Gandhi took an active role in India's national affairs. After her father died, she went on to become prime minister in 1966. However, hers was a troubled tenure. Found guilty of employing illegal election practices, Indira Gandhi was ousted by her political opponents in 1977. Determined to return to power, she was re-elected to parliament in 1980 and again served as prime minister until her death in 1984. She was assassinated by two of her own security guards, Sikhs who were motivated by religious reasons. Her son and successor, Rajiv Gandhi (1944–1991), was also assassinated, in 1991.

THE MIDDLE EAST

When was modern Israel established?

As a modern state, Israel was formed by decree in 1948. In the wake of World War II (1939–1945), the United Nations (UN) formed a special committee to address the British control of Palestine, the region in the Middle East (southwest Asia) that borders the Mediterranean Sea to the west, Lebanon to the north, Syria and Jordan to the east, and Egypt (the Sinai Peninsula) to the southwest; the narrow piece of land comes to a point in the south, where it fronts the Gulf of Aqaba. In November 1947, the United Nations (UN) carved Israel out of the Palestine region; areas of Palestine that were not designated as part of Israel were divided between neighboring Arab countries.

Modern Israel's first leader, David Ben-Gurion (1886–1973), proclaimed an independent Israel on May 14, 1948. Born in Poland, Ben-Gurion had arrived in Palestine as a young man of about twenty and became extremely active in efforts to assert Jewish autonomy in the region. He served as prime minister from 1949 to 1953, and again between 1955 and 1963. But Israel's history goes back much farther than these twentieth-century events. And, having such a long history, it is also a complicated one.

Israel was an ancient kingdom in Palestine, formed under King Saul in 1020 B.C.E. Israel included the lands in Canaan, the Promised Land of the Hebrew tribes who descended from the people that Moses (fourteenth–thirteenth century B.C.E.) led out of Egypt. But the kingdom was subsequently divided and by the eighth century B.C.E. it had ceased to exist. Nevertheless, the area remained home—and holy land—to the Hebrews (Israelites) who had settled there.

The entire region of Palestine, including the kingdom of Israel, subsequently came under the control of various empires. Palestine saw the rule of the Assyrians, the Chaldeans, the Persians, the Macedonians (under Macedonian king Alexander the Great; 356–323 B.C.E.), and the Romans (the area was the Roman province of Syria in the time of Jesus). After Roman rule, Palestine was, with only one exception, ruled by various Muslim (Islamic) dynasties, including the Ottoman Empire (1516 to 1917). It was in 1917 that Palestine came under control of the British, who proclaimed in the Declaration of Balfour to support the establishment of a national home for the Jews living there. However, Britain reversed this policy in 1939, at the same time the area was seeing an influx of Jewish people who were escaping persecution in Europe. Jews in Palestine opposed British control, and at the same time fighting intensified between Jews and Arabs.

The 1948 decision by the UN to establish a Jewish homeland resulted in nearly two years of fighting between Israelis and Arabs in the region. And though boundaries among the various states were determined anew in 1949, fighting in the region continued with the Arab-Israeli wars of 1956, 1967, 1973–74, and 1982. Unrest prevailed throughout the 1980s and into the 1990s, when the two sides began discussions to resolve the long conflict.

THE SOVIET BLOC

Who coined the term "iron curtain"?

It was former British Prime Minister Winston Churchill (1874–1965). In a March 1946 speech in Fulton, Missouri, he remarked that "an iron curtain has descended across the Continent." The statesman, who had been instrumental in coordinating the Allied victory in World War II (1939–1945), was commenting on Soviet leader Joseph Stalin's (1879–1953) tactics in Eastern Europe, which indicated the Soviets were putting up barriers against the West—and building up Soviet domination behind those barriers.

Just as he had issued warnings of the threat posed by Nazi Germany prior to World War II, Churchill astutely observed the rapidly emerging situation in Eastern Europe: In 1946 the Soviets installed Communist governments in neighboring Romania and in nearby Bulgaria; in 1947 Hungary and Poland came under Communist control as well; and the following year, Communists took control of Czechoslovakia. These countries, along with Albania, Yugoslavia, and East Germany, soon formed a coalition of Communist allies—and the Eastern bloc was formed. The United States and its democratic allies formed the Western bloc. The stage was set for the Cold War (1945–1990).

How was the Soviet Union formed?

The Soviet Union was officially created in 1922 when Russia joined with Ukraine, Belorussia, and the Transcaucasian Federation (Armenia, Azerbaijan, and Georgia) to form the Union of Soviet Socialist Republics (U.S.S.R.). These republics were later joined by nine others, and territories were redrawn so that by 1940 the union consisted of fifteen Soviet Socialist republics: Armenia, Azerbaijan, Belorussia (now Belarus), Estonia, Georgia, Kazakhstan, Kirghiz (now Kyrgyzstan), Latvia, Lithuania, Moldavia (now Moldova), Russia, Tadzhikistan (also spelled Tajikistan), Turkmenistan, Ukraine, and Uzbekistan.

How many leaders did the Soviet Union have?

From its formation in 1922 (just five years after tsarist Russia had fallen in the revolution of 1917), the Union of Soviet Socialist Republics (U.S.S.R.) had only ten leaders. But just five of these had meaningful tenure, either due to length of time served or true authority: Lenin, Stalin, Khrushchev, Brezhnev, and Gorbachev.

After tsarist Russia ended with the revolution of 1917, Bolshevik leader Vladimir Lenin (1870–1924) became head of the Soviet Russian government as chairman of the Council of People's Commissars (the Communists), dissolving the elected assembly and establishing a dictatorship. This lasted six years: When Lenin died of a stroke in 1924, Joseph Stalin (1879–1953)—who had been an associate of Lenin—promptly eliminated his opposition and in 1929 established himself as a virtual dictator. Stalin ruled the U.S.S.R. during World War II (1939–1945), and though he was aligned with the United States, Britain, and the other Allied nations during that conflict, soon after the war, he began a buildup of power in Eastern Europe, leading to the Cold War (1945–1990). Even though Stalin's domestic policies were extremely repressive and he ruled largely by terror, he remained in power until his death in 1953.

After Stalin died, the Soviet Union entered a brief period of struggle among its top leaders: Deputy Premier Georgy Malenkov (1902–1988), a longtime Stalin aide, came to power. In 1955 Malenkov was forced to resign, and he was succeeded by his (and Stalin's) former defense secretary, Nikolai Bulganin (1895–1975). However, Bulganin was a premier in name only; the true power rested with Communist Party secretary Nikita Khrushchev (1894–1971), who expelled Bulganin and officially took power as premier in 1958.

Khrushchev denounced the oppression of the long Stalin years, which had ended only five years earlier, and worked to improve living standards. On the international front, he pursued a policy of "peaceful coexistence" with the West and even toured the United States in 1959, meeting with President Dwight D. Eisenhower (1890–1969). In 1960 a U.S. reconnaissance plane was shot down over the U.S.S.R., raising doubts among the Soviets about Khrushchev's policy toward the West. Further troubles at home resulted

Josef Stalin

from widespread hunger due to crop failures. Meantime, Khrushchev advanced the cause of Soviet space exploration, beginning the so-called space race with the United States. Eventually, his stance on international issues, which included a rift with Communist China, led to his downfall. He was removed from power in October 1964.

Khrushchev's ouster (which was a forced retirement) had been engineered by his former ally and political adviser Leonid Brezhnev (1906–1982). With Khrushchev out of the way, technically Brezhnev was to lead the country along with Premier Alexei Kosygin (1904–1981). But as head of the Communist Party, it was Brezhnev who truly held the power. By the early 1970s, Brezhnev emerged as the Soviet chief—even though Kosygin remained in office until 1980. During his administration, Brezhnev kept tight control over the Eastern bloc (Communist countries), built up the Soviet Union's military (in what became an arms race with the United States), and did nothing to try to reverse the downward trend of the Soviet Union's economy.

When Brezhnev died in 1982, he was succeeded by Yuri Andropov (1914–1984). However, Andropov died two years later and Konstantin Chernenko (1911–1985) replaced him as premier. When Chernenko, too, died an untimely death in March 1985, Mikhail S. Gorbachev (1931–) became head of the Communist Party and leader of the Soviet Union. With Gorbachev, the reign of the old guard of Stalin-trained leaders had come to an end. Gorbachev's policies of openness to the West and economic development led to the disintegration of the Soviet Union, with Communist rule ending in 1991 and each Soviet republic setting up its own government.

73

OTHER REGIONS

MEXICO

Why was the election of Vicente Fox a landmark?

The July 2000 election of businessman-turned-politician Vicente Fox (1942–) was monumental in Mexico's political history because it ousted the Institutional Revolutionary Party (PRI) that had ruled the nation for seventy-one years. It was a victory not only for Fox but for his National Action Party (PAN). The former Coca-Cola Company executive had turned to politics in the 1980s, following a highly successful career in business. In 1987 Fox was elected to the national Chamber of Deputies, and in 1995 he was voted in as governor of his home state of Guanajuato. He promised voters economic and political reform, with a particular emphasis on ridding the nation's government of seemingly endemic corruption. Fox was sworn into office on December 1, 2000, for a six-year term. He served until the end of his term in November 2006 and then returned with his family to his home state of Guanajuato.

AFRICA

What former world leader was convicted of war crimes in 2012?

Charles Taylor, who ruled Liberia from 1997 until his resignation in 2003, was convicted of war crimes and crimes against humanity in April 2012, by a special court set up by Sierre Leone and the United Nations. Taylor was accused of assisting the Revolutionary United Front group in Sierra Leone. This group recruited child soldiers. It has been alleged that Taylor also harbored al Qaeda terrorists during his time as leader of Liberia.

LAW

What was the Draconian Code?

The Draconian Code was the body of law, or set of rules, established by Athenian ruler Draco. The Code was characterized by very punitive measures implemented for what today would be considered relatively minor offenses. Debtors were penalized very severely, sometimes even forced to go into slavery. The death penalty was used for a wide variety of offenses. The harshness of the code explains the etymology of the word "draconian."

What was Roman law?

It was the system of law used by the Romans from the eighth century B.C.E. until the fall of the empire (Rome, in the West Roman Empire, was toppled in 476 C.E.; the East Empire fell in 1453 C.E.). Justinian the Great (483–565), the emperor of the East Roman Empire, is credited with codifying (writing and organizing) Roman law by ordering the collection of all imperial statutes and of all the writings of the Roman jurists (judges and other legal experts).

Justinian appointed the best legal minds in the empire to assemble, write, publish, and update the code; work began early in his reign and continued until the time of Justinian's death, in 565. The result was the *Corpus juris civilis (Body of Civil Law)*, also called the *Justinian Code*. It consists of four parts: the Codex (a collection of imperial statutes), the Digest (the writings and interpretations of Roman jurists), the Institutes (a textbook for students), and the Novels (the laws enacted after the publication of the Codex).

Though largely suspended during the Middle Ages (500–1350), it was kept alive in the canon law of the medieval church and was handed down through the centuries. It forms the basis of modern civil law in most of continental Europe and in other non-English-speaking countries, as well as in the state of Louisiana. Nations or states whose systems of justice are based on civil law rely not on precedents set by the courts (which is the common law system of the United States and Great Britain), but rather on the letter of the law—the statutes themselves.

75

What is common law?

Common law means case law or judge-made law—the collection of judicial opinions that create a body of jurisprudence. It is the system of justice that prevails in Great Britain and the United States, where the precedents (past decisions) of the courts are used as the basis of the legal system. It is sometimes referred to as customary law since justices consider prevailing practices (customs) in order to arrive at their decisions.

In many countries, the justice system is a combination of the civil law handed down by the Romans under Justinian and the common law formulated in England. Private cases (often and confusingly called civil cases) are largely the realm of civil law (in other words, the statutes prevail); whereas criminal cases (in which crimes have been committed against society) are the realm of common law (i.e., decisions are based on precedent).

What was trial by ordeal?

It was an irrational way of determining someone's guilt or innocence used in older times. After the fall of Rome (476), Roman law gave way to the laws of the various Germanic (also called barbarian) tribes in Europe. If someone was charged with a crime, he or she was deliberately injured in some way: If the injury (from a heated iron bar or immersion into hot water, for example) healed within a prescribed number of days (usually three), the person was declared innocent. If the wound failed to heal, the verdict was guilty. This method for determining innocence or guilt was also called divination, since the court was trying, through the ordeal, to divine (discover intuitively) whether the accused person was guilty.

Trial by ordeal gave way to a far more practical, and certainly more rational, form of trial, in which judge and jury presided over the presentation of a case and employed written code or precedent or both to arrive at a verdict. But divination (literally, to predict by supernatural means) was used as recently as the 1600s, when women in Puritan New England were charged with witchcraft. A suspect was bound up with rope and immersed in water. If she sank, she was innocent; if she floated, she was declared guilty (the "reasoning" being that only someone with supernatural power could float under the circumstances). Those found guilty by this form of trial were put to death.

What was the Code Napoleon?

In 1800, just after Napoleon Bonaparte (1769–1821) had come to power in France, he appointed a commission of legal experts to consolidate all French civil law into one code. The process took four years; the so-called Code Civil went into effect on March 21, 1804, the same year that Napoleon named himself emperor of France (which he did in December). The laws thus took on the alternate name of the Code Napoleon or the Napoleonic Code. It went into force throughout France, Belgium, Luxembourg, and in other French territories and duchies in Europe.

The code represented a compromise between Roman law and common (or customary) law. Further, it accommodated some of the radical reforms of the French Revolution (1789–99). The Code Civil set forth laws regarding individual liberty, tenure of property, order of inheritance, mortgages, and contracts. It had broad influence in Europe as well as in Latin America, where civil law is prevalent. As opposed to the common law of most English-speaking countries, civil law judgments are based on codified principles, rather than on legal prece-

What was trial by battle?

Like trial by ordeal, trial by battle was a method of "justice" used predominately during the Middle Ages (500–1350). When noblemen had disputes, they would engage in a duel with one other: The assumption was that the person who was in the right would have God on his side, and he would emerge the victor in combat. No questions asked. This form of trial was gradually replaced by trial by jury.

dent. For example, under the Code Civil an accused person is guilty until proven innocent (as opposed to common law, which holds that a person is innocent until proven guilty).

What is habeas corpus?

The writ of habeas corpus (which is roughly translated from the Latin as "you should have the body") is considered a cornerstone of due process of law. It means that a person cannot be detained unless he or she is brought in person before the court so the court can determine whether or not the person is being lawfully held.

The notion dates back to medieval England; many historians believe that habeas corpus was implied by the Magna Carta (1215): Article 39 states, "No freemen shall be taken or imprisoned … or exiled or in any way destroyed … except by the lawful judgment of his peers or by the law of the land." The writ was reinforced by Britain's Habeas Corpus Amendment Act of 1679, which stated that the Crown (king or queen) cannot detain a prisoner against the wishes of Parliament and the courts. The English introduced the concept in the American colonies. And when the U.S. Constitution (1788) was written, it declared (in Article I, Section 9) that habeas corpus "shall not be suspended, unless when in cases of rebellion or invasion the public safety may require it." For example, during the Civil War (1861–1865), President Abraham Lincoln (1809–1865) suspended habeas corpus; and during Reconstruction (1865–1877), it was again suspended in an effort to combat the activities of the Ku Klux Klan.

Today habeas corpus law generally refers to an attempt by an inmate to argue that his underlying criminal trial and conviction were plagued by unconstitutional proceedings. For example, a habeas corpus claim may consist of a claim that the inmate was provided with ineffective assistance of counsel, in violation of the Sixth Amendment, or by a fundamentally unfair trial proceeding, in violation of the due process of the Fourteenth Amendment.

INTERNATIONAL LAW

What is international law?

As interpreted by Dutch jurist and humanist Hugo Grotius (1583–1645), natural law prescribes the rules of conduct among nations, resulting in international laws. His 1625 work, titled *Concerning the Law of War and Peace,* is considered the definitive text on international law, asserting the sovereignty and legal equality of all states of the world. But the notion also had its detractors, English philosopher Thomas Hobbes (1588–1679) among them. Hobbes insisted that since international law is not enforced by any legal body above the nations themselves, it is not legitimate.

Since the seventeenth century, however, international law has evolved to become more than just theory. During the 1800s and early 1900s, the Geneva Conventions (1864, 1906, 1929, 1949) and the Hague Conventions (1899, 1907) set forth the rules of war. Today, treaties (between two or among many countries), customary laws, legal writings, and conventions all influence international law, which is also referred to as "the law of nations." Further, it is enforced by the International Court of Justice (a United Nations body) as well as by world opinion, international sanctions, and the intervention of the United Nations (apart from the International Court of Justice).

What are the Geneva Conventions?

The Geneva Conventions are humanitarian treaties signed by almost all of the approximately 200 nations in the world today (there were 189 signatories as of 2003). The treaties were forged in Geneva, Switzerland, in 1864, 1906, 1929, and 1949. (The initial protocols, of 1864, gave rise to the Red Cross.) There were two amendments, called protocols, in 1977. In their entirety, the Geneva Conventions set standards for how signatory nations are to treat the enemy during war; they cover access to and treatment of battlefield casualties, treatment of prisoners of war (POWs), and the treatment of civilians.

The summaries of each convention and protocol are as follows:

- Convention I: For the Amelioration of the Condition of the Wounded and Sick in Armed Forces in the Field. Sets forth the protections for members of the armed forces who become wounded or sick.

- Convention II: For the Amelioration of the Condition of Wounded, Sick, and Shipwrecked Members of Armed Forces at Sea. Extends protections to wounded, sick, and shipwrecked members of the naval forces.

- Convention III: Relative to the Treatment of Prisoners of War, Geneva. Lists the rights of prisoners of war.

- Convention IV: Relative to the Protection of Civilian Persons in Time of War, Geneva. Deals with the protection of the civilian population in times of war. (All four Conventions were ratified as a whole in 1949.)

- Protocol I: Additional to the Geneva Conventions of 12 August 1949, and relating to the Protection of Victims of International Armed Conflicts. Extends protections to victims of wars against racist regimes and wars of self determination.

- Protocol II: Additional to the Geneva Conventions of 12 August 1949, and relating to the Protection of Victims of Non-International Armed Conflicts. Extends protections to victims of internal conflicts in which an armed opposition controls enough territory to enable them to carry out sustained military operations.

The Geneva Conventions, along with the Hague Conventions (1899, 1907), comprise much of what is called International Humanitarian Law (IHL). Because so many nations of the world have ratified both the Geneva Conventions and the Hague Conventions, they are considered customary international law, which means they are binding on all nations.

What are the Hague Conventions?

They are international treaties (1899, 1907) covering the laws and customs of war. The first Hague Convention developed out of the Peace Conference of 1899, held in The Hague (The Netherlands) and convened by Russian tsar Nicholas II (1868–1918). Among the original goals was limiting the expansion of armed forces. Though the representatives there, from twenty-six nations (including the United States), failed to agree on a resolution to limit such expansion, they did agree on certain rules of engagement for war on land and at sea.

They also adopted the Convention for the Pacific Settlement of International Disputes. This convention set up the permanent international court of arbitration and justice, still in existence today. The court is in The Hague, where it is housed in the Peace Palace, a gift of American industrialist and philanthropist Andrew Carnegie (1835–1919). A later convention, the Second Hague Peace Conference, was held in 1907; representatives of forty-four nations met for a period of four months.

The convention of 1907 modified and added to the first. Delegates resolved to meet again in 1915, but that conference was not held due to the outbreak of the First World War. The Hague Conventions were the forerunners of the League of Nations and the United Nations.

U.S. LAW AND JUSTICE

How was the makeup of the U.S. Supreme Court decided?

Article III of the U.S. Constitution (1788) states that the "judicial Power of the United States, shall be vested in one supreme Court." It goes on to describe the high court's jurisdiction, but it does not specify how the court was to be formed or how many justices it would consist of. These matters were left to Congress, which passed the Judiciary Act of 1789 that created the federal court system. The law provided that the Supreme Court would have a chief justice and five associate justices. The original six were Chief Justice John Jay and Associate Justices James Wilson, William Cushing, John Blair, John Rutledge, and James Iredell.

Since 1869 the Court has consisted of nine members: the chief justice and eight associates who, once named, serve for life. Justices are appointed by the president but must be approved by the Senate (according to Article 2 of the Constitution). To avoid partisanship, Congress is prevented from lowering the salaries of any of the justices, and justices can only be removed from the bench by impeachment (a formal document that charges a public official with misconduct). Cases reach the high court through appeal: Lower-court decisions that are formally challenged by filing a petition for writ of certiorari to the Court. The justices decide cases by majority vote.

79

The justices of the U.S. Supreme Court in 2012: Top row (left to right): Associate Justice Sonia Sotomayor, Associate Justice Stephen G. Breyer, Associate Justice Samuel A. Alito, and Associate Justice Elena Kagan. Bottom row (left to right): Associate Justice Clarence Thomas, Associate Justice Antonin Scalia, Chief Justice John G. Roberts, Associate Justice Anthony Kennedy, and Associate Justice Ruth Bader Ginsburg.

Does the chief justice have additional powers vis-à-vis the other justices?

Yes, the chief justice has additional powers and duties. It has often been said that the chief justice is "first among equals." The chief justice has the assignment power—the power to assign opinions to a justice of his choice—if he is in the majority.

The chief justice gives the oath of office to the president, assigns judges to the special Foreign Intelligence Surveillance Court, and presides over the Judicial Conference of the United States. The chief justice also provides reports to Congress on the state of the federal judiciary.

Who was the first chief justice of the U.S. Supreme Court?

President George Washington appointed John Jay (1745–1829) to the post, along with five associate justices: James Wilson, John Rutledge, William Cushing, John Blair, and James Iredell. Jay's was an impressive resume by the time of his appointment: He had been a member of the Continental Congress, over which he presided as president in 1778 and 1779; erved as U.S. minister to Spain (1779, during the American Revolution); and joined American statesman Benjamin Franklin (1706–1790) and the rest of the American peace commission in Paris (in 1782) to draw up the treaty ending the war with Britain. Once the new republic was established, Jay remained at the fore: He became President Washington's secretary of foreign affairs (1784–89) and, along with Alexander Hamilton (1755–1804) and James Madison (1751–1836), authored the *Federalist Papers* (1787–88), which explained the Constitution for the benefit of the states as they considered ratification.

What were the Jim Crow laws?

They were laws or practices that segregated blacks from whites. They prevailed in the American South during the late 1800s and into the first half of the 1900s. Jim Crow was a stereotype of a black man described in a nineteenth-century song-and-dance act. The first written appearance of the term is dated 1838, and by the 1880s it had fallen into common usage in the United States. Even though in 1868 Congress passed the Fourteenth Amendment, prohibiting states from violating equal protection of all citizens, southern states passed many laws segregating blacks from whites in public places.

In short, the laws were both manifestation and enforcement of discrimination. They permeated all aspects of American society, as whites and blacks used separate bathrooms, different hotels, different railway cars, and played in separate sports leagues. During the civil rights movement of the 1950s and 1960s, public pressure increased and exposed the unfairness of Jim Crow/segregation laws.

What was the Supreme Court's role in racial segregation?

Though most segregation laws (or "Jim Crow laws") were overturned by decisions of the Supreme Court during the 1950s and 1960s, the Court was righting its own wrong: In the late 1800s, during the years following the Civil War (1861–1865) and the abolition of slavery, the Supreme Court made rulings that actually supported segregation laws at the state level. The most famous of these was the 1896 case of *Plessy v. Ferguson,* in which the High Court upheld the constitutionality of Louisiana's 1890 law requiring "separate-but-equal" facilities for whites and blacks in railroad cars. The separate but equal doctrine provided that the government did not violate the equal protection clause of the Fourteenth Amendment by mandating separate facilities based on race as long as the facilities were roughly equal.

The lone dissent in *Plessy v. Ferguson* was authored by Associate Justice John Marshall Harlan, from a slaveholding family in Kentucky, who famously wrote:

In view of the Constitution, in the eye of the law, there is in this country no superior, dominant, ruling class of citizens. There is no caste here. Our Constitution is color-blind, and neither knows nor tolerates classes among citizens. In respect of civil rights, the humblest is the peer of the most powerful.

Because of this dissent and his lone dissent in an earlier case—*Civil Rights Cases* (1883)—Harlan became known as the "Great Dissenter."

Following the *Plessy v. Ferguson* decision, states went on to use the separate-but-equal principle for fifty years, passing Jim Crow laws that set up racial segregation in public schools, transportation, and in recreation, sleeping, and eating facilities. This meant there were drinking fountains, benches, restrooms, bus seats, hospital beds, and theater sections designated as "Whites Only" or "Colored." One Arkansas law even provided that the witnesses being sworn in to testify in a courtroom be given different Bibles depending on the color of their skin.

The U.S. Supreme Court invalidated the "separate but equal" doctrine—at least in of education—in its historic decision in *Brown v. Board of Education* (1954). *Brown v. Bre. Education* was a consolidation of cases from Kansas, South Carolina, Virginia, and I

What was Operation Falcon?

It was the code name for the mid-April 2005 roundup of more than 10,000 fugitives in one week; the coordinated nationwide effort was led by the U.S. Marshals Service. Together with officers from 960 federal, state, and local law enforcement agencies, the marshals arrested 10,340 people who were wanted for various crimes, many of them violent. The operation took place during Crime Victims Rights Week. More than 150 of the fugitives were wanted for murder, 550 for sexual assault charges, and more than 600 for armed robberies. There were also escaped prisoners and criminal suspects among those arrested. Operation Falcon was a landmark in law enforcement because of the sheer number of arrests; previous coordinated efforts had nabbed only hundreds of fugitives.

The lead case involved Oliver Brown, who sued on behalf of his young daughter Linda Brown, who was not allowed to attend an all-white school near her home in Topeka, Kansas.

The parents were supported in their fight by the NAACP (National Association for the Advancement of Colored People), whose legal counsel included future U.S. Supreme Court Justice Thurgood Marshall (1908–1993). On May 17, 1954, the Supreme Court unanimously ruled that segregated schools do violate the equal protection clause, overturning the separate-but-equal doctrine previously upheld by *Plessy v. Ferguson.* The Brown decision eventually led to the desegregation of nearly every aspect of American public life—including swimming pools, sporting events, restaurants, hotels, and prisons.

FAMOUS U.S. TRIALS

What were the Salem witch trials?

A series of trials in Salem, Massachusetts, in 1692, the proceedings against 200 people accused of witchcraft became allegory for searching out or harassing anyone who holds unpopular views. Indeed, the nineteen hangings that resulted from the witch hunt provide students of history with a cautionary tale about the hazards of mass hysteria.

In the seventeenth century, people widely believed in witchcraft and that those who wielded its supernatural power could perform acts of ill will against their neighbors. Courts somewhat regularly heard cases involving the malice of witches: Before the notorious trials of 1692, the records of colonial Massachusetts and Connecticut show that seventy witch cases had been tried, and eighteen of the accused were convicted. But nothing had reached the scale of the 1692 witch hunt. In January of that year, the daughter and niece of Reverend Samuel Parris began exhibiting strange behavior. Upon examination by a doctor, the conclusion was that the young girls (ages nine and eleven) were bewitched. Compelled to ame those who had bewitched them, the girls named a Carib Indian slave who worked in minister's home, and two other women—one a derelict and the other an outcast. They arrested. Hearings were held and others were accused, including upstanding members community whose only "crime" seemed to be their opposition to Reverend Parris.

The home of Judge Jonathan Corwin, who presided over many of the cases in Salem, Massachusetts, is the only remaining historical building with ties to the witch trials.

Members of his congregation became corroborative witnesses. By May, jails in Salem and Boston were filled with suspected witches awaiting trial. The court, now with a docket of some seventy cases, convened on June 28.

Through the summer months and into September, fifty of the accused confessed to practicing witchcraft, twenty-six were convicted, and nineteen were executed. The colonial governor of Massachusetts became alarmed by the number of convictions; he ordered the Salem court to disband and commenced hearings of the remaining cases in a superior court. Of fifty still accused, the court indicted only twenty-three; of these, there were only three convictions—all of which were overturned. In 1693 the colonial governor pardoned those whose cases were still pending and declared that witchcraft was no longer an actionable offense.

Who was John Peter Zenger?

John Peter Zenger (1697–1746) was a New York City printer who was accused of seditious libel in 1735. His case changed the definition of libel in American courtrooms and laid the foundation for freedom of the press.

The German-born Zenger immigrated to the American colonies in 1710, when he was thirteen years old. He found a job as a printer's apprentice, working on the colony's official newspaper, the *New York Gazette*. Fifteen years later he began his own operation, which w mostly concerned with printing religious pamphlets.

In 1733 New York received a new colonial governor from England: William quickly earned the contempt of the colonists, both rich and poor. Prosperous busir who opposed Cosby and his grievous tactics approached Zenger, offering to back a newspaper that he would both edit and publish. Zenger agreed and on November 5, 1733, the first issue of the *Weekly Journal* was released. It included scathing criticisms of the royal governor, raising Cosby's ire. After burning several issues of the papers, Cosby had Zenger arrested in November 1734. The editor-publisher continued to operate the journal from inside his jail cell, dictating editorials to his wife through the door.

Zenger's case went to trial in August 1735. Prominent Philadelphia attorney Andrew Hamilton (1676–1741), considered the best lawyer in the colonies, came to Zenger's defense. Hamilton admitted his client was guilty of publishing the papers, but, he argued, that in order for libel to be proved, Zenger's statements had to be both false and malicious. The prosecution contested the definition of libel, asserting that libelous statements are any words that are "scandalous, seditious, and tend to disquiet the people." The court agreed with the prosecution, and Hamilton was therefore unable to bring forth any evidence to support the truth of the material Zenger printed in the *Weekly Journal*. The defense argument was not heard until the closing statement was made by Hamilton; his summation stands as one of the most famous in legal history. He accused the court of suppressing evidence, urging the jury to consider the court's actions "as the strongest evidence," and went on to declare that liberty is the people's "only bulwark against lawless power…Men who injure and oppress the people under their administration provoke them to cry out and complain."

The brilliant attorney closed by urging the gentlemen of the jury to take up the cause of liberty, telling them that by so doing, they will have "baffled the attempt of tyranny." The seven jury members were convinced by Hamilton's impassioned speech and found Zenger not guilty. It was considered one of the earliest cases of jury nullification—a process by which jurors ignore settled law to reach their decision.

Discharged from prison the next day, Zenger returned to his printing business, publishing the transcripts of his own trial. While colonial officials were reluctant to accept the case's ruling on the definition of libel, the case became famous throughout the American colonies. And once the colonists had thrown off England's royal rule and established a new republic, the nation's founding fathers codified the Zenger trial's ruling in the Bill of Rights: The First Amendment to the U.S. Constitution guarantees freedom of the press.

Why was the Dred Scott decision important?

The decision in the case of Dred Scott pronounced the Missouri Compromise (1820) unconstitutional and served to deepen the divide between North and South, helping pave the way for the Civil War (1861–1865).

In the mid-1800s Dred Scott (c. 1795–1858), who had been born into slavery in Virginia, tried to claim his freedom on the basis that he had traveled with his owner, a doctor, in Wisconsin and Illinois, where slavery had been prohibited by the Missouri Compromise. By the compromise, Congress decided to admit Missouri as a slavery state and Maine as a free state, and declared that the territories north of the 36th parallel (present-day Missouri's southern border) were free, with the exception of the state of Missouri.

After a lifetime of slavery, Dred Scott sued Missouri for his freedom in April 1846. The 84 case, which hinged on Scott's travels in free territories in the North, went through two trials; the second was granted due to a procedural error in the first. In 1850, at the conclusion freed—his sentence had been reduced by Illinois governor Adlai Stevenson in exchange for the inmate's contribution to testing for malaria during World War II (1939–1945). He lived out his life in Puerto Rico, where he married, earned a master's degree, performed charitable works, and taught.

What was the "monkey trial"?

The July 1925 trial of Dayton, Tennessee, public schoolteacher John T. Scopes (1900–1970) was dubbed the "monkey trial" because at issue was Scopes' teaching of evolution in his classroom. Having yielded to religious beliefs in creationism (the story of human origins told in the Bible's book of Genesis), Tennessee state law prohibited teaching public school students about the theories of English naturalist Charles Darwin (1809–1882).

John Scopes

Darwin's scientifically credible work *The Origin of Species* argued that humans had descended from apelike creatures. Celebrated attorney Clarence Darrow (1857– 1938) defended Scopes; lawyer and former presidential candidate William Jennings Bryan (1860–1925), known as the "Great Commoner," argued for the prosecution. For twelve days in the summer of 1925, the small town in eastern Tennessee became the site of a showdown between modern scientific thought and traditional fundamentalism, or as some observed, between cosmopolitan and rural America. Spectators crowded the courtroom, eventually forcing the proceedings to be moved to the courthouse lawn. Journalists issued daily reports, which were published in newspapers across the country. It was headline writers who dubbed the case the "monkey trial."

Darrow made history when he called Bryan himself to the stand; it was a daring move on the defense attorney's part, but since Bryan eagerly accepted the summons, the judge allowed the questioning. Darrow first got Bryan to agree that every word in the Bible is true; then he set in to reveal the hazards of such a literal interpretation, asking, for example, how Cain had found himself a wife if he, Adam, Eve, and Abel were the only four people on Earth at the time.

Darrow succeeded in shaking the prosecutor, who finally admitted that he did not believe Earth was made in six days. Bryan retaliated by accusing Darrow of insulting the Bible, to which Darrow replied, "I am examining you on your fool ideas that no Christian on earth believes." It was drama better than any novelist could write. Darrow lost the case, which was later overturned on a technicality. Scopes had only been charged a $100 fine for violating the state law, which was repealed in 1967. But the trial, preserved in the play and film *Inherit the Wind*, is still remembered today: Scopes' crime was not sensational, his trial did not break any legal ground, and the defense had not won a brilliant victory, but the proceedings, carried out in the midsummer heat of the American South, epitomized the era and, ultimately, made for a great story.

Why is the court-martial of Billy Mitchell famous?

The 1925 military trial of William "Billy" Mitchell (1879–1936) made headlines because of the defendant's open and controversial criticism of the U.S. military.

A U.S. general in World War I (1914–1918), Mitchell returned from the experience convinced that the future military strength of the country depended on air power. In fact, he had commanded the American expeditionary air force during the war in Europe and had even proposed to General John Pershing that troops be dropped by parachute behind German lines; Pershing dismissed the idea. The war over, in 1921 Mitchell declared that "the first battles of any future war will be air battles." But when the navy and war departments failed to develop an air service, Mitchell was outspoken about it, charging the military with incompetence, criminal negligence, and describing the administration as treasonable. Those were fighting words.

Charged with insubordination and "conduct of a nature to bring discredit upon the military service," Mitchell's trial began on October 28, 1925. After lengthy hearings, on December 17 of that year Mitchell was found guilty and was suspended without pay from the military for a period of five years. Congress entered the fray, proposing a joint resolution to restore Mitchell's rank, but President Calvin Coolidge (1872–1933) upheld the court's decision. Mitchell responded by resigning. He returned to civilian life but continued to write and speak about his belief in an air force. He died in 1936, about five years too soon to see his predictions come true: In surprise air raids on December 7, 1941, the Japanese attacked U.S. military installations in the Philippines and Hawaii. Though the U.S. military rose to the occasion, entering World War II and building an impressive and mighty air fleet, many observers felt the military could have been better prepared to stage that monumental effort had Mitchell's advice been heeded years earlier.

Who were the Scottsboro Boys?

The Scottsboro Boys were nine African American youths falsely accused of raping two white women aboard a railway car. They were called the Scottsboro Boys because the event and subsequent trials took place in Scottsboro, Alabama. The young defendants were Clarence Norris, Charlie Weems, Haywood Patterson, Olen Montgomery, Ozie Powell, Willie Roberson, Eugene Williams, Andy Wright, and Roy Wright.

Due to racial prejudice, the youths received a sham of a trial. Facing the death penalty, the young defendants received legal help from the International Labor Defense (ILD) group and, initially, the NAACP (the NAACP later dropped out). Though convicted, the U.S. Supreme Court reversed the conviction of one of the defendants in *Powell v. Alabama* (1932), ruling that criminal defendants facing the death penalty must have an attorney. Because the defendants did not receive counsel until moments before trial, the Court ruled their trial violated due process.

Later in *Norris v. Alabama* (1935), the U.S. Supreme Court reversed a subsequent conviction of another Scottsboro Boy because the jury selection process was filled with racial bias. All-white juries convicted the Scottsboro Boys on several occasions. Eventually several of the defendants were paroled. Alabama governor George Wallace pardoned Clarence Norris in 1976.

The plight of the Scottsboro Boys is seen as a national tragedy and a prime example of a miscarriage of justice.

Who was tried at Nuremberg?

Following World War II (1939–1945), twenty-two leaders of Nazi Germany were put on trial at Nuremberg's Palace of Justice. The International Military Tribunal began the proceedings on November 25, 1945, and they were not concluded until September 30 of the following year; the verdicts were announced on October 1. The site was deliberately selected by the Allies: The now bombed-out city of Nuremberg was considered a seat of Nazi power.

Though many, including Soviet leader Joseph Stalin (1979–1953) thought that Hitler's henchmen ought only to be tried as a show of justice before they were executed, others, notably U.S. chief prosecutor Robert Jackson (a U.S. Supreme Court justice; 1892–1954), believed due process of law must be observed. The American view prevailed.

The tribunal indicted twenty-three Nazi leaders on four counts: conspiracy, crimes against peace, war crimes, and crimes against humanity. One of the defendants, Robert Ley (1890–1945), committed suicide in prison before the trial began. The case against the Nazis was based on a mountain of written evidence, such as orders, reports, manifests, logs, letters, and diaries; the Germans had scrupulously recorded their evil deeds. The presentation of the documents was punctuated with live testimony of a German civilian contractor who, out of curiosity, had followed a Nazi detachment to an embankment where several thousand Jewish men, women, and children were shot and buried in a pit; and of a French woman, a survivor of the horrors of Auschwitz, recollecting a night when "children had been hurled into furnaces alive," since the Nazis had run out of fuel.

The atrocities were rendered unimaginably horrific by the sheer number of Nazi victims, which included 3.7 million (of the 5.7 million captured) Soviet troops who died in prison, 4 million Jews who died in extermination camps, and the murder of at least 2 million more Jews elsewhere. The defense was prohibited from employing a "you did it, too" argument, which would

What was Al Capone tried for?

Notorious American gangster Alphonse "Scarface Al" Capone (1899–1947), whose crime syndicate terrorized Chicago in the 1920s, was brought to trial for income tax evasion. After Chicago police had been unable to bring Capone to justice for his criminal activities, which included trafficking bootleg liquor, gambling, prostitution, and murder, the Federal Bureau of Investigation determined that the only way to prosecute the crime boss would be through violation of the tax laws. For two and a half weeks in October 1931, the case against Capone was heard in a Chicago courtroom. He was found guilty on five counts of tax evasion, sentenced to eleven years in prison, and charged $50,000 in fines and $30,000 in court costs. While his first jail cell, in Illinois's Cook County Jail, allowed him the luxuries of a private shower, phone conversations, telegrams, and even visits by other gangsters, including "Lucky" Luciano and "Dutch" Schultz, Capone was eventually moved to Alcatraz Island in San Francisco Bay, where he received no privileges. Released in 1939, Capone lived out his remaining years with his wife and son in Miami Beach, where his mental health deteriorated due to neurosyphillis.

have been an attempt to justify their actions by claiming it was all part of war. The Allies were determined to bring the Nazis to justice for their appalling and diabolical acts.

Among those tried at Nuremberg were Hitler's chief deputy Hermann Goering (1893–1946, whom a *New Yorker* correspondent covering the trials described as "a brain without a conscience"), foreign minister Joachim von Ribbentrop (1893–1946), and armaments minister Albert Speer (1905–1981). Goering and Ribbentrop were among the five men found guilty on all four counts against them; they were sentenced to hang. Six others were found guilty of crimes against humanity and were all sentenced to hang. A seventh man, Martin Bormann (1900–1945), who had been tried in absentia, was also sentenced to hang—if he were found to be alive. Seven others were also found guilty on one or two counts and were sentenced to prison terms, ranging from ten years to life. Three were acquitted on all four counts. Goering escaped his hanging: Though he was to be closely monitored by his jailers, he managed to secure a vial of cyanide, which he swallowed a few hours before his scheduled execution. Since Bormann was at large, ten Nazi leaders died in the three gallows that had been constructed in the prison gym of the Palace of Justice.

The trials at Nuremberg cemented the principle that wartime leaders are accountable under international law for their crimes and atrocities.

Why was Alger Hiss tried?

U.S. public official Alger Hiss (1904–1996) was tried for perjury during 1949 and 1950. His first trial ended in a hung jury, and the second trial concluded with a guilty verdict and a sentence of five years in prison. Hiss served four years and eight months before he was released and returned to private life. To this day many believe Hiss was framed by Republican politicians who charged President Harry Truman's (1884–1972) administration with employing Communists who acted as secret agents for the Soviet Union. The politically charged case was packed with intrigue, including the testimony of a *Time* magazine senior editor who was later revealed to be a perjurer and who used at least seven different aliases in a fourteen-year period; microfilm evidence stored in a hollowed-out pumpkin in the middle of a farm field; and an old typewriter, which later evidence and testimony revealed was probably a fake.

The case against Hiss was made amidst the Investigation of Un-American Activities of the House of Representatives. It was 1948 and the Cold War was on; distrust was running high. And when a man named Whittaker Chambers (an editor at *Time*) appeared before the House committee and claimed that Hiss had been a courier who had transported confidential government documents to the Soviets, Hiss, then president of the Carnegie Endowment for International Peace, became the subject of investigation. He was indicted and stood trial.

In spite of his distinguished career as a public servant (he had served in the State Department for eleven years); a parade of character witnesses who testified of his integrity, loyalty, and veracity; and his own vehement denial of the charges, the prosecution managed to bring enough evidence against him to convince a second jury that Hiss lied when he said the charges that he was a secret agent were "a complete fabrication." (The jury in Hiss's first trial deadlocked following more than fourteen hours of deliberation.)

Even after his conviction, Hiss's lawyers worked tirelessly to appeal the case; all attempts were denied. In 1957 Hiss published his own account of the case, *In the Court of Public Opinion*, in which he reasserted his innocence. Then in 1973, during the Watergate hearings, former White House counsel John Dean's (1938–) explosive testimony included the statement that he heard President Richard Nixon (1913–1994) say, "The typewriters are always the key…We built one in the Hiss case." In 1988 Hiss published again; the book was titled *Recollections of a Life*. Four years later, at the age of eighty-seven, Hiss appealed to the Russian government to examine their intelligence archives to see what they revealed about him; the response came back that there was "not a single document" substantiating the allegations that Hiss had collaborated with the Soviet Union's intelligence service. That same year, 1992, Hiss's son, Tony, wrote an article for the *New Yorker* magazine; it was titled "My Father's Honor."

Ethel and Julius Rosenberg

Why were the Rosenbergs tried?

Husband and wife Julius (1918–1953) and Ethel Rosenberg (1915–1953) were tried for conspiracy to commit wartime espionage. Arrested in 1950, the Rosenbergs were charged with passing nuclear weapons data to the Soviets, enabling the Communists to develop and explode their own atomic bomb—an event that had been announced to the American public by President Truman on September 23, 1949. As the realization set in that the United States could now be the victim of an atomic attack, the anxieties of the Cold War heightened. Citizens were encouraged to build bomb shelters, school children participated in air-raid drills, civil-defense films (such as *How Can I Stay Alive in an Atom Bomb Blast?*) were screened, and entire towns conducted tests of how residents would respond in the event of an "A-bomb."

Meanwhile, the leak of top-secret information from the Manhattan Project at Los Alamos, New Mexico, was traced to New York City machine-shop owner Julius Rosenberg, his wife, and her brother, David Greenglass. Historian Doris Kearns Goodwin writes that the "short, plump Mrs. Rosenberg looked more like one of my friends' mothers than an international spy." Indeed, the case marked the first time American civilians were charged with espionage; and the trial made international headlines. Though the Rosenbergs were only two of many involved in the conspiracy, theirs was the heaviest of the punishments handed down in the cases against the spy ring. For their betrayal and their refusal to talk, the Rosenbergs were sentenced to death; in issuing the sentence, Judge Irving Kaufman accused the couple of having "altered the course of history." The penalty rocked the world: As Supreme Court Justice Felix Frankfurter put it, they "were tried for conspiracy and sentenced for treason." They were electrocuted the evening of June 19, 1953, as New York's Union Square filled with an estimated 10,000 protesters.

What was the lasting effect of the Clarence Earl Gideon trials?

The lasting effect of Clarence Earl Gideon's famous case was that criminal defendants in state court who are facing felony charges have the right to attorneys. A fifty-one-year-old drifter charged with burglary in Panama City, Florida, Clarence Earl Gideon had two trials, in 1961 and 1963. But it's what happened between the two trials that continues to be important to every American today.

What might have been pretty standard fare in the day-to-day business of the American justice system (Gideon was charged with robbing a cigarette machine and a jukebox), the Gideon case instead made history when the defendant successfully argued that his constitutional rights had been denied when he was refused an attorney. The Sixth Amendment to the U.S. Constitution provides that those charged with a crime should receive the "assistance of counsel." But, the question was whether this Sixth Amendment freedom—which technically applied only in federal trials—would be extended to state criminal cases.

Existing law did not support Gideon's claim to an attorney. In *Betts v. Brady* (1942), the U.S. Supreme Court had ruled that the Sixth Amendment right to counsel was not extended to the state's via the due process clause of the Fourteenth Amendment. In other words, people like Gideon did not have a constitutional right to an attorney.

However, Gideon kept pressing the issue. Though he had a limited education, after a guilty verdict was handed down in his 1961 trial, Gideon knew enough about his rights to petition the Supreme Court, saying that his right to a fair trial (guaranteed by the Sixth Amendment) had been violated: Since he was not able to hire a lawyer to defend himself, the trial had not been fair. The petition, one of thousands the Supreme Court receives each year, somehow rose to the top.

The high court heard Gideon's case and appointed a prominent Washington D.C. lawyer named Abe Fortas to argue for Gideon at the Supreme Court. Fortas later became a Supreme Court justice. The U.S. Supreme Court overruled *Betts v. Brady*, ruling that "any person hailed into court, who is too poor to hire a lawyer, cannot be assured a fair trial unless counsel in provided for him." For Gideon, the opinion served to throw out the first trial; for the rest of America, it was assurance that regardless of the crime, a defendant would be guaranteed legal counsel.

With the benefit of that counsel, Gideon's case was re-tried in 1963. He was acquitted on all charges.

What are Miranda warnings?

Familiar to many Americans from TV police dramas, the Miranda warnings are a reading of the arrested person's rights: "You have a right to remain silent…anything you say can and will be used against you in a court. You have a right to consult with a lawyer…if you cannot afford a lawyer, one will be appointed for you.… "

Reading the defendant his rights became a requirement after the 1963 trial of Ernesto Miranda, a young Latino man accused of rape. He was found guilty and sentenced to twenty to thirty years imprisonment. But Alvin Moore, Miranda's court-appointed lawyer, had revealed through his questioning of a police officer that the defendant had not been notified of his right to the services of an attorney. The same police officer had taken Miranda's written confession following two hours of interrogation.

The case was appealed all the way to the U.S Supreme Court, which ruled 5-4 in Miranda's favor, on June 13, 1966. Chief Justice Earl Warren (1891–1974) reasserted that "prior to any questioning a person must be warned that he has a right to remain silent, that any statement he does make may be used as evidence against him, and that he has the right to…an attorney."

Miranda's first trial was thrown out, and in 1967 he again stood trial in Arizona. But the prosecution secured new evidence; the testimony of his estranged girlfriend that Miranda had confessed to her the rape he was charged with. He was convicted and again sentenced to twenty to thirty years in prison. Released on parole, Miranda died in a bar fight in January 1976. Ironically, police officers on the scene found cards in Miranda's pockets in the bar detailing the Miranda rights. Police officers, the courts, and defendants still remember the importance of the case—even if they can't recall Ernesto Miranda's name or crime.

Why is the ruling in *Roe v. Wade* controversial?

The 1973 Supreme Court decision in the case of *Roe v. Wade* legalized abortion in the United States and has probably engendered more public controversy than any other legal decision of the late twentieth century. Women's access to safe abortion continues to be the subject of debate, at issue in legal cases, and has inspired overzealous antiabortion activists to commit violence against doctors who perform abortions and office workers in women's health clinics. The seven Supreme Court justices who issued the majority decision became the recipients of thousands of letters of hatred, some of them threatening.

What was ABSCAM?

ABSCAM was an undercover operation conducted by the Federal Bureau of Investigation (FBI) to ferret out corrupt government officials and prosecute them. In 1978 agents began posing as American representatives of Arab businessmen whose company, the fictitious Abdul Enterprises Limited, was willing to buy political influence in the United States. (ABSCAM comes from the first two letters of the business name, with the word "scam" added to the end.) The trap was set. The first to be caught was Congressman Michael "Ozzie" Myers (1943–) of Pennsylvania, who was videotaped accepting a $50,000 bribe and saying, "I'm going to tell you something real simple and short—money talks in this business." Other officials also fell prey to the sting operation. All of them were arrested on charges of bribery and conspiracy. The first of seven trials got under way in 1980. None of the officials were acquitted; most faced fines and/or imprisonment; and all of them lost their offices. The wide net cast by ABSCAM had caught one U.S. senator, six representatives in Congress, one mayor, three members of the Philadelphia city council, one INS (Immigration and Naturalization Service) inspector, one lawyer, one accountant, and many of their associates. The FBI operation and the resulting trials and punishments sent a loud warning to any public official subject to influence.

The case was brought as a class-action suit (representing all pregnant women) by twenty-one-year-old Norma McCorvey (1947–), who has since the ruling reversed her feeling and joined the antiabortion camp as a "Right to Life" advocate. But in 1969, under the alias Jane Roe, McCorvey claimed that Texas's abortion law (on the books since 1859) violated her constitutional rights and those of other women. The other party named in the case was Texas district attorney Henry B. Wade (1914–2001), who argued to uphold Texas state law that punished anyone who gave an abortion. Despite the fact that the ruling in the case would do nothing to help McCorvey, for who even a favorable decision would come too late to end her unwanted pregnancy, her lawyers, Linda Coffee and Sarah Weddington, agreed to pursue the case as a test. The crux of the plaintiff's case is best summed up by arguments made before the Supreme Court, when in December 1971, Weddington argued that Texas's ability to compel women to bear children infringed on a woman's right to control her own life. It was therefore a violation of the Constitution (the Fourteenth Amendment), which forbids states to "make or enforce any law which shall abridge the privileges or immunities of citizens." In response to defense claims that the fetus is entitled to protection, Weddington averred, "the Constitution as I read it…attaches protection to the person at the time of birth." These arguments, and those of the defense, were presented twice to the Supreme Court; after the first presentation the seven justices then seated concluded that such an important decision should not be made until the two newly appointed justices could participate. In October 1972 the case was heard again. As it turned out, the two new judges represented one majority vote and one dissenting vote. The majority decision was read by Justice Harry Blackmun on January 22, 1973: The high court overturned all state laws restricting women's access to abortions.

The decision was based on the Court's opinion that existing laws banning abortions had been enacted to protect the health of American women (since abortion had previously been a risky medical procedure) and that with advances in medicine this protection was no longer necessary or valid. The court also agreed that the Constitution's implied right to privacy, as found in the "Fourteenth Amendment's concept of personal liberty…or in the Ninth Amendment's reservation of rights to the people, is broad enough to encompass a woman's decision to terminate her pregnancy." Two justices dissented in the opinion, with Justice Byron White writing that the court had sustained a position that "values the convenience, whim or caprice of the putative mother more than life or the potential life of the fetus." Nearly four decades after the landmark decision, opinion continues to divide along such lines. In subsequent decisions, the Court has upheld various restrictions on obtaining an abortion, but it has never overruled the central holding of *Roe v. Wade*.

What was the Gang of Four?

The Gang of Four was a group within China's Communist Party that, under the leadership of Mao Tse-tung's wife, Jiang Qing (1914–1991), twenty-one years his junior, carried out its own power-hungry agenda and plotted the takeover of the government from Chairman Mao (1893–1976).

A former stage and movie actress, Jiang was also an astute student of politics. In the late 1960s (at which time she had been married to Mao for some thirty years), she became associated with former army commander Lin Bao, and the pair conspired to stage a coup. In 1970, at a Communist Party conference, they announced that Lin had surpassed Mao as the leader of the people; one year later Lin and Jiang tried to overthrow Mao's government. Failing, Lin fled the country (his plane was later shot down), and Jiang succeeded in covering up her involvement in the affair. But she continued her subversive activities, associating with three other members of the politburo (the chief executive and political committee of the Communist Party). In 1974 Mao publicly admonished his wife and her cohorts, Wang Hongwen, Yao Wenyuan, and Zhang Chunquiao, to cease their power-seeking activities. Infighting in the party had already resulted in Mao's loss of influence. Two years later, on September 9, 1976, Mao died. The Gang of Four were arrested and thrown into prison. There they remained for years while the case against them was formulated, resulting in an indictment that consisted of 20,000 words.

Finally, on November 20, 1980, the Gang of Four, expanded to include six other conspirators, were put on trial—charged with counterrevolutionary acts, including sedition and conspiracy to overthrow the government, persecution of party and state leaders, suppression of the people, and plotting to assassinate Mao. During nearly six weeks of testimony, Jiang's machinations were revealed to the 600 representatives who attended the trial, held in an air force auditorium in western Beijing, as well as to the Chinese press (foreign press was prohibited from attending). Her laundry list of malicious acts as ringleader of the Gang of Four included public humiliation and even torture of Communist Party rivals, execution of her personal enemies, inspiring the fear of the masses, and purging the arts of anything that did not carry a revolutionary theme. Jiang, while not denying many of these acts, insisted that she had all along acted at the behest of her husband, Mao. During the explosive testimony and presentation of evidence, which included tapes and documents substantiating the state's case against Jiang, she made outbursts, was temporarily expelled from the courtroom, was dragged screaming from the courtroom twice, and even taunted her accusers into executing her, saying it would be "more glorious to have my head chopped off."

In the end Jiang and one other conspirator were found guilty and sentenced to death (later commuted to life in prison), and the eight others were also found guilty and charged with sentences ranging from sixteen years to life in prison. Jiang died on May 14, 1991, in what appeared to be a suicide.

Was despotic Romanian leader Nicolae Ceausescu brought to justice?

In the 1989 "trial" of Nicolae Ceausescu (1918–1989) and his wife Elena (1919–1989), justice may not have been served, but many believed the tyrannical Communist leader of Romania had indeed met with just desserts. The December 25 trial of the Ceausescus lasted all of sixty minutes: fifty-five minutes of questioning, to which the president's response was, "I do not recognize you...I do not recognize this court," followed by five minutes of deliberation. The court and judge were made up of the leaders in the popular

Nicolae Ceausescu

rebellion that had begun December 16 when a pro-democracy rally attended by some 350,000 people ended in the Romanian army's and Ceausescu's secret police attacking unarmed demonstrators, killing several hundred men, women, and children. In demonstrations that followed, the Romanian army, long resentful of the privileged status enjoyed by the president's secret police, turned on Ceausescu's government, handing over automatic weapons to insurgents, whom they now joined in a popular uprising.

On December 21 state television and radio came under the people's control, as did the Communist Party's central building and the royal palace, which were later found to be replete with luxuries and were also connected by a maze of tunnels. The Ceausescus and a few of their close associates tried to flee, but were captured on December 22—the same day that mass graves were found, revealing the secret police's torture and murder of several hundred men, women, and children. The rebels drove the Ceausescus around for three days, averting the still-loyal secret police. Realizing that time was not on their side, the captors assembled an "extraordinary military tribunal" in a small schoolroom at an army barracks. A defense lawyer was provided for Ceausescu; counsel urged the former president to plead guilty by reason of insanity. He refused. The charges against Ceausescu included genocide, the massacre of demonstrators, and subversion of the economy for his own benefit. One hour later, the guilty verdict was delivered. Asked if they wished to appeal the decision, the Ceausescus remained silent. They were promptly taken outside, where a squad opened fire on the former president and his wife. Videotape of the brutal killings (the squad had fired as many as thirty rounds) was shown on Romanian television. By December 30 the country was controlled by rebel forces.

What was the "trial of the twentieth century"?

As the century drew to a close, American historians, legal experts, and the public considered which of the many trials hailed as the trial of the twentieth century actually merited the title. But the criteria used by each person varied: some believed the most important trial was the most highly publicized; others believed it was a trial in which the verdict affected everyone; some thought it was a trial that most epitomized an era; and some believed the most important trial was the one that inspired the most public debate. Still others looked for a single trial that seemed to "have it all": notoriety, impact, reflections of society at large, and a controversial outcome.

The following are among the courtroom dramas that were mentioned:

The 1907 to 1908 trial of Harry Thaw (1871–1947), whose lawyers went through two trials (the first ended in a deadlocked jury) to convince jurors that Mr. Thaw suffered from "dementia Americans," a condition supposedly unique to American men that had caused Thaw to experience an uncontrollable desire to kill a man who had had an affair with his wife; the case took "innocent by reason of insanity" to new heights. The well-to-do, Harvard-educated Thaw was declared not guilty.

The 1921 case of Nicola Sacco (1891–1927) and Bartolomeo Vanzetti (1888–1927), Italian-born anarchists charged with and, amidst international uproar, found guilty of murder and robbery. So many people were convinced of the pair's innocence that demonstrations were mounted in cities around the world. They were executed in August 1927, but fifty years later Governor Michael Dukakis of Massachusetts signed a special proclamation clearing their names.

The Bruno Richard Hauptmann (1899–1936) trial of 1935: The German-born defendant was convicted of murdering the twenty-month-old son of celebrated aviator Charles A. Lindbergh (1902–1974) and his noted wife Anne Morrow Lindbergh (1906–2001), after the child was kidnapped from the family's Hopewell, New Jersey, home on March 1, 1932. For two and a half months, the world had prayed for the safe return of Charles Jr. But the toddler's body was found on May 12, two miles from the Lindbergh home. Public outrage demanded justice. Evidence surfaced that implicated Hauptmann, who was tried January 2 to February 13, 1935. Found guilty, he died by electrocution. Influential journalist H. L. Mencken noted that the trial, in which the conviction seemed to hinge on circumstantial evidence and which was attended by a "circuslike" atmosphere, was the "biggest story since the Resurrection." Though many remained convinced that officials had acted hastily to bring a case against Hauptmann and maintained that he'd been framed, efforts to clear his name continued to be denied into the 1990s.

The 1931 to 1937 trials of the so-called "Scottsboro boys": Nine men, ranging in age from twelve to twenty, who had been seized from several points along a forty-two-car train in northeastern Alabama and were promptly charged with raping two white women. Upon medical examination, the women showed no signs of having been raped—or even of having had intercourse in the time frame in question. Nevertheless, the court of public opinion in the segregated South saw to it that eight of the nine were convicted of the crime, in spite of overwhelming evidence and testimony supporting their innocence.

The 1995 criminal case of former football player O. J. Simpson (1947–), who was tried and acquitted in the murders of his former wife, Nicole, and her friend, Ronald Goldman. One observer said this trial had it all: "women, minorities, public interest, domestic violence, fallen hero," and through its live media coverage had "exposed the legal system to the public." In a subsequent civil trial, Simpson was held liable for the wrongful death of his former wife and Goldman.

Other trials routinely mentioned in considering the question included the cases of convicted murderers Leopold and Loeb; the infamous Scopes "monkey trial," which pitted faith against reason, religion against science, and tradition against modernity; the Nuremberg trials, which established a process that brought war criminals to justice; the case of Alger Hiss, who was "either a traitor or the victim of a framing for political advantages at the highest levels"; and the Rosenberg espionage case. Undoubtedly there are trials missing from even this long list: There can be no definitive and objective answer to the question.

Were any 9/11 conspirators convicted?

Many of the 9/11 conspirators died in their suicide-terrorist attacks. But, French citizen Zacarias Moussaoui (1968–) was convicted in a U.S. court in Alexandria, Virginia, in connection with the September 11, 2001, attacks that claimed nearly 3,000 lives. Moussaoui was taken into custody by the Federal Bureau of Investigation (FBI) in August 2001; a flight instructor in Minnesota, where he was training, had reported him as suspicious. After the September terrorist attacks, Moussaoui continued to be held as the possible twentieth hijacker (one of the flights on 9/11 had four hijackers; the other three flights each had five).

For the next three years, the suspected terrorist was the subject of a sometimes dramatic legal battle: Moussaoui insulted the U.S. District judge hearing his case, attempted to fire his lawyers, and pleaded guilty only to later change his mind. On April 22, 2005, the case came to close when Moussaoui admitted his guilt in front of a packed courtroom. In 2006, he received a life sentence.

What is the status of the death penalty in the United States?

The death penalty still exists in thirty-four states. Critics insist that the death penalty constitutes "cruel and unusual" punishment in violation of the Eighth Amendment of the U.S. Constitution. In *Furman v. Georgia* (1972), the Supreme Court by a 5-4 vote invalidated the death penalty statute of Georgia and nullified the death penalty nationwide. The Court determined that the death penalty law did not provide enough guidance for jurors to determine whether individual defendants should receive the ultimate punishment.

Legislators went to work and crafted more detailed death-penalty laws that contained both aggravating and mitigating factors for jurors to consider. In *Gregg v. Georgia* (1976), the Court upheld the death penalty statute in Georgia.

While the Court has not invalidated the death penalty on its face, it has narrowed the application of death penalty. It has provided that certain types of defendants cannot be put to death. For example, the Court has ruled:

Coker v. Georgia (1977)—those convicted of rape cannot be executed.

Ford v. Wainwright (1986)—the mentally insane cannot be executed.

Atkins v. Virginia (2002)—mentally retarded inmates cannot be executed.

Roper v. Simmons (2005)—those who commit murder as juveniles cannot be executed.

Kennedy v. Louisiana (2008)—child rapists cannot be executed.

The death penalty remains one of the most divisive issues in modern society. Complicating the issue is that numerous defendants have been released from death row—on the verge of execution—after DNA evidence showed that they did not commit the crime for which they were convicted. Because of these wrongful convictions, several states issued moratoriums on the death penalty.

Still, proponents of the death penalty insist that the ultimate punishment serves both deterrence and retribution rationales.

WAR AND CONFLICT

THE TROJAN WAR

What was the Trojan War?

According to Greek legend, the Trojan War was a ten-year siege, c. 1200 B.C.E., on the ancient city of Troy (also called Ilium). The Greek poet Homer (c. 850–? B.C.E.) chronicled the Trojan War in his epic the *Iliad*. According to Homer, the (Greek) Mycenaeans, under their great king Agamemnon, set out to conquer the city of Troy, situated on the Turkish coast at the southwestern part of the Hellespont. The Hellespont, now called the Dardanelles, and the Bosporus are narrow straits that connect the Aegean Sea with the Black Sea. As such, they are the gateway between Europe and Asia, and in Mycenaean times they held the key to control of the profitable Black Sea trade. In hopes of taking over that trade, Agamemnon's army attacked the powerful city of Troy, launching the decade-long campaign. The mythological war likely reflected a real war that was fought over the Dardanelles about 1200 B.C.E.

What is a Trojan horse?

Thanks to the Greek poet Homer (c. 850–? B.C.E.), a Trojan horse has come to symbolize anything that looks good but is actually subversive. According to his Trojan War epic the *Iliad*, after nearly ten years of fighting the Trojans for control of their city, the Greek Mycenaean army built a huge wooden horse on wheels and offered it as a gift to their enemy. Leaving the "peace offering" outside the city walls of Troy, the Mycenaean army then departed. Despite warnings (including one from the Trojan princess Cassandra), the Trojans accepted the gift, and they opened the gates and wheeled the huge wooden horse into the city. It was a naive move: Once the horse was inside the city gates, Mycenaean soldiers who were hidden inside the wooden structure took Troy by storm, ending the decade-long campaign and taking control of the lucrative Black Sea trade.

THE PELOPONNESIAN WAR

What was the Peloponnesian War?

It was the war fought between the Greek city-states of Athens and Sparta between 431 and 404 B.C.E.; it left Athens ruined. The beginning of the war signaled the end of the golden age of Greece.

As the city-states (which were self-ruling regions made up of a city and the surrounding territory) developed, an intense rivalry grew between Athens and Sparta. The Spartans recruited allies into the Peloponnesian League (the Peloponnese Peninsula forms the southern part of mainland Greece), and together they attacked the Athenian Empire, which had been gaining power.

The war consisted of three stages: The first was the Archidamian War (431–421 B.C.E.), named for Archidamus, the Spartan king who led the unsuccessful attacks on fortified Athens. In 421 the so-called Peace of Nicias (421 to 413 B.C.E.) began, which was negotiated by Athenian politician Nicias. But this truce was broken when an Athenian commander promoted counterattacks on Athens's aggressors in 418 and 415 B.C.E. The attacks on the Peloponnesian League were unsuccessful, and so the Ionian War broke out (413–404 B.C.E.). After years of fighting, the Ionian War finally ended in victory for Sparta, after the Peloponnesian League had not only gained the support of Persia to defeat Athens but had successfully encouraged Athens's own subjects to revolt. Athens surrendered to Sparta, ending the Peloponnesian War.

PAN–HELLENISM

Why was Macedonian king Alexander known as "the Great"?

The Macedonian king Alexander the Great (356–323 B.C.E.) has passed through history as a legendary figure, a reputation attributable to the fact that he conquered virtually all of the known world in his day. In effect, he was king of the world, though his tenure in that role was relatively brief.

Born in the Greek city-state of Macedonia, Alexander was the son of King Philip II (382–336 B.C.E.), who had risen to power three years earlier. He had an upbringing and education befitting a young Greek prince: Alexander was tutored by Greek philosopher Aristotle (384–322 B.C.E.) and was trained in athletics and war. His studies of Greek literature and art would later combine with his skill as a warrior to produce a formidable conqueror. Inspired by Greek culture, he also possessed the military prowess and cunning necessary to spread Hellenism (Greek culture) throughout the known world.

At the age of sixteen, Alexander began running the government of Macedonia while his father, King Philip, waged military campaigns to protect and expand his kingdom. At the age of seventeen, Alexander joined his father on the battlefield, where he commanded a section of the army to defeat Thebes. When Philip was assassinated in 336 B.C.E., Alexander acted quickly to assert his claim to the throne. Having done so by 335 B.C.E., he continued to carry out his father's campaigns, securing Greece and the Balkan Peninsula by the fall of that year. He followed this with an all-out offensive on the Persian Empire, long the enemy

Alexander the Great is honored by this statue in Thessaloniki, Greece.

of Greece. Supremely courageous and confident in his own abilities as well as in his troops (which numbered in the tens of thousands), by the fall of 331 B.C.E. Alexander had defeated the Persian army and along the way claimed Egypt.

The centuries-old Persian Empire crumbled, and the young Macedonian king proclaimed himself "Lord of Asia." Still, he pressed on, claiming Afghanistan (where he solidified his claim by marrying a young princess) and then India. He was poised to take the Arabian peninsula, in 324 B.C.E., when he died of fever. He was thirty-three. His vast kingdom, which he had ruled leniently, but nevertheless authoritatively, was divided among his former generals.

THE ROMAN CONQUEST

How was Rome able to conquer Greece?

After Alexander the Great died in 323 B.C.E., his generals divided his empire into successor states, but Greece remained under Macedonian control. Though the Greeks would fight the armies of the Macedonian kings into the 200s B.C.E., they would not achieve independence, and instead associations of Greek city-states again fought each other.

Meanwhile, just to the west, Rome had been conquering lands to become a formidable power in the Mediterranean and soon began to look eastward to expand its authority. When Rome conquered Macedonia in 197 B.C.E., Greece was liberated. Fifty years later, in 146 B.C.E., Greece was conquered by Rome and was divided into provinces. While the city-states had no military or political power, they nevertheless flourished under Roman rule. And the Romans,

101

Why is Hannibal considered so important?

Hannibal (247 B.C.E.–183 B.C.E.) is considered a skilled military leader and strategist far ahead of his times, who sometimes led his Carthaginian troops to victories over much larger Roman forces. For example, in 216 B.C.E., he and his troops engaged and trapped a much larger Roman force of more than 85,000 troops in Cannae during the Second Punic War. Hannibal and his troops killed more than 50,000 Roman soldiers—probably the most devastating defeat Roman soldiers ever suffered.

Eventually, Hannibal was forced to retreat, as the Romans had too many resources. Rome won the Second Punic War in 201 B.C.E. Hannibal fled to present-day Turkey. He eventually committed suicide rather than surrender to the Romans.

who had first started borrowing from Greek thought and culture around 300 B.C.E., were soon spreading Greek ideas, art, and religion throughout their empire, giving rise to the Greco-Roman culture inherited by modern western civilization.

What were the Punic Wars?

The Punic Wars were three major campaigns that Rome waged to expand its empire. Messina (a present-day province of Sicily, Italy) was the site of the First Punic War, which began in 264 B.C.E. when warring factions in the trade and transportation center called for assistance from both Carthage and Rome. The Carthaginians arrived first and secured the city. But the Romans, who had girded their navy for the battle, arrived and drove the Carthaginians out (241 B.C.E.), conquering Sicily. Messina became a free city but was allied with Rome.

The rivalry between Rome and Carthage did not end there: The Second Punic War (218–201 B.C.E.) was largely fought over control of Spain. When the great Carthaginian general Hannibal (247–183 B.C.E.) captured the Roman-allied city of Sagunto, Spain, in 218, he then crossed the Alps and invaded Italy, where he was met by and then defeated the Roman armies. The deciding battle in the Second Punic War was fought in the North African town of Zama (southwest of Carthage) in 202 B.C.E. It was there that the Romans under general Scipio Africanus (236–183 B.C.E.) crushed the Carthaginians under Hannibal. Rome exacted payments from Carthage, and Carthage was also forced to surrender its claims in Spain. In 201 B.C.E. the two powers signed a peace treaty, which held for five decades.

The Third Punic War erupted in 149 B.C.E. when the Carthaginians rebelled against Roman rule. By 146 B.C.E. Carthage, which had been richer and more powerful than Rome when the Punic Wars began, was completely destroyed in this third and final conflict with the Roman army.

THE SACKING OF ROME

If the Roman Empire was so powerful, why did it fall?

One could argue that the Roman Empire collapsed under its own weight: It had become too vast to be effectively controlled by any one ruler.

By the close of the Punic Wars in 146 B.C.E., Greece, Macedonia, and the Mediterranean coasts of Spain and Africa had been brought under Roman control. Within a century, Rome again began to expand overseas. Under the Roman general Pompey (106–48 B.C.E.), eastern Asia Minor, Syria, and Judea (Palestine) were conquered. Next, Gaul was conquered by Pompey's rival, Julius Caesar (100–44 B.C.E.), adding the territory west of Europe's Rhine River to the Roman world. In 31 B.C.E., in the Battle of Actium, Octavian (63 B.C.E.– 14 C.E.; Julius Caesar's adopted son and heir) defeated the forces of Mark Antony (c. 83–30 B.C.E.) and Cleopatra (69–30 B.C.E.), queen of Egypt, and in 30 B.C.E. Egypt became a Roman province.

In 27 B.C.E. Octavian became the first Roman emperor and was known as Augustus, meaning "exalted." Though Octavian's rule marked the beginning of the long period of stability called the Pax Romana, the Roman Empire had become so large—stretching across Europe and parts of Africa and the Middle East—that only a strong, central authority could govern it. During the 200 years of the Pax Romana, Rome's emperors gradually grew more powerful, to the point that after death an emperor was worshiped by the people.

But soon there were threats to this central control, not the least of which was the spread of Christianity, as well as invasions from the Germanic Goths and the Persians. Theodosius I (379–395) was the last emperor to rule the entire Roman Empire. When he died in 395 C.E., the empire was split into the West Roman Empire and the East Roman Empire, setting the stage for the decline of the Romans.

The West Roman Empire came under a series of attacks by various Germanic tribes including the Vandals and the Visigoths (the western division of the Goths), who invaded Spain, Gaul (in western Europe), and northern Africa. These assaults eventually led to the disintegration of the West Roman Empire by 476.

The East Roman Empire remained more or less intact, but it became known as the Byzantine Empire and was predominately a Greek-oriented culture from 476 until 1453, when it fell to the Turks.

ATTILA THE HUN

Was Attila the Hun really a savage?

While Attila (c. 406–453) may have possessed some of the worthwhile qualities of a military leader, the king of the Huns was no doubt a ruthless and fierce figure. He is believed to have ascended through the ranks of the Hun army, coming to power as the leader of the nomadic group in 434. By this time, the Huns (who originated in central Asia) had occupied the Volga River valley in the area of present-day western Russia.

At first, like his predecessors, he was wholly occupied with fighting other barbarian tribes for control of lands. But under Attila's leadership, the Huns began to extend their power into central Europe. He waged battles with the eastern Roman armies, and, after murdering his older brother and co-ruler Bleda in 445, went on to trample the countries of the Balkan Peninsula and northern Greece—causing terrible destruction along the way. As Attila continued westward with his bloody campaigns, which each Hun fought using his own weapons and his own savage technique, he nearly destroyed the foundations of Christianity.

But the combined armies of the Romans and the Visigoths defeated Attila and the Huns at Châlons (in northeastern France) in June 451, which is known as one of the most decisive battles of all time. From there, Attila and his men moved into Italy, devastating the countryside before Pope Leo I (c. 400–461) succeeded in persuading the brutal leader to spare Rome. (For this and other reasons, Leo was later canonized, becoming St. Leo.) Attila died suddenly—and of natural causes—in 453, just as he was again preparing to cross the Alps and invade Italy anew.

THE MIDDLE AGES

What was the Norman Conquest?

The Norman Conquest is the brief but critical period in British history that began when the French duke William of Normandy (c. 1028–1087) sailed across the English Channel in 1066 and invaded England. This was upon the death of what would turn out to be England's last Anglo-Saxon king, Edward the Confessor (c. 1003–1066). While William became known as William the Conqueror (and he did conduct a brutal conquest of Anglo-Saxon England), he might have had reason to believe he could claim the English throne upon King Edward's death: The named successor, Harold (c. 1022–1066), of the powerful Wessex family, had two years earlier become shipwrecked off the coast of France, where he reportedly took an oath that he would, upon King Edward's death, support William of Normandy (who was King Edward's distant cousin) as heir.

Hearing of Edward's death, William and his army set sail for England, where Harold had already assumed the throne as King Harold II. But Harold had previously quarreled with his brother Tostig, and the noble Wessex family was divided and engaged in a power struggle. Tostig was joined in his fight by the Norwegians, who at the same time that William was landing on England's southern coast invaded from the north. Thus, William and his troops entered England without opposition (since Harold was focusing his efforts elsewhere). Though the king defeated the Norwegians and Tostig (who was slain in battle), he would not emerge the victor in his subsequent battle with William: On October 14 the two met in battle at Hastings, near the entrance to the Strait of Dover. Though he fought valiantly, Harold was killed.

William was crowned at Westminster Abbey on Christmas Day 1066. Within a few years, by 1070, he had killed many Anglo-Saxon nobles and the rest he deprived of their land. In the twenty-one years of his reign, William imposed Norman aristocracy on England, required that French be spoken at court, and drew England closer to Europe. He ruled until his death in 1087, after which the Norman nobility mixed with what was left of the Anglo-Saxons. It is this intermingling that produced the English language—from the German tongue of the Anglo-Saxons combined with the Norman French. William's descendants (albeit distantly so) have ruled England ever since his takeover in 1066.

Who was Genghis Khan?

He was a Mongol conqueror who rose to power in the early thirteenth century to rule over one of the greatest continental empires the world has seen. Born Temüjin (c. 1167– 1227),

A huge statue of Genghis Khan on horseback stands atop a visitor center on the banks of the Tuul River a little over 100 miles from the capital of Mongolia, Ulan Bator. The statue is over 120 feet tall and is covered in stainless steel.

he was named Genghis Khan, meaning "universal ruler," in 1206. He was a fearless military leader, a brilliant strategist, and a ruthless subjugator, known for his brutal methods.

Temüjin was the first-born son of the leader of a small nomadic clan. When he was a young boy, his father was killed by a neighboring tribe (Tatars) and thus he rose to the status of chief. But instead of allowing a boy to lead them, clan members abandoned Temüjin and his family. He survived the hard-scrabbled youth of a destitute nomad. But by all accounts, he seemed destined to become a great leader.

By the time he was twenty years old, Temüjin had managed to forge alliances with various tribal leaders and claimed the leadership of a small clan. By 1189 he united two Mongol tribes, which he organized to conquer the rival Tatars by the year 1202. At a conference of Mongol leaders in 1206, Temüjin was pronounced the Great Ruler, or Genghis Khan, of the Unified Mongolian State. He began a transformation of the Mongol tribes, dividing them into military units, each one supported by a number of households. He imposed law and order, promoted education, and stimulated economic prosperity. Within five years, Mongol society was changed from a nomadic-tribal to a military-feudal system. Thus organized, Genghis Khan prepared his troops to expand the Mongolian empire.

Genghis Khan's armies embarked on a series of military campaigns, claiming land and subjugating peoples—sometimes using barbaric methods. By 1213 he controlled northern China to the Great Wall. By 1219 he controlled most of China and began campaigns into the Muslim world. When he died in the field in 1227, Genghis Khan commanded the vast territory from China to the Caspian Sea. He was succeeded by his sons, who continued to expand the Mongol holdings. His grandson was Kublai Khan (1215–1294), under whose leadership the Mongolian empire reached its pinnacle.

Who was Tamerlane?

Tamerlane (1336–1405) was a central Asian conqueror who gained power in the late 1300s. His Islamic name was Timur; Tamerlane is the English version. He was a barbaric warrior and a brilliant military leader whose fearsome tactics earned him the name Tamerlane the Terrible. By 1370 he was a powerful warlord whose government was centered in the province of Samarkand, in present-day Uzbekistan. In 1383 he launched a series of conquests that lasted more than twenty years and gained him control of a vast region including Iraq, Armenia, Mesopotamia, Georgia, Russia, and parts of India. He died in 1405, while on an expedition to conquer China. His body was entombed in an elaborate mausoleum, which is considered a treasure of Islamic art. After his death, his sons and grandsons fought for control of his dynasty, which remained intact for another hundred years. Tamerlane and his heirs built Samarkand into a great city; in its day it was a center for culture and scholarship in central Asia.

What was the Hundred Years' War?

The term refers to a succession of wars between England and France. The fighting began in 1337 and did not end until 1453. However, the period was not one of constant warfare, as truces and treaties brought about breaks in the military action between the countries. The reasons for the conflicts were many: England was trying to hang onto its provinces on the European continent; the French threw their support behind the Scots, who had their own battles with the English; the French wished to control the commercial center of Flanders (present-day Belgium), where the English had set up a profitable wool trade; and finally, the two countries disagreed about who should control the English Channel, the body of water that lies between them.

To further complicate matters, marriages between the English and French aristocracy meant that heirs to either throne could find themselves with a foreign relative, allowing them to lay claim to authority over the other country as well. When the first war broke out in 1337, King Edward III (1312–1377) of England claimed the French throne on the basis of the fact that his mother, Isabella, was the daughter of France's King Philip IV (called Philip the Fair; 1268–1314) and the sister of three French kings. Over the course of the next century, even though England won most of the battles and for a brief time controlled France (1420–22), it was the French who ultimately won the war in 1453. England lost all its territory on the continent, except Calais, which was also later taken by the French (in 1558).

How did Joan of Arc become a warrior?

Joan of Arc (called the Maid of Orleans; c. 1412–1431) gained fame for leading the French into victory over the English in the Battle for Orleans in 1429. A year before the battle, the English forces had invaded northern France and took possession of an area that included the city of Reims, where all of France's kings were crowned in the cathedral. Thus, Charles VII (1403–1461), whom France recognized as their king, had never had a proper coronation. It is said that Joan, an extraordinarily devoted Catholic who was then just a teen, appealed to Charles to allow her to go into battle against the English who were besieging Orleans. Though he was skeptical of her at first (she claimed to have heard the voices of saints), he eventually conceded. In the battlefield, Joan also overcame the doubts of the French troops and their leaders, who were understandably hesitant to follow the young girl's lead. She proved to them that she was not only capable but also successful. In April 1429, in just ten days' time, Joan led the French to victory over the English, who fled Orleans.

Still determined to see Charles properly crowned, Joan proceeded to lead a military escort for the king into Reims, where he was at last coronated on July 17, 1429—with Joan of Arc standing beside him. Next she determined that Charles should authorize her to try to free Paris from English control. Again the king acquiesced, but this time with dire results: She was captured by the French Burgundians (English sympathizers and loyalists), who turned her over to the English. Believing she was a heretic (by all reports Joan of Arc was clairvoyant), the English burned her at the stake in Rouen, France, on May 30, 1431. She is still considered a national hero of France. Recognizing Joan of Arc for her unswerving faith and for having valiantly pursued what she believed her mission to be, the Catholic Church canonized Joan of Arc in 1920. The feast day of St. Joan of Arc is celebrated on May 30.

What was the impact of the Hundred Years' War?

After waging war with each other for more than a century, in 1453 both England and France emerged as stronger, centralized governments. As the governments had gained strength, the nobility in both countries found themselves with less power and influence than they had enjoyed previously, and the system of feudalism, which before the war had been necessary in the absence of a larger, protective entity, was on the decline. In their strategies against each other, both countries had developed new military tactics. And though England had fewer resources than did France, it still managed to assert itself at sea, marking the beginning of that country's naval prowess.

What were the Hussite Wars?

The Hussite Wars were fought in the former kingdom of Bohemia (part of present-day Czech Republic) between 1420 and 1433. The country was plunged into the thirteen-year war by festering hostilities between papal forces and Bohemian peasants (the Hussites, named such since they were followers of religious reformer Jan Huss; c. 1373–1415). In the Four Articles of Prague (1420), the Hussites called for freedom of preaching, limits to church property holding, and civil punishment of mortal sin. The fighting ended in 1433 with the compromise of the Counsel of Basel and three years later was officially ended by the Compact of Iglau (1436), in which a faction of the Hussites agreed to accept the Holy Roman Emperor as king. The peasants had succeeded nevertheless in asserting Bohemian nationalism and had severed the country's ties to Germany.

What was the Peasants' War?

Fought in 1524 and 1525, the war was in part a religious one that came during the Reformation. It was the greatest mass uprising in German history. In 1517 the German monk Martin Luther (1483–1546) had begun questioning the authority of the Roman Catholic Church. He soon had followers—nobles and peasants alike—and his reform movement spread, giving birth to Protestantism (the Christian beliefs practiced by those who protested against the Catholic Church). While many Protestants were sincere in their faith, some had their own motives for following the movement. German peasants looked to the Reformation to end their oppression at the hands of the noble lords. When the peasants revolted at the end of 1524, they were forcibly suppressed. Some 100,000 peasants died. Prior to the uprising, they had aimed to get Martin Luther's endorsement, but he declined to give it.

107

RENAISSANCE AND THE ENLIGHTENMENT

What was the Gunpowder Plot?

In 1605 a group of twelve men, who believed the English government to be hostile to Roman Catholics, laid plans to blow up the Houses of Parliament while King James I (1566–1625) and government officials were there. Their scheme was discovered, however, and all of the conspirators were put to death. The event is remembered today in two ways: On the night of November 4, which was when the plot was supposed to be carried out, the English hold a festival in which Guy Fawkes (1570–1606), the conspirator who originated the Gunpowder Plot, is burned in effigy. Further, the vaults beneath the Houses of Parliament are searched before each new session.

Who was Cardinal Richelieu?

Cardinal Richelieu (1585–1642) was a leading political leader and religious figure in France. A bishop in the Catholic Church, he also achieved great success in politics, serving as King Louis XIII's chief advisor. He consolidated power domestically in France by bringing nobles into line. He also was a master at foreign policy, not only centralizing power in France but also undermining the Habsburg Dynasty (France's chief rival for dominance in Europe). Richelieu also counseled his predecessor Cardinal Jules Mazarin. Richelieu's vision and execution were essential to French successes in the seventeenth century, including the later dominance of France as the world power under King Louis XIV (1638–1715), also known as Louis the Great.

What was the Thirty Years' War?

The Thirty Years' War (1618–48), like the Hundred Years' War, was actually a series of related conflicts, rather than one long campaign. The conflict in Europe began as a religious one, with hostility between Roman Catholics and Protestants; but it eventually turned political before it was ended with the Peace of Westphalia. The war had four periods: the Bohemian (1618–24), the Danish (1625–29), the Swedish (1630–34), and the Swedish-French (1635–48).

In Bohemia (part of present-day Czech Republic) the trouble began in the capital of Prague when the archbishop authorized the destruction of a Protestant church. The act angered Bohemian Protestants and those elsewhere in Europe, who believed it was their right—granted by the Peace of Augsburg (1555)—to worship as Lutherans. When Holy Roman Emperor Matthias (1557–1619) failed to intervene on behalf of the Protestants, Prague became the scene of mayhem in May 1618. Disorder continued in Bohemia even as a new emperor ascended to the throne of the Holy Roman Empire. King Ferdinand II (1578–1637), a Habsburg, wielded an enormous amount of power, and in 1620 he squelched the Bohemian rebellion, which cost the Bohemians their independence. Further, Catholicism was reinstated as the state religion. These events caused other Protestant lands within the Holy Roman Empire to take notice. Soon the kings of Denmark, Sweden, and France entered into their own campaigns fighting King Ferdinand II for control of German lands. But the conflicts weren't strictly about religious freedom: Reducing the authority of the powerful Habsburg family became a primary objective as well.

What was the Peace of Westphalia?

In 1644, with Europe torn by the Thirty Years' War (1618–48), a peace conference was convened in Westphalia, Germany. But the negotiations were four long years in the making: The fighting continued until 1648, when the Peace of Westphalia was finally signed. Under this treaty, France and Sweden received some German lands. The agreement also made important allowances for Europe's religions: Not only was Lutheranism given the same due as Catholicism, but Calvinism, the religious movement begun by Frenchman John Calvin (1509–1564), was also was given the official nod. In short, the treaty not only ended the religious warfare in Europe, but it provided for some measure of religious tolerance.

Since the pact recognized the sovereignty of all the states of the Holy Roman Empire, it effectively dissolved the empire. Therefore, historians view the Peace of Westphalia as the beginning of Europe's modern state system.

What was the Great Northern War?

It was a war undertaken at the beginning of the eighteenth century that challenged Sweden's absolute monarchy and imperialism. During the seventeenth century, Sweden had become a power in the Baltic region, gradually bringing more and more territory under its control. Even the Peace of Westphalia (1648) had granted some German lands to Sweden. But much of Sweden's prosperity and expansion during this period had been under the rule of Charles XI (1655–1697). When he was succeeded by his young son, Charles XII (1682–1718) in 1697, the tides were about to turn for Sweden.

In 1700 an alliance formed by Denmark, Russia, Poland, and Saxony (part of present-day Germany) attacked Sweden, beginning the Great Northern War. Sweden readily defeated Denmark and the Russians that same year. But Poland and Saxony proved to be more formidable foes, and Charles XII spent almost seven years fighting—and eventually defeating—them. But the Russian army was to have another chance at the Swedish, and this time they were successful, defeating Charles XII's forces in 1709 at Poltava (Ukraine). Charles fled the country as the war continued and did not return until 1714. Four years after that, the monarch was killed as he observed a battle (in what is present-day Norway). Much of the country's lands in the Baltic were surrendered, and Sweden's period of absolute monarchy came to an end.

What was the Seven Years' War?

It was a worldwide conflict that began in 1756 between Prussia and Austria, who fought over control of Germany—and over who would be the supreme power in Europe. Great Britain threw its support behind King Frederick II (the Great; 1712–1786) of Prussia. But by the following year Austria was supported not only by France, but also by Sweden, most of the German states, and, very importantly, Russia. (Spain joined the fighting on the side of Austria also, but it was not until late in the game—after 1762.) With such alliances forged among the European states, the conflict soon spilled over, manifesting itself in the colonies of North America and India, where the French and British fought each other for control.

In order to assert his authority in Europe, Prussia's King Frederick had launched many military initiatives and was in a weakened state by the time his army faced the Austrians in 1756. He was spared certain defeat only by an event in Russia in 1762: Upon the death of Tsarina Elizabeth Petrovna (1709–1762), who had feared King Frederick, Peter III (1728–

1762) ascended the Russian throne. Peter, unlike his predecessor, held Frederick in high esteem, and he proceeded to withdraw Russia's support from Austria and reach a peace agreement with Austria's enemy, Prussia. He died that same year.

The Seven Years' War ended the next year, on February 15, 1763, with the signing of a peace agreement in Saxony, Germany. The area that Austria had fought to control remained, for the most part, under Prussian rule, positioning Prussia as a leading European power. There were no other territorial changes in Europe as a result of the war. In North America and India, Britain emerged from the conflicts as the victor—and as the colonial power.

COLONIALISM

How did the British come to control much of North America during colonial times?

British and French explorers laid claim to many parts of what is now the United States. During the late 1600s and into the mid-1700s, the two European powers fought a series of four wars in their struggle for control of territory in North America. Three of the wars broke out in Europe before they spread to America, where British and French colonists fought King William's War (1689–97), Queen Anne's War (1702–13), and King George's War (1744–48). King William's War saw no gains for either side. After Queen Anne's War, however, both sides signed the Treaty of Utrecht, in which France ceded Newfoundland, Acadia, and the Hudson Bay territory to Britain.

The struggle between England and France was not settled until a fourth war, the French and Indian War (1754–63), from which Britain emerged the victor.

What was the French and Indian War?

The French and Indian War (1754–63) was the last major conflict in North America before the Revolutionary War (1775–83). During colonial times, both Britain and France had steadily expanded their territories into the Ohio River valley. Since the fur trade prospered in this region, both countries wished to control it. But as the French encroached on their territory, the British colonists sent an ultimatum to them. This message was delivered by none other than George Washington (1732–1799), who had been sent by the British governor. But the French made it clear that they did not intend to back down. So in 1754 Washington (now a lieutenant colonel) and 150 troops established a British outpost at present-day Pittsburgh, not far from where the French had installed themselves at Fort Duquesne. That spring and summer fighting broke out.

Washington met the French, and though he and his troops mustered a strong resistance, there were early losses for the British. But a reinvigorated British force, under the leadership of Britain's secretary of state William Pitt (1759–1806), took French forts along the Allegheny River in western Pennsylvania and met French troops in battle at Quebec. In 1755 Washington was made colonel and led the Virginia troops in defending the frontier from French and Indian attacks. Though the British finally succeeded in occupying Fort Duquesne in 1758 (at which time Washington temporarily retired to his farm in Virginia), fighting continued until 1763, when the Treaty of Paris ended the war.

The British won the spoils, gaining control of all French lands in Canada as well as French territories east of the Mississippi River, with the exception of New Orleans. (The city was ceded to Spain, along with its holdings west of the Mississippi; Spain had become an ally to France late in the war, in 1762.) In exchange for Havana, Cuba, Spain turned over Florida to the British. France, which had once controlled a vast region of America, retained only two small islands off the coast of Newfoundland, Canada, and the two Caribbean islands of Martinique and Guadeloupe.

AMERICAN REVOLUTION

Why is Paul Revere's ride so well known?

The April 18, 1775, event was famous in its own right but was memorialized by American writer Henry Wadsworth Longfellow (1807–1882) in his poem, "Paul Revere's Ride." The verse contains an error (or perhaps Longfellow simply took literary license) about the night that the American Revolution (1775–83) began: The light signal that was to be flashed from Boston's Old North Church (one light if the British were approaching the patriots by land and two if the approach was by sea) was sent not to Revere; it was received by Revere's compatriots in Charlestown (now part of Boston proper). However, Revere did ride that night—on a borrowed horse. He left Boston at about 10:00 P.M. and arrived in Lexington at midnight to warn Samuel Adams and John Hancock, who were wanted for treason, that the British were coming. The next day, April 19, the battles of Lexington and Concord were fought, starting the Revolutionary War in America.

As an American patriot, Revere (1735–1818) was known for his service as a special messenger, so much so that by 1773 he had already been mentioned in London newspapers. Revere also participated in the Boston Tea Party in 1773.

Did the American colonies have any allies in their fight against the British?

Yes. France—which was, of course, a longtime rival of Great Britain's—was a key ally to the Americans, supplying them with some 90 percent of their gunpowder. France also controlled numerous ports and helped American ships with safety and supplies. Thousands of French troops assisted in the war effort as well.

Who was Rochambeau?

Jean-Baptiste Donatien de Vimeur, the Comte de Rochambeau (1725–1807), was a French military leader and noble who assisted the American colonists in the American Revolutionary War against the British. He had previously fought in the Seven Years War, distinguishing himself at the Battle of Minorca.

In 1780, Rochambeau was given command of a special French force of more than 7,000 French troops who were sent with the task of helping General George Washington in his fight against the British. He helped Washington win the Battle of Yorktown with a decisive victory over British military leader Charles Cornwallis (1738–1805).

111

What other patriot rode on a different path than Revere to warn about the British invasion?

William Dawes (1745–1799) also rode from Boston to Lexington to warn Samuel Adams and John Hancock of the pending British invasion and threat. Dawes and Revere both arrived in Lexington. They later rode together to Concord with Dr. Samuel Prescott. The three riders dispersed when they ran into a group of British soldiers.

Dawes has been largely ignored historically—at least on a general level, while Paul Revere is a household name taught to American schoolchildren.

Why was Bunker Hill important in the American Revolution?

The June 1775 battle on the hills outside Boston proved to be the bloodiest battle of the war. After the fighting in April at Lexington and Concord, more British troops arrived in Boston in late May. The Americans fortified Breed's Hill, near Bunker Hill, and on June 17, the British were ordered to attack the Americans there. The patriots, who needed to conserve ammunition, were given the famous direction not to fire until they saw the whites of their enemies' eyes. The patriots succeeded in driving the British back on their first two charges. But on the third charge, the patriots fled. The Battle of Bunker Hill resulted in more than 1,000 injured or dead British soldiers and 400 American soldiers killed or wounded.

Were all the battles of the American Revolution waged in the Northeast?

No, there was also fighting in the southern colonies. But the struggle between the American colonists and the British was further complicated in the South by the presence of slaves. Landowners feared that any fighting in the vicinity would inspire slaves to revolt against them. Knowing this, the British believed they could regain control of the southern colonies more readily than those in the north. In November 1775, the British governor of Virginia offered to free any slaves who would fight for the British. As many as 2,000 black slaves accepted the offer and took up arms. But there were also patriots in the South: It was Virginian Patrick Henry (1736–1799) who uttered the famous words, "Give me liberty or give me death."

In late February 1776, patriot forces confronted and defeated pro-British colonists near Wilmington, North Carolina. The British troops who were sailing from Boston, Massachusetts, to North Carolina to join the loyal colonists arrived too late to help. They instead sailed on to Charleston, South Carolina, which was also the scene of fighting that summer.

FRENCH REVOLUTION

What was the Oath of the Tennis Court?

It was the oath taken in June 1789 by a group of representatives of France's third estate, who having been rejected by King Louis XVI (1754–1793) and the first and the second estates vowed to form a French national assembly and write their own constitution. The pledge set off a string of events that began the French Revolution (1789–1799).

French society had long been divided into three classes, called "estates": members of the clergy were the first estate, nobles comprised the second, and everyone else made up the third. When philosophers such as Jean-Jacques Rousseau (1712–1778) came along and challenged the king's supreme authority by promoting the idea that the right to rule came not from God but from the people, it fueled the discontent felt by the long-suffering peasants and the prosperous middle class, who paid most of the taxes to run the government but who had no voice in it. In short, these people were the disenfranchised third estate.

A government financial crisis brought on by the expense of war forced King Louis XVI to reluctantly call a meeting of the representatives of all three estates, called the Estates General, which had last convened in 1614. During the May 5, 1789, meeting at Versailles, the third estate attempted to seize power from the nobility, the clergy, and the king by insisting that the three estates be combined to form a national assembly in which each member had one vote; since the third estate had as many representatives as the other two combined, the people would at last have a voice. When the attempt failed, the representatives of the third estate gathered on a Versailles tennis court, where they vowed to change the government. Louis XVI began assembling troops to break up the meeting. Meantime, an armed resistance movement had begun to organize. The situation came to a head on July 14, 1789, with the storming of the Bastille in Paris.

What was the Reign of Terror?

It refers to the short but bloody period in French history that began in 1793 and ended July 1794. During this time revolutionary leader Maximilien Robespierre (1758–1794) led a tribunal that arrested, tried, and put to death more than 17,000 people—most of them by guillotine.

In the reforms that followed the 1789 Oath of the Tennis Court and the capture of the Bastille, France was transformed into a constitutional state, and French subjects became French citizens. An elected legislature (the Constituent Assembly) was given control of the government. Robespierre was elected first deputy from Paris and was the leader of the radical popular party. In this new era, those who had been associated with the old regime or those who opposed the French Revolution became the subjects of persecution. In January 1793 King Louis XVI (1754–1793) and his wife, Marie Antoinette (1755–1793), were executed, beginning the Reign of Terror that saw thousands more (mostly those who had made up the power-

Louis XVI

113

ful first and second estates) suffer a similar fate at the hands of the revolutionaries. To escape certain death, many fled the country; this included top-ranking military officials, which made room for the rapid advancement of young military officers such as Napoleon Bonaparte (1769–1821).

The Reign of Terror ended on July 28, 1794, when Robespierre himself was put to death. As he gained power and influence, the revolutionary leader also had become increasingly paranoid, even putting two of his friends to death in 1794. He was overthrown on July 27 by the Revolution of 9th Thermidor and the next day died by guillotine.

How long did the French Revolution last?

The Revolution lasted some ten years, and it grew increasingly violent as it progressed. It began in mid-1789 when the government found itself nearly bankrupt, and due to festering discontent among the commoners (the prosperous middle class included), that crisis quickly grew into a movement of reform. The Revolution ended in 1799 when French general Napoleon Bonaparte (1769–1821) seized control of the government. Democracy had not been established in France, but the Revolution had ended the supreme authority of the king, had strengthened the middle class, and had sent the message across Europe that the tenets of liberty and equality are not to be ignored.

What was the Brumaire Coup d'état?

It was the overthrow on November 9, 1799, of the French revolutionary government. The coup put Napoleon Bonaparte (1769–1821) in power as one of three consuls intended to head the government.

When did the Napoleonic Wars begin and end?

The Napoleonic Wars began shortly after Napoleon Bonaparte (1769–1821) took power and lasted until 1815, when he was finally defeated at the Battle of Waterloo. Ever the general, Napoleon used his power to keep France at war throughout his reign.

After the Coup d'état of 18th Brumaire (November 1799), which had put Napoleon in power, he at first instituted peace, but it was short-lived: In May 1800 he marched across the Alps to defeat the Austrians, ending the war with them that had begun eight years earlier. Britain, fearing a growing European power on the continent, had declared war on France in 1793; by 1802, having grown tired of battle, the country agreed to peace with Napoleon in the Treaty of Amiens. But the calm in Europe was not to last. By

Napoleon Bonaparte

1803 the diminutive but power-hungry Napoleon (nicknamed the Little Corporal) had begun to plot an invasion of Britain. Declaring himself emperor in 1804, he initiated a series of campaigns across Europe, and by 1806 most of the continent was under his control. He remained, of course, unable to beat the British, whose superior navy gave them supremacy at sea.

But the various alliances (called coalitions) formed by European countries against Napoleon eventually broke him. After he had been defeated in Russia in 1812, the European powers that had long been held in submission by Napoleon formed a sixth and final coalition against him: Great Britain, Russia, Sweden, Prussia, and Austria met Napoleon's army at the momentous Battle of the Nations at Leipzig, Poland, from October 16 to 19, 1813. Napoleon was defeated there in what is sometimes called the War of Liberation, and he retreated to France. The following March, the allies making up the Sixth Coalition took Paris; Napoleon's generals were defeated. He abdicated the throne on April 6. However, that was not the end of the Napoleonic era: Exiled to the Mediterranean island of Elba, Napoleon returned to Paris on March 20, 1815, believing he could recover power in the unstable atmosphere that followed his abdication. Three months later he was defeated at the Battle of Waterloo, on June 18. It was the last battle of the Napoleonic Wars. He was exiled to St. Helena Island, where he died in 1821.

What happened at Trafalgar?

Cape Trafalgar, on the southwest coast of Spain, was in 1805 the scene of a decisive victory for Great Britain over Napoleon Bonaparte's (1769–1821) navy. Other than a one-year respite in 1802, France and Britain had been at war with each other since 1793. Napoleon remained determined to conquer Britain, just as he had most of continental Europe. But when his fleets met those of decorated English Admiral Horatio Nelson (1758–1805) off the coast of Spain, the certain defeat and destruction of Napoleon's navy ended the emperor's hopes of invading England.

The confrontation at Trafalgar was the culmination of a two-year game of cat and mouse between Nelson's fleets and the French under the direction of Admiral Pierre-Charles Villeneuve (1763–1806), whose sole objective was to invade Britain. To prevent this from happening, in 1803 Nelson began a two-year blockade of Villeneuve and the French navy at Toulon, France (on the Mediterranean coast). When the French fleets escaped Toulon, attempting to lure the British out to sea, Nelson chased them all the way across the Atlantic—to the West Indies and back—before the showdown off Spain's coast, where the French were joined by Spanish fleets. Meantime, the coast of England remained protected by the British navy, leaving no opportunity for invasion by the French.

On October 21, 1805, seeing the enemy sailing out of Trafalgar, Nelson formed his fleet of twenty-eight ships into two columns, intending to divide and conquer the combined French and Spanish force of thirty-three ships. About noon that day, as they prepared for the confrontation, Admiral Nelson sent out one of the most famous commands of naval history: "England expects that every man will do his duty." While the British prevailed, destroying Napoleon's fleet in less than four hours' time, Nelson was fatally wounded by a sharpshooter, and the English navy hero died just as victory was his. The brave Nelson had seen fate coming: The night before Trafalgar, he had revised his will, and just before the battle had begun, he told Captain Henry Blackwood (1770–1832), "God bless you, Blackwood, I shall never speak to you again." Nevertheless, Nelson died knowing that he had won, uttering the still famous words, "Thank God, I have done my duty."

115

Why did the Russians burn Moscow?

The September 14, 1812, torching of their own city was directed by Tsar Alexander I (1777–1825), who wished to prevent Napoleon Bonaparte (1769–1821) and his invading armies from reaping the benefits of anything Russian. Through a series of wars, Napoleon had dominated most of Europe by 1805. The authority of Alexander was certainly threatened by the French emperor. In 1805 and 1807 Russia suffered major losses in battles with Napoleon's armies. In the face of these defeats, what Alexander did next was a stroke of genius, though he had many detractors at the time. Napoleon's forces, though victorious, were weary from fighting and were unable to pursue the Russian armies further. So, Alexander made peace with the emperor in the Treaty of Tilsit (1807). The Russian ruler vowed support of Napoleon, and for his part, Napoleon believed Alexander had extended him a hand of friendship. Instead, the cunning Russian ruler had bought himself and his country the time they needed to gird themselves against the powerful Napoleon.

By 1812 Russia, its economy dependent on exports, resumed trade with Great Britain, Napoleon's archenemy. This prompted the return of Napoleon's troops to Russia: Later that year the French emperor marched into Russia with a force of as many as 600,000 men, but the Russians still delivered Napoleon a crushing defeat. The Russian army had relied on guerrilla warfare tactics, including burning their own countryside. Napoleon returned to Paris in defeat by the end of the year.

WAR OF 1812

What caused the War of 1812?

The war between the young United States and powerful Great Britain largely came about because of France. After the French navy was crushed by the British under Admiral Nelson (1758–1805) at the Battle of Trafalgar, Napoleon turned to economic warfare in his long struggle with the British: He directed all countries under French control not to trade with Great Britain. Its economy dependent on trade, Britain struck back by imposing a naval blockade on France, which soon interfered with U.S. shipping. Ever since the struggle between the two European powers began in 1793, the United States tried to remain neutral. But the interruption of shipping to and from the continent and the search and seizure of ships posed significant problems to the American export business: In 1807 Great Britain had issued an Order in Council that required even neutral vessels destined for a continental port to stop first in England; Napoleon countered with the Milan Decree, which stated that any neutral vessel that had submitted to British search be seized.

Back in America, the people of New England, the region most dependent on shipping, nevertheless vehemently opposed entering into war with the British. But the country's economy was depressed as a result of the interruption of exports, and the U.S. Congress declared war on June 18, 1812. In these days before telegraph and radio, the United States did not know that two days before, on June 16, Britain had withdrawn its Orders in Council, lifting its policy of shipping interference, which had been the chief reason for the war declaration. Thus the two countries engaged in fighting for the next two and a half years. On December 24, 1814, the Treaty of Ghent officially ended the war. But once again, poor communication led to fighting: Two weeks after the treaty was signed, troops in New Orleans, unaware of this event, fought for control over the Mississippi River in the worst battle of the entire conflict. Though both the United States and Great Britain claimed victory in the War of 1812, neither side had gained anything.

Who were the War Hawks?

The War Hawks were a group of Republicans in the U.S. Congress who advocated war with Great Britain. Elected in 1810, the congressmen took office in 1811, the failure of the Erskine agreement fresh in their memories: That bit of 1809 diplomacy, arranged by British minister to the United States George Erskine and the then U.S. secretary of state James Madison (1751–1836), would have provided for the suspension of Britain's maritime practices that interfered with U.S. shipping, but the agreement fell apart when Erskine was recalled from office. The relationship between the United States and Great Britain, tenuous since 1807 due to trade embargoes and the impressment of American sailors into British service, deteriorated.

The newly elected congressmen were tired of the failure of diplomacy to resolve maritime problems with the British; they further felt that the British were challenging the young United States through their policies, which purportedly included British aid to American Indians in the Northwest. War Hawk leader Henry Clay (1777–1852) was named Speaker of the House, and Congress soon passed a series of resolutions to strengthen the army and navy. When Congress was called upon by President James Madison to declare war on the British in June of 1812, it was the War Hawks who swung the close vote. Thus the War of 1812 was declared. Some historians believe the true motive behind the War Hawks was not resolution of the shipping problems, but rather the desire to annex parts of southern Canada to the United States.

What was the Creek War?

The Creek War—sometimes called the Red Stick War—was a war between different tribes of the Creek Nation conducted during the War of 1812. Sometimes, it is considered part of the War of 1812. The Red Sticks were a group of Creeks (sometimes called Upper Creeks) who opposed assimilation and concessions to the United States government. They opposed the Lower Creeks, who were more willing to accede to the U.S. government.

A military commander from Tennessee named Andrew Jackson (1767–1845) earned praise for his bravery and skill in leading U.S. troops and Lower Creek troops in several victories over the Upper Creeks. His most famous victory in the Creek War occurred at the Battle of Horseshoe Bend in central Alabama. Jackson later catapulted from war hero to two-terms as U.S. president.

TEXAS WAR OF INDEPENDENCE

What does "Remember the Alamo" mean?

The saying was a rallying cry for Texans in their war for independence from Mexico. The movement for independence had begun in the winter of 1835 to 1936, when the people of Texas decided to cut off relations with Mexico, and soon turned into a war when the Mexican

117

The Alamo in San Antonio, Texas, remains a popular attraction for tourists from all over the world.

government sent a force of some 4,000 troops, under the command of General Antonio López de Santa Anna (1794–1876), to squelch the rebellion. As the Mexican army approached, the force of about 150 men who were determined to defend the city of San Antonio retreated to the Alamo, a Spanish mission built in the previous century. There they were joined by another fifty men but were still no match for the Mexicans, who kept the Alamo under siege for thirteen days—from February 23 to March 6, 1836. The Texans, low on ammunition, ceased to return fire. On the morning of March 6, Santa Anna's troops seized the Alamo. The fierce frontiersmen, Davy Crockett (1786–1836) among them, are believed to have fought using the butts of their rifles. All the Texans who fought that day at the Alamo died.

Meantime, General Sam Houston (1793–1863) had assembled his forces, and with the rallying cry "Remember the Alamo" (and their fellow Texans who had bravely fought and died there), he set out to face the Mexican army and secure independence. This he did, at San Jacinto, Texas, on April 21, 1836, in a quick and decisive battle that had caught Santa Anna's troops by surprise. The following day the Mexican general was captured and made to sign a treaty giving Texas independence.

MEXICAN WAR

What caused the Mexican War?

The two-year war (1846–48) was fought over the United States' annexation of Texas. The events that led up to the conflict began in 1837 when President Andrew Jackson (1767–1845) recognized Texas as independent (this was just after Texas had won its war with Mexico). Republic of Texas' President Sam Houston (1793–1863) felt that protection against a Mexican invasion may be necessary, so he eyed annexation to the United States. In the meantime, Mexican president Antonio Lopez de Santa Anna (1794–1876) warned that such an action on the part of the United States would be "equivalent to a declaration of war against the Mexican Republic." In June 1844 the U.S. Senate rejected a proposed annexation treaty. But later that year Democratic Party nominee James K. Polk (1795–1849), an ardent expansionist, was elected president. Because the annexation of Texas had figured prominently in his campaign platform, outgoing President John Tyler (1790–1862) viewed Polk's victory as a public mandate for annexation, and he recommended that Congress pass a joint resolution to invite Texas into the union. Congress did so in February, and President Tyler signed the resolution on March 1, 1845, three days before leaving office.

Mexico responded by breaking off diplomatic relations with the United States. A border dispute made the situation increasingly tenuous: Texas claimed that its southern border was the Rio Grande River, while Mexico insisted it was the Nueces River, situated farther north. In June President Polk ordered Brigadier General Zachary Taylor (1784–1850) to move his forces into the disputed area. In November the U.S. government received word that Mexico was prepared to talk. Polk dispatched Congressman John Slidell (1793–1871) to Mexico to discuss three other outstanding issues: the purchase of California (for $25 million), the purchase of New Mexico (for $5 million), and the payment of damages to American nationals for losses incurred in Mexican revolutions. This last point was critical to the negotiations, as Polk was prepared to have the United States assume payment of damages to its own citizens in exchange for Mexico's recognition of the Rio Grande as the southern border of Texas.

But upon arrival in Mexico City, Slidell was refused the meeting—President José Joaquín Herrera (1792–1854) had bowed to pressure, opposing discussions with the United States. When Polk received news of the scuttled talks, he authorized General Taylor to advance through the disputed territory to the Rio Grande. Meanwhile, Mexico overthrew President Herrera, putting into office the fervent nationalist General Mariano Paredes y Arrillaga (1797–1849), who reaffirmed Mexico's claim to Texas and pledged to defend Mexican territory.

While Polk worked through Slidell to get an audience with the Mexican government, the attempts failed, and on May 9 the Cabinet met and approved the president's recommendation to ask Congress to declare war. The next day news arrived in Washington that on April 25 a sizeable Mexican force had crossed the Rio Grande and surrounded a smaller American reconnaissance party. Eleven Americans were killed and the rest were wounded or captured. On May 11 Polk delivered a message to Congress, concluding, "Mexico has…shed American blood upon the American soil.… War exists … by the act of Mexico herself." By the time the war was officially declared on May 13, just more than one year after Polk had been sworn into office, General Taylor had already fought and won key battles against the Mexicans and had occupied the northern Mexico city of Matamoros.

What did the United States gain from the Mexican War?

The Mexican War (1846–48) was officially ended when the U.S. Senate ratified the Treaty of Guadalupe Hidalgo on March 10, 1848. By the treaty, Mexico relinquished roughly half its territory—New Mexico and California—to the United States. Mexico also recognized the Rio Grande as its border with Texas.

Who was the Gadsden Purchase named after?

The Gadsden Purchase was named after James Gadsden (1788–1858), the U.S. minister to Mexico in 1853. Gadsden was given instructions to purchase more land from Mexico. He did so with what became known as the Gadsden Purchase.

Gadsden had military experience, having served under General Andrew Jackson during the War of 1812. He later left the army and was appointed commissioner to oversee the removal (the unlawful removal) of Seminole Indians in Florida and Georgia to the western United States. He then served as president of a railroad company.

Mexico received payments in the millions from the United States, which also assumed the payment of claims of its citizens. Five years later under the terms of the Gadsden Purchase, the United States purchased a small portion of land from Mexico for another $10 million, which was widely regarded as further compensation for the land lost in the war. The territory the United States gained was in present-day Arizona and New Mexico, south of the Gila River.

CRIMEAN WAR

What was the Crimean War?

The Crimean War was fought from 1853 to 1856 between Russian forces and the allied armies of Britain, France, the Ottoman Empire (present-day Turkey), and Sardinia (part of present-day Italy). The Crimean Peninsula, which juts out into the Black Sea and is today part of Ukraine, was the setting for many of the battles. The source of the conflict was Russia's continued expansion into the Black Sea region—which if left unchecked would have resulted in strategic and commercial advantages for Russia. But Russia was unable to muster the strength it needed to combat the powerful alliance formed by the European countries and the Ottoman Empire. The war was ended with the signing of the Treaty of Paris (1856), which required Russia to surrender lands it had taken from the Ottoman Empire and abolished Russian navy and military presence in the Black Sea region. It was the first conflict that was covered by newspaper reporters at the front.

WAR OF REFORM

What was the War of Reform?

It was the period in Mexican history from 1858 to 1861 when the federalist government collapsed and civil war ensued. In 1858 President Ignacio Comonfort (1812–1863), who had become Mexico's leader when he helped overthrow President Antonio Lopez de Santa Anna (1794–1876) in 1855, felt political pressure and fled the country. Benito Júarez (1806–1872), who had served as minister of justice and minister of the interior, assumed the presidency. His position was immediately opposed by centralists who rallied around rebellious army forces. Under this pressure, the federalists, led by Juárez, withdrew from Mexico City and set up the capital at Veracruz, on the Gulf Coast. There they had control over customs receipts, which allowed them to purchase arms and finance their government. Eventually they defeated the centralists and reentered Mexico City, in January 1861. Juárez was elected president later that year, but his authority was challenged again with the arrival of the French, who quickly put Maximilian (1832–1867) in power as emperor of Mexico. Juárez led the country in a successful campaign against the French, who were expelled in 1867 when Juárez resumed the presidency. He died in office in 1872.

What does "Fifty-four forty or fight" mean?

The slogan refers to a dispute between the United States and Great Britain over Oregon Country, which an 1818 treaty allowed both nations to occupy. This was the territory that began at 42 degrees north latitude (the southern boundary of present-day Oregon) and extended north to 54 degrees 40 minutes north latitude (in present-day British Columbia). During the 1830s and early 1840s American expansionists insisted that U.S. rights to the Oregon Country extended north to latitude 54 degrees 40 minutes, which was then the recognized southern boundary of Russian America (roughly present-day Alaska).

The eleventh president of the United States, James K. Polk (1795–1849), used the slogan in his political campaign of 1844. After he was elected, Polk settled the dispute with Great Britain (in 1846), and the boundary was set at 49 degrees north, the northern boundary of what is today Washington State and the border between the United States and Canada. This agreement—reached without the fight threatened in the slogan—gave the United States the territory lying between 42 and 49 degrees north latitude and Great Britain the territory between 49 degrees and 54 degrees 40 minutes north latitude as well as Vancouver Island. The United States' portion is present-day Washington, Oregon, and Idaho as well as parts of Montana and Wyoming.

AMERICAN CIVIL WAR

Was the Civil War fought because of slavery?

For years, American schoolchildren learned that the question of slavery was the only cause of the Civil War (1861–1865): With nineteen free states and fifteen slave states making up the Union, Abraham Lincoln (1809–1865) had called the country "a house divided" even before he became president. While slavery was central to the conflict, many believe the bloody four-year war had other causes as well.

By the mid-1800s important differences had developed between the South and the North—and many maintain these differences, or vestiges of them, are still with the country today. The economy in the South was based on agriculture while the North was industrialized; the ideals and lifestyles of each region reflected these economic realities. Southerners believed their agrarian lifestyle was dependent on the labor of slaves. For a long time, slavery was viewed by some as a necessary evil. But by the early 1800s the view that slavery is morally wrong was beginning to take hold. Northern abolitionists had begun a movement to end slavery in the states. But, except for a small antislavery faction, these views were not shared in the South.

There were other factors that contributed to the declaration of secession and the formation of the Confederacy, although some still argue these factors were merely smoke screens for the defense of slavery. Disputes between the federal government and the states had limited the power of the states, and this policy was called into question by Southerners. Further, the political party system was in disarray in mid-1850s America. The disorder prompted feelings of distrust for the elected politicians who set national policy. Before the 1860 presidential election, Southern leaders urged that the South secede from the Union if Lincoln, who had publicly taken a stand against slavery, won.

How did the Civil War begin and end?

Unhappy with the outcome of the 1860 presidential election, in which Abraham Lincoln (1809–1865) was elected, and fearing a loss of their agrarian way of life, the Southern states began to make good on their promise to secede if Lincoln won the presidency: South Carolina was the first (in December of that year). In January 1861 five more states followed: Mississippi, Florida, Alabama, Georgia, and Louisiana. When representatives from the six states met the next month in Montgomery, Alabama, they established the Confederate States of America and elected Jefferson Davis (1808–1889) president. Two days before Lincoln's inauguration, Texas joined the Confederacy. (Virginia, Arkansas, North Carolina, and Tennessee joined in April, shortly after the Civil War had already begun.)

The Civil War, also called the War of Secession and the War Between the States, began on April 12, 1861, when Southern troops fired on Fort Sumter, a U.S. military post in Charleston, South Carolina. Brutal fighting continued for four years. On April 9, 1865, General Robert E. Lee (1807–1870) surrendered his ragged Confederate troops to General Ulysses S. Grant (1822–1885) of the Union at old Appomattox Court House, Virginia. The war had not only been between the states, it had also been between brothers: the conflict divided the nation. The Civil War took more American lives than any other war in history.

Why did Andrew Johnson vow he would burn Nashville before surrendering it?

It seems a strange thing for a politician to say about his home state's capital city. Andrew Johnson had served Tennessee in both the U.S. House of Representatives (1843–53) and the U.S.

What battle is sometimes called the bloodiest battle in the Civil War?

The Battle of Stones River (in Murfreesboro, Tennessee) is sometimes called the bloodiest battle of the Civil War, because of the high percentage of losses on each side. Union commander William Rosecrans (1819–1898) and Confederate leader Braxton Bragg (1817–1876) engaged in a series of conflicts that left nearly 13,000 Union casualties and nearly 12,000 Confederate casualties. The conflict left no clear winner, though historians have said that the Union gained morale by driving the Confederates from Murfreesboro into a retreat southward.

An illustration by Janet Lange of the battlefield at Gettysburg, published in *Journal Universel,* 1863.

Senate (1857–62); he had also been governor (1853–57). But after the Civil War broke out, the Southern democrat made a surprising move: he sided with the Union. This show of allegiance was largely owing to Johnson's strongly held belief that the South's secession was unconstitutional. Having thus made his stand, President Abraham Lincoln (1809–1865) saw fit to appoint Johnson as the Union's military governor in Tennessee. When rebel forces surrounded Nashville and seemed poised to take it, Johnson proclaimed he would sooner burn the city before surrendering it. But he was forced to do neither: In mid-December 1864 Union forces used the hand-cranked Gatling gun (invented in 1861) to help defeat the Confederate forces.

Why was the battle at Gettysburg important?

The 1863 battle, fought when the two sides met accidentally in the southern Pennsylvania town, was a turning point in the Civil War. From July 1 to 3 General George Meade (1815–1872) led his troops (about 90,000 strong) to defeat the advancing Confederate troops (numbering some 75,000) under General Robert E. Lee (1807–1870). The Union win effectively stopped Lee's invasion of the North.

The following November 19 President Abraham Lincoln (1809–1865) made the historical address at Gettysburg, as he dedicated part of the battlefield as a national cemetery. Beginning with the now-famous words "Four score and seven years ago our fathers brought forth upon this continent a new nation, conceived in Liberty, and dedicated to the proposition that all men are created equal," the short speech (which Lincoln rewrote many times) closed by issuing a rallying cry for the nation as a whole, saying, "we here highly resolve that the dead shall not have died in vain—that the nation shall, under God, have a new birth of freedom—and that governments of the people, by the people, and for the people, shall not perish from the earth."

123

INDIAN WARS

What was the Battle of Tippecanoe?

The battle near present-day Lafayette, Indiana, took place on November 7, 1811, when U.S. troops under the command of General William Henry Harrison (1773–1841) defeated the Shawnee Indians while their leader, Tecumseh (1768–1813), was away.

Before the November battle, the Shawnee Indians had been steadily pushed back from their ancestral lands along the Cumberland River in Kentucky. Once they settled in the Ohio River valley, they formed a wall of resistance to further pressure. Resistance fighting began in 1763 and did not end until thirty years later (1793) when the American forces of General Anthony Wayne (1745–1796) defeated the Shawnee at Fallen Timbers in northwest Ohio. Tecumseh was twenty-five years old at the time of this critical defeat of his people. He became determined, despite the counsel of the tribe elders, to halt the westward movement of the Shawnee. Tecumseh and his brother, Tenskwatawa (c. 1768–1834), built a settlement on Tippecanoe Creek near the Wabash River, Indiana. Called Prophet's Town, it became a rallying point for those Indians who resisted displacement by colonists. Soon the Shawnee who had settled at Prophet's Town were joined by bands of Wyandot, Potawatomi, Miami, and Delaware Indians. The British became aware of Tecumseh's defiance and soon supplied Prophet's Town Indians with arms to use against the Americans.

In 1810 the governor of the Indiana Territory, William Henry Harrison (1773–1841), requested a meeting with Tecumseh. But both were suspicious of each other and could reach no agreement for peace. Settlers who were aware of Tecumseh's armed resistance movement pressured President James Madison (1751–1836) to take action, which he did: Under orders from the president, Harrison set out in the fall of 1811 with a force of 1,000 men. Arriving at Tippecanoe on November 6, he met with the Indians under a flag of truce and then made camp about a mile away from Prophet's Town. Tecumseh was visiting the Creek Indians in Alabama at the time, trying to rally their support in the white resistance movement. But his brother, Tenskwatawa, rallied the men at Prophet's Town, and at the break of day, they attacked Harrison's camp. Hand-to-hand fighting ensued in an icy drizzle. The Indian alliance retreated and though Harrison took heavy losses, he had managed to destroy Prophet's Town.

The battle undermined Tecumseh's initiative and launched the career of Harrison. In 1840, after successful military duty and service in the U.S. Congress, Harrison rode a wave of public support all the way to the White House to become the ninth president. His campaign slogan was "Tippecanoe and Tyler, too" (John Tyler was his running mate). Eventually the Shawnee were pushed into Kansas. Tecumseh became an ally of the British in the War of 1812 (1812–14) and was killed in the fighting.

What was the Sioux uprising?

The uprising took place in August and September 1862, in southwestern Minnesota, when the Sioux there suddenly had been made to give up half their reservation lands. Their situation was made worse by crop failures. While the government debated over whether it would make the payments it owed to Indian nations in gold or in paper currency, the Sioux were also without money. The U.S. agent at the Sioux reservation refused to give out any food to the Indians until their money arrived from Washington. The Sioux people were hungry and angry, and white observers could see there was trouble coming and warned the government. But the situation soon erupted in August when four young men having a shooting contest suddenly fired into a party of whites, killing five people. The Sioux refused to surrender the four men to the authorities, and, under the leadership of Chief Little Crow (c. 1820–1863), they raided white settlements in the Minnesota River valley. A small U.S. military force sent out against the Sioux was annihilated. Meantime, white settlers fled the region in panic.

On September 23, Minnesota sent out 1,400 men who defeated Little Crow at the Battle of Wood Lake. The raids had already claimed the lives of 490 white civilians. Thirty-three Sioux were killed in the fighting with the military. While most of the Indians who had taken up arms fled to the Dakotas, the government began to round up native men who were suspected of participating in the campaign against white settlers. More than 300 men were tried and sentenced to death, many of them on flimsy evidence. Episcopal bishop Henry Whipple (1822–1901) interceded on their behalf, making a personal plea to President Abraham Lincoln (1809–1865). The bishop was able to get 265 death sentences reduced to prison terms. But thirty-eight Sioux men, accused of murder or rape, were hung in a public ceremony on December 26, 1862. The Sioux reservation lands were broken up, and the remaining Sioux were dispersed. Minnesota nevertheless continued to man military posts in that part of the state for years to come.

The events during and after the uprising were brutal for both sides, but many observers had seen that the treatment of the Sioux was going to lead to conflict: One missionary, after witnessing the harsh way the policy with the Indians had been carried out, wrote to Bishop Whipple, saying, "If I were an Indian I would never lay down the war club while I lived."

What was "Custer's Last Stand"?

The term refers to the defeat of General George A. Custer (1839–1876) at the Battle of Little Bighorn on June 25, 1876. Custer had a national reputation as a Civil War general and Indian fighter in the west, and when he and his troops were outnumbered and badly beaten by the Sioux led by Sitting Bull (c. 1831–1890)—just as the country was about to celebrate the hundredth anniversary of the Declaration of Independence—the result was a stunning reversal in the national mood.

Little Bighorn was part of a series of campaigns known collectively as the Sioux War. Several events led to the conflict that became Custer's Last Stand. The Sioux were non-treaty Indians, which means they had refused to accept the white-dictated limits on their territory. They were outraged at the repeated violation of their lands by the onrush of miners to new gold strikes in the Black Hills of South Dakota. Further, there had been eight attacks by the Sioux on the Crow who were living on reservation land. Finally, Sitting Bull, the chief of the Hunkpapa band of Sioux, refused government demands that he and his people return to reservation lands. Meanwhile, unbeknownst to the government's military strategists, by spring 1876 Sitting Bull had been joined in his cause by other groups of northern Plains tribes, including the Cheyenne led by Crazy Horse (c. 1842–1877). With the government ready to use force to return Sitting Bull and his band of Sioux to reservations, the stage was set for a conflict—bigger than any Washington official had imagined.

On June 25 Custer rode into Montana territory with his Seventh Cavalry to meet the Sioux. Despite orders to simply contain the Indians and prevent their escape, he attacked. While historians remain divided on how Custer could have been defeated on that fateful June day, one thing remains certain: Custer and his men were badly outnumbered. Having divided his regiment into three parts, Custer rode with about 225 men against a force of at least 2,000—the largest gathering of Indian warriors in Western history. Custer and his soldiers all died. The fighting continued into the next day, with those Indians that remained finally disbanding and returning to their designated territory. Meantime, Sitting Bull and his band retreated into Canada. Returning to the United States five years later, in 1890, Sitting Bull was killed by authorities.

The battle became the subject of countless movies, books, and songs. It's remembered by some Native Americans as a galvanizing force—proof that brave men who fight for what they believe in can win.

BOER WARS

What were the Boer Wars?

They were conflicts between the British and the Afrikaners (or Boers, who were Dutch descendants living in South Africa) at the end of the nineteenth century, in what is today South Africa. The first war, a Boer rebellion, broke out in 1880 when the British and the Afrikaners fought over the Kimberley area (Griqualand West), where a diamond field had been discovered. The fighting lasted a year, at which time the South African Republic (established in 1856) was restored. But the stability would not last long: In 1886 gold was discovered in the Transvaal, and though the Afrikaner region was too strong for the British to attempt to annex it, they blocked the Afrikaners' access to the sea. In 1899 the Afrikaner republics of the Orange Free State and the Transvaal joined forces in a war against Britain. The fighting raged until 1902, when the Afrikaners surrendered. For a time after the Boer War (also called the South African War), the Transvaal became a British crown colony. In 1910 the British government combined its holdings in southern Africa into the Union of South Africa.

SPANISH–AMERICAN WAR

What caused the Spanish–American War?

The 1898 war, which lasted only a matter of months (late April to mid-August), was fought over the liberation of Cuba. During the 1870s the Cuban people rebelled against Spanish rule. But once that long rebellion had been put down, peace on the Caribbean island did not hold: Worsening economic conditions prompted revolution in 1895. American leaders, the bloody American Civil War (1861–1865) still in their memories, feared that while the Cuban rebels could not win their battle against the Spanish, neither were the Spanish strong enough to fully put down the insurrection. Meanwhile, the American public, fed by a steady stream of newspaper accounts reporting oppressive conditions on the island, increasingly supported U.S. intervention in the Cuban conflict.

In November 1897, President William McKinley (1843–1901) did intervene, but it was through political, rather than military, pressure. As a result, Spain granted Cuba limited self-government within the Spanish empire. However, the move did not satisfy the Cuban rebels, who were determined to achieve independence from Spain; the fighting continued. Rioting broke out in Havana, and in order to protect Americans living there, the United States sent the battleship *Maine* to the port on January 25, 1898. On February 15, an explosion blew up the *Maine*, killing more than 200 people. Blame for the blast was promptly— and history would later conclude wrongly—assigned to Spain. While President McKinley again made several attempts to pressure Spain into granting Cuba full independence, it was to no avail. Nevertheless, on April 19, the U.S. Congress passed a joint resolution recognizing an independent Cuba, disclaiming American intention to acquire the island, and authorizing the use of the American army and navy to force Spanish withdrawal. On April 25, the United States formally declared that the country was at war with Spain.

In the months that followed, American forces battled the Spanish and Spanish loyalists in Cuba and the Spanish-controlled Philippines. There was also military activity on Puerto Rico; however, the American forces there met little resistance. Once Santiago, Cuba, was surrendered by the Spanish after the battle at San Juan Hill in July 1898, it would only be a matter of weeks before a cease-fire was called and an armistice was signed (on August 12), ending the brief war.

What was the charge up San Juan Hill?

On July 1, 1898, during the Spanish–American War, Colonel Theodore Roosevelt (1858–1919) led his American troops, known as the Rough Riders, on an attack of the Spanish blockhouse (a small fort) on San Juan Hill, near Santiago, Cuba. Newspaper reports made Roosevelt and the Rough Riders into celebrities, and even after he became a U.S. president, Teddy Roosevelt remarked that "San Juan was the great day of my life."

Then-colonel Teddy Roosevelt standing atop San Juan Hill with his Rough Riders.

San Juan Hill was part of a two-pronged assault on Santiago. While the Rough Riders regiment attacked the Spanish defenses at San Juan and Kettle Hills, another American division, led by General Henry Lawton (1843–1899), captured the Spanish fort at El Caney. The success of the two initiatives on July 1 combined to give the Americans command over the ridges surrounding Santiago. By July 3 the American forces had destroyed the Spanish fleet under the command of Admiral Pascual Cervera y Topete (1839–1909). On July 17 the Spanish surrendered the city.

Though the victory was critical to the outcome of the war, the assault on Kettle Hill and San Juan Hill had come at a high price: 1,600 American lives were lost, in a battle that had seen American troops—black and white—fight the Spanish shoulder to shoulder.

What is the Treaty of Paris?

There has been more than one Treaty of Paris. The following international agreements were signed in the French capitol:

- In 1763 representatives of Great Britain, France, and Spain signed a treaty, which, along with the Treaty of Hubertusburg (February 15, 1763), ended the Seven Years' War (1756–63).

- On September 3, 1783, the Treaty of Paris, which had been under negotiation since 1782, was signed by the British and the Americans, represented by statesmen Benjamin Franklin (1706–1790), John Adams (1735–1826), and John Jay (1745–1829). The agreement officially ended the American Revolution (1775–83), establishing the United States as an independent country and drawing the boundaries of the new nation—which extended west to the Mississippi River, north to Canada, east to the Atlantic Ocean, and south as far as Florida, which was given to Spain.

- In 1814 and 1815 treaties were signed ending the Napoleonic Wars, which the French ruler Napoleon Bonaparte (1769–1821) had begun shortly after taking power in 1799.

- In 1856, European nations signed a treaty in Paris ending the Crimean War (1853–56) and outlawing the wartime practice of privateering.

- The Treaty of Paris that was signed December 10, 1898, settled the conflict that had resulted in the Spanish–American War (1898). This treaty provided for Cuba's full independence from Spain. It also granted control of Guam and Puerto Rico to the United States. The pact further stipulated that the United States would pay Spain $20 million for the Philippine Islands.

- In 1951, in the wake of World War II (1939–1945), Belgium, France, Italy, Luxembourg, the Netherlands, and West Germany signed the Treaty of Paris, which established the European Coal and Steel Community (ECSC). The desire was to bring about economic and political unity among the democratic nations of Europe. This agreement paved the way for the European Union, which was effected by the Maastricht Treaty, an economic agreement signed by representatives of twelve European countries, in the Netherlands in 1992.

MEXICAN REVOLUTION

What does "¡Viva Zapata!" mean?

It was the cry that went up in support of the rebel general Emiliano Zapata (1879–1919), whose chief concern during the Mexican Revolution (1910–20) was the distribution of land to the people.

An advocate of Mexico's lower classes, Zapata began revolutionary activities against the government of Porfirio Díaz (1830–1915) as early as 1897. Zapata rose to prominence in helping the liberal and idealistic Francisco Madero (1873–1913) overthrow Díaz in 1911. With Madero placed in power, Zapata promptly began pressing his co-conspirator for a program to distribute the hacienda (large estate) lands to the peasants. Rebuffed by Madero that same year, Zapata drafted the agrarian Plan of Ayala and renewed the revolution. Madero's government never achieved stability and proved to be ineffective, prompting a second overthrow in 1913: Victoriano Huerta (1854–1916) seized power from Madero, whom he had helped put into office, and in the chaos surrounding the coup, Madero was shot and killed.

But Zapata refused to support Huerta and remained a leader of the revolution, continuing his crusade for the people—who supported him with cheers of "¡Viva Zapata!," meaning "long live Zapata!" The bitter fighting of the revolution continued and soon those who had supported the slain Madero—including Zapata and Pancho Villa (1878–1923)—threw their backing behind another revolutionary, Venustiano Carranza (1859–1920). In 1914 Carranza's forces occupied Mexico City and forced Huerta to leave the country. No sooner had Carranza taken office than the revolutionaries began fighting among themselves. Zapata and Pancho Villa demanded dramatic reforms and together they attacked Mexico City in 1914. Five years later, and one year before the end of the revolution, Carranza's army ambushed and assassinated Zapata in his home state of Morelos.

Why did the U.S. government send troops after Pancho Villa?

Pancho Villa (1878–1923) was sought by the U.S. government because in 1916 he and his followers attacked Americans on both sides of the border. In 1915 the United States decided it would back the acting chief of Mexico, Venustiano Carranza (1859–1920), even as he faced attacks from two of his fellow revolutionaries, Emiliano Zapata (1879–1919) and Pancho Villa. Four years earlier, Villa had himself sought to control Mexico after the fall of President Porfirio Díaz. When the United States cut off the flow of ammunition to the rebels, Villa, who was a fierce fighter, earned himself a reputation as a bandit, seeking revenge on Americans in Mexico by stopping trains and shooting the passengers. In 1916 Villa raided the small New Mexico village of Columbus, where he killed eighteen people. The attack prompted President Woodrow Wilson (1856–1924) to send U.S. soldiers to hunt Villa down and capture him. Though thousands of men were put on the initiative under General John Pershing (1860–1940), they never caught up with the bandit. Wilson withdrew the forces from Mexico after the government there expressed resentment for the U.S. effort—which the Mexican people, President Carranza included, viewed as a meddlesome American interference in the Mexican Revolution (1910–20). The revolution ended three years later, after ten years of fighting and disorder.

WARS IN ASIA

What was the Chinese–Japanese War?

It was a war fought in 1894 to 1895 over control of Korea, which was a vassal state of China. When an uprising broke out in Korea in 1894, China sent troops in to suppress it. Korea's ports had been open to Japan since 1876 and in order to protect its interests there, Japan, too, sent troops to the island nation when trouble broke out. But once the rebellion had been put down, the Japanese troops refused to withdraw. In July 1894 fighting broke out between Japan and China, with Japan emerging as the victor, having crushed China's navy. A peace treaty signed on April 17, 1895, provided for an independent Korea (which only lasted until 1910, when Japan took possession) and for China to turn over to Japan the island of Taiwan and the Liaodong Peninsula (the peninsula was later returned to China for a fee after Russia, Germany, and France forced Japan to do so). The war, though relatively brief, seriously weakened China, and in the imperialist years that followed, the European powers scrambled for land concessions there.

What caused the Russo–Japanese War?

From 1904 to 1905 the war was fought by Russia and Japan over their interests in China (particularly Manchuria) and Korea—areas of strategic importance to each country. Before fighting broke out Japan moved to settle the conflict, but the overture was rejected by Tsar Nicholas II (1868–1918), and Japan soon severed all diplomatic relations (on February 6, 1904) with Russia. Two days later the Japanese issued a surprise attack on Russian ships at Lushun (Port Arthur), Manchuria. On February 10 Japan officially declared itself at war with Russia. The battles—both on land and at sea—went badly for the Russian forces, which could not be adequately reinforced or supplied to meet the powerful and disciplined Japanese. Early in 1905, the war effort already unpopular back home, revolution broke out in Russia, further weakening the country's resolve.

After an eight-month siege at Lushun, it became clear that Russia could no longer muster a fight. Further, the war was expensive for Japan, which sought the intervention of the United States in settling the conflict. President Theodore Roosevelt (1858–1919) became involved in mediating the dispute; a peace treaty was signed September 5, 1905, at a shipyard in Portsmouth, New Hampshire, following one month of deliberations. The terms of the treaty were these: Both nations agreed to evacuate Manchuria; Russia ceded to Japan the southern half of Sakhalin Island, which lies between the two countries (the island was ceded back to Russia after World War II); Korea became a Japanese protectorate; and Russia transferred to Japan the lease of China's Liaodong Peninsula. And so Japan emerged as a power onto the world scene.

For his peacemaking efforts what honor did President Roosevelt receive?

Theodore Roosevelt received the Nobel Peace Prize in 1906 for his mediation efforts at Portsmouth, New Hampshire, that led to an end to the Russo–Japanese War of 1904–1905. It took several weeks of contentious discussions, but Roosevelt saw the matter through to a successful conclusion.

Roosevelt became the first U.S. President to win the Nobel Peace Prize. Woodrow Wilson would win in 1919 for his efforts in helping to end World War I, and President Barack

Obama would win in 2009 for his efforts at improving international diplomacy. Jimmy Carter would win the award in 2002—but that was more than twenty years after he left office.

RUSSIAN REVOLUTION

What was Bloody Sunday?

The January 22, 1905, event, which is also known as Red Sunday, signaled the beginning of revolutionary activity in Russia that would not end until 1917. On that winter day the young Russian Orthodox priest Georgi Gapon (1870–1906), carrying a cross over his shoulder, led what was intended to be a peaceful workers' demonstration in front of the Winter Palace at St. Petersburg. But, as the London Times correspondent reported that day, when the crowd was refused entry into the common gathering ground of the Palace Square, "the passions of the mob broke loose like a bursting dam." Despite Father Gapon's thinking that they too would join the workers in protest, the Cossack guards and troops, still loyal to the Romanov tsar Nicholas II (1868–1918), shot into the crowd of demonstrators, killing about 150 people—children, women, and young people among them.

Father Gapon, who had intended to deliver to the tsar a petition on behalf of the workers, was injured during the day's events and later fled in exile. His thinking that the palace guards would come over to the workers' side was not his only miscalculation: Tsar Nicholas was not even at the palace that Sunday, having left days earlier. But Nicholas's reign was threatened by his troops' response to the gathering crowd: So horrific was the bloodshed that the snow-covered streets of St. Petersburg were stained in red, and the correspondent for the French newspaper *Le Matin* reported that the Cossacks had opened fire "as if they were playing at bloodshed." The event sent shockwaves through the country, where hostilities had been mounting against Nicholas's ineffective government. It also stirred up unrest elsewhere, including in Moscow—where, in a related event, the tsar's uncle, Grand Duke Serge, was killed in early February. The death was a sure sign that popular anger had been focused on the tsar and his family. In the countryside, the peasants rose up against their landlords, seizing land, crops, and livestock.

The events foreshadowed the downfall of tsarist Russia: Though the outbreak in 1905 was unsuccessful in effecting any change and Nicholas remained in power for twelve more years, he was the last tsar to rule Russia.

Who was Rasputin?

Grigory Rasputin (1872–1916) was a Russian mystic and quasi-holy man who rose from peasant farmer to become adviser to Tsar Nicholas II (1868–1918) and his wife, Tsarina Alexandra (1872–1918). Sometime in 1905 or shortly thereafter, Alexandra had come into contact with Rasputin; when he demonstrated that he was able to effectively treat Nicholas's and Alexandra's severely hemophiliac son Alexis (1904–1918), Rasputin quickly gained favor with the Russian rulers. But the prime minister and members of the legislative assembly, the Duma, could see Rasputin was a disreputable character, and they feared his influence on the tsar. They even tried to exile Rasputin, but to no avail.

By 1913, one year before the outbreak of World War I (1914–1918), the Russian people had become acutely aware of Tsar Nicholas's weaknesses as a ruler—not only was his government subject to the influence of a pretender like Rasputin, but the events of Bloody Sunday had irreversibly marred the tsar's reputation. That year the Romanov dynasty was marking its 300th anniversary: members of the royal family had ruled Russia since 1613. But public celebrations, intended to be jubilant affairs, were instead ominous, as the crowds greeted Nicholas's public appearances with silence.

Russia's entry into World War I proved to be the beginning of the end for Nicholas, with Rasputin at the front and center of the controversy that swirled around the royal court. During the first year of fighting against Germany, Russia suffered one military catastrophe after another. These losses did further damage to the tsar and his ministers. In the fall of 1915, urged on by his wife, Nicholas left St. Petersburg and headed to the front to lead the Russian troops in bat-

Grigory Rasputin

tle himself. With Alexandra left in charge of government affairs, Rasputin's influence became more dangerous than ever. But in December 1916, a group of aristocrats put an end to it once and for all when, during a palace party, they laced Rasputin's wine with cyanide. Though the poison failed to kill Rasputin, the noblemen shot him and deposited his body in a river later that night. Nevertheless, the damage to Nicholas and Alexandra had already been done: By that time virtually all educated Russians opposed the tsar, who had removed many capable officials from government office, only to replace them with the weak and incompetent executives favored by Rasputin. The stage had been set for revolution.

What was the Bolshevik Revolution?

It was the November 1917 revolution in which the Bolsheviks, an extremist faction within the Russian Social Democratic Labor Party (later renamed the Russian Communist Party), seized control of the government, ushering in the Soviet age. The event is also known as the October Revolution since by the old Russian calendar (in use until 1918), the government takeover happened on October 25.

The Bolshevik Revolution was the culmination of a series of events in 1917. In March, with Russia still in the midst of World War I (1914–1918), the country faced hardship. Shortages of food and fuel made conditions miserable. The people had lost faith in the war effort and were loathe to support it by sending any more young men into battle. In the Russian capital of Petrograd (which had been known as St. Petersburg until 1914), workers went on strike and rioting broke out. In the chaos (called the March Revolution), Tsar Nicholas II (1868–1918) ordered the legislative body, the Duma, to disband; instead, the representatives set up a provisional government. Having lost all political influence, Nicholas abdicated the throne on March 15. He and his family were imprisoned and are believed to have been killed in July of the following year.

Hearing of Nicholas's abdication, longtime political exile Vladimir Lenin (1870–1924) returned from Europe to Petrograd, where he led the Bolsheviks in rallying the Russian people with calls for peace, land reform, and worker empowerment; their slogan was "Land, Peace, and Bread." The Bolsheviks grew in numbers and became increasingly radical, in spite of efforts by the provisional government headed by revolutionary Alexander Kerensky (1881–1970) to curb the Bolsheviks' influence. The only socialist member of the first provisional government, Kerensky's government proved ineffective and failed to meet the demands of the people. He also failed to end the country's involvement in World War I, which the Bolsheviks viewed as an imperialistic war.

On November 7 the Bolsheviks led workers and disgruntled soldiers and sailors in a takeover of Petrograd's Winter Palace (the scene of Bloody Sunday in 1905), which had become the headquarters of Kerensky's provisional government. By November 8 the provisional government had fallen.

What was the Red Terror?

The Red Terror was the brutal coercion used by the Communists during the tumultuous years of civil unrest that followed the Bolshevik Revolution of November 1917. After the revolution, the Bolsheviks, now called Communists, put their leader, Vladimir Lenin (1870–1924), into power.

Delivering on the Bolshevik promise to end the country's involvement in World War I (1914–1918), Lenin immediately called for peace talks with Germany, ending the fighting on the eastern front. (Germany and the other Central Powers would be prevented from victory on the western front by the entry of the United States into the war that same year.) But the Brest-Litovsk Treaty, signed March 3, 1918, dictated harsh—and many believed humiliating—terms to Russia, which was forced to give up vast territories including Finland, Poland, Belarus, Ukraine, Moldavia, and the Baltic states of Estonia, Latvia, and Lithuania.

Meantime, Russians had elected officials to a parliamentary assembly. But when the results were unfavorable to Lenin (of the 703 deputies chosen, only 168 were Communists), he ordered his troops to bar the deputies from convening, and so the assembly was permanently disbanded. In its place, Lenin established a dictatorship based on Communist secret police, the Cheka. Further, the radical social reforms he had promised took the form of government takeover of Russia's industries and the seizure of farm products from the peasants. Lenin's hard-handed tactics created opposition to the Communists—colloquially known as the Reds. The opposition organized their White army, and civil war ensued. In September 1918 Lenin was nearly assassinated by a political opponent, prompting Lenin's supporters to organize the retaliative initiative that came to be known as the Red Terror. Though thousands of Communist opponents were killed as a result, the unrest in Russia would not end until 1920. And some believe the ruthless repression of the Red Terror lasted into 1924.

133

Who was Leon Trotsky?

Leon Trotsky (1879–1940) was a Marxist leader who later joined the Bolshevik Revolution under Lenin's leadership. He was a charismatic leader of the Red Army and later served as the People's Commissar of Military and Naval Affairs of the Soviet Union under Lenin.

After Lenin's death, Trotsky became opposed to the growing power of Joseph Stalin. Trotsky eventually had to flee the country, as Stalin had him expelled from the Communist Party and exiled from the country. Trotsky first went to Turkey and then later went to Mexico, where he lived for more than a decade. He was assassinated there in 1940 by Soviet agent Ramon Mercarder (1913–1978).

WORLD WAR I

How did World War I begin?

Though the Great War, as it was called until World War II (1939–1945), was sparked by the June 28, 1914, assassination of Archduke Francis Ferdinand of Austria-Hungary (1863–1914), the war in Europe had been precipitated by several developments. National pride had been growing among Europeans; nations increased their armed forces through drafts; and colonialism continued to be a focus of the European powers, as they competed with each other for control of lands in far-off places. Meantime, weapons and other implements of war had been improved by industry, making them deadlier than ever. So on that June day in the city of Sarajevo (then the capital of Austria-Hungary's province of Bosnia and Herzegovina), when a gunman named Gavrilo Princip (1894–1918) shot down Archduke Ferdinand, it is not surprising that Austria-Hungary responded with force. Since Princip was known to have ties to a Serbian terrorist organization, Austria-Hungary declared war on Serbia. Both sides, however, believed that the battle would be decided quickly. But instead fighting would spread, involving more countries. Four years of fighting—aided by the airplane, the submarine, tanks, and machine guns—would cause greater destruction than any other war to that date.

What alliances were forged during World War I?

In its declaration of war against Serbia in late July 1914, Austria-Hungary was joined in early August by its ally Germany, which together formed the Central Powers. In October 1914 Bulgaria and the Ottoman Empire joined the Central Powers.

When the fighting began, France, Britain, and Russia threw their support behind Serbia, and together were known as the Allies. The Allies declared war on the Ottoman Empire in November 1914, after Turkish ships bombarded Russian ports on the Black Sea and Turkish troops invaded Russia. Eventually, twenty more nations joined the Allies, but not all of them sent troops to the front. Belgium, Montenegro, and Japan joined the Allies in August 1914, with Japan declaring war on Germany and invading several Pacific islands to drive out the Germans. In 1915 Italy and San Marino joined; as fighting wore on, in 1916, Romania and Portugal became Allied nations; and 1917 saw the entry of eight countries, most notably the United States and China, but also Liberia, Greece, Siam, Panama, Cuba, and Brazil. Before the war ended in 1918, Guatemala, Haiti, Honduras, Costa Rica, and Nicaragua all became supporters of the Allies.

What did the *Lusitania* have to do with World War I?

World War I (1914–1918) was already under way when in May of 1915 a German U-boat sank a British passenger ship, the SS *Lusitania*, off the coast of Ireland. The ship had been launched in 1907 by Britain's Cunard Line to become the largest passenger ship afloat. When she was downed in the North Atlantic, 1,200 civilians, including 128 American travelers, were killed. President Woodrow Wilson (1856–1924) warned Germany that another such incident would force the United States into entering the war. Germany heeded the warning only for a time.

Why did the United States get involved in World War I?

When war broke out in Europe in August 1914, Americans opposed the involvement of U.S. troops, and President Woodrow Wilson (1856–1924) declared the country's neutrality. But as the fighting continued and the German tactics threatened civilian lives, Americans began siding with the Allies.

After the sinking of the passenger liner SS *Lusitania*, Germany adopted restricted submarine warfare. But early in 1917 Germany again began attacking unarmed ships, this time American cargo boats, goading the United States into the war. Meantime, German U-boats were positioning to cut off shipping to and from Britain, in an effort to force the power to surrender. Tensions between the United States and Germany peaked when the British intercepted, decoded, and turned over to President Wilson a telegram Germany had sent to its ambassador in Mexico. The so-called "Zimmermann note," which originated in the office of German foreign minister Arthur Zimmermann (1864–1940), urged the German officials in Mexico to persuade the Mexican government into war with the United States—in order to regain lost territory in Texas, New Mexico, and Arizona. The message was published in the United States in early March. One month later, on April 6, 1917, the U.S. Congress declared war on Germany after President Wilson had asserted that "the world must be made safe for democracy."

How did World War I end?

Though the United States had been little prepared to enter the war, the American government mobilized quickly to rally the troops—and the citizens—behind the war effort: In April 1917 the U.S. Regular Army was comprised of just more than 100,000 men; by the end of the war, the American armed forces stood some five million strong. It was the arrival of the U.S. troops that gave the Allies the manpower they needed to win the war. After continued fighting in the trenches of Europe, which had left almost ten million dead, in November 1918, Germany agreed to an armistice and the Central Powers finally surrendered. In January 1919 Allied representatives gathered in Paris to draw up the peace settlement.

How were Europe's lines redrawn as a result of World War I?

The treaties that came out of the Paris Peace Conference (1919–20) redrew Europe's boundaries, carving new nations out of the defeated powers. The Treaty of Versailles forced Germany to give up territory to Belgium, Czechoslovakia, Denmark, France, and Poland.   **135**

Germany also forfeited all of its overseas colonies and turned over coal fields to France for the next fifteen years. The treaties of St. Germain and Trianon toppled the former empire of Austria-Hungary (whose archduke had been assassinated in 1914, triggering the war) so that the separate nations of Austria and Hungary were formed, each occupying less than a third of their former area. Their former territory was divided among Italy, Romania, and the countries newly recognized by the treaties: Czechoslovakia, Poland, and the kingdom that later became Yugoslavia. The Treaty of Sevres took Mesopotamia (present-day Iraq), Palestine, and Syria away from the Ottoman Empire, which three years later became the Republic of Turkey. Finally, Bulgaria lost territory to Greece and Romania. However, these new borders would serve to heighten tensions between some countries, as the territorial claims of the newly redrawn nations overlapped with each other.

How did the Treaty of Versailles pave the way for World War II?

In the aftermath of World War I (1914–1918), Germany was severely punished: One clause in the Treaty of Versailles even stipulated that Germany take responsibility for causing the war. In addition to its territorial losses, Germany was also made to pay for an Allied military force that would occupy the west bank of the Rhine River, intended to keep Germany in check for the next fifteen years. The treaty also limited the size of Germany's military. In 1921 Germany received a bill for reparations: It owed the Allies $33 million.

While the postwar German government had been made to sign the Treaty of Versailles under the threat of more fighting from the Allies, the German people nevertheless faulted their leaders for accepting such strident terms. Not only was the German government weakened, but public resentment over the Treaty of Versailles soon developed into a strong nationalist movement—led by German chancellor and führer Adolf Hitler (1889–1945).

What was the League of Nations?

The League of Nations was the forerunner to the United Nations. It was an international organization established by the Treaty of Versailles at the end of World War I (1914–1918). Since the United States never ratified that treaty, it was not a member.

The league was set up to handle disputes among countries and to avoid another major conflict such as the Great War (which is how World War I was referred to until the outbreak of World War II). But the organization proved to be ineffective; it was unable to intervene in such acts of aggression as Japan's invasion of Manchuria in 1931, Italy's conquest of Ethiopia during 1935 to 1936 and occupation of Albania in 1939, and Germany's takeover of Austria in 1938.

The League of Nations dissolved itself during World War II (1939–1945). Though unsuccessful, the organization did establish a basic model for a permanent international organization.

THE ERA BETWEEN THE WORLD WARS

What was Nazism?

Short for national socialism, "Nazi" was a derisive abbreviation that held. The Nazi doctrine rests on three philosophies: extreme nationalism, anti-Semitism, and anticommunism. As one of the Central Powers, Germany's defeat in World War I (1914–1918) resulted in severe punishment of that country and its seriously diminished role in Europe. The doctrines of Nazism took hold there, appealing to the masses with promises of a rebuilt Germany.

The "bible" of Nazism was Adolf Hitler's *Mein Kampf* (*My Struggle*; 1923), which asserted the superiority of a pure Aryan race (Aryans are non-Jewish Caucasians, particularly those of northern European descent), led by an infallible ruler (called "the führer"); the reestablishment of a German empire (the Third Reich); and the systematic annihilation of people whom Nazis perceived to be Germany's worst enemies, Jews and Communists. Nazis ruled Germany from 1933, when Hitler rose to power as head of the National Socialist German Workers' Party. In their own country, they enforced their policies through a secret police (the Gestapo), storm troops (called the SS), and Hitler's bodyguard (called the SA). Elsewhere in Europe, the Nazis used sheer force in imposing their system. Their aggression and ruthlessness resulted in World War II (1939–1945). During the Holocaust (1933–45), Nazi soldiers, led by "Hitler's henchmen," persecuted and exterminated upwards of twelve million people, at least half of whom were European Jews. Nazism ended in 1945, when Hitler killed himself and Germany lost the war. The doctrine, which demonstrated how detrimentally powerful a theory can be, was outlawed thereafter. Sadly, the late twentieth century saw a resurgence of "neo-Nazism" among extremists in Germany and the United States.

What was the importance of Hitler's beer hall putsch trial?

The 1924 trial of German chancellor and führer Adolf Hitler (1889–1945) and nine other men, charged with treason for their attempted coup (in German, putsch) of late 1923, marked the beginning of Hitler's seemingly unstoppable rise to power.

As the leader of the Nazi Party (National Socialists German Workers' Party), Hitler had gained enough of a following to believe that he had the support of the people to recreate a powerful German empire and rid it of its "mongrel-like" quality. A speech by Bavarian leader Gustav von Kahr in a Munich beer hall on the night of November 8, 1923, reinforced the belief that many people sympathized with Hitler's message. But in a march through Munich the following day, the still-loyal German regular army and the Bavarian state police opened fire on the Nazi demonstrators and their sympathizers, killing sixteen and arresting Hitler and his nine co-conspirators. Their trial began on February 26, 1924: Over the course of twenty-five days, aided by radio and newspaper coverage, Hitler held forth (in one case taking four hours to respond to a single question), earning him the overwhelming support of the German people. His impassioned appeals turned what ought to have been an open-and-closed case of treason against him into an indictment of the German government. His basic argument was this: "I cannot declare myself guilty. True, I confess to the deed, but I do not confess to the crime of high treason. There can be no question in an action which aims to undo the betrayal of this country in 1918." Hitler was referring to the German surrender in World War I (1914–1918).

Nevertheless, he and nine others were convicted of treason. Hitler was sentenced to five years in prison, where he wrote the first volume of his infamous work *Mein Kampf* (*My Struggle*), which revealed his frightening theories of racial supremacy and his belief in the Third Reich. Released after only nine months, Hitler walked out of prison more popular than he had been before his highly publicized trial.

SINO–JAPANESE WAR

What was the Sino–Japanese War?

This dispute between China and Japan (who had not that long ago clashed in the Chinese–Japanese War of 1894–95) began in 1937 and was absorbed by World War II (1939–1945). The trouble between the Asian powers began when Japan, having already taken Manchuria and the Jehol Province from China, attacked China again. Though China was in the midst of internal conflict—with the nationalist forces of Generalissimo Chiang Kai-shek (1887–1975) fighting the Communists under Mao Tse-tung (1893–1976)—China turned its attention to fighting the foreign aggressor. The fighting between the two countries continued into 1941 before war was officially declared by China. In so doing, China was at war not only with the Japanese but with Japan's Axis allies—Germany and Italy—as well. The conflict then became part of World War II, which ended with the surrender of Japan to the Allies in September 1945.

What was the Nanking Massacre?

One of the most brutal chapters in modern history, the Nanking Massacre, also called the Rape of Nanking, was a mass execution of hundreds of thousands of unarmed Chinese civilians by invading Japanese soldiers in December 1937 and January 1938. No one knows for certain how many people were murdered in the mass killings, but most estimates place the number at 300,000, with another 80,000 people raped and tortured, including women and children.

SPANISH CIVIL WAR

What caused the Spanish Civil War?

From 1936 to 1939, two sides fought for control of Spain: the nationalists and the loyalists. The insurgent nationalists were aristocrats, military leaders, Roman Catholic clergy, and members of a political group called the Falange Party; they were supported by Nazi Germany (under Adolf Hitler [1889–1945]) and fascist Italy (under Benito Mussolini [1883–1945]) in their effort to wrest control. The loyalists were liberals, socialists, and communists; they were supported by the Soviet Union (under Joseph Stalin [1879– 1953]). A number of non-Spanish idealists, who believed saving the republic from the fascist rebels was worth dying for, joined the ranks of the loyalists to form the International Brigade. (In his novel, *For Whom the Bell Tolls*, Ernest Hemingway [1899–1961], who had covered the war as a correspondent, wrote about one young American man who took up arms on behalf of the loyalist effort.) The nationalists, under Generalissimo Francisco Franco (1892–1975), won the war when they captured Madrid in March 1939, beginning an era of harsh right-wing rule. And, as with any war, the fascist victory had come at a dear price: Hundreds of thousands dead and massive destruction throughout the country.

Who was Generalissimo Franco?

Generalissimo Francisco Franco (1892–1975) was the fascist leader of Spain from 1939 until 1973. He rose to power in the Spanish Civil War (1936–39) as he led a rebel nationalist army against the loyalist forces. Capturing Madrid in 1939, Franco assumed the role of head of government. Though he and the nationalists had received considerable help from Nazi Germany and fascist Italy to win the civil war, when fighting broke out in World War II (1939–1945), Spain stayed neutral (at least nominally so). In 1947, with the fighting in Europe over, Franco declared himself monarch of Spain and ruled as an authoritative dictator. Two years before he died, he stepped down as head of state, though he retained the title generalissimo, meaning "commander in chief." Franco named as his successor Prince Juan Carlos (1938–). When Franco died in 1975, Juan Carlos I became the first Spanish monarch to control Spain

Generalissimo Francisco Franco

since his grandfather, King Alfonso XIII (1886–1941), was deposed in 1931 to make way for the brief republic (which was later overthrown by Franco and the nationalists). King Juan Carlos played an important role in transforming Spain into a modern democracy.

WORLD WAR II

What was the Munich Pact?

It was a failed effort to appease the territory- and power-hungry German leader Adolf Hitler (1889–1945) in the days leading up to World War II (1939–1945). After Germany annexed neighboring Austria in the Anschluss of March 1938, it became known that Hitler had designs on the Sudetenland, a heavily German region of Czechoslovakia. With World War I (1914–1918) a fresh memory, and European nations still recovering from heavy losses, Europe's powers were eager to avoid another conflict. On September 29 and 30, 1938, British Prime Minister Neville Chamberlain met with Hitler in Munich; they were joined by Italian dictator Benito Mussolini, a German ally, and French Premier Edouard Daladier, a Czech ally. Czechoslovakia did not have any representatives at the conference. The leaders quickly worked out a plan for Germany to occupy the Sudetenland. Chamberlain considered Czechoslovakia's concession a reasonable price to pay for peace on the continent. But the effort to assuage Hitler was not successful: In March 1939 Germany moved to occupy the rest of Czechoslovakia; on September 1, Germany marched into Poland, and World War II began.

How did World War II begin?

The war began on September 1, 1939, when Germany invaded Poland, which was soon crushed by German chancellor and führer Adolf Hitler's (1889–1945) war machine. But while the Nazis moved in from the west, Poland was under attack by the Soviets from the north and east. The events in the Eastern European country had set the stage for a major conflict.

After Poland, the Germans moved into Denmark, Luxembourg, the Netherlands, Belgium, Norway, and France, taking control as they went. By June 1940 only Great Britain stood against Hitler, who was joined by Axis power Italy. Before long, fighting had spread into Greece and northern Africa.

In June 1941 Germany invaded the Soviet Union, enlarging the scope of the conflict again. With the world's focus on war-torn Europe, Japan executed a surprise attack on the U.S. naval base at Pearl Harbor, Hawaii, in December 1941, which drew Americans into the war. The war would not end until 1945.

How many countries were part of the Axis powers?

The Axis, which was forged in 1936, included an alliance of three nations: Germany, Italy, and Japan. These major powers were joined by six smaller countries, the Axis satellites: Albania, Bulgaria, Finland, Hungary, Romania, and Thailand. But together these countries never comprised the unified front and strength that the Allied powers did.

Germany started the war on September 1, 1939, and was joined in June 1940 by Italy and Albania. In the middle of 1941 Bulgaria, Hungary, Romania, and Finland joined the Axis effort. Japan, which was already fighting with China (in the Sino–Japanese War), entered the fray on December 7, 1941, with its attack on the U.S. naval base at Pearl Harbor, Hawaii. Thailand was the last Axis country to enter the war, on January 25, 1942.

Which countries comprised the Allies in World War II?

The three major Allied powers were Great Britain, the United States, and the Soviet Union. Their leaders, Winston Churchill (1874–1965), Franklin Roosevelt (1882–1945), and Joseph Stalin (1879–1953), were referred to as the Big Three. They and their military advisors developed the strategy to defeat the Axis countries—though Stalin, for the most part, acted alone on the Soviet front. China, which had been at war with Asian rival Japan since 1937, also joined the Allies. Forty-six other countries became part of the Allied front before the war was over.

Germany invaded Poland on September 1, 1939, and within days Great Britain entered into fighting against Germany. Australia, New Zealand, India, France, South Africa, and Canada also allied with Great Britain, as did Norway, Denmark, Belgium, the Netherlands, and Luxembourg in 1940—all of them under siege by Nazi Germany. Greece entered the war later that year, as did Yugoslavia in the spring of 1941. On June 22, 1941, the Soviet Union entered the war. And in the days after the Japanese bombing of the U.S. naval base at Pearl Harbor, Hawaii, on December 7, 1941, twelve more Allied countries became involved in the war, chief among them, the United States and China. (The others, with the exception of Czechoslovakia, were all Caribbean and Latin American countries: Panama, Costa Rica, the Dominican Republic, Haiti, Nicaragua, El Salvador, Honduras, Cuba, and Guatemala.) The year 1942 saw three more countries join the Allies—Mexico in May, Brazil in August, and Ethiopia in December. In 1943 and 1944—in what were perhaps the darkest days of the war—Iraq, Bolivia, Iran, and Columbia signed on as Allied nations, followed by the tiny country of San Marino (significant since it is situated wholly within the boundaries of Axis power Italy), Colombia, and Liberia. February and March of 1945 saw another wave of nations siding with the Allies: the South

American countries of Ecuador, Paraguay, Peru, Chile, Venezuela, Uruguay, and Argentina; along with the Middle Eastern countries of Egypt, Syria, Lebanon, and Saudi Arabia. Mongolia (the Mongolian People's Republic), in Central Asia, was the last to join the Allies, on August 9, 1945. Of course, the level of support each Allied nation lent to the war effort varied. But it was significant that the list of Allied nations grew longer with each year that the war was fought.

What was the Atlantic Charter?

On the eve of direct U.S. involvement in World War II (1939–1945), President Franklin D. Roosevelt (1882–1945) met with British Prime Minister Winston Churchill (1874–1965) on board a ship off the coast of Newfoundland, Canada. There the two leaders drew up a program of peace objectives known as the Atlantic Charter, which they signed on August 14, 1941. In addition to other peacetime goals, the charter roughly contained Roosevelt's Four Freedoms, which he had outlined in his speech to Congress on January 6, 1941, as the legislative body considered passage of the Lend-Lease Act. Roosevelt believed that freedom of speech and expression, freedom of worship, freedom from want, and freedom from fear should prevail around the world.

Briefly, in the Atlantic Charter the two leaders stated that neither of their countries sought new territories; that they respected the right of the people of each country to choose their own form of government; that no country ("great or small, victor or vanquished") would be deprived access to the raw materials it needed for its own economic prosperity; that countries should cooperate to improve labor standards and social security; that after the "final destruction of the Nazi tyranny, all the men in all the lands may live out their lives in freedom from fear and want"; and that a "wider and permanent system of general security" would be necessary to ensure peace. (This last statement alludes to the future establishment of the United Nations.)

Why did the Japanese attack Pearl Harbor?

There is still disagreement among historians, military scholars, and investigators about why the island nation of Japan issued this surprise attack on the U.S. military installation at Pearl Harbor, Hawaii. Some believe that Japan had been baited into making the attack in order to marshal public opinion behind U.S. entry into World War II (1939–1945); others maintain that the United States was unprepared for such an assault, or at least, the Japanese believed Americans to be in a state of unreadiness; and still others theorize that Pearl Harbor was an all-or-nothing gamble on the part of Japan to knock America's navy out of the war before it had even entered into the fray.

In 1941 Japanese troops had moved into the southern part of Indochina, prompting the United States to cut off its exports to Japan. In fall of that year, as General Hideki Tojo (1884–1948) became prime minister of Japan, the country's military leaders were laying plans to wage war on the United States. On December 7 Pearl Harbor, the hub of U.S. naval power in the Pacific, became the target of Japanese attacks, as did the American military bases at Guam, Wake Island, and the Philippines. But it was the bombing of Pearl Harbor that became the rallying cry for Americans during the long days of World War II—since it was at this strategic naval station, which had been occupied under treaty by the U.S. military since 1908, that Americans had felt the impact of the conflict.

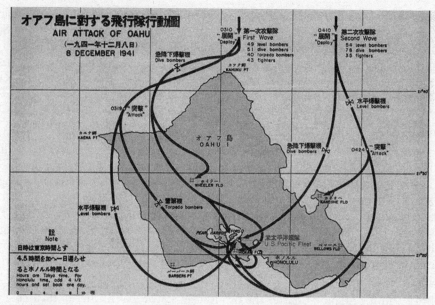

Originally published in "Reports of General MacArthur," this map shows the location of the Japanese fleet and the flight paths the bombers took (note: the date indicates December 8 instead of December 7 because it is in Japanese time.

What happened at Pearl Harbor?

On the night before the attack, the Japanese moved a fleet of thirty-three ships to within 200 miles of the Hawaiian island of Oahu, where Pearl Harbor is situated. More than 300 planes took off from the Japanese carriers, dropping the first bombs on Pearl Harbor just before 8:00 A.M. on December 7, 1941. There were eight American battleships and more than ninety naval vessels in the harbor at the time. Twenty-one of these were destroyed or damaged, as were 300 planes. The biggest single loss of the day was the sinking of the battleship USS *Arizona*, which went down in less than nine minutes. More than half the fatalities at Pearl Harbor that infamous December day were due to the sinking of the Arizona. By the end of the raid, more than 2,300 people had been killed and about the same number were wounded.

Pearl Harbor forever changed the United States and its role in the world. When President Franklin D. Roosevelt (1882–1945) addressed Congress the next day, he called December 7 "a date which will live in infamy." The United States declared war against Japan, and on December 11 Germany and Italy—Japan's Axis allies—declared war on the United States. The events of December 7 had brought America into the war, a conflict from which it would emerge as the leader of the free world.

Who was the "Desert Fox"?

The Desert Fox was the nickname of skilled German military leader Erwin Rommel (1891–1944), who led German forces in the North African Campaign of 1940 to 1943. He was known for quick tactical decisions and excellent strategy. A decorated officer in World War I, Rommel wrote a book entitled *Infantry Attacks* about his various battles in World War I.

He led a Panzer (tank) division, called the Ghost Division, that advanced on French forces at an alarming pace. During the North African campaign, he had many successful battles in the deserts of Egypt and Libya. Rommel actively participated in military campaigns—something that some high-ranking officer do not do. Robert Kapp wrote for *The Washington Post* in his July 1942 article entitled "Erwin Rommel of Africa: His Military Fame Will Outlast the War": "His personal bravery in battle has been attested time and again. He really leads his troops into battle and on one occasion, according to report, took part in the repulse of an enemy tank attack."

Rommel often disagreed with German führer Adolf Hitler and reportedly participated in a plot to assassinate him. Rommel treated captured soldiers humanely—unlike some other German military commanders. Rommel killed himself in October 1944, in exchange for a promise from Hitler that his family would be protected and spared from death.

What did the U.S. Supreme Court rule about the internment of Japanese-American citizens?

The U.S. Supreme Court upheld the internment of Japanese-American citizens in *Korematsu v. United States* (1944). The Court ruled 6-3 that the judgment of military officials' must be interpreted in the context of the times, including that Japan was an enemy of the United States and that there were some Japanese Americans who would be loyal to Japan.

Three justices—Owen J. Roberts, Frank Murphy, and Robert Jackson—dissented. All three wrote dissenting opinions. Murphy called the interment "one of the most sweeping and complete deprivations of constitutional rights in the history of this nation in the absence of martial law."

THE WAR IN EUROPE

What happened at Anzio?

Anzio, Italy, was the site of a four-month battle between Allied troops and the Germans during World War II (1939–1945). On January 22, 1944, more than 36,000 Allied troops and thousands of vehicles made an amphibious landing at Anzio, which is situated on a penin-

When did the first U.S. troops begin fighting in World War II?

Late in 1942 the United States sent its first troops across the Atlantic, making amphibious landings in North Africa, followed by Sicily and the Italian peninsula. The first Allied landings were in Morocco (Casablanca) and Algeria (Oran and Algiers) on November 8 of that year. (Algiers became the Allied headquarters in North Africa for the duration of the war.) The combined forces of the initial landing included more than 100,000 troops, launching the American military effort in the Atlantic theater of conflict. One American newspaper headline announced: "Yanks Invade Africa."

sula jutting into the Tyrrhenian Sea. But German soldiers, led by Field Marshal Albert Kesserling (1885–1960), were able to surround the Allied forces, containing them along the shoreline into May of that year. Fighting was intense, with an estimated 60,000 casualties, about half on each side. On May 25, 1944, the Germans withdrew in defeat, enabling the Allies to march toward Rome (thirty-three miles to the north-northwest). The taking of Anzio was a tactical surprise on the part of the U.S. and British, and their eventual victory there was a turning point for the Allies in the war.

What happened at Normandy?

Normandy, a region in northwestern France that lies along the English Channel, is known for the June 6, 1944, arrival of Allied troops, which proved to be a turning point in World War II (1939–1945). Officially called Operation Overlord (but known historically as D-Day) and headed by General Dwight D. Eisenhower (1890–1969) of the United States, the initiative had been in the planning since 1943 and it constituted the largest seaborne invasion in history. After several delays due to poor weather, the Allied troops crossed the English Channel and arrived on the beaches of Normandy on the morning of June 6. Brutal fighting ensued that day, with heavy losses on both sides. At the end of the day, the Allied troops had taken hold of the beaches—a firm foothold that would allow them to march inland against the Nazis, eventually pushing them back to Germany. While it was a critical Allied victory (which history has treated as the beginning of the end for German chancellor and führer Adolf Hitler [1889–1945]), the invasion at Normandy was still to be followed by eleven more months of bloody conflict; Germany would not surrender until May 7 of the following year.

What American general was the First Supreme Allied Commander of Europe?

That honor went to five-star general Dwight D. Eisenhower (1890–1969), who was also Chief of Staff of the United States Army. Eisenhower oversaw Operation Overlord, headed Operation Torch in North Africa, and Operation Avalanche—the Allied invasion of Italy.

Eisenhower exited World War II as an unquestioned military hero in the eyes of the American public. He later parlayed that into a successful political career, serving as the thirty-fourth president of the United States. He served two terms in office, from 1953 to 1961.

What was the Battle of the Bulge?

The term refers to the December 16, 1944, German confrontation with the American forces in the Ardennes Mountains, a forested plateau range that extends from northern France into Belgium and Luxembourg. Even though Germany appeared to be beaten at this late point in the war, Hitler rallied his remaining forces and launched a surprise assault on the American soldiers in Belgium and Luxembourg. But Germany could not sustain the front, and within two weeks the Americans had halted the German advance near Belgium's Meuse River (south of Brussels). The offensive became known as the Battle of the Bulge because of the protruding shape of the battleground on a map.

The Ardennes were also the site of conflict earlier in World War II, in 1940, as well as in World War I, in 1914 and 1918.

THE WAR IN THE PACIFIC

Did General MacArthur vow to return?

Two weeks after the Japanese bombing of the U.S. military bases at Pearl Harbor and the Philippines, Japan invaded the Philippine Islands. General Douglas MacArthur (1880–1964), the commander of the U.S. Army forces in the Far East, led the defense of the archipelago. He had begun to organize his troops around Manila Bay when, in March 1942, he received orders from the president to leave the islands. When he reached Australia, MacArthur said, "I shall return," in reference to the Philippines. Under new commands, MacArthur directed the Allied forces' offensive against Japan throughout the Southwest Pacific Islands. After a string of successes, on October 20, 1944, MacArthur made good on his promise, landing on the Philippine island of Leyte, accompanied by a great invasion force. By July of the following year, the general had established practical control of the Philippines. When Japan surrendered in August, MacArthur was made the supreme commander of the Allies, and as such, he presided over the Japanese surrender aboard the USS *Missouri* on September 2. He received the Medal of Honor for his defense of the Philippines, but he wasn't the only hero in the MacArthur family: His father, Arthur MacArthur (1845–1912), had received the nation's highest military award during the Civil War (1861–1865).

What was the Bataan Death March?

It was one of the most brutal chapters of World War II (1939–1945). On April 9, 1942, American forces on the Bataan Peninsula, Philippines, surrendered to the Japanese. More than 75,000 American and Filipino troops became prisoners of war (POWs). On April 10, they were forced to begin a sixty-five-mile march to a POW camp. Conditions were torturous—high temperatures, meager provisions, and gross maltreatment. The troops were denied food and water for days at a time; they were not allowed to rest in the shade; they were indiscriminately beaten; and those who fell behind were killed. On stretches where some troops were transported by train, the boxcars were packed so tightly that many POWs died of suffocation. The forced march lasted more than a week. Twenty thousand men died along the way.

But the end of the march was not the end of the horrors for the surviving POWs. About 56,000 men were held until the end of the war. They endured starvation, torture, and horrific cruelties; some were forced to work as slave laborers in Japanese industrial plants and some became subjects of medical experiments. In August 1945 their POW camp was liberated by the Allied forces, and the surviving troops were put on U.S. Navy vessels for the trip home. As part of the United States' 1951 peace treaty with Japan, surviving POWs were barred from seeking reparations from Japanese firms that had benefited from their slave labor. This injustice continued to be the subject of proposed Congressional legislation into the early 2000s, with no positive outcome for the veterans.

Why was the Battle of Midway important in World War II?

It was the turning point for the allied forces fighting the Japanese in the Pacific. The battle for Midway Island (actually two small islands situated about 1,300 miles west-northwest of Honolulu, Hawaii) began on June 4, 1942. The Japanese aimed to control Midway as a position from which its air force could launch further attacks on Hawaii. As the Japanese fleet approached the islands, which were home to a U.S. Navy base (established in 1941), U.S. forces attacked. Fighting continued until June 6. The Japanese were decisively defeated, losing four aircraft carriers; the United States lost one. The victory proved that Allied naval might could overcome Japan's.

What happened on Iwo Jima?

During the month of February 1945 Allied forces and the Japanese fought for control of Iwo Jima, a small island in the northwest Pacific Ocean, 759 miles south of Tokyo. Japan was using Iwo Jima as a base from which to launch air attacks on U.S. bombers in the Pacific. Capturing the island from the Japanese became a key objective for the United States. On February 19, 1945, the Fourth and Fifth U.S. Marine Divisions invaded the island. Fighting over the next several days claimed more than 6,000 U.S. troops. On the morning of February 23, after a rigorous climb to the top of Mount Suribachi (Iwo Jima's 550-foot inactive volcano), U.S. Marines planted an American flag. Though small, it was visible from around the island. Later that day, a larger flag was raised atop Mount Suribachi by five marines and a navy hospital corpsman. The moment was captured by American news photographer Joe Rosenthal. His famous photo became the inspiration for the U.S. Marine Corps Memorial (dedicated November 10, 1954) in Arlington, Virginia.

How many were killed by the A-bomb that was dropped on Nagasaki?

The death toll from the explosion, on August 9, 1945, was about 40,000. But, as in Hiroshima, thousands more died later due to radiation exposure from the atomic bomb. American military strategists believed that the first A-bomb, on Hiroshima, would force Japan's leaders to surrender. But when they did not, the second bomb was dropped on Nagasaki, an important seaport and commercial city. That catastrophic attack on Japan brought an end to the war, on August 14. Japan signed the surrender agreement on September 2 aboard the U.S. battleship *Missouri*, in Tokyo Bay.

WORLD WAR II ENDS

What are V-E Day and V-J Day?

V-E Day stands for Victory in Europe Day, and V-J Day stands for Victory over Japan Day. After the German surrender was signed in Reims, France (the headquarters of General Dwight D.

What was the *Enola Gay*?

It was the American B-29 bomber that dropped the first atomic bomb ever used in warfare. On August 6, 1945, the *Enola Gay* flew over Hiroshima, Japan, to drop an A-bomb over the city. The explosion killed an estimated 80,000 people and leveled an area of about five square miles in Hiroshima, an important manufacturing and military center. Thousands more died later from radiation exposure.

Eisenhower [1890–1969]), in the wee hours of May 7, 1945, U.S. president Harry S. Truman (1884–1972) declared May 8 V-E Day—the end of the World War II fighting in Europe.

But it was not until the Japanese agreed to surrender on August 14, 1945, that World War II ended. September 2, 1945, was declared the official V-J Day since it was then that Japan signed the terms of surrender on the USS *Missouri* anchored in Tokyo Bay.

Were any countries besides Switzerland neutral during World War II?

Yes, in its official stance of neutrality, Switzerland was joined by Spain, Portugal, Sweden, Turkey, and Argentina. However, postwar findings indicated the neutrality of these countries—with the exception of Argentina—was not an absolute policy. (Some have described these countries as only nominally neutral.) A 1998 report released by U.S. Undersecretary of State Stuart Eizenstat indicated that the Swiss had converted Nazi gold to Swiss francs and that Germany had used that exchange to buy minerals from Spain, Portugal, Sweden, and Turkey. The report further pointed out that Sweden had allowed a quarter of a million Nazi troops to cross its country in order to reach neighboring Finland, where the Germans fought Soviet forces.

Eizenstat, who headed a U.S. government effort to determine where Nazi gold ended up, was assisted in his research by State Department historians. Although the investigation's reports were critical of these neutral countries, Eizenstat also pointed out that all the countries were in difficult positions during the conflict. For example, Switzerland was completely surrounded by German-occupied countries. Nevertheless, Jewish groups brought lawsuits against the Swiss government and three Swiss banks for their role in converting looted Nazi gold into currency during World War II.

What was the Berlin airlift?

It was the response during 1948 and 1949 to the Soviet blockade of West Berlin. After World War II (1939–1945), the German city had been divided into four occupation zones: American, British, French, and Soviet. But following the conclusion of the war, it did not take long for the Cold War (1945–1990) between the Western powers and the Soviet Union to heat up. When the Americans, British, and French agreed to combine their three areas of Berlin into one economic entity, the Soviets responded by cutting the area off from all supply routes. In June 1948 all arteries—road, rail, and water—into West Berlin were blocked by Soviet troops. Since Berlin was completely surrounded by the Soviet occupation zone, the Soviets clearly believed the blockade would be an effective move that would prompt the Western countries to pull out. But the move failed: The Americans, British, and French set up a massive airlift. For the next eleven months, West Berlin was supplied with food and fuel entirely by airplanes. The Soviets lifted the blockade in May 1949, and the airlift ended by September.

COLD WAR

What is NATO?

NATO stands for the North Atlantic Treaty Organization, a military alliance formed on April 4, 1949, when twelve countries signed the North Atlantic Treaty in Washington, D.C. The original twelve NATO countries were Belgium, Canada, Denmark, France, Iceland, Italy, Luxembourg, the Netherlands, Norway, Portugal, the United Kingdom, and the United States. Each member nation agreed to treat attacks on any other member nation as if it were an attack on itself. In other words, any aggressor would have to face the entire alliance. This was NATO's policy of deterrence, a way of discouraging any attacks by the Soviet Union or other Eastern bloc countries. The organization had the further benefit of discouraging fighting among the member countries.

Three years after it was formed, the alliance was joined by Greece and Turkey (in 1952). West Germany followed three years after that, in 1955, and Spain joined in 1982. After the fall of communism and the reunification of East and West Germany (c. 1990), all of Germany joined the alliance. At this point, with the Cold War (1945–1990) over, many wondered what purpose the organization could serve. After all, the Soviet threat was no longer existent. However, other conflicts loomed on the horizon, including those in Bosnia and Herzegovina and in the Albanian republic of Kosovo. Fearing the civil war in the former Yugoslav republic would spread, NATO sent in troops on the side of the Bosnian government. NATO also formed the Partnership for Peace in 1994: This program was joined by more than twenty countries, among them former Eastern bloc nations, including Russia. Though these nations are not full members in the NATO alliance, the Partnership for Peace provides for joint military planning among signing nations. On March 12, 1999, three former Eastern bloc nations were given full membership in NATO: Poland, Czechoslovakia, and Hungary. Observers hailed the additions as evidence that Europe is becoming more unified. On April 23, 1999, the 50th anniversary of the alliance's founding, the nineteen NATO member nations gathered in Washington, D.C., to commemorate the event, just after NATO had begun airbombing Yugoslavia to pressure the government there to accept international terms aimed at bringing peace to the nation's Kosovo province, where ethnic conflicts between Serbs and Albanians had turned deadly.

NATO is governed by the North Atlantic Council, which is made up of the heads of government of member nations or their representatives. It was headquartered in Paris until 1967, at which time the offices were moved to Brussels, Belgium.

What was the Warsaw Pact?

The Warsaw Pact was the Eastern bloc countries' answer to the North Atlantic Treaty Organization (NATO). Seeing the Western nations form a strong alliance, in May 1955 the Soviet Union and its allies met in Warsaw, Poland, where they signed a treaty agreeing that they, too, would mutually defend one another. The eight member nations were Albania (which withdrew in 1968), Bulgaria, Czechoslovakia, East Germany, Hungary, Poland, Romania, and the Soviet Union. The Warsaw Pact was headquartered in Moscow and, in addition to discouraging attacks from Western bloc/NATO countries, the organization also sought to quell any democratic uprisings in Warsaw Pact nations.

But in 1990 the pact and the Soviet Union's control of it weakened as democracy movements in member nations could not be put down. As the former Eastern bloc countries underwent relatively peaceful revolutions, Warsaw Pact members began announcing their intentions to withdraw from the organization. East Germany withdrew when it was reunified with West Germany, and the restored Germany joined NATO (in 1990). The Warsaw Pact was dissolved by the remaining member nations in 1991.

What was the Bay of Pigs?

Bay of Pigs is the name of an unsuccessful 1961 invasion of Cuba, which was backed by the U.S. government. About 1,500 Cuban expatriates living in the United States had been supplied with arms and trained by the U.S. Central Intelligence Agency (CIA). On April 17, 1961, the group of men who opposed the regime of Cuba's Fidel Castro (1926–) landed at the Bahia de Cochinos (Bay of Pigs) in west-central Cuba. Most of the rebels were captured by the Cuban forces; others were killed. In order to secure the release of the more than 1,100 men who had been captured during the invasion, private donors in the United States accumulated $53 million in food and medicine, which was given to Castro's government in exchange for the rebels' release. The failed invasion came as a terrible embarrassment to the Kennedy administration, and many believe the Bay of Pigs incident directly led to the Cuban Missile Crisis.

What was the Cuban Missile Crisis?

The 1962 events, which happened very quickly, nevertheless constituted a major confrontation of the Cold War (1945–1990). After the disastrous Bay of Pigs invasion, when the United States backed Cuban expatriates in an attempt to oust Fidel Castro (1926–), the Soviet Union quietly began building missile sites in Cuba. Since the island nation is situated just south of Florida, when U.S. reconnaissance flights detected the Soviet military construction projects there, it was an alarming discovery. On October 22, 1962, President John F. Kennedy (1917–1963) demanded that the Soviet Union withdraw its missiles from Cuba. Kennedy also ordered a naval blockade of the island. Six days later, the Soviets agreed to dismantle the sites, ending the crisis.

What was the impact of the Soviet invasion of Afghanistan?

When the Soviet Union invaded Afghanistan in December 1979, to bolster a pro-Communist government in the Middle Eastern nation, no one could have anticipated the far-reaching effects of this decision—effects that would be felt decades later and around the globe. What immediately followed was a ten-year civil war, in which Soviet troops fought Afghan guerrillas, or the mujahideen. The war in Afghanistan became a jihad, or holy war, and a rallying point for many Muslims, with the conflict drawing young men from across the Muslim world to fight on the side of the guerillas. According to The 9/11 Commission Report, "mosques, schools, and boarding houses served as recruiting stations in many parts of the world, including the United States." The war was a virtual stalemate for seven years. But a turning point came in 1986 after the United States and Great Britain supplied shoulder-fired surface-to-air missiles to the Afghan guerrillas. The weaponry gave the scrubby ground forces a fighting

A declassified map that was used by the CIA during the Cuban missile crisis shows the range of Soviet-provided missiles and the cities they threatened in the United States.

chance against Soviet air power. As The 9/11 Commission Report asserts, together with Saudi Arabia, the United States supplied billions of dollars worth of secret assistance to rebel Afghan groups resisting the Soviet occupation. Thus supported, in April 1988 the Afghans declared victory, and early the next year the Soviet troops began to withdraw.

The war was over, but it had fueled an extremist Islamic ideology (the jihad as holy war) and put into place an infrastructure out of which emerged a powerful and deadly terrorist network. Though most Muslims hold peaceful views, a minority of Muslims view all non-Muslims as unbelievers. It was from this minority, trained and financed as a result of the Afghan War, that the global network of terrorists called al Qaeda emerged.

WARS IN SOUTHEAST ASIA

Who were the Khmer Rouge?

The Khmer Rouge (or Red Khmer) were a group of Cambodian Communists led by radical Marxist leader Pol Pot (1925–1998). Between 1970 and 1975 the Khmer Rouge guerrilla force, supported by Communists from neighboring Vietnam, waged a war to topple the U.S.-supported government of Lon Nol (1913–1985). On April 16, 1975, Lon Nol's regime fell, and the next day the Khmer Rouge seized the Cambodian capital, Phnom Penh. The ruthless revolutionary leader Pol Pot became prime minister of a Communist Cambodia and instituted a reign of terror. In his attempt to turn Cambodia into an agriculture-based society, the Khmer Rouge systematically emptied the cities, forcibly moving the people onto collective farms where they performed hard labor. Anyone thought to be opposed to the Khmer Rouge was killed. An estimated two million people died—by execution, overwork, and starvation. Pol Pot's "experiment" had failed, and his efforts to revolutionize Cambodia amounted to nothing short of genocide.

A Vietnamese invasion ousted the Khmer Rouge in 1979 and installed a new leadership. But civil wars were fought throughout the 1980s. The warring factions, who had made various alliances among themselves, finally signed a peace treaty in 1991. Under the watchful eye of the United Nations, elections were held in 1993. The resulting constitution provided for a democratic government with a limited monarchy. At that point, the Cambodian leadership seemed to come full circle—with Norodom Sihanouk (1922–) being crowned king in 1993: In 1970 Sihanouk had been deposed by Lon Nol, whose regime later became the target of the Khmer Rouge. During his lifetime Sihanouk made strides in establishing Cambodia's independence, and he enjoyed great public support. Due to failing health, he abdicated the throne in November 2004 and was succeeded by his son, Norodom Sihamoni (1953–).

For decades after Pol Pot was deposed, he continued to lead a revolutionary force of the Khmer in Cambodia, though he remained under house arrest by Ta Mok. His own men turned against him in early 1998, and Pol Pot died in April of that year. In December the last main fighting force of the Khmer Rouge surrendered to the Cambodian government. The event was broadcast on national television. Though some Khmer leaders remained in hiding and small bands of guerrilla fighters were thought to still exist, the radical Marxist group, which had terrorized Cambodia, no longer presented a threat to the government.

What were the "killing fields"?

After Communist leader Pol Pot (c. 1928–1998), head of the Khmer Rouge, took over the Cambodian government in 1975, he ordered a collectivization drive, rounding up anyone who was believed to have been in collusion with or otherwise supported the former regime of Lon Nol (1913–1985). The government-instituted executions, forced labor (in so-called re-education camps), and famine combined to kill one in every five Cambodians, or an estimated two million people, during Pol Pot's reign. He was removed from power in the Vietnamese invasion of 1978 to 1979, and he died in hiding in 1998.

On December 29 of that year, two former Khmer Rouge leaders surrendered to authorities: Khieu Samphan, age sixty-seven, and Nuon Chea, seventy-one. The two appeared in a televised news conference. Asked if he was sorry for the suffering that claimed the lives of millions of Cambodians, Khieu Samphan looked straight at the questioner and answered in English: "Yes, sorry, very sorry." Nuon Chea, said, "We are very sorry, not just for the human lives but also animal lives that were lost in the war." However, neither Samphan nor Chea accepted personal responsibility for the killing fields. While Samphan pled not to be tried for his crimes and Prime Minister Hun Sen (1950–) of Cambodia seemed inclined toward closing the book on this dark chapter in the country's history, there was public outcry to bring the former Khmer leaders to justice. Supporters of a trial assert that Cambodia will have no peace until someone is punished for the killing fields—for the Khmer's genocidal regime.

KOREAN WAR

Why did the United States get involved in the Korean War?

Americans became involved in the Korean conflict when the United Nations (UN), only five years old, called upon member countries to give military support to South Korea, which had been invaded by troops from Communist-ruled North Korea on June 25, 1950. The United Nations considered the invasion to be a violation of international peace and called on the Communists to withdraw. When they did not, sixteen countries sent troops and some forty countries sent supplies and military equipment to the aid of the South Korean armies. About 90 percent of the UN aid came from the United States. But North Korea received aid too— the Chinese sent troops and the Soviet Union provided equipment for them to sustain the war, which lasted until July 27, 1953. After three years of fighting, an armistice was called, but a formal peace treaty was never drawn up between the neighboring countries, prompting the United States to maintain military forces in South Korea in an effort to discourage any further acts of aggression from the north.

VIETNAM WAR

What caused the Vietnam War?

In the simplest terms, the long conflict in Southeast Asia was fought over the unification of Communist North Vietnam and non-Communist South Vietnam. The two countries had

151

been set up in 1954. Prior to that, all of Vietnam was part of the French colony of Indochina. But in 1946, the Vietnamese fought the French for control of their own country. The United States provided financial support to France, but the French were ultimately defeated in 1954. Once France had withdrawn its troops, an international conference was convened in Geneva to decide what should be done with Vietnam. The country was divided into two partitions, along the 17th parallel. This division of land was not intended to be permanent, but the elections that were supposed to reunite the partitions were never held. Vietnamese president Ho Chi Minh (1892–1969) took power in the north while Emperor Bao Dai (1913–1997), for a while, ruled the south.

But the Communist government in the north opposed the non-Communist government of South Vietnam and believed the country should still be united. The North Vietnamese supported antigovernment groups in the south and over time, stepped up aid to those groups. These Communist-trained South Vietnamese were known as the Viet Cong. Between 1957 and 1965, the Viet Cong struggled against the South Vietnamese government. But in the mid-1960s, North Vietnam initiated a large-scale troop infiltration into South Vietnam, and the fighting became a full-fledged war.

China and the Soviet Union provided the North Vietnamese with military equipment, but not manpower. The United States provided both equipment and troops to non-Communist South Vietnam in its struggle against the Viet Cong and North Vietnam. By 1969 there were more than half a million American troops in South Vietnam. This policy was controversial back in America, where protests against involvement in the Vietnam War continued until the last U.S. troops were brought home in 1973. In January of that year, the two sides had agreed to a cease-fire, but the fighting broke out again after the American ground troops left. On April 30, 1975, South Vietnam surrendered to North Vietnam and the war, which had lasted nearly two decades, ended. North Vietnam unified the countries as the Socialist Republic of Vietnam.

For its part, the North Vietnamese called the conflict a "war of national liberation": They viewed the long struggle as an extension of the earlier struggle with France. They also perceived the war to be another attempt by a foreign power (this time the United States) to rule Vietnam.

Why did the United States get involved in Vietnam?

The policy of involvement in the Vietnam conflict began in the mid-1950s when President Harry S. Truman (1884–1972) provided U.S. support to the French in their struggle to retain control of Vietnam, which was then part of French Indochina. In the Cold War era (1945–1990), government leaders believed that the United States must come to the assistance of any country threatened by communism. Truman's successors in the White House, Presidents Dwight D. Eisenhower (1890–1969), John F. Kennedy (1917–1963), and Lyndon B. Johnson (1908–1973), also followed this school of thought, fearing a "domino effect" among neighboring nations—if one fell to communism, they'd all fall.

What was the Tet Offensive?

The Tet Offensive was a turning point in the Vietnam War (1954–1975). The assault began during Tet, a festival of the lunar new year, on January 30, 1968. Though a truce had been

What was the My Lai Massacre?

It was a horrific chapter in American military history, during which U.S. troops fighting in South Vietnam took the small village of My Lai on March 16, 1968. The incident did not come to light until more than a year later, after which time it became clear that the unit of 105 soldiers who entered My Lai that morning had faced no opposition from the villagers. Even so, at the end of the day as many as 500 civilians, including women and children, lay dead. Though charges were brought against some of the men, only the commander of the company, Lt. William Calley (1943–), was convicted. His sentence of life imprisonment for the murder of at least twenty-two people was later reduced to twenty years, and he was released on full parole in November 1974.

called for the holiday, North Vietnam and the Viet Cong issued a series of attacks on dozens of South Vietnamese cities, including the capital of Saigon, as well as military and air installations. American troops and the South Vietnamese struggled to regain control of the cities, in one case destroying a village (Ben Tre) in order to "save it" from the enemy. Fighting continued into February. Though the Communist North ultimately failed in its objective to hold any of the cities, the offensive was critical in the outcome of the war: As images of the fighting and destruction filled print and television media, Americans saw that the war was far from over, despite pre-Tet reports of progress in Vietnam. The Tet Offensive strengthened the public opinion that the war could not be won. It altered the course of the American war effort, with President Lyndon Johnson (1908–1973) scaling back U.S. commitment to defend South Vietnam.

Why did so many Americans protest U.S. involvement in the Vietnam War?

The Vietnam War (1954–1975) divided the American public: The antiwar movement maintained that the conflict in Southeast Asia did not pose a risk to U.S. security (contrary to the "domino effect" that Washington, D.C., foresaw), and in the absence of a threat to national security, protesters wondered, "What are we fighting for?" Meanwhile, President Lyndon B. Johnson (1908–1973) slowly stepped up the number of troops sent to Vietnam. Many never came home, and those who did came home changed. Mass protests were held, including the hallmark of the era, the sit-in. Protesters accused the U.S. government of not only involving Americans in a conflict in which the country had no part, but of supporting a corrupt, unpopular—and undemocratic—government in South Vietnam.

Those Americans who supported the nation's fight against communism eventually became frustrated by the United States' inability to achieve a decisive victory in Vietnam. Even for the so-called hawks, who supported the war, the mounting costs of the war hit home when President Johnson requested new taxes. As the casualty count soared, public approval of U.S. participation in Vietnam dropped. By the end of the 1960s, under increasing public pressure, the government began to withdraw American troops from Vietnam. The evacuation of the ground troops was not complete until 1973. But even then, soldiers who were missing in action (MIAs) and prisoners of war (POWs) were left behind.

THE MIDDLE EAST

What is the basis of the conflict over the Gaza Strip and the West Bank?

The conflict is rooted in Jewish and Arab claims to the same lands in the Palestine region, which was under British control between 1917 and 1947. The Gaza Strip is a tiny piece of territory along the eastern Mediterranean Sea and adjacent to Egypt. After the nation of Israel was established and boundaries were determined by the United Nations (UN) in 1947, the Gaza Strip—bounded on two sides by the new Israel—came under Egyptian control. The Arab-Israeli war of 1967 resulted in Israeli takeover and occupation of Gaza. But unrest continued, and in 1987 and 1988 the region was the site of Arab uprisings known as the Intifada. A historic accord between the Palestine Liberation Organization (PLO) and Israel, signed in May 1994, provided for Palestinian self-rule in the Gaza Strip. This has been in effect since—though peace in the region remains elusive, as extremists on both sides of the conflict stage sporadic acts of violence.

The West Bank (which does not neighbor the Gaza Strip) is an area on the east of Israel, along the Jordan River and Dead Sea. The West Bank includes the towns of Jericho, Bethlehem, and Hebron. The holy city of Jerusalem is situated on the shared border between Israel and the West Bank. By the UN mandate that established the independent Jewish state of Israel in 1948, the West Bank area was supposed to become Palestinian. But Arabs who were unhappy with the UN agreement in the first place attacked Israel, and Israel responded by occupying the West Bank. A 1950 truce brought the West Bank under the control of neighboring Jordan; this situation lasted until 1967, when Israeli forces again occupied the region. Israelis soon began establishing settlements there, which provoked the resentment of Arabs. The Intifada uprisings that began in the Gaza Strip in 1987 soon spread to the West Bank. In 1988 Jordan relinquished its claim to the area, but fighting between the PLO and Israeli troops continued. Peace talks began in 1991, and the agreements that provided for Palestinian self-rule in the Gaza Strip also provided for the gradual return of West Bank lands to Palestinians. The city of Jericho was the first of these lands.

In August 2005, Israel began pulling out of the Gaza Strip after thirty-eight years of occupation. Some Israeli settlers resisted Prime Minister Ariel Sharon's call for withdrawal; but Sharon insisted the move was a critical step toward peace and securing Israel's future.

What were the Camp David Accords?

Camp David Accords is the popular name for a 1979 peace treaty between Israel and Egypt. The name stuck since President Jimmy Carter (1924–) met with Israel's Menachem Begin (1913–1992) and Egypt's Anwar Sadat (1918–1981) at the presidential retreat at Camp David, Maryland. The treaty was actually signed on March 26, 1979, in Washington, D.C., with Carter as a witness to the agreement between the warring Middle Eastern nations.

The pact, which was denounced by Arab countries, provided for the return of the Sinai Peninsula to Egypt. The mountainous area, adjacent to Israel and at the north end of the Red Sea, had been the site of a major campaign during the Arab-Israeli War of 1967 and had been occupied by Israel since. The transfer of the peninsula back to Egypt was completed in 1982. The Camp David Accords had also outlined that the two sides would negotiate Palestinian autonomy in the occupied West Bank and Gaza Strip. However, Sadat was assassinated in 1981, and this initiative saw no progress as a result of the Camp David Accords.

What is the Wye Accord?

Officially called the Wye River Memorandum, the accord outlined a limited and interim land-for-peace settlement between Israel and Palestine. It was signed October 23, 1998, by Israeli Prime Minister Benjamin Netanyahu (1949–) and Palestinian leader Yasser Arafat (1929–2004) at a summit held at Wye Mills, on the banks of Maryland's Wye River. The meeting was the follow-up to the 1993 Middle East Summit in Oslo, Norway. There, after months of talks, both sides agreed to an interim framework of Palestinian autonomy in the West Bank and Gaza Strip. The Wye meeting was the opportunity for both sides to make good on the promises made in Oslo.

The Wye Accord was brokered after a twenty-one-hour bargaining session mediated by U.S. president Bill Clinton (1946–). The points of the agreement included developing a security plan to crackdown on terrorism; the withdrawal of Israeli troops from an additional 13 percent of the West Bank (along with a commitment for future additional withdrawals); a transfer of roughly 14 percent of the West Bank from joint Israeli-Palestinian control to Palestinian control; Palestinian agreement that anti-Israeli clauses in its national charter would be removed; Israel's guarantee that it would provide two corridors of safe passage between the Gaza Strip and the West Bank; Israeli release of 750 Palestinian prisoners; and the opening of a Palestinian airport in Gaza.

The Knesset, Israel's parliament, approved the accords on November 17, 1998. But by December Israel suspended its obligations in the Wye, citing Palestinian failure to comply with the accords. Benjamin Netanyahu's successor, Prime Minister Ehud Barak (1942–), pledged to resume implementing the Wye Accord but at the same time delayed its timetable, saying the measures should be included in a final peace agreement with the Palestinians. On September 4, 1999, the two sides met again at Sharm al-Sheikh, Egypt, where they agreed on a new timetable for the Wye. That document was signed by Barak and the Palestinian Authority's Arafat and was witnessed by diplomats from Egypt, Jordan, and the United States (Secretary of State Madeleine Albright). But both Barak and Arafat faced mounting political opposition at home, posing immediate challenges to the revised agreement, which stalled again.

What was Camp David II?

In July 2000, President Bill Clinton (1946–) invited Israeli and Palestinian Authority leaders to the presidential retreat at Camp David, Maryland, to hammer out a final peace agreement in the Middle East. In what could have been the major breakthrough in the conflict, Israeli prime minister Ehud Barak (1942–) agreed to a Palestinian state, including the West Bank and East Jerusalem, and the administration of all Jerusalem holy sites by a third party (i.e. neither Israel nor Palestine). In exchange, Palestinian leader Yasser Arafat (1929–2004) was asked to sign an "end of conflict" addendum to the final agreement, which would have required him to bring the militant Arab group Hamas under control and end all Palestinian attacks on Israelis. But Arafat refused the deal. The July 11–25 meeting ended without an agreement. Violence erupted again in Israel, beginning the Second Intifada.

The lodge at Camp David.

What is the Roadmap for Peace?

It is a plan for lasting peace in the Palestinian-Israeli conflict. The roadmap was announced by the Bush administration on March 14, 2003, after several months of working with Russian, European Union, and United Nations (UN) officials to develop the plan, which calls for a permanent two-state solution. The roadmap outlines specific, actionable steps to be taken by each side in the conflict. The U.S. State Department described it as a "performance-based and goal-driven roadmap, with clear phases, timelines, target dates, and benchmarks aiming at progress through reciprocal steps by the two parties in the political, security, economic, humanitarian, and institution-building fields." In announcing the roadmap, President George W. Bush (1946–) called for an end to the recent wave of violence (intifada) in the Middle East, for authoritative Palestinian leadership, and for Israeli readiness to comply. He asked for Israeli and Palestinian leaders to contribute to and discuss the roadmap, and he repeated his call for "all parties in the Middle East to abandon old hatreds and to meet their responsibilities for peace." In 2009, Israeli leader Benjamin Netanyahu (1949–), the country's prime minister, debated and discussed with President Barack Obama, the merits of a settlement freeze on the West Bank. The two have disagreed over the implementation of the Roadmap for Peace.

LATIN AMERICA & THE CARIBBEAN

Who was Che Guevara?

Ernesto "Che" Guevara (1928–1967) was an idealist who became involved in revolutionary movements in at least three countries. The Argentinean, who had earned his degree in medicine in Buenos Aires in 1953, believed that social change and the elimination of poverty could only come about through armed conflict. Guevara met Fidel Castro (1926–) in Mexico in 1954 and served his guerrilla forces as a physician and military commander during the

Cuban Revolution (1956–1959). Once in power, Castro appointed Guevara as president of the National Bank of Cuba. Between 1965 and 1967 Guevara became active in leftists movements in Congo and in Latin America. He was leading a force against the Bolivian government when he was killed in 1967.

What was the Chiapas uprising?

Also called the Zapatista uprising, it was a January 1994 revolt staged by Mayan rebels in Chiapas, Mexico's southernmost state. On New Year's Day, members of the Zapatista Army of National Liberation (EZLN) launched a coordinated attack on four municipal capitals and a Mexican army headquarters in the remote region. With the cry of "tierra y libertad" ("land and liberty"), the armed insurgents invoked the name and spirit of Emiliano Zapata (1879–1919), Mexico's early twentieth-century revolutionary leader. The EZLN, or "Zapatistas," destroyed government offices, burned land deeds, and freed prisoners. At least 135 people died in the rebellion.

On January 12, after eleven days of heavy fighting, a cease-fire was called. The next month peace talks began between EZLN representatives and the Mexican government. Negotiations between the two sides proved to be a frustrating and lengthy process. Seeking "democracy, liberty, and justice for all Mexicans," the EZLN called for government reforms, including local autonomy, as well as land redistribution and other measures to aid the region's impoverished indigenous population. In February 1996 the two sides signed the San Andrés Accords and agreed to more talks. But in August of that year, the dialog stalled; the EZLN said it would not return to the negotiating table until the government implemented the San Andrés Accords.

Meanwhile, pro-government paramilitary groups with ties to Mexico's ruling PRI party (Institutional Revolutionary Party) made their presence known in Chiapas. There were violent episodes, the most horrific of which occurred on December 23, 1997, when the pro-government paramilitary group Paz y Justicia (Peace and Justice) brutally attacked a group of unarmed indigenous people in the village of Acteal. A total of forty-five people, mostly women and children, were slaughtered, and twenty-five more were injured.

The turbulence in Chiapas is fueled by deep-seated antigovernment feelings among the indigenous (Mayan) population. Despite the fact that it is rich in natural resources (including coffee, corn, timber, and oil), it is one of the poorest regions of Latin America; the wealth of Chiapas rests in the hands of a few. In 1990 half of the population in the state was malnourished, 42 percent had no access to clean water, 33 percent was without electricity, and 62 percent did not have a grade-school education. It was no coincidence that the 1994 uprising took place the same day that the North American Free Trade Agreement (NAFTA) went into effect: According to one Zapatista leader, NAFTA was the "death sentence" for Mexico's poor farmers, who would now have to compete with farmers north of the border. In 2012 they gained more supporters internationally from an Internet campaign, but no big government changes occurred.

PERSIAN GULF WAR

Why was the Persian Gulf War important?

The six-week war, telecast around the world from start to finish (February–April 1991), was significant because it was the first major international crisis to take place in the post–Cold

War era. The United Nations proved to be effective in organizing the coalition against aggressor Iraq. Leading members of the coalition included Egypt, France, Great Britain, Saudi Arabia, Syria, and the United States. The conflict also tested the ability of the United States and the Soviet Union (then still in existence as such) to cooperate in world affairs.

What did President George H. W. Bush mean when he said the United States had to "draw a line in the sand"?

President George H.W. Bush (1924–) was reacting to Iraqi leader Saddam Hussein's (1937–2006) act of aggression, when on August 2, 1990, his troops invaded neighboring Kuwait. The United Nations (UN) gave Iraq until January 15, 1991, to withdraw from Kuwait. Iraq failed to comply. The "line in the sand" that Hussein crossed was soon defended: On January 16, 1991, Operation Desert Storm was launched to liberate the Arab nation of Kuwait from Iraq, whose military dictator had not only invaded Kuwait but proclaimed it a new Iraqi province. Bush averred, "This will not stand," and in order to protect U.S. oil supplies in the country, the president mobilized U.S. forces, which were joined by a coalition of thirty-nine nations, to soundly and quickly defeat Iraq.

WAR IN THE BALTICS

What caused the Bosnian War?

To understand the war in Bosnia (1992–1995) it is important to review the history of Yugoslavia. Treaties at the end of World War I (1914–1918) dissolved the Austro-Hungarian Empire, creating separate nations of Austria and Hungary and dividing their former territory into three new countries: Czechoslovakia, Poland, and the Kingdom of Serbs, Croats, and Slovenes.

The various factions within the Kingdom of Serbs, Croats, and Slovenes struggled for power. In 1929 King Alexander I (1888–1934), an ethnic Serbian, dismissed the national parliament, did away with the constitution (1921), and declared an absolute monarchy. He also changed the country's name to Yugoslavia. The government was then dominated by ethnic Serbs, who had settled in the region as early as the seventh century C.E. and were converted to Eastern Christianity (Orthodox Christianity) by the ninth century. But the Serbian authority was challenged by the nation's ethnic Croats, whose ancestors had settled in the region by the seventh century C.E. and were converted to Western Christianity (Roman Catholicism) by the Franks. To try to end the struggle, in 1939 Croats were given limited autonomy within Yugoslavia. The arrangement was short-lived: Yugoslavia was invaded by the Axis powers in April 1941 during World War II (1939–1945).

The war over, in 1946 Yugoslavia was divided into six federated republics: Bosnia and Herzegovina, Croatia, Macedonia, Montenegro, Serbia, and Slovenia. But the lines of demarcation between these republics paid little regard to the ethnic boundaries of Serbs, Croats, and Muslims (who have been in the region since 1526, when it was invaded by Turks). Federal power was in the hands of Communist leader Josip Broz Tito (1892–1980). At first

Tito tied his government to the Soviet Union; he directed the nationalization of land, industry, utilities, and natural resources. But after 1948 he pursued a policy of nonalignment.

In the 1980s Yugoslavia's economy weakened, exacerbating regional differences. Tensions among ethnic groups flared. In 1991, as communism fell across Eastern Europe, Yugoslavia began to break apart. By March 1992 four of its republics had declared independence: Croatia, Slovenia, Macedonia, and Bosnia and Herzegovina. What remained of Yugoslavia were Serbia and Montenegro.

Serbs living in Bosnia and Herzegovina objected to the declaration of independence, which had been approved by the republic's Croats and Muslims. Fighting broke out in Bosnia, centered around the capital city of Sarajevo. Troops from Serbia entered the region to back the ethnic uprising in Bosnia. As with many civil wars, the conflict divided families and friends. Evidence mounted that the Serbs, under the direction of leader Radovan Karadžić (1945–), were engaged in a program of ethnic cleansing, including the mass murder of tens of thousands of Muslim refugees. In May 1995, after the Serbian military in Bosnia refused to comply with a United Nations (UN) ultimatum, the North Atlantic Treaty Organization (NATO) began a campaign of strategic air strikes on Serbian targets. The NATO assaults weakened the Serbs and brought them to the negotiating table in November 1995, when U.S. mediators helped broker a peace agreement in Dayton, Ohio. A single state (Bosnia and Herzegovina) was re-established; it was to be governed through a power-sharing arrangement among Serbs, Croats, and Muslims. But the conflict in Yugoslavia was not over; by 1998 the region's ethnic disputes erupted into another civil war, this time in the Kosovo province.

In 2003 Yugoslavia was effectively dissolved with the establishment of the country of Serbia and Montenegro through a peace accord brokered by officials from the European Union (EU). The new arrangement gave greater autonomy to each republic. (In 2006 Montenegro ended its union with Serbia and became an independent country.)

What happened to the "Butcher of Bosnia"?

During the Bosnian war, Radovan Karadžić (1945–), the former president of the Serb Republic and commander of its armed forces, earned himself the ignominious nickname "the Butcher of Bosnia" for directing the massacres and mass victimization of enemies, many of them Muslims. Following the war, the United Nation's International Court Tribunal for the former Yugoslavia (ICTY) in The Hague issued two indictments of Karadžić, charging him with genocide, war crimes, and crimes against humanity. Karadžić disappeared in 1996 and was at large until his arrest in Belgrade in July 2008. He remains in the custody of the International Criminal Tribunal for the former Yugoslavia.

In early December 1998, North Atlantic Treaty Organization (NATO) forces arrested Karadžić henchman General-Major Radislav

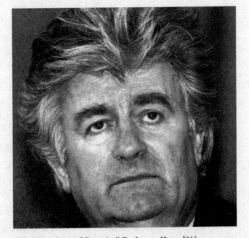

"The Butcher of Bosnia," Radovan Karadžić.

159

Krstic (1948–). The high-ranking Serbian official was believed to have taken part in the July 1995 massacre of as many as 8,000 Muslims in the eastern Bosnian town of Srebrenica. On August 2, 2001, Krstic was found guilty of genocide, persecutions for murders, cruel and inhumane treatment, terrorizing the civilian population, forcible transfer and destruction of personal property of Bosnian Muslim civilians, and murder as a violation of the Laws and Customs of War; he was sentenced to forty-six years in prison. After appeals, in April 2004, Krstic's sentence was reduced to thirty-five years based on the court's belief that he had aided and abetted acts of genocide but had not instigated them. He was transferred to Great Britain to serve out his sentence.

Another high-ranking Serbian military leader who faced charges of genocide before the ICTY was General Ratko Mladic (1942–). As the former commander of the Bosnian Serb forces in Bosnia and Herzegovina, Mladic was considered responsible for the "serious breaches" of international humanitarian law committed by the Bosnian Serb forces between May 1992 and July 1995, including the massacre at Srebrenica. His indictment also included charges of war crimes and crimes against humanity. He was at large for sixteen years until his arrest in Serbia in May 2011.

KOSOVO

What caused the fighting in Kosovo?

The conflict in Kosovo, like that in Bosnia, was ethnic-based. Kosovo is a province at the southern end of Serbia; it neighbors Albania and the former Yugoslav republic of Macedonia. Many Albanians still live in Kosovo and see themselves more closely aligned with Albania, to the southwest, than with Yugoslavia. Thus, a separatist movement began, which caused mounting tension between ethnic Albanians and Serbian authorities.

Early in 1998 Serbian forces and Yugoslav army units moved to suppress the Kosovo Liberation Army (KLA), the guerrilla force that sought independence for the province's Albanian population. In October Yugoslav President Slobodan Milosevic (1941–2006) agreed to end the crackdown—but this was only after the North Atlantic Treaty Organization (NATO) had repeatedly threatened air strikes. However, in the months that followed Milosevic's stated compliance, there was more violence against ethnic Albanians. By January 1999 hundreds had been killed and more than a quarter million people were displaced from their homes—many of them seeking shelter in makeshift huts in the forest. Victims included the elderly, women, and children. On March 23, 1999, Yugoslav's Serb parliament rejected NATO demands for autonomy in Kosovo as well as the plan to send NATO peacekeeping troops into the troubled province. The following day, NATO launched a campaign of air strikes against Yugoslavia, with the intent to weaken Milosevic and force him to comply with international demands to settle the conflict. After more than fifty days of air strikes, which included some controversial and deadly errors on NATO's part, it appeared that while NATO was winning the air campaign against Yugoslavia, the Serbian government of Yugoslavia was winning a ground campaign against the Kosovar Albanians: Of the estimated 1.8 million ethnic Albanians in Yugoslavia, Milosevic's forces had driven out or killed all but 130,000. Meantime, evidence of Serb atrocities toward ethnic Albanians mounted, as mass graves were discovered and survivors who fled Kosovo reported horrific tales of torture and rape at the hands of the Serbs.

Ultimately NATO's Operation Allied Force was successful. On June 10, 1999, after a seventy-seven-day air campaign, the bombing was temporarily suspended because Yugoslav forces had begun to fully withdraw from Kosovo. The withdrawal was in compliance with an agreement drawn up between NATO and the Federal Republic of Yugoslavia and Republic of Serbia on the evening of June 9. By June 20 the Serb withdrawal was complete and a multinational security force was established to keep the peace. That same day NATO announced that it had formally terminated the air campaign. NATO personnel were reassigned as peacekeepers and to move humanitarian aid, including food, water, tents, and medical supplies. Though the crisis in Kosovo was over, the aftermath was immense: It was estimated that by the end of May 1999, 1.5 million people, or 90 percent of the Kosovar population, had been expelled from their homes and a quarter million Kosovar men were missing. Further, there was mounting evidence that ethnic Albanians had been the victims of genocide. This evidence included the discoveries of mass graves; reports of mass executions, expulsions, and rape; and the systematic destruction of property and crops.

In 2003, in a peace accord brokered by the European Union, the nation of Serbia and Montenegro was established, with each republic receiving greater autonomy. The nation of Yugoslavia no longer existed. (In 2006 Montenegro ended its union with Serbia and became an independent country.)

CHECHNYA

What was the conflict over Chechnya?

Since the 1990s separatist factions have been fighting for the independence of the tiny Russian republic (at just more than 6,000 square miles in area, it is about the size of Hawaii).

Chechnya's population falls into three main ethnic groups: Chechens (the majority), Ingush, and Russian. The religion of the Chechen and the Ingush peoples is Islam, while the Russian population is mostly Orthodox Christian. After the breakup of the Soviet Union, the region remained with the new Russian Federation as the Chechen-Ingush republic. But dissent grew, and in 1991 a rebel faction led by Dzhokhar Dudayev (1944–1996) took control of the government. Chechnya separated from Ingushetia to form two separate republics in 1992.

In 1994 Russian troops invaded to reclaim the Chechen capital of Grozny, an oil and manufacturing center. By this time two factions existed among the rebels: One was a nationalist movement and the other a fundamentalist Islamic movement. In 1995 the conflict spilled over into neighboring regions, as Chechen militants began a series of terror attacks. In June of that year gunmen seized a hospital in Budyonnovsk, about ninety miles north of the Chechen border, in the Stavropol territory, and held 1,800 people hostage for six days. More than one hundred people were killed and hundreds were injured. In 1996 Chechen terrorists seized another hospital, holding 2,000 hostages, this time in neighboring Dagestan; at least twenty-three people were killed. Russia's military strikes in Chechnya continued until a ceasefire was negotiated in 1996, by which time dissident leader Dudayev had been killed.

Even after a peace treaty was signed in 1997, ending the First Chechen War, the status of Russia's "breakaway republic" remained unclear. In 1999 the battle over Chechnya's status was taken straight to the Russian capital of Moscow, where five bombings in four weeks claimed 300 lives; Islamic militants in Chechnya were blamed. The Kremlin responded with force, leveling Grozny by early 2000 and displacing a quarter of a million people from their homes. A pro-Moscow administration was put into place.

Violence related to the Chechen conflict continued throughout Russia. Suicide bombings alone claimed more than 260 lives between 2002 and 2004.

There were large-scale assaults as well: In October 2002 Chechen militants took more than 700 people hostage at a Moscow theater; after a two-day standoff, Russian Special Forces stormed the building, killing forty-one Chechen fighters and 129 hostages. In August 2004 two airliners crashed within minutes of each other after taking off from the same airport; ninety people died in the crashes, which Russian president Vladimir Putin (1952–) labeled terrorism. And on September 1, 2004, thirty-two armed militants seized an elementary school in Beslan, North Ossetia, a region bordering Chechnya. The terrorists held some 1,200 hostages for forty-eight hours, at which time Russian forces stormed the building; 335 people died, most of them children. Leaders of the Chechen nationalist movement distanced themselves from these terrorist acts, the responsibility for which was claimed by a militant Chechen Muslim group.

Chechnya continued to be unstable, with Putin resolved to a hard-line approach to the breakaway republic. In elections held in March 2003, voters reportedly approved a new constitution that declared Chechnya to be part of Russia. But critics found the election results irregular, with almost 96 percent of voters expressing support for the referendum. Months later, pro-Moscow leadership was elected in the person of Deputy Prime Minister Ramzan Kadyrov; critics called it a puppet regime.

In March 2005 Chechen nationalist leader Aslan Maskhadov (1951–2005) was killed in a Russian assault. His death was seen as a victory for Moscow; Maskhadov, who had briefly been president (1997–1999) of an independent Chechnya, was generally viewed as a moderate who believed an honest dialogue between the two sides could bring an end to the decade-long conflict. In April 2009, the insurgency in Chechenya officially ended, though there are still occasional outbreaks of violence in the region.

AFRICA

What was "Black Hawk Down"?

Though the U.S. military uses the term to communicate any crash of one of its Black Hawk helicopters, the phrase is closely associated with events in Mogadishu, Somalia, on October 3, 1993. The term became synonymous with that day after American journalist Mark Bowden wrote a book, by the same title, describing a disastrous U.S. raid on a Mogadishu warlord. The book was turned into a movie in 2001.

The background is this: Somalia threw off its colonial constraints in 1960 to become an independent nation. But warring factions within the impoverished east African nation made a stable central government elusive. After staging a 1969 coup, Soviet-influenced army commander Mohammed Siad Barre (1919 or 1921–1995) established a military dictatorship in Somalia. His authoritarian rule, which was marked by human rights abuses, lasted until

1991 when he was deposed in a popular uprising (he died in exile four years later). The nation of about eight million people was in chaos, and many were starving. International donations of food were hijacked and used by competing warlords to secure weapons from other nations, thus furthering civil strife. After a 1992 cease-fire, the United Nations (UN) sent peacekeepers to Somalia and launched a humanitarian relief operation. Outgoing U.S. President George H.W. Bush (1924–) supported the UN effort by approving a deployment of 25,000 American troops to Somalia to help secure trade routes over which badly needed food supplies could move. In 1993 the United States, then led by President Bill Clinton (1946–), reduced the number of troops to less than half the original deployment.

Trouble was ignited on June 5, 1993, when twenty-four Pakistani soldiers, in Somalia as part of the UN operation, were killed in an ambush. The warlord thought to be responsible for the massacre was Mohammed Farah Aidid. Somalia's government ordered Aidid's arrest. His capture was an imperative to peace: He and his followers were staging a violent rebellion against the provisional Somali government, led by Aidid rival Ali Mahdi. Over the next several months, UN and U.S. forces launched several attacks on what were believed to be Aidid clan strongholds, but Aidid himself remained an elusive target.

On October 3 U.S. elite forces launched an assault on a Mogadishu hotel believed to be an Aidid hideout. They were met with an ambush. Over the following seventeen hours, U.S. troops, including a military mission to rescue downed Black Hawk helicopter crews, engaged in a battle with armed Somalis in the streets of Mogadishu. Eighteen American servicemen were killed; the bodies of some were dragged through the streets of the city. Another eighty-four American soldiers were wounded. Hundreds of Somalis were killed in the fighting. Video footage of the chaos was shown on international television. The Battle of Mogadishu, as it is officially called, was the most intense combat firefight experienced by U.S. troops since Vietnam. On October 7, President Clinton signed orders to withdraw all American troops from Somalia. The United States pulled out in 1994, and the UN peacekeepers followed in 1995. Even after a 2002 reconciliation conference, Somalis had not secured a central government by 2004. The country remained impoverished, strife-ridden, and lawless. The UN and other non-governmental organizations (NGOs) worked to provide much-needed humanitarian relief to Somalis.

Some military and foreign affairs experts point to the Battle of Mogadishu as a primary reason for American reluctance to engage troops in the world's hotspots in the 1990s.

What happened in the Rwandan genocide?

On April 6, 1994, the airplane carrying Rwandan president Juvenal Habyarimana (1937–1994), of Rwanda's majority Hutu ethnic group, was shot down by unknown attackers. The event touched off, or was used as an excuse for, what one journalist described as a "premeditated orgy of killing" in which ethnic Hutu extremists carried out a campaign of mass murder against minority Tutsis. Ten years after the horrific events, the *Chicago Tribune*'s Africa correspondent recounted how Rwanda's "Hutu majority, equipped with machetes and called to action by government radio announcements, slaughtered neighbors, friends, co-workers. Priests killed parishioners who sought refuge in churches. Teachers murdered pupils. Hundreds of thousands of women were raped, children burned or drowned, bodies pushed into mass graves." The massacre continued for three months, ending only when Tutsi fighters managed to seize the capital at Kigali and take power.

In 2004 the Rwandan government released its official estimate of the death toll: 937,000 people were murdered, making it the worst ethnic cleansing the world has seen since the Holocaust during World War II (1939–1945). But, unlike the Holocaust, which was carried out by a dictatorial military machine, the Rwandan genocide was carried out by the masses. In the aftermath, more than 150,000 people were accused of participating in the massive violence, though the Rwandan courts had only tried a small fraction of those—no more than 10 percent in ten years. An estimated two million Hutus, many who probably feared retribution, had fled to neighboring countries after the Tutsis gained power. The genocide had happened at the hands of many.

In the decade since the Rwandan genocide, Rwandans, and the world, have grappled with difficult and perhaps unanswerable questions. How could so many people (Hutus) have participated in the mass cleansing? Experts point to Rwanda's deeply divided history; the ri-

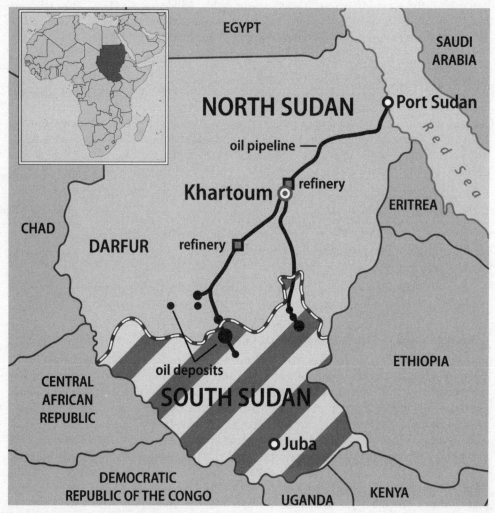

A map of the Sudan, showing the Darfur region.

valry between Hutus and Tutsis dates back hundreds of years—since the Tutsis first arrived in the central African region in the fourteenth century. How could the world body have "allowed" such an event to happen, particularly with the Nazi Holocaust a not-too-distant memory? Again, there is no easy answer. The United Nations withdrew its people when the violence began in April 1994, but some UN officials estimated later that perhaps as few as 5,000 troops might have been able to prevent the annihilation. The United States did not intervene in the Rwandan genocide; the recent images of dead American soldiers being dragged through the streets of Mogadishu, Somalia (in October 1993), had left the country reticent to involve itself in the world's hotspots. But, even with the lesson of Rwanda, experts wondered how the international response might differ today.

What was the crisis in Darfur, Sudan?

The brutal violence, really a genocide, in Darfur began in February 2003, and was still ongoing two years later as United Nations (UN) negotiators tried to broker a peace agreement. Sudanese government troops and government-backed Arab militia, called the janjaweed, were engaged in a violent campaign that targeted black African civilians from the Fur, Massalit, and Zaghawa ethnic groups in the western Sudanese state of Darfur (which is about the size of Texas). Reports from the Human Rights Watch and UN agencies working in Sudan indicated that large-scale bombing and burning campaigns had destroyed entire villages, tens of thousands of Darfurians had been raped and killed, and as many as two million had been displaced by early 2005. International relief efforts were hampered by ongoing violence, putting millions of women and children at risk of starvation and disease. Observers called for an international response to the crisis to avert "another Rwanda." In April 2005 the UN Security Council referred the Darfur situation to the International Criminal Court. Two peace agreements—in 2006 and in 2011—have stopped much of the horrific ethnic cleansing. The 2011 agreement, called the Doha Agreement, was between the Sudan government and the Liberation and Justice movement.

The Darfur crisis was part of a greater and older conflict in Sudan. The east African nation, whose neighbors include Egypt to the north and Ethiopia to the east, was in 2005 the scene of Africa's oldest civil war. Since 1984, the conflict had pit the Arab (Muslim) north against the Christian and animist south. But diplomatic efforts to resolve that decades-old conflict failed. The Muslim regime based in the national capital of Khartoum was unwilling to share power and wealth. Thus, when Khartoum was hit with a rebellion in 2003, it retaliated by inciting the brutality in Darfur. Diplomats worked to resolve the north-south civil conflict, offering Sudan a package of debt relief and development aid that could reach $100 million. Critics of that plan said that incentives were not enough, and that sanctions should be levied against the nation to pressure the government to move toward ceasefire.

TERRORISM

What happened after the 1993 World Trade Center bombing?

During the Federal Bureau of Investigation (FBI) investigation that followed the February 26, 1993, tragedy, it was learned that the World Trade Center was one of several intended targets of an Islamic extremist group. The bomb explosion in lower Manhattan killed six people and started a fire that sent black smoke through the 110-story twin towers, injuring hundreds and forcing 100,000 people to evacuate the premises.

Days later, on March 4, twenty-five-year-old Mohammed A. Salameh, an illegal Jordanian immigrant, was arrested in Jersey City, New Jersey. Salameh was later found to be a follower of self-exiled Islamic fundamentalist leader Sheik Omar Abdel Rahman (1938–), who was wanted by Egypt for having incited antigovernment riots in 1989. In June investigators seized Arab terrorists they accused of plotting to blow up several New York City sites, including the United Nations headquarters and the Holland and Lincoln tunnels. U.S. authorities then arrested Rahman and imprisoned him on suspicion of complicity in the World Trade Center bombing. On October 1, 1995, a federal jury found Rahman and nine other militant Muslims guilty of conspiring to carry out a campaign of terrorist bombings and assassinations aimed at forcing Washington to abandon its support of Israel and Egypt.

The 1993 bombing foreshadowed the terrorist strikes of September 11, 2001, which destroyed the landmark twin towers of the World Trade Center in lower Manhattan and launched what came to be called a global war on terrorism.

What happened in the Oklahoma City bombing?

The attack took place at 9:02 A.M. on April 19, 1995, when a truck bomb exploded outside the Alfred P. Murrah Federal Building in Oklahoma City, Oklahoma. Of the 168 people who were killed, 19 were children. Another 500 people were injured. The blast, which investigators later learned had been caused by a bomb made of more than two tons of ammonium nitrate and fuel oil, sheered off the front half of the nine-story building and left a crater eight feet deep and thirty feet wide. Nearby buildings were damaged or destroyed, including a YMCA day care center where many children were seriously injured. The force of the explosion shattered windows blocks away. Survivors of the blast and others in the vicinity began rescue efforts right away. Eventually more than 3,600 people from around the country participated in rescue operations, including police, firefighters, and members of the Federal Emergency Management Agency (FEMA).

Police and Federal Bureau of Investigation (FBI) agents arrested members of an American right-wing militant group who were suspected of wanting to avenge the April 19, 1993, FBI/ATF raid on the Branch Davidian religious compound in Waco, Texas. Former army buddies Timothy J. McVeigh (1968–2001), then twenty-seven, and Terry L. Nichols (1955–), then forty, were indicted on August 10, 1995, on eleven charges each. The two were tried separately and convicted in federal court. McVeigh was found guilty of murder and conspiracy in June 1997, and a federal jury sentenced him to death. He was executed by lethal injection in June 2001.

Nichols was later found guilty of conspiracy and involuntary manslaughter, but in January 1998 the jury deadlocked on the sentence, which was then to be decided by the judge. In early June it was decided that Nichols would serve life in prison.

Officials believe the Murrah Federal Building was targeted in the antigovernment attack because it housed fifteen federal agencies, including offices of the Social Security Administration (SSA), Housing and Urban Development (HUD), the Drug Enforcement Administration (DEA), and the Bureau of Alcohol, Tobacco, and Firearms (ATF), as well as several defense department offices and a government-run day care center.

Was the Madrid commuter train bombing an act of terrorism?

Spanish officials concluded that the March 11, 2004, bombing of packed commuter trains in Madrid was an act of terrorism, likely motivated by Spain's arrest of dozens of al Qaeda suspects after the September 11, 2001, attacks on the United States. (At least three of those arrested in Spain were charged with helping organize the 9/11 attacks.) On March 11, 2004, ten backpacks loaded with dynamite exploded on four trains at the height of morning rush hour, killing 191 people and injuring 1,800. In the investigation that followed, officials uncovered other terrorist plots, including suicide bombings and assassinations aimed at interrupting Spain's court system that tries terrorist suspects. The discoveries led officials to conclude that their nation had become a "crossroads" for Muslim extremists, in part because of Spain's proximity to northern Africa. In April 2004, as authorities closed in on the hideout of the suspected Madrid bombing ringleader, a Tunisian man, and his associates, the suspects blew up their apartment. A total of sixty-two suspects were arrested in 2004 in association with the train bombings.

9/11

What was the chronology of events on September 11, 2001?

The sequence of events related to the terrorist attacks on 9/11 were as follows (all times are eastern daylight time):

8:46 A.M.: A passenger plane crashes into the north tower of New York City's World Trade Center. At first it is assumed to be an accident. But within hours, it is learned that the plane was American Airlines Flight 11, which had been commandeered by hijackers shortly after takeoff from Boston headed to Los Angeles. It carried eighty-one passengers (including five hijackers) and eleven crewmembers.

9:03 A.M.: A second passenger plane slams into the south tower of the World Trade Center and explodes. United Airlines later announces that this was Flight 175, another Boston-Los Angeles plane; it carried fifty-six passengers (including five hijackers) and nine crewmembers. Both towers of the World Trade Center are in flames.

9:21 A.M.: Bridges and tunnels leading into New York City are closed. Within the hour, Mayor Rudolph Giuliani (1944–) orders an evacuation of Manhattan south of Canal Street.

9:25 A.M.: All flights in the United States are grounded. It is the first time in history that the Federal Airlines Administration (FAA) halts all flights.

9:30 A.M.: President George W. Bush (1946–), scheduled to speak at a grade school in Sarasota, Florida, remarks that the nation has been the target of an "apparent terrorist attack."

9:45 A.M.: A third passenger plane crashes into the east wall of the Pentagon in Arlington, Virginia. The plane was American Airlines Flight 77, carrying fifty-eight passengers (including five hijackers) and six crewmembers. It originated at Washington, D.C.'s Dulles International Airport and was headed to Los Angeles. After being hijacked, the plane made a U-turn over the Ohio-Kentucky border to return to the Washington, D.C.-area, where it hit its intended target.

9:45 A.M.: The White House is evacuated.

10:05 A.M.: The south tower of the World Trade Center collapses.

10:10 A.M.: A large section of the Pentagon collapses.

10:10 A.M.: A fourth passenger plane crashes in a field in Somerset County, in southwestern Pennsylvania (outside of Pittsburgh). It was United Airlines Flight 93, originating in Newark, New Jersey, and bound for San Francisco. After being hijacked, the plane made a U-turn over Ohio and was headed for a target in Washington, D.C. (later thought to be Camp David, the White House, or the U.S. Capitol building). After learning via cell phones of the other hijackings, a group of passengers stormed the cockpit in an effort to take the plane, which crashed in the countryside. The plane carried thirty-seven passengers (including four hijackers) and a crew of seven. There were no survivors.

10:24 A.M.: The FAA reports that it has diverted all incoming transatlantic flights to Canada.

10:28 A.M.: The north tower of the World Trade Center falls. The collapse of each tower blankets lower Manhattan in smoke and ash, turning the brilliantly sunny day to darkness.

10:45 A.M.: All federal office buildings in the nation's capital are evacuated.

2:00 P.M.: Senior FBI sources reveal to the media that they are working under the assumption that the four airplanes that crashed were part of a terrorist attack. The FBI later learns the identities of all nineteen hijackers (there were five on board each plane, except Flight 93, which had four).

4:00 P.M.: Media reports indicate that U.S. officials have credible evidence tying the morning's attacks to Saudi militant Osama bin Laden (1957–2011).

5:20 P.M.: Building 7 (a forty-seven-story structure) of the World Trade Center complex collapses. Nearby buildings are in flames.

How many died in the September 11 attacks?

About 3,000 people died that day as a result of the terrorist attacks on the United States. The strikes on New York's World Trade Center claimed 2,602 lives, and another 125 died at the Pentagon, outside Washington, D.C. (The numbers include firefighters and police officers who died as part of the rescue effort.) The victims on board the hijacked flights, which were used as terrorist weapons, numbered an additional eighty-seven on American Airlines Flight 11, which crashed into the North Tower of the World Trade Center; sixty on United Airlines Flight 175, which

The National 9/11 Memorial at Ground Zero, New York City.

crashed into the South Tower of the World Trade Center; fifty-nine on American Airlines Flight 77, which slammed into the Pentagon; and forty on United Airlines Flight 93, which crashed in rural Somerset County, Pennsylvania.

In February 2005 officials announced that they had exhausted all possible methods of identifying the human remains recovered at Ground Zero. Of the 2,749 people reported missing at the World Trade Center, positive identification had been made on 1,161 people. The rest were presumed dead; 2,749 death certificates were issued related to the World Trade Center attack.

What was the 9/11 Commission?

It was the ten-member group created by a congressional act signed by the president on November 27, 2002. The bipartisan commission, consisting of five Republicans and five Democrats, was chosen by Congress to look into how the attacks of September 11, 2001, could have happened and how such a tragedy could be avoided in the future. During its investigation, the commissioners and their staff reviewed more than 2.5 million pages of documents, interviewed more than 1,200 people in ten countries, held nineteen days of hearings, and took public testimony from 160 witnesses. The commission wrapped up its work in all due speed, publishing a full report less than two years after it received its mandate. The 567-page report chronicles the events of 9/11, looks at the roots and growth of the "new terrorism," reviews the U.S. response to the attacks and to previous assaults (including the August 1998 U.S. embassy bombings in Kenya and Tanzania), and recommends changes to prevent further terrorist strikes. The report was made available as a book and an online document, and was presented "to the American people for their consideration."

Among the key disclosures in the report were that the commission found "no credible evidence that Iraq and al Qaeda cooperated on the attacks against the United States." That finding was immediately dismissed by the White House in June 2004. The commission also reported that the original plan for the al Qaeda attacks on the U.S. homeland included a total of ten hijacked airplanes, striking targets on the East and West coasts; the plan was dismissed by al Qaeda leader Osama bin Laden as too complex. In the aftermath of the 9/11 attacks and the U.S.-led retaliatory strikes on Afghanistan, the commission believed that al Qaeda had become more decentralized, with cell leaders assuming greater authority for decision-making.

THE WAR ON TERROR

What is the War on Terror?

In his remarks the evening of September 11, 2001, President George W. Bush (1946–) vowed that "America and our friends and allies join with all those who want peace and security in the world, and we stand together to win the war against terrorism." TV newscasts were soon emblazoned with the message, "America's War on Terror," or simply, "The War on Terror." The events of 9/11 catapulted the free world into a new era, in which conflicts no longer were limited to wars between nations. There was a new enemy, which knew no national boundaries, whose "army" was covert, and which mercilessly targeted civilians.

Acknowledging that the new threat could not be met by the United States alone, the Bush administration began forging an alliance of nations that together would use diplomacy, take military action, and coordinate intelligence and law enforcement efforts to combat terrorists around the globe. On September 12, 2001, Secretary of State Colin Powell (1937–) called for a "global coalition against terrorism." Eventually the Bush administration put together an alliance of eighty-four countries, called the Global Coalition Against Terrorism, "united against a common danger, and joined in a common purpose."

The strike on Afghanistan, called Operation Enduring Freedom, was the first military strategy in the new war. The next major initiative was the war in Iraq. While those operations were underway, terrorist strikes continued around the globe. In March 2004, following the commuter train blasts in Spain, President Bush remarked that "the murders in Madrid are a reminder that the civilized world is at war. And in this new kind of war, civilians find themselves suddenly on the front lines. In recent years, terrorists have struck from Spain, to Russia, to Israel, to East Africa, to Morocco, to the Philippines, and to the United States. They've targeted Arab states such as Saudi Arabia, Jordan, and Yemen. They've attacked Muslims in Indonesia, Turkey, Pakistan, Iraq, and Afghanistan. No nation or region is exempt from the terrorists' campaign of violence."

When was the Office of Homeland Security formed?

The Office of Homeland Security was organized in the days following the September 11, 2001, terrorist attacks. President George W. Bush (1946–) chose Pennsylvania governor Tom Ridge (1945–) as the first Office of Homeland Security advisor. Ridge was sworn in on October 8, 2001. The office was elevated to the department level on November 25, 2002, when President Bush signed into law the Homeland Security Act, creating the Department of Homeland Security (DHS) and making Ridge a cabinet-level administrator.

The DHS consolidated several existing agencies and pledged to carry out new initiatives to protect the nation from further attacks (to the extent this is possible). Agencies and subdepartments within the DHS's purview eventually included the Transportation Security Administration, Customs and Border Protection, Immigration and Customs Enforcement, the Federal Emergency Management Agency (FEMA), Information Analysis and Infrastructure Protection offices, U.S. Citizenship and Information Services (formerly the Immigration and Naturalization Service, or INS), an office for Civil Rights and Civil Liberties, the U.S. Coast Guard, and the U.S. Secret Service.

On February 15, 2005, Ridge was succeeded by Michael Chertoff (1953–), a former U.S. Circuit Court judge. Chertoff had also worked as an assistant attorney general; in that position, he helped trace the 9/11 terrorist attacks to the al Qaeda network and worked to increase information sharing within the Federal Bureau of Investigation (FBI) and with state and local officials. In 2009, Janet Napolitano became secretary of homeland security.

What is the Patriot Act?

The USA Patriot Act is a controversial, 342-page law passed by a wide majority of Congress and signed by President George W. Bush (1946–) in October 2001. It is an acronym for the Uniting and Strengthening America by Providing Appropriate Tools Required to Intercept and Obstruct Terrorism.

It was designed to strengthen national security following the 9/11 terrorist attacks. The legislation relaxes federal surveillance laws, granting authorities broad leeway to gather information on U.S. citizens and resident foreigners. It also expands the government's prosecutorial powers against suspected terrorists and their associates. The complex act, which contains 168 sections, allows the nation's intelligence and law enforcement agencies to, among other things, monitor email and financial transactions without securing a subpoena, use wiretapping without a court order, and require Internet service providers (ISPs) to hand over usage data on customers.

One of the most controversial sections of the Patriot Act is the so-called "library provision," which allows government officials to secretly subpoena books, records, papers, documents, and other items from businesses, hospitals, and other organizations. Critics feared that the government could use the provision to snoop into the lives and habits of innocent Americans. The reaction to the provision was so strong that, according to the American Civil Liberties Union (ACLU), five states and 375 communities in forty-three states had passed anti-Patriot Act resolutions by spring 2005. Another contentious section of the Patriot Act allows the delayed notification of search warrants; this is called the "sneak and peek" provision because it lets federal officials search a suspect's home without telling the individual until later.

While many legislators and security experts hailed the Patriot Act provisions as necessary in combating terrorism and securing the homeland, others immediately saw the legislation as a serious infringement of civil rights. Supporters pointed to the hundreds of charges brought against suspected terrorists, as well as hundreds of convictions, as a result of the Patriot Act. But critics, including legislators, the ACLU, conservative groups, and many citizens, called the act unconstitutional—and unpatriotic. A top ACLU representative said, "Cooler heads can now see that the Patriot Act went too far, too fast and that it must be brought back in line with the Constitution." The fallout included charges of abuses by law enforcement, the introduction of alternate legislation in Congress to revise or repeal sections of the act, as well as challenges in court.

Despite court challenges and public opposition to certain portions of the law, the vast majority of the Patriot Act is still good law. In May 2011, President Barack Obama signed extensions to several of the key, controversial provisions of the Patriot Act, including ones that provide for roving wiretaps, searches of business records (including libraries), and conducting surveillance of those suspected of engaging in lone-wolf terrorist acts.

What was the controversy about the Guantanamo detainees?

After the 9/11 attacks, the U.S. military began holding terror suspects at a detention center at the naval base at Guantanamo Bay, Cuba. (The U.S. Navy has occupied Guantanamo since the Spanish–American War, in 1898, paying an annual lease to Cuba.) The White House labeled the detainees "enemy combatants"; the controversy came when they were not charged with any crimes, yet they continued to be held.

The first detainees were transported to Guantanamo, or "Camp Gitmo," in January 2002, after being captured in Afghanistan. But no charges were made against any detainees until more than two years later, in February 2004. American lawyers challenged the Bush administration policy at Guantanamo, saying that it was a violation of the due process clause

171

of the U.S. Constitution. In January 2005 one district court judge agreed with the prosecution, saying that the Constitution applied to the prisoners: They could not be deprived of their liberty without due process.

The U.S. Supreme Court has ruled that certain aspects of Gitmo—or at least certain denials of process to those held captive at Gitmo violate the Constitution or some version of international law. In *Hamdan v. Rumsfeld* (2006), the U.S. Supreme Court ruled that certain military commissions set up by the Bush Administration to try those charged at Gitmo violated a key provision of the Geneva Conventions.

In *Boumediene v. Bush* (2008), the U.S. Supreme Court ruled that those at Gitmo did have a right to contest the constitutionality of their confinement in a U.S. federal court. "The laws and Constitution are designed to survive, and remain in force, in extraordinary time," Justice Anthony Kennedy wrote for the majority. The majority opinion drew a strong rebuke from dissenting Justice Antonin Scalia, who wrote: "The nation will live to regret what the court has done today."

Nevertheless, the facility at Guantanamo Bay remains open, although President Barack Obama had pledged to close the facility upon taking office.

Why did NATO respond to the 9/11 attacks?

The North Atlantic Treaty Organization (NATO) responded to the terrorist attacks on the United States because its charter states that an attack on any member nation is considered an attack on the alliance. The language is contained in Article 5 of the NATO Treaty, signed April 4, 1949, in Washington, D.C.: "The Parties agree that an armed attack against one or more of them in Europe or North America shall be considered an attack against them all and consequently they agree that, if such an armed attack occurs, each of them, in exercise of the right of individual or collective self-defense…will assist the Party or Parties so attacked." It was the first time Article 5 had been invoked by NATO since its founding.

On September 12, 2001, NATO convened a special meeting in response to the attacks on American soil and afterward issued a statement saying, in part, that the United States could rely on the support and assistance of NATO if it was found that the attack was directed from abroad. The organization's secretary general, Lord Robertson (1946–), strongly condemned the attacks and called for the "international community and the members of the Alliance to unite their forces in fighting the scourge of terrorism."

The invocation of Article 5 was confirmed by NATO on October 2, after U.S. Ambassador-at-Large Frank Taylor briefed the organization's chief decision-making body on the investigations into the terrorist attacks. The North Atlantic Council determined that the information provided by Taylor confirmed "that the individuals who carried out the attacks belonged to the world-wide terrorist network of al Qaeda, headed by Osama bin Laden and protected by the Taleban regime in Afghanistan."

At a press conference held October 8, Secretary General Lord Robertson announced NATO's full support for the U.S.-led invasion of Afghanistan. The following day it was confirmed that NATO assets had been deployed to the eastern Mediterranean to establish a presence in the region. But the alliance did not take a lead role in the military effort to oust the Taliban from Afghanistan.

What is al Qaeda?

Al Qaeda (Arabic, meaning "the base") is a global network of terrorists who banded together during the 1990s and proclaimed to be carrying out a holy war on non-Islamic nations. The group knows no national boundaries, though certain nations, including Afghanistan, were known to be al Qaeda strongholds. Led by the elusive Osama bin Laden (1957–2011), a wealthy exiled Saudi, the group conducted terrorist training programs in several Muslim (mostly Middle Eastern) countries and was funded by loyalists around the world. One of the United States' first actions following the September 11, 2001, terrorist attacks on the World Trade Center and Pentagon (which were later confirmed to have been carried out by al Qaeda operatives) was to freeze bank accounts of persons and organizations with suspected ties to the terrorist group.

The roots of al Qaeda can be traced to the Soviet invasion of Afghanistan in 1979, when thousands of Muslims, including bin Laden, joined the Afghan resistance. The ten-year conflict was a rallying point for Islamic extremists. Bin Laden returned home to Saudi Arabia in 1989, determined to perpetuate a holy war (jihad) by maintaining the funding, organization, and training that had made the Afghan resistance victorious against the Soviets. By the early 1990s he emerged as a leader in the Muslim world, proclaiming his goal to reinstate the Caliphate, a unified Muslim state. He also proclaimed the United States to be an enemy to Islam; he considered the nation responsible for all conflicts involving Muslims. The Saudi government rescinded his passport in 1994, and bin Laden fled his homeland. He eventually found safe harbor in Taliban-ruled Afghanistan. According to the report issued by the 9/11 Commission, bin Laden's declaration of war came in February 1998, when he and fugitive Egyptian physician Ayman al Zawahiri "arranged from their Afghanistan headquarters for an Arabic newspaper in London to publish what they termed a fatwa issued in the name of a 'World Islamic Front.'" The statement claimed that America had declared war against God and his messenger, and they called for retaliation.

Under bin Laden's direction, al Qaeda carried out several attacks on American targets, including the August 7, 1998, bombings of U.S. embassies in Kenya and Tanzania, which killed 258 and injured 5,000, and the September 11, 2001, attacks on the World Trade Center and Pentagon, which killed nearly 3,000 people. After the Global Coalition Against Terrorism, led by U.S. forces, launched its attack on Afghanistan in October 2001, bin Laden was believed to have fled for Pakistan. Capturing him and other al Qaeda leaders and operatives was the key objective of the United States in its efforts to dismantle the terrorist network.

What is the Taliban?

It is the ultraconservative faction that ruled Afghanistan from late 1996 until December 2001, when its government crumbled following a U.S.-led military campaign. The Persian word *taleban* means "students"; the group was made up of Afghan refugees who, during the Soviet invasion (1979–89), had fled their country for Pakistan, where they attended conservative Islamic religious schools. After the Soviet withdrawal from Afghanistan and amidst the unrest that ensued, the Taliban rose to prominence. They gained control of the nation region by region, eventually taking the capital of Kabul in 1996.

While in power, the group put into force strict laws based on a fundamental interpretation of Islam. The Taliban excluded women from Afghan society, and it allowed the nation to become a training ground for Islamic terror groups such as al Qaeda. Very few nations of the world recognized the Taliban government. Its human rights abuses, principally the complete disenfranchisement of women and girls, were decried by the international community. But the breaking point came after the September 11, 2001, terrorist attacks on the U.S. homeland: When the American government requested that the suspected mastermind of those attacks be extradited from Afghanistan to the United States, the Taliban refused. The group was forcibly ousted in the brief military campaign that followed. In December 2001 the United Nations (UN) convened a conference in Bonn, Germany, where leaders of anti-Taliban ethnic factions decided on a post-Taliban transitional government, led by Pashtun leader Hamid Karzai (1957–). (The Pashtuns are the dominant group in Afghanistan, representing about 42 percent of the population. The next largest group is the Tajik, which represents about 27 percent of the population in the highly fragmented nation of 28.5 million people.) Attendees also agreed to a UN-led peacekeeping operation. Though ethnic rivalries and sporadic conflicts continued under the transitional government, Afghanistan made strides in

Not all Afghanis supported the Taliban, not by any stretch of the imagination. This photo shows a group of opposition fighters led by Shah Massood organizing a strike against the Taliban in 1996.

building a stable, democratic government. One encouraging sign of reform came in March 2005, with the appointment of Habiba Sarabi (1956–), the first woman to become a provincial governor in Afghanistan history. Sarabi was chosen by the president for her post, which she assumed in late March.

However, the Taliban is still an active and dangerous insurgent force in Afghanistan. American military members, and those believed to aid or support the United States, are still targets for the remaining Taliban supporters.

When did the U.S.-led operation in Afghanistan begin?

Joined principally by the United Kingdom, the U.S.-led military strikes on Afghanistan began on October 7, 2001, twenty-six days after the terrorist attacks on the U.S. homeland. The goals were to weaken the Taliban government and root out terrorist cells in the Middle Eastern nation. Al Qaeda leader Osama bin Laden (1957–2011), the suspected 9/11 mastermind, was also a target. The strikes on Afghanistan, which the United States called Operation Enduring Freedom (OEF), were the first in the new war on terror.

OEF's primary goal—ousting the ruling Taliban government—was achieved relatively quickly. By mid-November, the combined efforts of the U.S. military, British, and

Afghanistan's Northern Alliance, managed to take control of major cities, including the capital of Kabul. In late December an interim government was established at a UN-convened conference in Bonn, Germany. In June 2002 Hamid Karzai (1957–) was overwhelmingly elected as transitional president by the loya jirga, the traditional Afghan assembly of ethnic leaders; the transitional government was to run Afghanistan until national elections could be held in 2004. Despite strides in establishing the new government, fighting continued in the rugged mountainous terrain of eastern Afghanistan. Operation Anaconda was the name given to the U.S. military's effort to combat Taliban pockets of resistance, root out terrorist cells, and capture key al Qaeda leaders, including Osama bin Laden (though he had reportedly fled to neighboring Pakistan). Violence also preceded the October 2004 election.

What are WMD?

WMD are weapons of mass destruction: nuclear, biological, or chemical weapons that can cause extensive casualties. The term emerged during World War II (1939–1945); the abbreviated "WMD" became part of everyday language in the late 1990s and early 2000s, as the world's superpowers and the United Nations turned their attention to serious threats posed by rogue states and terrorists in a post-Cold War society.

Following the launch of the 2003 Iraq war, WMD were regularly in the news. The Bush administration and its chief ally, British Prime Minister Tony Blair (1953–), faced sharp public criticism when no weapons of mass destruction were found in Iraq. The presence of WMD in that rogue state had been the justification for the controversial invasion. In 2004 President Bush appointed a bipartisan commission to look into why U.S. intelligence agencies had concluded that Iraq possessed WMD. In late March 2005 the commission released to the public an unclassified version of its report. The conclusion: Intelligence errors had overstated Iraq's WMD programs. It stated, "The daily intelligence briefings…before the Iraq war were flawed…. This was a major intelligence error." The commission outlined seventy-four recommendations to improve intelligence-gathering among the United States' fifteen spy agencies. The classified version of the report contained information on the intelligence community's assessments of the nuclear programs of many of the "world's most dangerous reactors." It also provided more details on intelligence concerning the al Qaeda terrorist network.

In Britain, the intelligence failures concerning Iraq spurred a years-long controversy, which damaged Blair's approval ratings and posed tragic consequences. In addition to the loss of life in Iraq, British weapons inspector David Kelly took his own life after publicly accusing the government of overstating the need for war. As in the United States, Britain took steps to tighten controls on its intelligence-gathering to prevent errors in judgment.

Despite the fact that no WMD were found in Iraq, the White House stood firm on the decision to invade Iraq. On September 11, 2004, the Office of the Press Secretary released a fact sheet titled, "Three Years of Progress in the War on Terror." The document stated in part, "We were right to go into Iraq. We removed a declared enemy of America, who had defied the international community for 12 years, and who had the capability of producing weapons of mass murder, and could have passed that capability to the terrorists bent on acquiring them. Although we have not found stockpiles of weapons of mass destruction, in the world after September 11th, that was a risk we could not afford to take."

175

When did Operation Iraqi Freedom begin?

The U.S.-led multinational military campaign in Iraq began on March 19, 2003, with air strikes on the capital of Baghdad; ground forces moved into southern Iraq from neighboring Kuwait. After taking the southern city of Basra, U.S. marines and army infantry moved northward, toward the capital. U.S. troops took control of Baghdad on April 9, after which images of gleeful Iraqis dismantling statues and other symbols of Saddam Hussein's despotic rule flooded the American media. Coalition forces, American troops, and U.S.-backed Kurdish fighters then pressed into northern Iraq, including Tikrit, Saddam's hometown and a loyalist stronghold. On April 14 Tikrit fell. The war seemed to be near conclusion, but the hard combat had only begun—and would continue for years, even after the end of major combat was declared.

When did the major combat phase of Operation Iraqi Freedom end?

President George W. Bush (1946–) declared an end to major combat on May 1, 2003. But the stabilization of Iraq was far from over; the fighting continued more than two years later, the result of an increasingly violent Iraqi insurgency. Faced with the ongoing resistance, in December 2004 the number of U.S. troops in the war-torn nation was increased from 130,000 to 150,000.

Most of the casualties occurred after the declared end of major combat: On April 8, 2005, the Pentagon reported that there had been 1,543 American fatalities in the war to date—1,174 in hostile actions and 369 in nonhostile actions, including accidents during routine maneuvers. Of the 1,543 U.S. military deaths, 1,404 died after the declared end of major combat, 1,065 of them from hostile action. More than 7,000 had been injured to date.

In addition to the American fatalities, the British military had reported eighty-six deaths as of early April 2005; Italy, twenty-one; Ukraine, eighteen; Poland, seventeen; Spain, eleven; Bulgaria, eight; Slovakia, three; Estonia, Thailand, and the Netherlands, two each; and Denmark, El Salvador, Hungary, Kazakhstan, and Latvia, one each.

The figures fueled criticism for the lingering war, with some observers wondering if stabilization was possible in the fractious nation. There were several factors contributing to the growing lists of casualties and injuries: Coalition forces were frequently ambushed in attacks from resistance fighters and suicide bombers; U.S. troops faced continued combat in parts of Baghdad and its outskirts; the southern towns of Najaf and Kufa were holdouts of resistance; and there was intense fighting in the Sunni cities of Fallujah, Ramadi, and Samarra, which remained under insurgent control even after the transfer of political authority from the United States to the interim Iraqi authority on June 28, 2004.

In October 2011, President Barack Obama announced that by the end of the year virtually all U.S. soldiers would leave Iraq, and the last troops left in December 2011.

When was Saddam Hussein captured?

The former Iraqi leader, known for his cruelty, was caught on December 14, 2003, eight months after the fall of Baghdad. Hussein (1937–2006) was found in Ad Dawr, about nine miles from his hometown of Tikrit. He was said to be hiding "like a rat," in a hole across the Tigris River from one of his palaces. His six-to-eight-foot bunker was equipped with a basic ventilation system and was camouflaged with bricks and dirt. A disheveled Hussein had in his possession about $750,000 as well as arms, which he did not use. The former dictator was taken into custody in what U.S. defense secretary Donald Rumsfeld called a "surprisingly peaceful manner." Despite that, Hussein reportedly remained defiant and unrepentant: When he was asked about the thousands of people killed and dumped into mass graves during his regime, he dismissed his victims as "thieves."

The news of his capture prompted jubilation in Baghdad and across the nation: Crowds of Iraqis flooded into the streets to celebrate the end of his brutal rule. But his hometown of Tikrit, considered a loyalist stronghold, remained quiet. The news of his capture was welcomed by leaders around the globe. In a short televised address from the White House, President Bush remarked that Hussein would "face the justice he denied to millions." Bush also reassured the Iraqi people that they would "not have to fear the rule of Saddam Hussein ever again." Hussein was held for questioning in Iraq. Upon the June 28, 2004, transfer of authority, Iraq was given legal custody of the former ruler, who became a criminal defendant instead of a prisoner of war. He was convicted by an Iraqi court of numerous charges of murder and sentenced to death by hanging. He was executed on December 30, 2006.

What was the Abu Ghraib prison scandal?

News of the atrocities of Abu Ghraib, where Iraqi prisoners were being held by members of the U.S. military during Operation Iraqi Freedom, first surfaced in April 2004 when shocking photographs began appearing in the American media. The photos depicted an array of hideous abuses, all of them in violation of the Geneva Conventions for the treatment of prisoners of war.

The deep troubles first surfaced in spring 2003 when International Red Cross and human rights groups complained that American troops had been mistreating Iraqi prisoners. The U.S. Army launched an investigation into its prison system; a fact-finding mission was eventually led by Major-General Antonio Taguba, who completed his report in February 2004. It stated that one police company at Abu Ghraib had committed "sadistic, blatant, and wanton criminal abuses." The Taguba report also found that "supervisory omission was rampant" at the prison. More investigations and reports followed, taking into account other prisons under Central Command. Some of the reports tied prisoner deaths to the abuses.

The scandal sent shockwaves around the world and sparked an intense debate about how such abuses could have happened. The tortures were labeled by some as "unauthorized actions taken by a few individuals." But others believed they were a manifestation of policy that had gone wrong. The scandal soon widened: By May 2004 British newspapers began reporting abuses by British troops. While Prime Minister Tony Blair (1953–) apologized for any mistreatment Iraqi prisoners may have suffered at the hands of British troops, President Bush went on Arabic television to denounce the abuses as "abhorrent"; he stopped short of an apology, saying that the mistreatment "does not represent the America that I know." Both nations moved quickly to bring charges against several soldiers shown in the pictures. The guilty verdicts, and subsequent sentences, began being handed down in May 2004. Between 2004 and 2006, eleven different American soldiers were court-martialed for their involvement in the scandal.

The prison scandals fueled criticism of the controversial war in Iraq. They also prompted a deadly backlash from the Arab world: Insurgents in Iraq began a series of kidnappings of

177

When was Saddam Hussein finally found?

In December 2004, almost two years after the war began, Hussein was found hiding in the cellar of an Iraqi house. He was in desperate condition, had gone unshaved for months, and he looked terrible, but he had nearly one million dollars in cash on his person.

Paul Bremmer, leader of the U.S. occupation, declared, "Ladies and gentlemen, we've got him." Hussein was turned over to the provisional Iraqi government. After a lengthy trial, he was found guilty of crimes against the nation and executed in May 2006.

Americans and British citizens working in Iraq, many of them ending in ghastly and widely publicized killings. Between spring 2004 and spring 2005 more than 200 foreigners were taken captive in Iraq; more than thirty of them were killed by their kidnappers.

Was the Iraq War finally over?

Not by a long shot. One would think that the execution of the tyrant might bring peace, but Iraq was bitterly divided between Sunni, Shi'ite, and Kurd. As well, many Iraqis had turned against the American occupiers, saying that had brought neither democracy nor running water. As a result, the Iraq War—which still was not an officially "declared" conflict—dragged on.

One naturally wonders how U.S. personnel were able to maintain their morale, and the short answer is that they did not do so. Many continued to serve, heroically, and to receive the appreciation of their fellow Americans, but the trials were severe for nearly all of them. Military suicides began to increase as early as 2004, and by 2010 they had exceeded all previous records. The Bush administration continued to stand firm in Iraq and maintained that democracy would be the result.

Did the Obama administration bring clarity to the situation in Iraq?

Not right away. Obama was elected by a slim margin, and unlike George W. Bush, he proceeded cautiously. Obama had promised, for example, to close the detention center at Guantanamo Bay immediately, but this did not happen. He began a slow reduction of U.S. forces in Iraq, but at the same time he kept a sharp eye on Afghanistan. Many of those who voted for him expressed their disappointment with Obama during his first year in office. The major change took place in 2010.

When did President Obama declare combat operations had ceased?

The magic date was assigned to September 1, 2010. A symbolic handover from American officials to Iraqis took place in Baghdad. It was announced that 50,000 uniformed Americans would remain in Iraq, but that they would be in support positions and would only be used in combat when the situation was dire.

Time magazine noted that the troops scheduled to go home were exhausted, but held their heads high. What had they accomplished? They had defeated Saddam Hussein's army in 2004, then taken down the Sunni insurgency in Fallujah, and finally they had defeated the

Shi'ite Mahdi army. To what extent the troops—men and women—had changed because of their experience was more difficult to say. Many went home with metal legs and arms or with synthetic compounds inside their bones, but there were internal changes as well. It was unlikely that anyone who served in Iraq for a long time would ever be completely the same.

For how long was Osama bin Laden able to evade the U.S. military?

President Bush had declared in 2001 that Osama bin Laden was wanted "dead or alive," but it took until the spring of 2011 for the terrorist leader to be tracked down. U.S. Special Forces acted on tips that led them to a hideout in northwest Pakistan. That country was a U.S. ally, making the matter more difficult, but President Obama gave the go-ahead, and he, Secretary of State Hillary Clinton, and other officials waited and watched as a Special Forces unit attacked the compound where Bin Laden was hiding. Osama bin Laden was killed in the firefight, and the American military chose to drop his body into the Indian Ocean rather than deliver it to any earthly burial.

Bin Laden's death closed a chapter in American foreign policy, but he had accomplished more than he knew. The United States, in the spring of 2011, was tangibly different from the nation of September 2001. Some of the changes were technical in nature—the country was awash in cell phones, for example—but there were psychological and social scars as well. Few Americans trusted their government to the same extent as ten years earlier, and a significant majority were pessimistic about the future. Some of this sentiment stemmed from the economic situation; the rest came from the ten-year war.

What was the Arab Spring?

In the early winter of 2010–2011, there was a marked rise in tension throughout the Arab World. Veteran observers, including those in the U.S. State Department, brushed off the early indicators of something really big because they had seen similar signs before. This time, however, both the leading Arab regimes and the United States were about to reap a whirlwind of discontent.

The fighting began in Tunisia, one of the smaller Arab nations. Eight demonstrators were killed in early January of 2011; their deaths led to a full-fledged revolution in that country. Within three weeks, President Ibn Saud, who had been in power for twenty-seven years, was forced to step down from office. By then, the student uprisings had spread to Cairo.

Was that it for the war in Iraq?

So far as the majority of Americans went, that was it. Weary of hearing about either Iraq or Afghanistan, many Americans simply closed their ears to the news reports of the next three years, which suggested that both the Taliban and Iraqi insurgents were once more on the rise. Even a terrible civil war in Syria—beginning in 2012—could not rouse Americans from their slumber, and it was difficult to blame them. President Obama swayed first one way and then the next on Syria: he was unable to develop a coherent foreign policy toward that nation.

179

Were the Arab Spring protestors mainly students?

Students were at the vanguard, but it is fair to say that many other young people, and quite a few middle-aged protesters as well, were ready to join the movements spreading throughout the Arab world. Discontent had built and simmered for more than a generation, with millions of young people seeking the right moment to chastise their dictators. The key difference in 2011, as opposed to, say, 1991, was that the young people had modern technology, including cell phones and computers, with which to coordinate their actions.

The results were stunning. The leader of Tunisia fell first and was followed by Egypt's Hosni Mubarak (governed 1981–2011), who had been in power ever since the death of Anwar Sadat in 1981. Bashar al-Assad managed to hang on in Syria, but that nation soon degenerated into a terrible civil war that practically ruined the country. About the only Arab regime that remained truly unaffected was Saudi Arabia, and this is because the state-controlled police turned out early enough to thwart the protestors.

What was the situation in the Middle East in 2014?

Americans, on the whole, were utterly tired of hearing about Iraq and Afghanistan. Even so, they were shocked, in the early summer of 2014, to learn that a new movement which seemed to combine all the worst aspects of their Middle Eastern foes had arisen. Known as the Syria-Iraq movement, this appeared to be a spontaneous uprising of those who wanted to combine the Arab regimes in Syria and Iraq.

Acting with speed and astonishing ease, the militia of this new group practically put the newly formed Iraqi army out of business in June and July 2014. Entire regiments of the Iraqi army simply folded when matched up against the militia, and it seemed for a time that Baghdad itself might fall to the insurgents. President Obama declared that Iraq had to win this war, and he approved the sending of thousands of Americans to act as military advisers.

What is ISIS/ISIL?

The rise of ISIL (Islamic State of Iraq and the Levant), or ISIS (Islamic State of Iraq and Syria), was little short of amazing. In 2013, most Americans had heard neither the name nor the goals of the movement; during the late summer of 2014, however, Americans became alarmed as they heard of beheadings and mass executions. At one point it seemed possible that the ISIL forces would capture Baghdad; this was thwarted by the use of American air power. Whether ISIL would continue to be a major power in the region was open to question, but as of the autumn of 2014, its forces controlled one-sixth of Syria and one-quarter of Iraq.

ISIL was the original name of this group of extremists, with the name ISIS coming shortly afterward. In either case, the aims and goals of the leaders are the same: the creation of a pan-Islamic state where Sharia law—a fundamentalist version of that taught by the Prophet Muhammad—would prevail.

Who is Edward Snowden?

In the early summer of 2013, Americans were stunned and dismayed to learn that many government secrets had been leaked to international organizations, much of the work being done by twenty-nine-year-old Edward Snowden (1983–). Born in New Jersey, he enjoyed a normal middle-class life and education, and he joined the Central Intelligence Agency in

What role will technology like the Internet play in warfare?

Many nations have already been using computers to spy on both enemies and friends. Experts in programming learn how to hack into business and government databases to extract information on everything from new weapons to where personnel are stationed. Countries like China, for instance, also conduct espionage using computers and can also track the activities of dissidents. In the United States, the National Security Agency (NSA) has been a concern to American citizens who believe they are being spied on even when they are not suspected terrorists or foreign agents.

2006. In 2012 to 2013, while working as a contractor for the National Security Agency (NSA), Snowden chose to leak hundreds of thousands of classified documents. When questioned, he replied that he and his generation of young Americans believed that surveillance was both illegal and immoral and that he was pleased to use the most modern technology to thwart his former employers. Whether Snowden is a hero (as some claim), a villain (as others assert), or simply a misguided person depends very much on the worldview of the person making the pronouncement. As of this printing, Snowden is currently hiding in Russia from American authorities.

How dominant was the U.S., militarily speaking, in the year 2014?

American defense spending—in the neighborhood of 600 billion annually—slightly exceeded that of all other nations in the world combined. The U.S. active military—including all sections of the Armed Forces—came to slightly more than 1.5 million. And to take a special case, that of naval power, the United States possessed nineteen aircraft carriers—most of them state of the art—compared to twelve for the rest of the world combined.

Was there a number two?

No. In 2014, the United States stood ahead of all friends and foes by such a margin that no one could really count as an effective second. Some people might point to the British, French, and Russian militaries, but all of them combined would not even come close to equaling American military power. Others might look to the People's Republic of China, which certainly had performed amazing economic feats, but which still lagged the United States by a long way, militarily speaking. America's world position in 2014 was rather like that of the doleful answer given to Queen Victoria. In 1852, while her royal yacht was positioned to observe the America's Cup sailing race, Queen Victoria commented that she saw that the United States was first. And who was second, she inquired? "Madam, there is no second" was the sad answer.

What was the state of guerrilla or insurgency actions around the world in 2014?

The world seemed quieter in 2014 than usual, but it was the calm that comes after many years of covert actions, insurgencies, and counterinsurgencies. Experts pointed to certain areas of success, such as the Democratic Republic of the Congo, which was more peaceful than at any time in the previous decade.

181

POLITICAL AND SOCIAL MOVEMENTS

How old is nationalism?

Nationalism, a people's sense that they belong together as a nation because of a shared history and culture, and often because of a common language and/or religion, emerged at the close of the Middle Ages (500–1350). By the 1700s several countries, notably England, France, and Spain, had developed as "nation-states," groups of people with a shared background who occupy a land that is governed independently. As political and economic entities, the nation-states were preceded by fiefs, tribes, city-states, and empires, which overlapped each other as organizing units, dividing peoples' loyalties.

By the 1800s nationalism had become a powerful force, and the view took hold that any national group has the right to form its own state. Because of this belief, called national self-determination, some nations achieved independence (including Greece, which gained freedom from Turkey in 1829, and Belgium, which won self-rule from the Netherlands in 1830); others formed new, larger countries (both Italy and Germany were created by the unification of numerous smaller states, Italy in 1870 and Germany one year later); and still others carved smaller states out of great empires (for example, the breakup of the Austro-Hungarian Empire following World War I [1914–18] resulted in the formation of the independent countries of Austria, Hungary, Czechoslovakia, Poland, and, later, Yugoslavia, which itself has now broken up into Slovenia, Macedonia, Croatia, Kosovo, Bosnia and Herzegovina, and Montenegro).

In the United States, nationalism in the 1800s took the form of Manifest Destiny, the mission to expand the country's boundaries to include as much of North America as possible. By the end of the century the United States had claimed all of its present-day territory.

While nationalism is a source of pride and patriotism and has had many positive results, some leaders (notably German dictator Adolf Hitler [1889–1945]) have carried it to extremes, initiating large-scale movements that resulted in the persecution of other peoples and in the hideous practice of ethnic cleansing.

183

The boundary lines that were drawn on the world map at the end of the twentieth century were largely the result of nationalistic movements, some of which had resulted in conflicts—and some of which remained unresolved.

What was the nonviolent Indian reform movement?

It was the movement led by Indian nationalist leader Mohandas Gandhi (1869–1948), whose methods of protest included staging boycotts, fasting, conducting prayer vigils, and visiting troubled areas in an attempt to end conflicts. Gandhi, whom the people called Mahatma (meaning "great-souled"), was determined to bring about change in India—to bring an end to British control of the country and to topple the ages-old caste system (the strict social structure) there. Gandhi believed that it took great courage to not engage in violence, and he began campaigns of passive resistance, which he called satyagraha (meaning "firmness in truth").

Gaining a wide following, Gandhi's acts of civil disobedience did bring about changes in his homeland, where he is revered as the founder of an independent India (1947). He remained faithful to his nonviolent beliefs throughout his life. He also adhered to a firm policy of religious tolerance. It was for this reason that the spiritual and nationalist leader was killed by Nathuram Godse, a Hindu extremist in 1948.

What was the May Fourth movement?

It was a mass movement that emerged in China after May 4, 1919, when students in Beijing protested one of the outcomes of the peace conference held at Versailles earlier that year to officially settle World War I (1914–1918): Japan, which had seized German territories in China during the war, was given control of the holdings. Student demonstrators criticized a weakened Chinese government for allowing the Japanese occupation. Following the death of powerful leader Yuan Shih-k'ai (1859–1916), the country's central government crumbled. In northern China local military leaders (called warlords) rose to power, continually challenging the authority of the capital at Beijing. Meanwhile, revolutionary leader Sun Yat-sen (1866–1925) had begun promoting his three great principles—nationalism, democracy, and people's livelihood—in southern China, where he gained the support of military leaders in the region. At about the same time, Chinese intellectuals had begun attacking traditional culture and society, urging government reforms and the modernization of industry. The May Fourth movement fanned the fires of revolution. The movement would have far-reaching—and unforeseen—results. And some might argue that the story has not yet played out.

In 1919 Sun reorganized the Kuomintang (Nationalist) Party and began recruiting student followers. Two years later he became president of a self-proclaimed national government of the Southern Chinese Republic, establishing the capital at Guangzhou (Canton). His sights were set on conquering northern China. Intent on toppling the northern warlords to reunify the country, in 1924 Sun began cooperating with both the Soviets and the Communist groups that had been formed by students following the 1919 protest. Under Sun's leadership, the Nationalist Party began preparing for war. But Sun, who is regarded as the "father of modern China," would not live to see the culmination of his plans: He died of cancer in 1925. Under military leader Chiang Kai-shek (1887–1975), the Kuomintang turned on its Communist members, whose leaders fled in fear of the generalissimo. In 1928, following a two-year military campaign, Chiang led the nationalists to capture Beijing, reuniting China under one government for the first time in twelve years. His rule of China lasted until 1949, when Communists won control of the mainland and Mao Tse-tung (1893–1976) became the first chairman of the People's Republic of China. The expelled Chiang and his followers established a Chinese nationalist government on the island of Taiwan. Back on the mainland, Mao's Great Leap Forward, his massive collectivization of agriculture and industry, brought economic failure and a two-year famine to China in the late 1950s.

What is Solidarity?

It was a worker-led movement for political reform in Poland during the 1980s which contributed greatly to the downfall of communism. The movement was inspired by Pope John Paul II's June 1979 visit to his native Poland, where, in Warsaw, he delivered a speech to millions, calling for a free Poland and a new kind of "solidarity." (As scholar and author Timothy Garton Ash noted, "Without the Pope, no Solidarity. Without Solidarity, no Gorbachev. Without Gorbachev, no fall of Communism.")

Lech Walesa

Shipyard electrician Lech Walesa (1943–) became the leader of Solidarity, formed in 1980 when fifty labor unions banded together to protest Poland's Communist government. The unions staged strikes and demonstrations. By 1981 Solidarity had gained so many followers that it threatened Poland's government, which responded (with the support of the Soviet Union) by instituting martial law in December of that year. The military cracked down on the activities of the unions, abolishing Solidarity in 1982 and arresting its leaders, including the charismatic Walesa. But the powerful people's movement, which had also swept up farmers (who formed the Rural Solidarity), could not be suppressed. Martial law was lifted in mid-1983 but the government continued to exert control over the people's freedom. That year Walesa received the Nobel Peace Prize for his efforts to gain workers' rights and prevent violence. Solidarity continued its work for reform.

In 1989, with the collapse of communism on the horizon (people's movements in Eastern Europe had combined with Soviet leader Mikhail Gorbachev's policy of glasnost to herald the system's demise), the Polish government reopened negotiations with Solidarity's leadership. Free elections were held that year, with the labor party candidates gaining numerous seats in Parliament. In 1990 Walesa was elected president, at which time he resigned as chairman of Solidarity. Poland's Communist Party was dissolved that year.

What was the anti-apartheid movement?

It was an international movement to throw out the decades-old system of racial segregation in South Africa. (The word apartheid means "separateness" in the South African language of Afrikaans.) Under apartheid, which was formalized in 1948 by the Afrikaner Nationalist Party, minority whites were given supremacy over nonwhites. The system further separated nonwhite groups from each other so that mulattoes (those of mixed race), Asians (mostly Indians), and native Africans were segregated. The policy was so rigid that it even separated native Bantu groups from each other. Blacks were not allowed to vote, even though they were and are the majority population. Apartheid was destructive to the society as a whole and drew protest at home and abroad. But the South African government adhered to the system, claiming it was the only way to keep peace among the country's various ethnic groups. In 1961 the government even went so far as to withdraw from the British Commonwealth in a dispute over the issue.

Protesters against apartheid staged demonstrations and strikes, which sometimes became violent. South Africa grew increasingly isolated as countries opposing the system refused to trade with the apartheid government. The no-trade policy had been urged by South African civil rights leader and former Anglican bishop Desmond Tutu (1931–), who led a nonviolent campaign to end apartheid and in 1984 won the Nobel Peace Prize for his efforts. During the 1980s the economic boycott put pressure on the white minority South African government to repeal apartheid laws. It finally did so, and in 1991 the system of segregation was officially abolished.

White South African leader F. W. de Klerk (1936–), who was elected in 1989, had been instrumental in ending the apartheid system. In April 1994 South Africa held the first elections in which blacks were eligible to vote. Not surprisingly, black South Africans won control of Parliament, which in turn elected black leader Nelson Mandela (1918–) as president; de Klerk was retained as deputy president. The two men won the Nobel Peace Prize in 1993 for their efforts to end apartheid and give all of South Africa's peoples full participation in government. In 1996 the work of the Truth and Reconciliation Commission, a panel headed by Desmond Tutu and charged with investigating the political crimes committed under apartheid, began work. Its investigations continued into 1999, with many findings proving controversial.

Who was Stephen Biko?

Stephen Biko (1946–1977) was a black leader in the fight against South African apartheid and white minority rule. In 1969 Biko, who was then a medical student, founded the South African Student's Organization, which took an active role in the black consciousness movement, a powerful force in the fight against apartheid. Preaching a doctrine of black self-reliance and self-respect, Biko organized protests, including antigovernment strikes and marches. Viewing such activities as a challenge to its authority and fearing an escalation of unrest, in August 1977, the white government had Biko arrested. Within one month, he died in prison. Evidence indicated he had died at the hands of his jailers, a revelation that only cemented antigovernment sentiment. Along with Nelson Mandela (1918–), who was imprisoned in South Africa from 1962 to 1990 for his political activities, Biko became a symbol of the antiapartheid movement, galvanizing support for racial justice at home and abroad.

What was the Soweto Uprising?

The Soweto Uprising referred to a protest by South African black school-aged youths that began on June 16, 1976. The youths protested the introduction of Afrikaans, a Dutch language, into their schools. They associated Afrikaans with the government's support of apartheid. More than 20,000 students participated in the protest, which resulted in more than 170 deaths. June 16 is now a public holiday, called Youth Day, in South Africa.

Tiananmen Square

What happened at China's Tiananmen Square?

In 1989 Beijing's Tiananmen Square, the largest public square in the world, became the site of a student protest and massacre. Three years before the demonstration, freedom of speech and other democratic beliefs began being espoused on university campuses. Increasing numbers of China's youth were demanding political reform. They found a sympathizer in the general secretary (the highest ranking officer) of the Communist Party, Hu Yaobang (1915–1989), who adhered to his liberal views, particularly concerning freedom of expression, despite criticism from conservatives in government. In January 1987 Hu was removed from his post; he died in April 1989, at which time students organized marches in his honor and demonstrated in favor of democratic reforms. On June 4, 1989, Chinese troops fired on the protesters in Tiananmen Square, killing more than 200 and later arresting anyone thought to be involved in China's pro-democracy movement. The actions raised fury around the world. International observers continued to monitor the tenuous situation in China, where evidence surfaced that the government was continuing its pattern of human rights violations.

THE ANTISLAVERY MOVEMENT

Which U.S. state was the first to abolish slavery?

Vermont was first, in 1777. On July 8 of that year Vermont adopted a state constitution that prohibited slavery. The first document in the United States to outlaw slavery, it read in part: "No male person, born in this country, or brought from over sea, ought to be holden by law, to serve any person, as a servant, slave or apprentice, after he arrives to the age of twenty-

187

one years, nor female, in like manner, after she arrives to the age of eighteen years, unless they are bound by their own consent, after they arrive to such age, or bound by law, for the payment of debts, damages, fines, costs, or the like." Vermont's constitution also gave suffrage to all men, regardless of race.

Vermonters were the first to put a black legislator in the state house, when Alexander Twilight (1795–1857) was elected as a representative in 1836. Twilight also earned another first: In 1823 he graduated from Vermont's Middlebury College to become the first black person in the nation to earn a college degree.

When did the antislavery movement begin?

In the United States, the campaign to prohibit slavery strengthened in the early 1800s. Across the Atlantic, abolitionists had successfully lobbied for the outlaw of slave trade in Great Britain by 1807. The following year, the U.S. government also outlawed the trade, but possession of slaves remained legal and profitable. In the 1830s the call to abolish slavery and emancipate slaves became an active movement in the United States, precipitated by a revival of evangelical religion in the North. Abolitionists, believing slavery to be morally wrong and in violation of Christian beliefs, called for an end to the system, which had become critical to the agrarian economy of the southern states, where plantations produced cotton, tobacco, and other crops for domestic and international markets.

Who were the leaders of abolition?

Leaders of the antislavery movement included journalist William Lloyd Garrison (1805–1879), founder of the influential antislavery journal *The Liberator* and of the American Anti-Slavery Society (established 1833); brothers Arthur (1786–1865) and Lewis (1788–1873) Tappan, prominent New York merchants who were also founders of the American Anti-Slavery Society; and Theodore Dwight Weld (1803–1895), leader of student protests, organizer of the American and Foreign Anti-Slavery Society, and author of *The Bible Against Slavery* (1837) and other abolitionist works.

Another leading abolitionist was a black man named Frederick Douglass. His *Narrative of the Life of Frederick Douglass, An American Slave* became a leading abolitionist book. The autobiography inspired many to join the abolitionist movement.

Underground Railroad conductor Harriet Tubman (c. 1820–1913) worked against slavery by helping to free hundreds of blacks who escaped slavery in the South, and headed for northern states and Canada. Writers such as Harriet Beecher Stowe (1811–1896), author of *Uncle Tom's Cabin* (1851–52), helped strengthen the abolitionist cause and were instrumental in swaying public sentiment. In the hands of some activists, the movement became violent: In 1859 ardent abolitionist John Brown (1800–1859) led a raid on the armory at Harpers Ferry (in present-day West Virginia), which proved a failed attempt to emancipate slaves by force.

What did the founding of Liberia have to do with the antislavery movement?

With the goal of transporting freed slaves back to their homeland, members of the American Colonization Society (organized 1816–17), made land purchases on the West African coast. The holdings were named Liberia, a Latin word meaning "freedom." The first black Americans arrived there in 1822. But the society's plan was controversial; even some abolitionists and blacks opposed it, as they believed the only answer to the question of slavery was to eradicate it from the United States and extend the full rights of citizenship to the freed slaves in their new American home.

Nevertheless, by 1860 11,000 freed black slaves from the United States had been settled there; eventually a total of 15,000 made the transatlantic voyage to a secured freedom in Liberia. The country was established as an independent republic on July 26, 1847.

Why did President Lincoln issue the Emancipation Proclamation before the end of the Civil War?

As the war raged between the Confederacy and the Union, it looked like victory would be a long time in the making: In the summer of 1862 things seemed grim for the federal troops when they were defeated at the Second Battle of Bull Run (which took place in northeastern Virginia on August 29–30). But on September 17, with the Battle of Antietam (in Maryland), the Union finally forced the Confederates to withdraw across the Potomac into Virginia. That September day was the bloodiest of the war. President Abraham Lincoln (1809–1865) decided that this withdrawal was success enough for him to make his proclamation, and on September 22, he called a cabinet meeting. That day he presented to his advisers the Preliminary Emancipation Proclamation.

The official Emancipation Proclamation was issued later, on January 1, 1863. This final version differed from the preliminary one in that it specified emancipation was to be effected only in those states that were in rebellion (i.e. the South). This key change had been made because the president's proclamation was based on congressional acts giving him authority to confiscate rebel property and forbidding the military from returning slaves of rebels to their owners.

Abolitionists in the North criticized the president for limiting the scope of the edict to those states in rebellion, for it left open the question of how slaves and slave owners in the loyal (Northern) states should be dealt with. Nevertheless, Lincoln had made a stand, which served to change the scope of the Civil War (1861–1865) to a war against slavery.

On January 31, 1865, just over two years after the Emancipation Proclamation, Congress passed the Thirteenth Amendment, banning slavery throughout the United States. Lincoln, who had lobbied hard for this amendment, was pleased with its passage. The Confederate states did not free their four million slaves until after the Union was victorious (on April 9, 1865).

When was slavery outlawed in Europe?

The slave trade ended in Britain in 1807, when authorities agreed with the growing number of abolitionists (those who argued that slavery is immoral and violates Christian beliefs) and outlawed the trade. In 1833 slavery was abolished throughout the British colonies as the culmination of the great antislavery movement in Great Britain. In the United States, the slave trade was prohibited in 1808, but possessing slaves was still legal. Consequently, trade on the black market continued until Britain stepped up its enforcement of its antislavery law by conducting naval blockades and surprise raids off the African coast, effectively closing the trade. The slave trade as it had been known officially came to an end after 1870, when it was outlawed throughout the Americas. Throughout the world, the United Nations works to abolish slavery and other systems of forced labor.

THE CIVIL RIGHTS MOVEMENT

What was the Niagara movement?

It was a short-lived but important African American organization that advocated "the total integration of blacks into mainstream society, with all the rights, privileges, and benefits of other Americans." Founded in Niagara Falls, Ontario, in 1905, the Niagara movement was led by writer, scholar, and activist W. E. B. Du Bois (1868–1963), who was then a professor of economics and history at Atlanta University.

Observers described the organization as the anti-Bookerite camp: Educator Booker T. Washington (1856–1915), who rose from slavery to found Alabama's Tuskegee Institute (1881), believed change for black people should be effected through education and self-improvement—not through demand. Washington opposed the social and political agitation favored by some reformers; the Niagara movement, on the other hand, placed the responsibility for the nation's racial problems squarely on the shoulders of its white population.

The thirty branches of the Niagara movement challenged conservative politics of the so-called "Tuskegee Machine" led by Booker T. Washington. Though the Niagara organization dissolved in 1909, the National Association for the Advancement of Colored People (NAACP) was heir to its ideology and activism. Du Bois helped found that organization, and from 1910 to 1934 edited its official journal, *The Crisis*, in which he published his views "on nearly every important social issue that confronted the black community."

How did the civil rights movement begin?

It began on Thursday, December 1, 1955, as Rosa Parks (1913–2005), a seamstress who worked for a downtown department store in Montgomery, Alabama, made her way home on the Cleveland Avenue bus. Parks was seated in the first row that was designated for blacks. But the white rows in the front of the bus soon filled up. When Parks was asked to give up her seat so that a white man could sit, she refused. She was arrested and sent to jail.

Montgomery's black leaders had already been discussing staging a protest against racial segregation on the city buses. They soon organized, with Baptist minister Martin Luther King Jr. (1929–1968) as their leader. Beginning on December 5, 1955, thousands of black people refused to ride the city buses: the Montgomery Bus Boycott had begun. It lasted more than a year (382 days) and ended only when the U.S. Supreme Court ruled that segregation on the buses

The statue of Booker T. Washington at Tuskeegee University, Tuskeegee, Alabama.

was unconstitutional. The protesters and civil rights activists had emerged the victors in this—their first and momentous—effort to end segregation and discrimination in the United States.

Parks, who lost her job as a result of the arrest, later explained that she had acted on her own beliefs that she was being unfairly treated. But in so doing Parks had taken a stand and had given rise to a movement.

What was the nonviolence movement?

The Reverend Martin Luther King Jr. (1929–1968) was committed to bringing about change by staging peaceful protests. He had carefully studied the works of Matahma Gandhi and was impressed by the Indian man's nonviolent commitment against injustice. King led a campaign of nonviolence as part of the civil rights movement. King rose to prominence as a leader during the Montgomery Bus Boycott in 1955, when he delivered a speech that embodied his Christian beliefs and set the tone for the nonviolence movement, saying, "We are not here advocating violence…. The only weapon we have…is the weapon of protest." Throughout his life, King staunchly adhered to these beliefs—even after terrorists bombed his family's home. King's "arsenal" of democratic protest included boycotts, marches, the words of his stirring speeches (comprising an impressive body of oratory), and sit-ins.

With other African American ministers King established the Southern Christian Leadership Conference (1957), which assumed a leadership role during the civil rights movement.

The nonviolent protest of black Americans proved a powerful weapon against segregation and discrimination: A massive demonstration in Birmingham, Alabama, in 1963 helped sway public opinion and motivate lawmakers in Washington to act when news coverage of the event showed peaceful protesters being subdued by policemen using dogs and heavy fire hoses. In response to the outcry over the event in Birmingham, President John F. Kennedy (1917–1963) proposed civil rights legislation to Congress; the bill was passed in 1964. That same year Martin Luther King Jr. received the Nobel Peace Prize for his nonviolent activism.

King's policy of peace was challenged two years later when the Student Nonviolent Coordinating Committee (SNCC), tired of the violent response with which peaceful protesters were often met, urged activists to adopt a more decisive and aggressive stance and began promoting the slogan "Black Power." The civil rights movement, having made critical strides, became fragmented, as leaders, including the highly influential Malcolm X (1925–1965), differed over how to effect change.

On April 4, 1968, King was in Memphis, Tennessee, to show his support for a strike of black sanitation workers when he was gunned down outside his hotel room shortly after 5:30 in the evening. As news of King's death swept over the nation, blacks in 168 American cities and towns responded with rioting, setting fire to buildings, and looting white businesses.

Commenting on the terror, radical African American leader Stokely Carmichael said, "When white America killed Dr. King last night, she declared war on us." The chaos continued for a week: When the rioting ended on April 11, there were 46 dead (most of them black), 35,000 injured, and 20,000 jailed. Nevertheless, the violent crime that claimed the leader's life and the violence that erupted after news spread of his death have not, decades later, overshadowed King's legacy of peace and his message of the brotherhood of all people.

What were the sit-ins?

Sit-ins were a practice of challenging segregation laws by sitting in establishments reserved for whites only. African American students in Greensboro, North Carolina, conducted a sit-in at Woolworth's, which touched off a wave of sit-ins in various cities across the Southeast, including a well-planned wave of sit-ins in Nashville, Tennessee.

The Greensboro sit-in was not the first use of the practice. Some African American activists performed sit-ins in the late 1930s and early 1940s against various segregation laws in places such as libraries, lunch counters, and other places of public accommodation.

What were the "freedom rides"?

The "freedom rides" were a series of bus rides designed to test the U.S. Supreme Court's prohibition of segregation in interstate travel. In 1960, in the case of *Boynton v. Virginia*, the Supreme Court ruled in favor of a Howard University student who charged that segregation laws at the Richmond, Virginia, bus station violated federal antisegregation laws. The Congress of Racial Equality (CORE) decided to test the enforcement of the federal law by initiating the freedom rides.

On May 4, 1961, thirteen people, black and white, boarded a bus for the South. Meant as a nonviolent means of protest against local segregation laws, the riders were nevertheless met with violence: When the bus reached Montgomery, Alabama, on May 20, a white mob was waiting; the freedom riders were beaten. Rioting broke out in the city, and U.S. marshals were sent to restore order. The interracial campaign to desegregate transportation was ultimately successful, but government intervention was required to enforce the laws, as numerous southern whites had demonstrated that they weren't going to comply voluntarily.

When did Martin Luther King Jr. give his "I Have a Dream" speech?

The occasion was the March on Washington on August 28, 1963. That summer day more than a quarter million people—lobbying for congressional passage of a civil rights bill—gathered at the Lincoln Memorial to hear speakers, including the charismatic and influential King (1929–1968). His eloquent words defined the movement and still inspire those who continue to work for reforms. Among his words were these: "I have a dream that one day this nation will rise up and live out the true meaning of its creed, 'We hold these truths to be self-evident; that all men are created equal.'"

Congress did pass the Civil Rights Act, in 1964. The most comprehensive American civil rights legislation since the Reconstruction (the twelve-year period that followed the

The Rev. Dr. Martin Luther King Jr. giving his "I Have a Dream" speech during the March on Washington, August 28, 1963.

Civil War), the act outlawed racial discrimination in public places, assured equal voting standards for all citizens, prohibited employer and union racial discrimination, and called for equality in education.

Who was Fred Shuttlesworth?

Fred Shuttlesworth (1922–2011) was an African American leader of the civil rights movement. Based in Birmingham, Shuttlesworth was co-founder of the Southern Christian Leadership Conference (SCLC) and pastor of a Baptist church in Birmingham.

He survived several attempts on his life, including a dynamite attack on his home. He was not afraid to speak his mind to fellow civil rights leaders, such as King, or to white authorities. He seemingly had no fear of death, as he vowed to kill segregation—or be killed by it. He later moved to Cincinnati where he served as pastor of a church there for many years.

Who was Medgar Evers?

Medgar Evers (1925–1963) was a civil rights leader from Mississippi who challenged segregation, voting discrimination, and other unfair practices against African Americans during his short life. He was assassinated by Byron De La Beckwith, a member of the White Citizens Council who was not convicted until more than thirty years later, in 1994. Two previous prosecutions in 1964 had led to hung juries.

What horrible event occurred in Philadelphia, Mississippi?

Three civil rights workers—James Chaney, Andrew Goodman, and Michael Schwermer—were murdered in Philadelphia, Mississippi, by members of the Ku Klux Klan, including a deputy sheriff of Neshoba County, named Cecil Ray Price. The murders symbolized the injustices occurring against African Americans and other civil rights workers (as Goodman and Schwermer were white). The three victims had been part of "Freedom Summer"—an extensive effort to challenge voting discrimination and other civil rights abuses in Mississippi.

Eighteen men, including Price, were put on trial for conspiracy to violate federal civil rights. *Mississippi Burning* (1988) was a critically-acclaimed movie about the murders of the three civil rights workers. The movie was nominated for several Academy Awards.

How were southern blacks prevented from voting?

Besides intimidation, there were three different methods used in southern states in the early part of the century to disenfranchise black citizens: 1) the poll tax; 2) literacy tests; and 3) grandfather clauses. The poll tax required a voter to pay a fee in order to exercise the right to vote. Literacy tests were implemented as a prerequisite for voting; this method also kept many poorly educated whites (unable to pass the exam) from casting their ballots as well.

Most southern states also adopted legislation by which voting rights were extended only to those citizens who had been able to vote as of a certain date—a date when few if any black men would have been able to vote. Since these laws made provisions for said voters' descendants as well, they were dubbed "grandfather clauses." Such attempts to deny citizens the right to vote were made unlawful in 1964 (by the Twenty-fourth Amendment, which outlaws the poll tax in all federal elections and primaries), in 1965 (by the Voting Rights Act, which outlawed measures used to suppress minority votes), and in 1966 (when poll taxes at the state and local levels were also declared illegal). Literacy tests and grandfather clauses were also struck down as unconstitutional.

What is the history of the Ku Klux Klan?

The Ku Klux Klan (KKK) is a white supremacist group originally formed in 1865 in Pulaski, Tennessee, when Confederate Army veterans formed what they called a "social club." The first leader (called the "grand wizard") was Nathan Bedford Forrest (1821–1877), a former general in the Confederate Army, who, on April 12, 1864, in the final days of the Civil War, led a massacre of 300 black soldiers in service of the Union Army at Fort Pillow, Tennessee.

As the unofficial arm of resistance against Republican efforts to restore the nation and make full citizens of its black (formerly slave) population, the Ku Klux Klan waged a campaign of terror against blacks in the South during Reconstruction (1865–1877), the twelve-year period of rebuilding that followed the Civil War. Klan members, cloaked in robes and hoods to disguise their identity, threatened, beat, and killed numerous blacks. While the group deprived its victims of their rights as citizens, their intent was also to intimidate the entire black population and keep them out of politics. White people who supported the federal government's measures to extend rights to all black citizens also became the victims of the fearsome Klan. Membership in the group grew quickly, and the Ku Klux Klan soon had a presence throughout the South.

In 1871 the U.S. Congress passed the Force Bill, giving President Ulysses S. Grant (1822–1885) authority to direct federal troops against the Klan. The action was successful, causing the group to disappear—but only for a time. In 1915 the society was newly organized at Stone Mountain, Georgia, as a Protestant fraternal organization (called "The Invisible Empire, Knights of the Ku Klux Klan, Inc."), this time widening its focus of persecution to include Roman Catholics, immigrants, and Jews, as well as blacks. Members of all of these groups became the target of KKK harassment, which now included torture, whippings, and public lynchings. The group, which proclaimed its mission of "racial purity," grew in number and became national, electing its own to public office in many states, not just the South. But the society's acts of violence raised the public ire, and by the 1940s, America's attention focused on World War II (1939–1945), and the Klan died out or went completely underground. The group had another resurgence during the 1950s and into the early 1970s, as the nation struggled through the era of civil rights. The Klan still exists today, fostering the extremist views of its membership and staging marches to demonstrate its presence on the American landscape. Such demonstrations are often attended by anti-Klan protestors.

TEMPERANCE

What was the temperance movement?

Temperance was an American movement that began in the mid-1800s to outlaw the manufacture and consumption of alcoholic beverages, which were viewed by many to be a corrupting influence on American family life. By 1855 growing public support to ban liquor resulted in thirty-one states making it illegal to some degree. But a national policy of temperance was still sought by many. During the 1870s temperance became one of the cornerstones of the growing women's movement. As the nation's women, joined by other activists, mobilized to gain suffrage (the right to vote), they also espoused sweeping cultural changes. In 1874 a group of women established the Woman's Christian Temperance Union (WCTU); in 1895 the Anti-Saloon League was formed. Such societies, which grew out of a fundamentalist spirit, found an increasing voice and eventually influenced legislators, many of whom were "dry" candidates that the societies had supported, to take federal action. Even President Woodrow Wilson (1856–1924) supported prohibition, as one of the domestic policies of his New Freedom program.

The movement met with success on January 16, 1919, when the Eighteenth Amendment to the U.S. Constitution (1788) was ratified, forbidding people to make, sell, or transport "intoxicating liquors" in the United States and in all territories within its jurisdiction. Though Congress, which proposed the amendment on December 18, 1917, provided states with a period of seven years in which to ratify the amendment, it took just over a year for it to be approved, such was the prevailing spirit among lawmakers. After the amendment was made, Congress passed the Volstead Act to enforce it. But government nevertheless found prohibition difficult to enforce. Bootleggers (who made their own moonshine—illegal spirits, often distilled at night), rum runners (who imported liquor, principally from neighboring Canada and Mexico), and speakeasies (underground establishments that sold liquor to their clientele) proliferated. Soon organized crime ran the distribution of liquor in the country, whose citizens had not lost their taste for alcoholic beverages. Prohibition was a failure on many levels.

The government now found itself with a bigger problem. As the Federal Bureau of Investigation (FBI) and police worked to control and end mob violence, and as the country suffered through the early years of the Great Depression, lawmakers in Washington reconsidered the amendment.

On February 20, 1933, the U.S. Congress proposed that the Eighteenth Amendment be repealed. Approved by the states in December of that year, the Twenty-first Amendment declared the Eighteenth Amendment null, and the manufacture, transportation, and consumption of alcoholic beverages was again legal in the United States, ending the thirteen-year period of Prohibition. Herbert Hoover (1874–1964), president at the time of repeal, called prohibition a "noble experiment."

WOMEN'S RIGHTS

When did the American suffragist movement begin?

In the 1840s American women began organizing and, in increasing numbers, demanding the right to vote. The movement was started by women who sought social reforms, including outlawing slavery, instituting a national policy of temperance (abstinence from alcoholic beverages), and securing better work opportunities and pay. These reformers soon realized that in order to make change they needed the power of the vote.

Among the leaders of the suffragist movement was feminist and reformer Elizabeth Cady Stanton (1815–1902). She joined with antislavery activist Lucretia Mott (1793–1880)

The family home of Elizabeth Cady Stanton in Seneca Falls, New York.

to organize the first women's rights convention in 1848 in Seneca Falls, New York, launching the woman suffragist movement. In 1869 Stanton teamed with Susan B. Anthony (1820–1906) to organize the National Woman Suffrage Association. That same year, another group was formed: the American Woman Suffrage Association, led by women's rights and antislavery activist Lucy Stone (1818–1893) and her husband Henry Brown Blackwell (1825–1909). In 1870 the common cause of the two groups was strengthened by the passage of the Fifteenth Amendment, which gave all men, regardless of race, the right to vote. When the two organizations joined forces in 1890, they formed the National American Woman Suffrage Association (NAWSA).

The founders of the American women's movement were followed by a new generation of leaders, which included Stanton's daughter, Harriot Eaton Blatch (1856–1940), as well as Alice Paul (1885–1977), who founded the organization that became the National Woman's Party, and organizer and editor Lucy Burns (1879–1966), who worked closely with Paul.

The suffragists appealed to middle-class and working-class women, as well as to students and radicals. They waged campaigns at the state level, distributed literature, organized meetings, made speeches, and marched in parades. They also lobbied federal legislators, picketed, and chained themselves to the White House fence. When jailed, many resorted to hunger strikes and were sometimes met with cruel treatment. The suffragists' fight was a fierce one; the opposition played on the widespread belief that if given the right to vote, women would neglect the traditional duties of wife and mother.

The movement gained strength during World War I (1914–1918). As men went off to fight the war in Europe, the women at home demonstrated themselves to be intelligent and involved citizens in the life of the country. A wartime suffragist poster declared in one long column, "As a war measure, the country is asking of women service as…farmers, mechan-

There was mounting pressure, from inside and outside the Muslim world, for this to change. The issue was an important focal point for the Human Rights Watch, an international watchdog group. In October 2004 a high-ranking Egyptian cleric spoke out on the contentious issue, saying, "It is the right of a Muslim woman to vote for and speak her opinion about whoever serves public or greater interests." He went on to clarify that he was "talking about Muslim women in all Muslim countries, in Egypt, Kuwait, and others." In 2006, the United Arab Emirates granted women the right to vote.

Suffrage for women has been won country by country and decade by decade. Further, within many countries, rights have been extended only gradually; for example, beginning with local elections. The first nations to extend broad voting rights to women were New Zealand in 1893, Australia and South Wales in 1902, and Finland in 1906. In the 1910s women in several European and Scandinavian nations, including Austria, Denmark, Germany, Luxembourg, the Netherlands, Norway, Poland, and Russia, won the right to vote—largely as a result of World War I (1914–1918). The 1920s added not only the United States and the United Kingdom (to a voting status equal to men), but about a dozen other nations, including the former Czechoslovakia and Sweden. Every decade since has added more nations to the tally.

Women have the right to vote in some Muslim nations, including Indonesia, as seen here ina 2009 photo of a polling station in Tuban, Bali.

How old is feminism?

Feminists—people who believe that women should have economic, political, and social equality with men—have existed throughout history; such women are often described in literature and by history as being "women before their time." But as a movement, feminism, which is synonymous with the women's rights movement, did not get under way until the mid-1800s, when women in the United States and Great Britain began organizing and campaigning to win the vote.

Early feminists (and feminists today) were likely influenced by the revolutionary work titled *A Vindication of the Rights of Woman,* published in 1792 by British author and educator Mary Wollstonecraft (1759–1797; her daughter was writer Mary Shelley of *Frankenstein* fame). Wollstonecraft attacked the convention of the day, charging that it kept middle-class and upper-class women in a state of ignorance, training them to be useless. A staunch promoter of education (she was self-educated), Wollstonecraft is credited with being the first major philosophical feminist.

199

What is the ERA?

The ERA stands for the Equal Rights Amendment, a constitutional amendment proposed by Congress in 1972. It stated that "equality of rights under the law shall not be denied or abridged by the United States or any state on account of sex." In proposing the amendment, Congress gave the states ten years in which to ratify it.

But by 1982 only thirty-five of the necessary thirty-eight states had approved the amendment, which then died. The failure to ratify the ERA was the result of disagreement over how the language would be interpreted. Supporters believed the amendment would guarantee women equal treatment under the law; opponents feared the amendment might require women to forfeit the financial support of their husbands and require them to serve in the military.

THE BIRTH CONTROL MOVEMENT

How did the birth control movement get started?

The decline in death rates, which has meant an overall increase in the world population, gave rise to the birth control movement. Scientific advances during the eighteenth and nineteenth centuries resulted in better food supplies, improved control and treatment of diseases, and safer work environments for those living in developed countries. These improvements combined with progress in medicine to save and prolong human lives. During the 1800s, the birth rate, which in earlier times had been offset by the death rate, became a concern to many who worried that population growth would outstrip the planet's ability to provide adequate resources to sustain life.

In 1798 British economist and sociologist Thomas Robert Malthus (1766–1834) published his *Essay on the Principle of Population*, arguing that populations tend to increase faster than do food supplies. He thereby concluded that poverty and suffering are unavoidable. Malthus viewed only war, famine, disease, and "moral restraint" as checks on population growth. In spite of or because of Malthus's assertions, during the 1800s the idea of birth control as a practical method to keep population growth in check gained momentum.

Early in the 1900s the movement found a leader in American Margaret Higgins Sanger (1883–1966), whose personal experience as a nurse working among the poor had convinced her that limiting family size is necessary for social progress. She became convinced that unwanted pregnancy should be avoided by using birth control methods. It was—and remains—controversial. Even though the distribution of birth control information was illegal at the time, Sanger advised people on the subject. In 1914 she founded a magazine called *The Woman Rebel*, and she sent birth control information through the mail. She was arrested and indicted. But she was not deterred. In 1916 in Brooklyn, New York, Sanger founded the first birth control clinic in the United States. In 1921 she organized the first American Birth Control Conference, held in New York. That same year she founded the American Birth Control League, which later became the Planned Parenthood Federation of America. As public support for the movement increased, Sanger succeeded in getting laws passed that allowed doctors to disseminate birth control information to their patients.

In other countries, Sanger's work inspired similar movements, but developed nations continue to have lower birth rates than do developing nations. With the world population now exceeding 7 billion, the fear of overpopulation has prompted continued interest in birth control and family planning.

POPULISM, PROGRESSIVISM, AND THE LABOR MOVEMENT

What was populism?

A commoners' movement, in the United States populism was formalized in 1891 with the founding of the Populist Party, which worked to improve conditions for farmers and laborers. In the presidential election of 1892, the party supported its own political candidate, the former (third-party) Greenback candidate James B. Weaver (1833–1912). Though Weaver lost, the Populists remained a strong force. In the next presidential election, of 1896, they backed Democratic Party candidate William Jennings Bryan (1860–1925), a self-proclaimed commoner who was sympathetic to the causes of the Farmers' Alliances and of the National Grange (reform-minded agricultural organizations) as well as the nation's workers.

Bryan lost to William McKinley (1843–1901), and soon after the election the Populist Party began to fall apart, disappearing altogether by 1908. Nevertheless, the party's initiatives continued to figure in the nation's political life for the next two decades and many populist ideas were made into laws, including the free coinage of silver and government issue of more paper money ("greenbacks") to loosen the money supply, adoption of a graduated income tax, passage of an amendment allowing for the popular election of U.S. senators (the Constitution provided for their election by the state legislatures), passage of antitrust laws (to combat the monopolistic control of American business), and implementation of the eight-hour workday. Since the early 1900s political candidates and ideas have continued to be described as populist, meaning they favor the rights of and uphold the beliefs and values of the common people.

What was the Progressive movement?

It was a campaign for reform on every level—social, political, and economic—in the United States. It began during the economic depression that was brought on by the Panic of 1873 and lasted until 1917, when Americans entered World War I (1914–1918).

During the first 100 years of the U.S. Constitution (1788), federal lawmakers and justices proved reluctant to get involved in or attempt to regulate private business. This policy of noninterference had allowed the gap to widen between rich and poor. The turn of the century was a time in America when early industrialists built fantastic mansions while many workers and farmers struggled to earn a living; when tenement houses sprang up in urban areas to meet (albeit horribly inadequately) the housing needs made present by a steady stream of immigrants; and when labor unions, which had only recently begun to organize, were beset by outbreaks of violence, hurting their fight for better treatment by employers. Observing these problems, progressive-minded reformers, comprised largely of middle-class

Americans, women, and journalists (the so-called "muckrakers"), began reform campaigns at the local and state levels, eventually effecting changes at the federal level.

Progressives favored many of the ideas that had previously been espoused by the Populists, including antitrust legislation to bust up the monopolies and a graduated income tax to more adequately collect public funds from the nation's well-to-do businessmen. Additionally, Progressives combated corrupt local governments; dirty and dangerous working conditions in factories, mines, and fields; and inner-city blight. The minimum wage, the Pure Food and Drug Act, and Chicago's Hull House (which served as "an incubator for the American social work movement") are part of the legacy of the Progressive movement.

When did the U.S. labor movement begin?

It began in the early 1800s, when skilled workers, such as carpenters and blacksmiths, banded together in local organizations with the goal of securing better wages. By the time fighting broke out in the Civil War (1861–1865), the first national unions had been founded—again, by skilled workers. However, many of these early labor organizations struggled to gain widespread support and soon fell apart. But by the end of the century, several national unions, including the United Mine Workers (1890) and the American Railway Union (1893), emerged. In the last two decades of the 1800s, violence accompanied labor protests and strikes while opposition to the unions mounted. Companies shared blacklists of the names of workers suspected of union activities; hired armed guards to forcibly break strikes; and retained lawyers to successfully invoke the Sherman Anti-Trust Act (of 1890) to crush strikes—lawyers who argued that strikes interfered with interstate commerce, which was declared illegal by the Sherman legislation (which had not been the intent of the lawmakers).

In the early decades of the 1900s, unions made advances, but many Americans continued to view organizers and members as radicals. The climate changed for the unions during the Great Depression (1929–1941). With so many Americans out of work, many blamed business leaders for the economy's failure and began to view the unions in a new light—as organizations created to protect the interests of workers. In 1935 the federal government strengthened the unions' cause in passing the National Labor Relations Act (also called the Wagner Act), protecting the rights to organize and to bargain collectively (when worker representatives, usually labor union representatives, negotiate with employers). The legislation also set up the National Labor Relations Board (NLRB), which still works today to penalize companies that engage in unfair labor practices. The constitutionality of the act was challenged in court in 1937, but the Supreme Court upheld the legislation.

The unions grew increasingly powerful over the next decade: By 1945 more than one-third of all nonagricultural workers belonged to a union. Having made important gains during World War II (1939–1945), including hospital insurance coverage, paid vacations and holidays, and pensions, union leaders continued to urge workers to strike to gain more ground—something leaders felt was the worker's right amidst the unprecedented prosperity of the postwar era. But strikes soon impacted the life of the average American: Consumers faulted the unions for shortages of consumer goods, suspension of services, and inflated prices. Congress responded by passing the Labor-Management Relations Act (or the Taft-Hartley Act) in 1947, which limits the impact of unions by prohibiting certain kinds of strikes, setting rules for how unions could organize workers, and establishing guidelines for how strikes that may impact the nation's health or safety are to be handled.

What was the first big union?

The first national union of note was the Knights of Labor, founded by garment workers in Philadelphia, Pennsylvania, in 1869. Recruiting women, blacks, immigrants, and unskilled and semiskilled workers alike, the Knights of Labor's open-membership policy provided the organization with a broad base of support, something previous labor unions, which had limited membership based on craft or skill, lacked. The organization set its objectives on instituting the eight-hour workday, prohibiting child labor (under age fourteen), instituting equal opportunities and wages for women laborers, and abolishing convict labor. The group became involved in numerous strikes from the late 1870s to the mid-1880s.

At the same time, a faction of moderates within the organization was growing, and in 1883 it elected American machinist Terence Powderly (1849–1924) as president. Under Powderly's leadership, the Knights of Labor began to splinter. Moderates pursued a conciliatory policy in labor disputes, supporting the establishment of labor bureaus and public arbitration systems; radicals not only opposed the policy of open membership, they strongly supported strikes as a means of achieving immediate goals—including a one-day general strike to demand implementation of an eight-hour workday. In May 1886 workers demonstrating in Chicago's Haymarket Square attracted a crowd of some 1,500 people; when police arrived to disperse them, a bomb exploded and rioting ensued. Eleven people were killed and more than 1,000 were injured in the melee. For many Americans, the event linked the labor movement with anarchy. That same year several factions of the Knights of Labor seceded from the union to join the American Federation of Labor (AFL). The Knights of Labor remained intact for three more decades, before the organization officially dissolved in 1917, by which time the group had been overshadowed by the AFL and other unions.

How old is the AFL-CIO?

The roots of the American Federation of Labor-Congress of Industrial Organizations (AFL-CIO), today a federation of national unions, date to 1881 when the Federation of Organized Trade and Labor Unions was formed in Pittsburgh, Pennsylvania, by trade union leaders representing some 50,000 members in the United States and Canada. Reorganizing in 1886, the association of unions changed its name to the American Federation of Labor (AFL) and elected Samuel Gompers (1850–1924) president.

Unlike the open-membership policy of the Knights of Labor (from whom the AFL gained numerous members in 1886), the AFL determined to organize by craft: At the outset, its member unions included a total of 140,000 skilled laborers. Gompers, who had immigrated to America from England in 1863, and became the first registered member of the Cigar-Makers' International Union in 1864, had been active in labor for more than two decades. Once chosen as president of the AFL, Gompers remained in that office, with the exception of only one year, until his death in 1924. During this nearly forty-year period, he shaped the labor federation and helped it make strides by determining a general policy that allowed member unions autonomy. Unlike the Knights of Labor, which pursued long-term goals such as Knights leader Terence Powderly's abstract objective of making "every man his own master—every man his own employer," the AFL focused its efforts on specific, short-term goals such as higher wages, shorter hours, and the right to bargain collectively (when an employer agrees to negotiate with worker/union representatives).

In the 1890s the AFL was weakened by labor violence, which evoked public fears. A July 1892 strike at the Carnegie Steel plant in Homestead, Pennsylvania, turned into a riot between angry steelworkers and Pinkerton guards. The militia was called in to monitor the strike, which five months later ended in failure for the AFL-affiliated steelworkers. Nevertheless, under Gompers's leadership, membership of the AFL grew to more than one million by 1901 and to 2.5 million by 1917, when it included 111 national unions and 27,000 local unions. The federation collected dues from its members, creating a fund to aid striking workers. The organization avoided party politics, instead seeking out and supporting advocates regardless of political affiliation. The AFL worked to support the establishment of the U.S. Department of Labor (1913), which administers and enforces statutes promoting the welfare and advancement of the American workforce, and the passage of the Clayton Anti-Trust Act (1914), which strengthened the Sherman Anti-Trust Act of 1890, eventually delivering a blow to monopolies.

The CIO was founded in 1938. In the early 1930s several AFL unions banded together as the Committee for Industrial Organizations and successfully conducted campaigns to sign up new members in mass-production facilities such as the automobile, steel, and rubber industries. Since these initiatives (which resulted in millions of new members) were against the AFL policy of signing up only skilled laborers by craft (the CIO had reached out to all industrial workers, regardless of skill level or craft), a schism resulted within the AFL. The unions that had participated in the CIO membership drive were expelled from the AFL; the CIO established itself as a federation in 1938, officially changing its name to the Congress of Industrial Organizations.

In 1955, amidst a climate of increasing anti-unionism, the AFL and CIO rejoined to form one strong voice. Today the organization has craft and industrial affiliates at the international, national, state, and local levels, with membership totaling in the millions.

Who were the Wobblies?

The Wobblies were the early radical members of the Industrial Workers of the World (IWW), a union founded in 1905 by the leaders of forty-three labor organizations. The group pursued short-term goals via strikes and acts of sabotage as well as the long-term goal of overthrowing capitalism and rebuilding society based on socialist principles. One IWW organizer proclaimed that the "final aim is revolution." Their extremist views and tactics attracted national attention, making IWW and Wobblies household terms during the early decades of the twentieth century.

Founded and led by miner and socialist William "Big Bill" Haywood (1869–1928) and mine workers agitator Mary "Mother" Jones (1830–1930), the IWW aimed to unite all workers in a camp, mine, or factory for the eventual takeover of the industrial facility. The union organized strikes in lumber and mining camps in the West, in the steel mills of Pennsylvania, and in the textile mills of New England. The leadership advocated the use of violence to achieve its revolutionary goals and opposed mediation (negotiations moderated by a neutral third party), collective bargaining (bargaining between worker representatives and an employer), and arbitration (third-party mediation). The group declined during World War I (1914–1918), when the IWW led strikes that were suppressed by the federal government. The organization's leaders were arrested and the organization weakened. Haywood was convicted of sedition (inciting resistance to lawful authority) but managed to escape the country. He died in the Soviet Union, where he was given a hero's burial for his socialist views.

The IWW never rose again to the prominent status of its early, controversial days. Many accounts of the group's history cite its demise in the 1920s. But, according to its own statement, the organization continued to "enjoy a more or less continuous existence" into the twenty-first century. As the IWW prepared to celebrate its one-hundredth anniversary in 2005, it continued to promote its original goal of organizing workers by industry rather than trade. Under the IWW's scheme, workers around the world would organize into one big union divided into six camps (or "departments"): agriculture and fisheries, mining and minerals, general construction, manufacture and general production, transportation and communication, and public service. In the early 2000s the IWW had a few dozen member unions in the United States, as well as branches in Australia, Japan, Canada, and the British Isles.

Who was Eugene Debs?

Debs (1855–1926) was a radical labor leader who in 1893 founded the American Railway Union (ARU), an industrial union for all railroad workers. Debs was a charismatic speaker, but he was also a controversial figure in American life around the turn of the century. In 1894 workers at the Pullman Palace Car Company, which manufactured railcars in Pullman, Illinois (near Chicago), went on strike to protest a significant reduction in their wages. Pullman was a model "company town" where the railcar manufacturer, founded by American inventor George W. Pullman (1831–1897) in 1867, owned all the land and buildings, and ran the school, bank, and utilities. In 1893, in order to maintain profits following declining revenues, the Pullman Company cut workers wages by 25 to 40 percent, but did not adjust rent and prices in the town, forcing many employees and their families into deprivation. In May 1894 a labor committee approached Pullman Company management to resolve the situation. The company, which had always refused to negotiate with employees, responded by firing the labor committee members. The firings incited a strike of all 3,300 Pullman workers. In support of the labor effort, Eugene Debs assumed leadership of the strike (some Pullman employees had joined the ARU in 1894) and directed all ARU members not to haul any Pullman cars. A general rail strike followed, which paralyzed transportation across the country. In response to what was now being called "Deb's rebellion," a July 2, 1894, federal court order demanded all workers to return to the job, but the ARU refused to comply. U.S. president Grover Cleveland (1837–1908) ordered federal troops to break the strike, citing it interfered with mail delivery. The intervention turned violent.

Despite public protest, Debs, who was tried for contempt of court and conspiracy, was imprisoned in 1895 for having violated the court order. Debs later proclaimed himself a socialist and became leader of the American Left, running unsuccessfully for president as the Socialist Party candidate five times, in 1900, 1904, 1908, 1912, and 1920. He actively supported the causes of the International Workers of the World (IWW), a radical labor organization founded in 1905.

He was arrested again in 1918, after giving a speech in Canton, Ohio, in which he criticized the U.S. war effort and entry into World War I. He was convicted of violating the Espionage Act of 1917, because he compared the draft to slavery and told members of the crowd that they were no better than mere cannon fodder. President Warren G. Harding commuted his sentence in 1921.

Who was César Chávez?

Mexican American farm worker César Chávez (1927–1993) was a labor union organizer and spokesperson of the poor. Born in Arizona, his family lost their farm when he was just ten years old; they became migrant workers in California, where farm production—particularly of grape crops—depended on the temporary laborers. Chavez knew the migrant worker's life intimately, and as a young man he began working to improve conditions for his people. In 1962 he organized California grape pickers into the National Farm Workers Association. Four years later this union merged with another to form the United Farm Workers Organizing Committee, or UFWOC (the name was changed to the United Farm Workers of America, or UFW, in 1973). An impassioned speaker known for squishing bunches of grapes in his hands as he delivered his messages, Chavez went on to lead a nationwide boycott of table grapes, since growers had refused to accept the collective bargaining of the UFWOC. By the close of the 1970s, California growers of all crops had accepted the migrant workers' union, now called the United Farm Workers. Like Martin Luther King Jr., Chavez maintained that nonviolent protest was the key to achieving change.

A poster announcing the César Chávez Day celebration.

Why was the fire at the Triangle Shirtwaist Factory important to the labor movement?

The March 25, 1911, blaze, which killed 146 people (most of them women), prompted public outrage and led to the immediate passage of fire safety legislation and became a rallying cry for labor reforms.

The Triangle Shirtwaist Factory occupied the top three floors of a Manhattan office building. It was one of the most successful garment factories in New York City, employing some 1,000 workers, mostly immigrant women. But the conditions were hazardous: The space was cramped, accessible only via stairwells and hallways so narrow that people had to pass single-file; only one of the four elevators was regularly in service; the cutting machines in the workroom were gas-powered; scraps of fabric littered the work areas; the water barrels (for use in case of fire) were not kept full; and the no-smoking rule was not strictly enforced. In short, it was an accident waiting to happen.

When the fire broke out on a weekend (the cause is unknown since the building was charred so badly), about half of the employees were there. Smoke and fire, however, were not the only causes of death: In the panicked escape, people were trampled, fell in elevator shafts, jumped several stories to the pavement below, and were killed when a fire escape melted and collapsed.

While the fire happened during a time of labor reform, those reforms had not come soon enough to save the lives of the Triangle Shirtwaist Factory employees, who had been subjected to extremely poor and dangerous working conditions. The disaster became a rallying cry for the labor movement: Tens of thousands of people marched in New York City in tribute to those who had died, calling attention to the grave social problems of the day.

In New York State, the fire safety reforms for factories came right away: The legislature appointed investigative commissions to examine factories statewide, and thirty ordinances in New York City were enacted to enforce fire prevention measures. One of the earliest was the Sullivan-Hoey Fire Prevention Law of October 1911, which combined six agencies to form an efficient fire commission. Soon factories were required to install sprinkler systems.

The Triangle Shirtwaist Factory fire became an object lesson for the entire nation,

The Triangle Shirtwaist Factory fire in 1911 killed 146 workers because the building lacked safety features that would have saved lives.

prompting the consolidation of reform efforts. The much-needed labor reforms, which addressed the miserable working conditions, did not come until years later.

COUNTERCULTURE, CONSUMERISM, AND THE ENVIRONMENT

What was the Beat movement?

The post-World War II era bred unprecedented prosperity and an uneasy peace in the United States. Out of this environment rose the Beat generation, alienated youths who rejected society's new materialism and threw off its "square" attitudes to reinvent "cool." The Beat generation of the 1950s bucked convention, embraced iconoclasm, and attracted attention. Mainstream society viewed them as anarchists and degenerates. But many American youths listened to and read the ideas of its leaders, including writers Allen Ginsberg, Jack Kerouac (whose novel *On the Road* 1957, was the bible of the Beat movement), William Burroughs, and Lawrence Ferlinghetti. The "Beatniks," as they were dubbed by their critics, believed in peace, civil rights, and radical protest as a vehicle for change. They also embraced drugs, mystical (Eastern) religions, and sexual freedom—all controversial ideas during the postwar era. Beat writers and artists found their homes in communities like San Francisco's North Beach, Los Angeles's Venice Beach, and New York City's Greenwich Village. The movement merged—or some would argue, gave birth to—the counterculture movements of the 1960s, including the hippies. Beat literature is the movement's legacy.

Who were the hippies?

Most hippies of the 1960s and 1970s were young (fifteen to twenty-five years old), white, and from middle-class families. The counterculture (anti-establishment) movement advocated peace, love, and beauty. Having dropped out (of modern society) and tuned in (to their own feelings), these flower

The hippie counterculture thrived in the 1960s and early 1970s, but the era of free love and drugs led to disease and death that effectively dampened the mood of the movement.

children were as well known for their political and social beliefs as they were for their controversial lifestyle: They opposed American involvement in the Vietnam War (1954–1975) and rejected an industrialized society that seemed to care only about money; they favored personal simplicity, sometimes living in small communes where possessions and work were shared, or living an itinerant lifestyle, in which day-to-day responsibilities were few if any; they wore tattered jeans and bright clothing usually of natural fabrics, grew their hair, braided beads into their locks, walked around barefoot or in sandals, and listened to a new generation of artists including the Beatles, the Grateful Dead, Jefferson Airplane, Bob Dylan, and Joan Baez.

Some hippies were also known for their drug use: Experimenting with marijuana and LSD, some hoped to gain profound insights or even achieve salvation through the drug experience—something hippie guru Timothy Leary told them was possible. New York City's East Village and San Francisco's Haight-Ashbury neighborhood became havens of this counterculture. The movement began on American soil, but was soon embraced elsewhere as well—principally in Canada and Great Britain.

What are "Nader's Raiders"?

They were (and are) investigators working with American lawyer and consumer advocate Ralph Nader (1934–). With the help of his research team, Nader wrote the landmark work *Unsafe at Any Speed*, in 1965; it charged that many automobiles weren't as safe as they should be or as consumers had the right to expect them to be. In part the book was responsible for passage in 1966 of the National Traffic and Motor Vehicle Safety Act, which set motor vehicle safety standards. Nader has continued his watchdog work, founding the Public Citizen Organization, which researches consumer products, promotes consumer awareness, and works to influence legislators to improve consumer safety.

While Nader may be the most recognizable face of consumer advocacy, the movement's roots predate his activism. As the consumer age dawned at the end of the 1800s and early

1900s, when mass-production techniques came into wide use, some observers decried industry standards (or lack thereof) that put the public who used their products at risk. The muckraking journalists of the early twentieth century disclosed harmful or careless practices of early industry, raising awareness and bringing about needed reforms. Upton Sinclair (1878–1968), for example, penned the highly influential novel *The Jungle* (1906), revealing scandalous conditions at meat-packing plants.

The public was outraged; upon reading Sinclair's work, President Theodore Roosevelt (1858–1919) ordered an investigation. Finding the novelist's descriptions to be true to life, the government moved quickly to pass the Pure Food and Drug Act and the Meat Inspection Act that same year (1906). Industry watchdogs continued their work in the early decades of the century: In 1929 Consumers' Research Inc. was founded, and in 1936, the Consumers Union was formed; both of these independent organizations test and rate consumer products. (Consumers Union publishes its reports in the monthly magazine *Consumer Reports*.)

Such consumer advocacy has served to heighten public awareness, compelling industry to make changes and improving the safety of products in general. Abuses still occur, but at roughly one hundred years into the consumer age, the work of consumer watchdogs like Nader's Raiders has made the consumer experience far less risky than it once was.

What did *Silent Spring* have to do with the environmental protection movement?

The 1962 work, by American ecologist Rachel Carson (1907–1964), cautioned the world on the ill effects of chemicals on the environment. Carson argued that pollution and the use of chemicals, particularly pesticides, would result in less diversity of life. The best-selling book had wide influence, raising awareness of environmental issues and launching green (environmental protection) movements in many industrialized nations.

What is the Kyoto Protocol?

It is an environmental agreement signed by 141 nations that agree to work to slow global warming by limiting emissions, cutting them by 5.2 percent by 2012. Each nation has its own target to meet. The protocol was drawn up December 11, 1997, in the ancient capital of Kyoto, Japan, and went into effect on February 16, 2005. The United States is not among the signatories: American officials said the agreement is flawed because large developing countries including India and China were not immediately required to meet specific targets for reduction. Upon the protocol's enactment, Japan's prime minister called on non-signatory nations to rethink their participation, saying that there was a need for a "common framework to stop global warming." Environmentalists echoed this call to action.

What is the Occupy movement?

The Occupy movement is an international movement designed to address social and economic disparities and to make the economic power structure more equitable. The Occupy Movement uses the slogan "We are the 99 percent," signifying that the power structure and financial empires of world governments serve the interests of the extremely wealthy 1 percent of the world.

Occupy movements or protests have occurred throughout the world. For example, 200,000 people protested in Rome, Italy, in October 2011, protesting economic conditions.

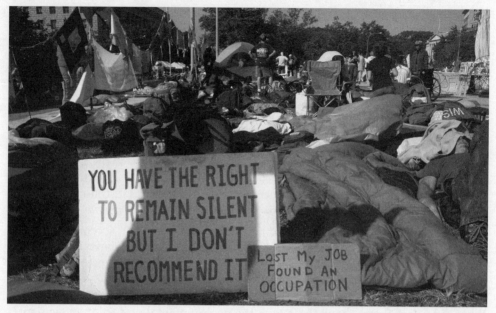

A campsite for Occupy DC (part of the Occupy Wall Street movement) protesters in Freedom Plaza, Washington, D.C.

Occupy Wall Street, which took place in the Wall Street District in New York City's Zuccotti Park in September 2011, marked the movement in the United States.

Occupy movements have sprung up in various cities across the United States. Occupiers camp out on government property, carrying signs and creating symbolic tents to send the message that they will occupy government land until the government responds to the financial wrongs and abuses of the country.

RELIGION AND PHILOSOPHY

RELIGION

What are the basic beliefs of Buddhism?

Buddha taught the Four Noble Truths: existence is suffering; the cause of suffering is desire; through total transcendence (called nirvana) one may suspend suffering; and to end suffering one must follow a certain path—called the Eightfold Noble Path. The path prescribes moral conduct, specifically: 1) knowing the truth; 2) resolving to resist evil; 3) using speech properly—so as not to hurt others; 4) demonstrating respect for life, morality, and property through ones actions; 5) working in a job that does not harm others; 6) making an effort to free one's mind of evil; 7) mindfulness (or controlling one's thoughts and feelings); and 8) concentration. In some places, the beliefs and practices of Buddhism are combined with those of Hinduism and the Shinto religion.

Who is the Dalai Lama?

The Dalai Lama is the spiritual leader of Lamaism, a Buddhist sect in Tibet. The title, first bestowed on a Lamaist leader in 1578, translates as "teacher whose wisdom is great as the ocean." The title has been bestowed 13 times since: Followers believe that the Dalai Lama is continually reborn. Monks go in search of a young boy who was born at about the same time as the Dalai Lama died. They seek other signs of continuity as well before identifying the "new" Dalai Lama, who the monks educate and train to assume the leadership role.

What is Zen?

Also called Zen Buddhism, it is a sect of Buddhism practiced predominately in Japan and China. The religion is based on meditation rather than on the strict moral doctrine of Buddhism. It was founded in China in the fifth century A.D. by Bodhidharma, an Indian Buddhist monk and missionary. He taught that sudden enlightenment can be achieved through the

211

practice of meditation (or "wall-gazing"). The religion defines enlightenment as the direct seeing of one's original nature.

What is Hinduism?

Hinduism, an ancient religion that originated about 1500 B.C. and developed over thousands of years, encompasses the beliefs and practices of the numerous religious sects of India. Each sect has its own philosophy and form of worship. It is a polytheistic religion—believing in many gods as well as in one great god, or universal spirit, called Brahman. Hindu doctrine is centered on sacred scriptures including the Veda, which includes the Upanishads (dialogues describing sacrificial rituals and religious ceremonies), the Puranas (stories about Hindu gods and goddesses), and the Mahabharata, which contains the Bhagavad Gita (or "the Song of the Lord," in which the god Krishna discusses the meaning of life with a warrior-prince on the eve of battle). Hindus worship alone at temples, which are dedicated to divinities. Followers also practice yoga, believing that it leads to knowledge and union with God.

The Dalai Lama, pictured in December 2004, was awarded the Nobel peace prize in 1989 for his nonviolent efforts to free Tibet from China.

What is Shinto?

Shinto is the dominant religion of Japan. Its traditions call for the reverence of ancestors, prayer, and the observance of rituals. It is polytheistic, believing in many gods (kami), who are thought to be the forces behind nature as well as behind human conditions such as sickness, healing, and creativity. Followers of the Shinto religion believe these spirits are housed in shrines. Private shrines are erected in homes while public shrines can be highly elaborate, including multiple buildings as well as gardens. The latter are the goals of many religious pilgrimages; pilgrims pray and make offerings (of money and flowers) to the spirits.

Originating in Japan in ancient times, Shinto has an interesting modern history: In 1882 religious organizations were divided into two groups—state shrines and sectarian shrines. State Shinto was controlled by the government, which went so far as to proclaim divine origins for the Japanese emperor. After World War II (1939-45), state Shinto crumbled and Emperor Hirohito (1901-1989) was compelled to renounce his divinity. Sectarian Shinto religion still thrives in Japan today, where it has more than 3 million followers.

What is the difference between the Hebrew Bible and the Old Testament?

The Hebrew Bible is made up of 24 books. The Old Testament used by Christians consists of the same books as those of the Hebrew Bible, but they are arranged differently and many books are divided, resulting in more books in the Old Testament than in the Hebrew Bible.

Among Christians, the Old Testament varies between Protestantism and Roman Catholicism: Protestants include 39 books in the Old Testament while Roman Catholics add seven

books, called the Apocrypha, to their version, for a total of 46 books. The books of the Apocrypha resemble those of the Old Testament, but since they were written later than most of the Old Testament (probably 300 B.C.-A.D. 70), both Protestants and Jews treat them separately. The Bibles used by all three religions—Judaism, Roman Catholicism, and Protestantism—begin with the same seven books: Genesis, Exodus, Leviticus, Numbers, Deuteronomy, Joshua, and Judges. The first five of these were written by Moses.

What are the Dead Sea Scrolls?

The scrolls are ancient manuscripts of great historical and religious importance. They were found in dry riverbed caves on the northwestern side of the Dead Sea (a salt lake situated between Israel, the West Bank, and Jordan). More than 800 scrolls have been found, with the most famous discoveries made in 1947. The Dead Sea Scrolls were found miles apart at a number of different sites, including Khirbat Qumran in the West Bank (formerly Israel). The texts date to different centuries but include fragments of every book of the Hebrew Bible (or Old Testament) except the Book of Esther. Some texts are almost identical to Bible texts used today, showing that much of the Old Testament is the same as it was 2,000 years ago.

Jews and Christians consider the Ten Commandments to be the summary of divine law, handed down by God to the prophet Moses.

What are the Ten Commandments?

Also called the Decalogue, the Ten Commandments appear in the Bible in the book of Exodus (20:2-17) and in the book of Deuteronomy (5:6-21). They are considered the summary of divine law as handed down by God to Moses, who not only heard them but received them in the form of writing on two stone tablets as he stood atop Mount Sinai (what is known today as Gebel Musa, on Egypt's Sinai Peninsula), where he had been summoned by God.

According to the Bible, the commandments, which are paramount in the ethical systems of Judaism and Christianity, are these: 1) Do not have any other god besides the Lord God; 2) Do not have or worship idols (carved images); 3) Do not make wrong use of the name of the Lord your God (or, do not take the name of the Lord in vain); 4) Keep the Sabbath day holy; 5) Honor your mother and your father; 6) Do not commit murder; 7) Do not commit adultery; 8) Do not steal; 9) Do not give false evidence against your neighbor; and 10) Do not covet your neighbor's household or lust after your neighbor's spouse.

People sometimes see the Ten Commandments as divided into two groups: the first group covers the relationship between people and God and the second covers relationships among people.

What is the Ark of the Covenant?

According to Judeo-Christian tradition, the Ark of the Covenant is a decorative box that holds the tablets containing the Ten Commandments, also called the Law. The Ark was constructed by skilled craftsmen in Sinai; it was made exactly to God's specifications, which are first mentioned in the Bible in Exodus 25:10-22. The Israelites carried the Ark with them into the Promised Land, where King Solomon (tenth century B.C.) built a permanent temple to house it. When the Babylonians captured Jerusalem in 586 B.C., the Ark was either destroyed or taken. If it survived, its location is a mystery that has intrigued scholars and archeologists, as well as popular culture. However, some scholars believe the Ark never really existed.

Why did people first believe that Jesus of Nazareth was the Messiah?

In his lifetime, Jesus of Nazareth (c. 6 B.C.-c. A.D. 30) was believed to be the Messiah for many reasons. These reasons are explained in detail in the New Testament, particularly in the four Gospels, Matthew, Mark, Luke, and John.

First, Jesus was thought to have been miraculously conceived by Mary, a virgin. In Luke 2:8-20, an angel is described as having spoken to shepherds tending their fields, telling them that "in this night in the city of David, a Savior is born unto you ... a Messiah, the Lord," and goes on to say that the sign (of the Messiah) is that they will find a baby wrapped in swaddling clothes. Also in Luke (2:36-38), a prophetess arrives and proclaims Mary's baby to be the "child to all who were looking for the liberation of the Jews."

Further, Jesus proclaimed himself to be the Son of God (as described, for example, in John 5:17-23). He demonstrated extraordinary healing powers, used parables to teach moral and spiritual ways, and carried a message of God's redeeming love. All of this was convincing enough that many—mostly the common people—became disciples, or followers, of Christ during his lifetime.

Why was Jesus feared by the authorities?

There were two reasons Jesus (c. 6 B.C.-c. A.D. 30) was feared by Palestine's leaders. First, as an advocate of the poor, he was an outspoken critic of the privileged as well as of Palestine's oppressive Roman rulers. (Palestine was part of the Roman province of Syria during the lifetime of Jesus.) Jesus openly accused the ruling class of hypocrisy and injustices. Second, some feared that if Jesus was the Messiah, he would lead a revolution. So the governors viewed him and his teachings as a threat to their authority.

Who were the apostles?

The apostles were 12 men chosen by Jesus Christ (c. 6 B.C.-c. A.D. 30) to be his close followers. The apostles helped spread the word that they believed Jesus to be the Son of God. Matthew 10:1 explains that Jesus gave the 12 authority to drive out unclean spirits and to cure every kind of illness.

In Matthew 10:2-4, the names of the 12 apostles are given as Simon Peter (who is later simply called Peter), Andrew, James, John, Philip, Bartholomew, Thomas, Matthew, James the son of Alphaeus, Thaddaeus, Simon the Zealot, and Judas Iscariot. But the lists of apostles found in Luke 6:13-16 and in Acts 1:13 differ from that found in Matthew. While both Luke and Acts cite (Simon) Peter, Andrew, James, John, Philip, Bartholomew, Thomas, Matthew, James the son of Alphaeus, Simon the Zealot, and Judas Iscariot, they do not name Thaddaeus, but rather Judas the son of James. In other words, the lists agree on 11 of the 12 names.

After Judas Iscariot betrayed Jesus Christ, Matthias was chosen by the apostles to take his place (this is described in Acts 1:21-26). He was considered eligible since, like the 11 remaining apostles, he accompanied Jesus from the time of Jesus's baptism until "the day he was taken up from us."

What is Golgotha?

Golgotha is the Hebrew name for Calvary, the site on a hillside outside ancient Jerusalem where Jesus Christ (c. 6 B.C.-c. A.D. 30) was crucified. Though the exact site is unknown, it is believed to be where the church of the Holy Sepulcher is located.

How old is Islam?

Islam, one of the world's largest religions, originated with the teachings of the prophet Muhammad (c. 570-632) during the early 600s. Muhammad was born in Mecca (in present-day Saudi Arabia) and was orphaned at the age of six. He was raised by relatives, who trained him as a merchant. When he was 25 years old he married a wealthy widow, Khadijah, who bore him several children. In about 610, Muhammad began having visions in which he was called upon by God (Allah). More than 600 of these visions were written down, becoming the sacred text known as the Koran (or Qur'an). By 613 Muhammad had attracted followers with his messages of one God, Allah's power, the duty of worship and generosity, and the doctrine of the last judgment. Followers of this new religion became known as Muslims, an Arabic word meaning "those who submit" (to Allah); and the religion itself became known as Islam (meaning submission).

Today, there are Muslims in every part of the world, but the largest Muslim communities are in the Middle East, North Africa, Indonesia, Bangladesh, Pakistan, India, and central Asia. Additionally, most of the people of Turkey and Albania are Muslim. It is the world's second-largest religion (after Christianity).

Who wrote the Koran?

The Koran (or Qur'an) contains the holy scriptures of Islam and was written by the followers of the prophet Muhammad (c. 570-632). It is not known whether these texts were written down during Muhammad's lifetime or after his death. It is known that the texts were codified (organized into a body) between 644 and 656. Muslims believe the angel Gabriel revealed the book to Muhammad, beginning in 610 and continuing until the prophet's death in 632. The Koran, meaning "recitation," consists of 114 verses (ayas) that are organized in chapters (suras).

Muslims believe the beautiful prose of the Koran to be the words of God himself, who spoke through Muhammad. Further, it is believed to be only a copy of an eternal book, which is kept by Allah. The Koran is also held up by Muslims as proof that Muhammad was indeed a prophet since no human is capable of composing such text. Among the most widely read texts today, the Koran is also taught orally so that even Muslims who are illiterate may know and be able to recite verses.

When did the Sunni and Shiah sects of Islam form?

It was during the 600s, not long after Muhammad's death, when Muslims split into two main divisions: Sunni and Shiah.

Sunnite Muslims, who account for most of the Islamic world today, believe that Islamic leadership passes to caliphs (temporal and spiritual leaders) who are selected from the prophet Muhammad's tribe.

The Shiites believe, however, that the true leaders of Islam descend from Ali (c. 600-661), Muhammad's cousin and the husband of Muhammad's daughter, Fatimah (called the Shining One; c. 616-633). Ali, who was the fourth caliph (656-61), is revered by Shiites as the rightful successor to the prophet Muhammad and are led by his descendants.

Shiites form the largest subgroup, but there are other sects within Islam as well: the Wahhabi Muslims are a puritanical sect; the Baha'is emerged from the Shiites; and the Is-maili Khoja Muslims have been in existence almost from the beginning of Islam. While Islamic practices may vary somewhat among the sects, all Islamic people uphold the Five Pillars of Faith.

What are Islam's Five Pillars of Faith?

Muslims practice adherence to the Five Pillars of Faith: 1) belief in Allah as the only God and Muhammad as his prophet; 2) prayer five times daily—at dawn, at noon, in the afternoon, in the evening, and at nightfall; 3) giving alms to the poor; 4) fasting from dawn until dusk during the holy month of Ramadan); and 5) making the pilgrimage (*hajj*) to the holy city of Mecca at least once during their lifetime.

Why is Mecca a holy city for Muslims?

Mecca, in western Saudi Arabia, is the birthplace of the prophet Muhammad (c. 570) and was his home until the year 622, when those who opposed him forced him to flee to Medina (a city about 200 miles north of Mecca). Muhammad later returned to Mecca and died there in 632.

Mecca is also the site of the Great Mosque, which is situated in the heart of the city. The outside of the mosque is an arcade, made up of a series of arches enclosing a courtyard. In that courtyard is the most sacred shrine of Islam, the Kaaba (or Caaba), a small stone building that contains the Black Stone, which Muslims believe was sent from heaven by Allah (God).When Muslims pray (five times a day, according to the Five Pillars of Faith), they face the Kaaba. It is also the destination of the *hajj*, or pilgrimage.

Does Muslim tradition teach Islam's affinities with other specific faiths?

According to the Koran, Muslims have a special relationship to certain other religious communities. Especially in post- *Hijra* texts, the Koran speaks of Muslims as having much in common with the "Peoples of the Book." The term originally referred to Jews and Christians and eventually expanded to include other communities as well. These groups were known as *dhimmis*, or protected communities. And the notion that "there is no compulsion in religious matters" (*din*, Koran 2:256) is surely a central concept in Islamic views of relations with other traditions. But there is no doubt that the ultimate goal is a return to the pristine unity in which all creation worships God together. There is also no doubt that non-Muslims living in largely Muslim nations have sometimes confronted odious restrictions in

Hajj pilgrims pray during the annual Muslim pilgrimage to the holy city of Mecca, 2002.

religious practice. The realities of inter-religious relations have not always been cordial, and much difficult work needs to be done on this matter all over the world. When it comes to acceptance of diversity, all human beings have a hard time moving from theory to practice.

Do Muslims, Christians, and Jews worship the "same God"?

"Allah" is an Arabic term that derives from a combination of the definite article ("the") al-, with ilah, an ancient Arabic term for "deity." "Allah" therefore means "the [only] deity," and that's what Christians and Jews generally mean by the word "God." Islamic tradition describes God further by means of the "Ninety-Nine Most Beautiful Names." Among these names are Merciful, Compassionate, All-Hearing, All-Seeing, All-Knowing, Oft-Returning, Just Judge, Giver of Life, Bringer of Death, Victorious, Beneficent, and Guide. Muslims traditionally meditate on these names as they ply their "rosary" beads. Christians and Jews will find nothing in the list that is in any way incompatible with their own fundamental beliefs.

What are some examples of specific, shared conceptions of God?

Like Christians and Jews, Muslims believe God created the universe from nothing and has communicated through a series of prophets. Allah is intimately involved in the events of human history, which ends for each individual with death, resurrection, judgment, and either reward in Heaven or punishment in Hell. As for the ultimate fate of the human race collectively, Muslim tradition holds that history will end with a cosmic conflict in which the Messiah will play

217

a role in subduing a figure very similar to the "Anti-Christ." From the Jewish perspective, the Ninety-Nine Names describe the God of the Hebrew Scriptures almost perfectly. From the Christian perspective, two essential aspects of God are conspicuously missing from the Islamic list of divine attributes: the notions that God has become flesh in the Incarnation and consequent Divinity of Jesus, and that God is both One and a Trinity of Father, Son, and Holy Spirit. Is the "God" of Jews and Christians and the "Allah" of Muslims the same supreme being? It is reasonable to say, at least, that they are so remarkably similar that members of the three faiths have ample reason for considering themselves siblings as "children of Abraham."

What "images of God" do Christians and Jews share with Muslims?

Most Jews and Christians are convinced their "own" supreme being is loving and kind, provident and generous, as well as thirsty for justice and equity. So are most Muslims. Of the "Ninety-Nine Most Beautiful Names" of God, the two by far most frequently invoked are "Gracious or Compassionate" and "Merciful." All but one of the Koran's 114 suras (chapters) begins with the phrase, "In the name of God, the Gracious and Merciful." One might say these two names are as important for Muslims as are the names Father, Son, and Holy Spirit heard in so many Christian invocations. Virtually every Muslim public speaker begins with that Koranic phrase and goes on to wish the audience the blessings and mercy of God.

The opening chapter of the Koran sets the tone of Muslim spiritual life and includes themes very similar to those of the Christian "Lord's Prayer":

> In the Name of God, the Compassionate and Merciful: Praise to God, Lord of the
> Universe.
> The Compassionate, the Merciful,
> Master of the Day of Judgment.
> You alone do we serve; from you alone do we seek help.
> Lead us along the Straight Path,
> the path of those who experience the shower of your grace,
> not of those who have merited your anger
> or of those who have gone astray. (Koran 1:1–7)

The text features several of the principal divine attributes. Compassion and mercy top the list and receive an emphatic second mention. In addition, God rules the "two worlds" (seen and unseen, i.e., the universe), takes account at Judgment, offers aid and grace, and manifests a wrathful side to those who prefer arrogant independence from the origin of all things. At the center of the prayer, the Muslim asks for guidance on the Straight Path, a path laid out and marked as the way of divine graciousness.

What were the Crusades?

The Crusades were a series of nine Christian military expeditions that took place during the end of the eleventh century and throughout the twelfth and thirteenth centuries. The stated goal of the Crusades was to recover from the Muslims the Holy Land of Palestine, where Jesus Christ (c. 6 B.C.-A.D. 30) lived. The word crusade comes from the Latin word crux meaning "cross," and Crusaders were said to have "taken up the cross."

The Crusades began with an impassioned sermon given by Pope Urban II (c. 1035- 1099) at Clermont, France, in November 1095. Earlier that year Byzantine emperor Alexius I Comnenus (1048-1118) had appealed to Urban for aid in fighting back the fierce Seljuk Turks. (The Seljuk Turks preceded the Ottoman Turks; the Seljuks were named for their traditional founder, Seljuq). Seeing the expansion of the Turks, who were Muslim, as a threat to Christianity, the Pope agreed to help. Not only did Urban rally support for the Byzantines in staving off the further advances of the Turks, he also advocated that the Holy Lands should be recovered from them. While the Arab Muslims who had previously controlled the Holy Land had allowed Christians to visit there, the Turks tolerated no such thing. Urban feared that if Palestine were not recovered, Christians would lose access to their holy places altogether.

But Urban also viewed the Crusades as a way of unifying western Europe: The feudal nobility there had long fought against each other. He believed a foreign war would unite them behind a common cause as Christians. Further, he hoped the Crusades would unite western with eastern (Byzantine) Europe behind one goal. If successful, the expeditions would also expand the pope's moral authority across a greater region.

En route from Clermont to Constantinople (present-day Istanbul, Turkey), where the Crusade was set to begin in August 1096, Urban continued to preach his message—at Limoges, Poitiers, Tours, Aquitaine, and Toulouse, France. The message found broad appeal, even if it appealed to something other than the people's religious sensibilities. Some of those who answered Urban's call took up arms not for the Christian cause, but for their own personal gain such as acquiring more land, expanding trade, or recovering religious relics. Many peasants "took up the cross" to escape hardships— in 1094 northern France and the Rhineland had been the site of flooding and pestilence, which was followed in 1095 by drought and famine.

The First Crusade actually turned into two. A Peasants' Crusade (which had never been Urban's intent) had gone ahead of the official expedition, and many lives were lost. It ended in failure. But the planned expedition, called the Crusade of Princes, ultimately succeeded in capturing Jerusalem in 1099. Western Christian feudal states were established at Edessa, Antioch, and Tripoli—all of which were placed under the authority of the Kingdom of Jerusalem. But Urban did not live to see the recovery of the Holy Land. And the Christian hold on Palestine was not to last, as the Muslims refused to give up the fight for control of lands they too considered to be holy. The Second (1147-49), Third (1189-92), Fourth (1202-04), Fifth (1217-21), Sixth (1228-29), Seventh (1248-54), and Eighth (1270) Crusades were prompted by a mix of religious, political, and social circumstances. The Crusades ended in 1291—almost 200 years after they had started—when the city of Acre, the last Christian stronghold in Palestine, fell to the Muslims, ending Christian rule in the East.

Yet another crusade, in 1212, was particularly tragic: Called the Children's Crusade, the expedition was led by a young visionary who had rallied French and German children to believe they could recover Jerusalem—since, as poor and faithful servants, they would have God on their side. As the children marched south across Europe, many of them died even before reaching the Mediterranean coast. Some believe that the Crusade was sabotaged, resulting in the children being sold into slavery in the East.

What was the controversy with Thomas Becket?

Archbishop of Canterbury Thomas Becket (c. 1118-1170) was killed by knights in the service of England's King Henry II (1133-1189); he had refused to be subservient to the monarch. In the long struggle between church and state, the story of St. Thomas Becket is a dramatic chapter. Born in London in about 1118, when he was in his twenties Becket entered into service for the archbishop of Canterbury, the spiritual head of the Church of England. He subsequently held various church offices, including archdeacon. When Henry II was coronated in 1154, becoming the worldly leader of the Church of England, he found in Becket one of his most vigorous champions. In 1162 Henry made him archbishop of Canterbury. But a transformation soon occurred in Thomas Becket, who put his spiritual duties first and began defending the church against the king's power. Henry, eager to increase royal authority, was determined to regain control over the church. A bitter struggle ensued between the two former friends. At one point, Becket fled the country because he was in fear for his life. When he returned to England six years later (in 1170), he renewed his opposition to the king, but nevertheless forced a reconciliation with him. Henry was still irked by Becket's open defiance to his authority, and he suggested to his knights that one among them might be brave enough to do away with him, ending the king's troubles. Four knights took the king at his word, and on December 29, 1170, they found Becket in Canterbury Cathedral and killed him as he made his evening prayers. Henry later did penance for the crime; Becket was canonized three years later.

What caused the East-West schism in the Catholic Church?

During the Middle Ages (500-1350) cultural, geographical, and even political differences caused an increasingly wide divide between East (the Catholic churches in eastern and southeastern Europe, as well as in parts of western Asia) and West (the Catholic churches of western Europe). In the 800s a series of theological disputes began between the highest authority of the Eastern (Byzantine) churches, called the patriarch of Constantinople (also called the ecumenical patriarch), and the pope—particularly about the pope's authority over Christians in the East. Finally, in 1054, Pope Leo IX (1002-1054) issued an anathema (a formal curse) against the patriarch of Constantinople, Michael Cerularius (c. 1000-1059), excommunicating him and his followers from the Roman Catholic Church. The church had officially split. Thereafter the Eastern Orthodox churches would accept the patriarch of Constantinople as the highest church authority (in other words, they did not acknowledge the primacy of the pope) and they would follow the Byzantine rite (ceremonies); in the West, Roman Catholics followed the Latin rite and continued to regard the pope as the Holy Father.

When the Ottoman Empire captured Constantinople (present-day Istanbul, Turkey) in 1453, Orthodox Christians in the East came under Muslim rule; this lasted into the 1800s. Though there are still differences between the Eastern Orthodox churches (the Greek Orthodox church, the Russian Orthodox church, etc.) and the Roman Catholic Church today, the rift between them was healed in 1964 when Pope Paul VI (1897-1978) met with Ecumenical Patriarch Athenagoras I (1886-1972) in Jerusalem. The following year, the two religious leaders lifted the mutual anathemas between their churches.

What was the Reformation?

It was a religious movement in Europe during the sixteenth and seventeenth centuries. It fomented inside the Catholic Church as people began questioning the church's doctrines, practices, and authority. While the movement was preceded by a swelling dissatisfaction with the church, the Reformation was officially, and some would say abruptly, begun in October 1517 when German monk and theology professor Martin Luther (1483-1546) nailed his Ninety-Five Theses to the door of the Castle Church at Wittenberg (Saxony, Germany),

What was the importance of Martin Luther's Ninety-Five Theses?

The Reformation as a movement began on October 31, 1517, when the German monk and theology professor Martin Luther (1483-1546) nailed his Ninety-Five Theses to the door of the Castle Church at Wittenburg (Saxony, Germany). The theses (which are arguments or assertions) questioned the value of indulgences (the pardons that were disseminated by the church) and condemned the sale of them. Luther had already begun to preach the doctrine of salvation by faith rather than by works, and during 1518 he went on to publicly defend his beliefs, which were in direct opposition to the church. The following year he expanded his argument against the church by denying the supremacy of the pope.

In 1521 Pope Leo X (1475-1521) declared Luther a heretic and excommunicated him. Ordered to appear before the Diet of Worms in April 1521, Luther refused to retract his statements of his beliefs, saying, "Unless I am convinced by the testimony of the Scriptures or by clear reason … I am bound by the Scriptures I have quoted and my conscience is captive to the Word of God." The following month, Holy Roman Emperor Charles V (1500-1558) issued the Edict of Worms, declaring Luther to be an outlaw and authorizing his death. But the Prince of Saxony, known by history as Frederick the Wise (1463-1525), saw fit to protect Luther, whom he had appointed as a faculty member at the University of Wittenberg (founded by Frederick the Wise in 1502). There Luther translated the New Testament into German and undertook a translation of the entire Bible. Luther continued the Protestant movement until his death in 1546.

launching an attack on the church. The movement continued through the Thirty Years' War (1618-48). And though the resolution to that conflict brought about a measure of religious stability in Europe, the force of the Reformation did not end there. Both the freedom of dissent and the Protestantism people know today are the byproducts of the movement.

What was the Counter Reformation?

Also called the Catholic Reformation, it was the Roman Catholic Church's response to the Protestant Reformation of the sixteenth century. Some parishioners and members of the Roman Catholic clergy had already been calling for reforms within the church for more than two centuries when in 1517 German monk and theology professor Martin Luther (1483-1546) nailed his Ninety-Five Theses to the door of the Castle Church at Wittenberg (Saxony, Germany). His theses attacked the doctrines and authority of the church, sparking the Reformation. The movement's leaders, called Protestants because they protested against the Catholic Church, changed the religious landscape of Europe by creating new Christian churches. But a movement to make changes inside the Catholic Church also began. The turning point came in 1534 when Paul III (1468-1549) became pope. Realizing that the church must respond to what it viewed as a religious crisis, Pope Paul convened the Council of Trent (in Italy), which was charged with reviewing all aspects of religious life. The ecumenical group met from 1545 to 1547, 1551 to 1552, and 1562 to 1563, and out of those deliberations emerged the modern Catholic Church. The Counter Reformation was aided by a group of priests and brothers known as the Jesuits, members of the Society of Jesus, a religious order of the Roman Catholic Church. The Jesuits were instrumental in spreading the word of the reforms and in promoting a new spirit within the Catholic Church.

Who are the Jesuits?

The Jesuits are members of a Roman Catholic religious order called the Society of Jesus. The group was founded by Saint Ignatius of Loyola (1491-1556). Born into nobility as Iñigo de Oñaz y Loyola, the Spaniard became a knight in 1517. In that capacity he fought against the French in their siege 1521 of Pamplona, northeast of Madrid. But he was seriously wounded in the battle and retreated to a commune in northeast Spain from 1522 to 1523. There Ignatius heard a religious calling and subsequently undertook a pilgrimage to Jerusalem (1523 to 1524). Committed to a religious life, he embarked on a program of disciplined writing and study in Spain and in Paris, France. Even before he was ordained in 1537, Ignatius had gained followers—the Spanish missionary Francis Xavier (1506-1552) among them. With his companions Ignatius founded the Society of Jesus in 1539; the religious order was approved by Pope Paul III (1468-1549) the following year. Jesuits are known for leading structured lives and for their self-discipline, commitment to the pope, and missionary work. They have a profound belief in education, and as such have long been leaders in learning and in the sciences. The order was suppressed in 1773 but restored in 1814.

What were the results of the Reformation?

The emergence of the Protestants (who got their name for protesting against the Catholic Church) was officially recognized by Holy Roman Emperor Charles V (1500-1558) with the Peace of Augsburg (1555), which granted the people the right to worship as Lutherans (the church named for reformer Martin Luther [1483-1546]). But the hostility between Catholic and Protestant countries erupted in 1618 with the Thirty Years' War. That series of conflicts, which had become increasingly political as it raged, was ended with the Peace of Westphalia, which, among other things, stipulated that Lutheranism and Calvinism (or Presbyterianism, founded by Frenchman John Calvin [1509-64]) be given the same due as Catholicism.

Through acts of state, both Catholicism and Protestantism took hold in Europe, with the northern countries, including those of Scandinavia, turning toward the new churches and the southern countries remaining Catholic. For the most part, the Reformation fostered an attitude of religious tolerance among Christians. However, conflict would continue (to the present day) in the British Isles: After Queen Elizabeth I (1533-1603) adopted a moderate form of Protestantism (called Anglicanism) as the official religion of England, English Protestants colonized Ulster (Northern) Ireland and in so doing gave rise to hostilities with their Irish-Catholic countrymen to the south.

For its part, the Catholic Church, too, underwent a period of reform (called the Counter Reformation), which rid the church of many of its pre-Reformation problems to emerge as a stronger religious body.

The Reformation had without question brought about greater religious freedom than had been known before. Among the churches that emerged during the Reformation are the Lutheran, the Anabaptist (ancestors to the Amish and Mennonite churches), the Presbyterian, the Episcopal, and the Congregational and Unitarian (formerly Puritan)—all of which have strong followings today, both in Europe and in North America, where they were established by the colonists.

Who were the Puritans?

The Puritans were members of a religious movement that began in England in the 1500s and lasted into the first half of the 1600s, when it spread to America as well. Influenced by the teachings of religious reformers John Wycliffe (c. 1330-1384) and John Calvin (1509-1564), the Puritans were so named because they wanted to "purify" the Anglican church (also known as the Church of England). They believed too much power rested with the church hierarchy (its priests, bishops, and cardinals), that the people (called the laity or lay members) should have more involvement in church matters, and that the ceremonies ought to be simplified to stress Bible reading and individual prayer. Further, they defied the authority of the pope, believing that each church congregation should have control of its own affairs, which should be guided by a church council (called a presbytery) made up of lay members.

These ideas are familiar to Americans today since they provided the basis not only for many Protestant churches but also influenced the formulation of U.S. government. When the Puritans faced persecution at home, they became religious pilgrims, traveling to the New World, where they established both their religious and social belief system.

PHILOSOPHY

What is philosophy?

From the Greek *philo*, meaning "love of," and *sophia,* meaning "wisdom," philosophy is literally a love of wisdom. In practice, it is the pursuit of understanding the human condi-

What was the Great Awakening?

The Great Awakening was an American religious movement that began in New England in the mid-1730s. At its center were the fire-and-brimstone sermons delivered by charismatic preachers such as Congregational minister Jonathan Edwards (1703-1758) and Anglican missionary George Whitefield (1714-1770). Revivals were another cornerstone of the movement: These were evangelistic meetings that moved around the countryside, from Maine to Georgia, converting (or awakening) people to Christianity—not through the doctrines of the church, but rather through the individual's own experience. The theology of the Great Awakening was Calvinist, stressing the depravity of man and the sovereignty of God and promoting the belief that faith, and not conduct, is the road to salvation. In its emphasis on the individual and its espousal that the individual is the final arbiter of truth, the movement had a profound effect on the spiritual and political character of what would soon become the United States. Since many vehemently opposed the movement, it also served to divide churches between the revivalists and the traditionalists. Thus, it diversified American religious life and promoted religious tolerance.

tion—how, why, and what it means to exist or *to be.* Philosophers use methods such as observation and questioning to discern the truth. Philosophy is traditionally divided between Eastern thought and Western thought. Further, Western thought consists of five branches: metaphysics (concerned with the nature of the universe or of reality); logic (the laws of reasoning); epistemology (the nature of knowledge and the process by which knowledge is gained); ethics (the moral values or rules that influence human conduct); and aesthetics (the nature of beauty or the criteria for art).

How old is Taoism?

It dates back to the sixth century B.C. when it was founded by Chinese philosopher Lao-tzu (c. 550 B.C.-?). Master Lao, as he was known, believed in inaction and simplicity, which he combined with religious practices to form the mystical philosophy of the Tao (Dao), the path of virtuous conduct. Lao-tzu reasoned that since humans face a "cloud of un-

Confucius was a highly revered Chinese philosopher who believed that the family is the model for all human relationships.

knowability," they ought not to react to things at all: He viewed the world as a pendulum, with the Tao as its hinge. Anyone who struggles against the current of life is like an insect caught at the end of a pendulum—swinging back and forth, and suffering with each movement. But by crawling along the hinge (Tao) to reach the top, a place of complete stillness is found. Lao-tzu advised that people do away with their desires, avoiding that which is extreme, extravagant, or excessive, and steer clear of any competition. Many of these ideas are embodied in a work usually ascribed to him, Tao-te Ching (Classic of the Way of Power). However, modern scholars now believe that tome to be the work of his followers.

Taoism is still relevant to many today. When it was developed some 26 centuries ago, the philosophy filled a spiritual void that was not addressed by the practical doctrines of traditional Confucianism. One legend has it that Lao-tzu rebuked a young Confucius (551-479 B.C.) for his pride. The Tao also contributed greatly to Buddhism, especially in its emphasis on meditation and sudden enlightenment.

One of the great thinkers of the Chinese Taoist school was teacher and philosopher Chuang-tzu (fourth century B.C.), who constructed an nonpolitical, transcendental philosophy that promoted an individual's spiritual freedom. His self-titled work (Chuang-tzu) is another classic of Taosim.

Why was Socrates condemned to death?

Socrates (c. 470-399 B.C.), the Greek philosopher who is credited, along with philosophers Plato (c. 428-347 B.C.) and Aristotle (384-322 B.C.), for laying the foundations of Western thought, had many followers in his own time. However, his ideas and methods were controversial, too, which led him to be tried before judges and sentenced to death, which he carried out by drinking hemlock (poison). He had been charged for not worshiping the Athenian gods and for corrupting the young.

Except for his time spent in military service, Socrates lived his entire life in Athens, where he was as well known for his disheveled appearance as for his moral integrity, self-control, and quest for wisdom. He lived during a time when attention was turning away from the physical world (of the heavens) and toward the human world (of the self, the community, and the law). He participated in this turning point by walking the streets of Athens, engaging people—including rulers who were supposed to be wiser than he—in conversation. In these conversations, he employed what came to be known as the "Socratic method" or dialectic, a series of seemingly simple questions designed to elicit a rational response. Through the line of questioning, which usually centered around a moral concept such as courage, the person being questioned was intended to realize that he did not truly know that which he thought he knew. Socrates's theory was that once the person being questioned realized his weak understanding, he could divest himself of false notions, and was then free to participate in the quest for knowledge. These philosophical "disputes," however, gained Socrates many enemies.

Though he left no writings, Socrates's student, Plato, documented his recollections of dialogues with his teacher. A staunch believer in self-examination and self-knowledge, Socrates is credited with saying that "the unexamined life is not worth living" (some ascribe the quote to Plato). Socrates also believed that the psyche (or "inner self") is what should give direction to one's life—not appetite or passions. A seminal figure in Greek (and Western) thought, philosophy that predates him is termed "pre-Socratic."

What was Plato's relationship to Socrates and Aristotle?

The Athens-born Plato (originally, Aristocles) was Socrates's disciple and Aristotle's teacher. The philosophies of these three men combined to lay the foundations of Western thought.

With the death sentence of his spiritual guide, Socrates, in 399 B.C., Plato's (c. 428-347 B.C.) dissatisfaction with the Athenian government reached its peak. Traveling throughout the Mediterranean after the death of Socrates, Plato returned to Athens in 387 B.C., and one mile outside of the city he established the Academy, a school of philosophy supported entirely by philanthropists; students paid no fees. One of the pupils there was young Aristotle (384-322 B.C.), who remained at the Academy for 20 years before venturing out on his own.

Plato wrote a series of dialogues in which Socrates figures prominently. The most highly regarded of these is the *Republic*, in which Plato discusses justice and the ideal state. It was his belief that people would not be able to eliminate injustice from society until rulers became philosophers: "Until all philosophers are kings, or the kings and princes of this world have the spirit and power of philosophy, and political greatness and wisdom meet in one, and those commoner natures who pursue either to the exclusion of the other are compelled to stand aside, cities will never have rest from their evils—no, nor the human race." Also on the subject of the ideal state, Plato wrote but did not finish Laws. His other works include *Symposium*, which considers ideal love; *Phaedrus*, which attacks the prevailing notions about rhetoric; *Apology*, which is a rendering of the speech Socrates delivered at his own trial

225

in 399 B.C.; and *Phaedo*, which discusses the immortality of the soul and which is supposed to be a record of Socrates's last conversation before he drank hemlock and died.

What is Plato's theory of forms?

The theory, or doctrine, of forms (also called the theory of ideas) is Greek philosopher Plato's (c. 428-347 B.C.) expression of his belief that there are forms that exist outside the material realm, and therefore are unchanging—they do not come into existence, change, or pass out of existence. It is these ideas that, according to Plato, are the objects or essence of knowledge. Further, he posited that the body, the seat of appetite and passion, which communes with the physical world (rather than the world of ideas or forms), is inferior to the intellect. He believed the physical aspect of human beings to be irrational while the intellect, or reason, was deemed to be rational.

The origins of Plato's theory can be traced to Socrates (c. 470-399 B.C.), who believed that the psyche (inner spirit) has intuitive access to divinely known principles or truths, which he attempted to formulate through his conversations with others. Indeed, the Socratic dialogues, written by Plato, reveal that Socrates was striving to define the exact nature of the traditional Greek moral virtues of piety, temperance, and courage.

Did Aristotle develop his own philosophy?

A student of Plato's for 20 years, Aristotle's ideas were unquestionably influenced by his teacher. However, Aristotle developed his own doctrine, which he applied to many subjects.

Aristotle rejected Plato's theory of forms (or theory of ideas). While Aristotle, too, believed in material (the physical being) and forms (the unchanging truths), unlike his teacher, he believed that it is the concrete (material) that has substantial being. Aristotle viewed the basic task of philosophy as explaining why and how things are, or how they become what they are. It is for this reason that Aristotle had not only a profound and lasting influence on philosophy but on scientific spirit.

Who were the great Islamic philosophers of the Middle Ages?

Three thinkers of the Islamic world stand out as important interpreters of Greek thought, and therefore, as a bridge between ancient philosophy and the Scholasticism of the Middle Ages: their Latin names are Avennasar, Averroës, and Avicenna.

Avennasar (c. 878-950), who studied with Christian Aristotelians in Baghdad (Iraq), proved so adept at applying the teachings of Aristotle (384-322 B.C.) to Muslim thought that he became known as "the second Aristotle" or the "second teacher." He posited that philosophy and religion are not in conflict with each other; rather, they parallel one another. Also known for his work in interpreting the great Aristotle for the Muslim world, Avicenna (980-1037) is sometimes referred to as the "third teacher." He was also the first to expand the distinction between essence and existence. Averroës (1126-1198) also was no stranger to Aristotle, writing commentaries on him as well as Plato (specifically, the *Republic*); he also wrote on religious law and philosophy as well as religion and logic.

Who were the great thinkers of Scholasticism?

Just as Islamic philosophers reinterpreted faith by applying reason, subordinating revelation to reason, Western philosophers endeavored to incorporate the doctrines of Greek philosophy into the theology of the Christian church. Leaders in this movement included St. Augustine (Augustine of Hippo), St. Anselm, and St. Thomas Aquinas.

Augustine of Hippo (354-430) lived during a time when the last vestiges of the pagan world of the Romans was giving way to Christianity. His theological works, including sermons, books, and pastoral letters, reveal a Platonic influence, foreshadowing the movement of Scholasticism that emerged more than six centuries later (during the eleventh century). Augustine believed that understanding can lead one to faith and that faith can lead a person to understanding. He also argued that Christians can understand the nature of the Trinity by examining their own nature (through introspection).

One of Scholasticism's founders, Anselm (c. 1033-1109) was a Benedictine monk who in 1093 became archbishop of Canterbury. He became famous for writing about the attributes of God (in his work Monologion) and for trying to prove the existence of God (in Proslogion) by rational means alone, arguing that God is that of which nothing greater can be thought; that of which nothing greater can be thought must include existence (if it did not, then something greater could be thought); and therefore God necessarily exists.

But the greatest figure of Scholasticism was St. Thomas Aquinas (1225-1274), who is also one of the principal saints of the Roman Catholic Church. In 1879 his philosophical works were declared the official Catholic doctrine by Pope Leo XIII (1810-1903). While he was teaching at universities in Cologne (Germany) and Paris between 1248 and 1272, Thomas Aquinas penned his major works, *Summa contra gentiles* (1259-64) and Summa theologica (1266-73). He discarded the Platonic leanings of St. Augustine (to whom truth was a matter of faith), interpreting Aristotle's naturalistic philosophy: Similar to the Islamic philosopher Avennasar (c. 878-950), who argued that religion and philosophy are not in conflict with each other, Thomas Aquinas believed faith and reason are in harmony with each other. His work is considered the greatest achievement of medieval philosophy, making the thirteenth century Scholasticism's golden age. Thomas Aquinas was canonized in 1323 and was proclaimed a doctor of the Catholic Church in 1567.

What were Sir Francis Bacon's beliefs?

The English philosopher, author, and statesman was one of the great minds of the Scientific Revolution of the 1500s and 1600s, during which the way that Europeans viewed themselves and the universe underwent a dramatic change. Bacon (1561-1626) believed that humankind's accepted notions about nature should be aggressively challenged. As a young man studying at Trinity College, he concluded that the Aristotelian system (or deductive logic) was without merit; Bacon favored observation (or inductive logic) as a system for interpreting and understanding nature. He argued that the understanding of nature was being held back by the blind acceptance of the beliefs of an-

English philosopher Sir Francis Bacon believed that nature was best understood by direct observation. (Original engraving by S. Freeman.)

cient philosophers such as Aristotle (384-322 B.C.) and Plato (c. 428-347 B.C.). A religious person, Bacon maintained that theology should not be questioned: He believed that rational inquiry can unlock the secrets of nature—but not of the human soul. Bacon therefore insisted on the separation of philosophy and theology, an idea that ran counter to the academic traditions of the time. Consequently he was a staunch proponent of educational and scientific reform.

Trained in law, Bacon served as a royal diplomat in France, was admitted to the bar, elected to Parliament, and served in public office (including the jobs of solicitor general and attorney general). He penned several seminal works, including *Essayes* (1597), which consists of practical wisdom and observations; *Advancement of Learning* (1605), a survey of the state of knowledge (Bacon was attempting to enlist the support of the king in the total reform of education and science in England); and *Novum Organum* (1620), in which he put forth his method for understanding nature by an inductive system, based on direct observation (versus Aristotle's deductive method, which was based on circumstantial evidence and prior conclusions).

Why is Descartes considered the "father of modern philosophy"?

French mathematician and philosopher René Descartes (1596-1650) was living in Holland in 1637 when he published his first major work, *Discourse on Method*. In this treatise, he extends mathematical methods to science and philosophy, asserting that all knowledge is the product of clear reasoning based on self-evident premises. This idea, that there are certitudes, provided the foundation for modern philosophy, which dates from the 1600s to the present.

Descartes may be best known for the familiar phrase "I think, therefore I am" (*Cogito ergo sum,* in Latin). This assertion is based on his theory that only one thing cannot be doubted, and that is doubt itself. The next logical conclusion is that the doubter (thinker) must, there-

What is empiricism?

Empiricism is the philosophical concept that experience, which is based on observation and experimentation, is the source of knowledge. According to empiricism, the information that a person gathers with his or her senses is the information that should be used to make decisions, without regard to reason or to either religious or political authority. The philosophy gained credibility with the rise of experimental science in the eighteenth and nineteenth centuries, and it continues to be the outlook of many scientists today. Empiricists have included English philosopher John Locke (1632-1704), who asserted that there is no such thing as innate ideas—that the mind is born blank and all knowledge is derived from human experience; Irish clergyman George Berkeley (1685-1753), who believed that nothing exists except through the perception of the individual, and that it is the mind of God that makes possible the apparent existence of material objects; and Scottish philosopher David Hume (1711-1776), who evolved the doctrine of empiricism to the extreme of skepticism—that human knowledge is restricted to the experience of ideas and impressions, and therefore cannot be verified as true.

fore, exist. The correlation to the dictum (I think, therefore I am) is dualism, the doctrine that reality consists of mind and matter: Since the thinker thinks and is, he or she is both mind (idealism) and body (matter, or material). Descartes concluded that mind and body are independent of each other, and he formulated theories about how they work together. Modern philosophers have often concerned themselves with the question of dualism.

Descartes's other major works include *Meditations on First Philosophy* (1641), which is his most famous, and *Principles of Philosophy* (1644). His philosophy became known as Cartesianism (from *Cartesius,* the Latin form of his name).

Why are Kant's philosophies still relevant?

Immanuel Kant (1724-1804) remains one of the great modern thinkers because he developed a whole new philosophy, one that completely reinterpreted human knowledge. A professor at Germany's Königsberg University beginning in 1755, Kant lectured widely and was a prolific writer. His most important work came somewhat late in life—after 1775. It was in that year that he undertook "a project of critical philosophy," in which he aimed to answer the three questions that, in his opinion, have occupied every philosopher in Western history: What can I know? What ought I do? For what may I hope?

Kant's answer to the first question (What can I know?) was based on one important conclusion: What a person can know or make claims about is only his or her experience of things, *not* the things in themselves. The philosopher arrived at this conclusion by observing the certainty of math and science: He determined that the fundamental nature of human reality (metaphysics) does not rely on or yield the genuine knowledge of science and math. For example, Newton's law of inertia—a body at rest tends to remain at rest, and a body in motion tends to remain in motion—does not change based on human experience. The law of inertia is universally recognized as correct and as such, is a "pure" truth, which can be relied on. But human reality, argued Kant, does not rest on any such certainties. That which a person has not experienced with their senses cannot be known absolutely. Kant therefore reasoned that free will cannot be proved or disproved—nor can the existence of God.

Even though what humans can know is extremely limited, Kant did not become skeptical. On the contrary, he asserted that "unknowable things" require a leap of faith. He further concluded that since no one can disprove the existence of God, objections to religion carry no weight. In this way, Kant answered the third question posed by philosophers: For what may I hope?

After arriving at the conclusion that each person experiences the world according to his or her own internal laws, Kant began writing on the problem of ethics, answering the second question (What ought I do?). In 1788 he published the *Critique of Practical Reason,* asserting that there is a moral law, which he called the "categorical imperative." Kant argued that a person could test the morality of his or her actions by asking if the motivation should become a universal law—applicable to all people: "Act as if the maxim from which you act were to become through your will a universal law." Kant concluded that when a person's actions conformed with this "categorical imperative," then he or she was doing his or her duty, which would result in goodwill.

Kant's theories have remained relevant to philosophy for more than two centuries: modern thinkers have either furthered the school of thought that Kant initiated or they have rejected it. Either way, the philosopher's influence is still felt. It's interesting to note that among his writings is an essay on political theory (*Perpetual Peace*), which first appeared in 1795: In it, Kant described a federation that would work to prevent international conflict; the League of Nations and the United Nations, created more than a century after Kant, are the embodiments of this idea.

What is the Hegelian dialectic?

It is the system of reasoning put forth by German philosopher Georg Hegel (1770-1831), who theorized that at the center of the universe there is an absolute spirit that guides all reality. According to Hegel, all historical developments follow three basic laws: Each event follows a necessary course (in other words, it could not have happened in any other way); each historical event repre-

German philosopher Georg Hegel (in an 1884 portrait) theorized that at the center of the universe there is an absolute spirit that guides all reality. (Original painting by Ernst Hader.)

sents not only change but progress; and one historical event, or phase, tends to be replaced by its opposite, which is later replaced by a resolution of the two extremes. This third law of Hegel's dialectic is the "pendulum theory" discussed by scholars and students of history: that events swing from one extreme to the other before the pendulum comes to rest at middle. The extreme phases are called the thesis and the antithesis; the resolution is called the synthesis. Based on this system, Hegel asserted that human beings can comprehend the unfolding of history. In this way, he viewed the human experience as absolute and knowable.

What is existentialism?

Existentialism is not a single school of thought but rather a label applied to several systems that are influenced by the theories of Danish philosopher Soren Kierkegaard (1813-1855). Existentialist thinkers consider one problem: human existence in an unfathomable universe. However, in considering this "plight," philosophers have arrived at different conclusions.

The founder of existentialism, Kierkegaard rejected the principles put forth by traditional philosophers such as Georg Hegel (1770-1831), who had considered philosophy as a science, asserting that it is both objective and certain. Kierkegaard overturned this assertion, citing that truth is not objective but rather subjective; that there is no such thing as universal truths; and that human existence is not understandable in scientific terms. He maintained that human beings must make their own choices, based on their own knowledge. When he wrote on the subject, Kierkegaard frequently used pseudonyms, a practice he defended by intimating that he was putting the onus on his readers to determine what is true—that they shouldn't rely on the "authority" of his philosophies.

In the twentieth century, heirs to Kierkegaard's school of thought included German philosopher Martin Heidegger (1889-1976), who rejected the label "existentialist," and the French writer Jean-Paul Sartre (1905-1980), the only self-proclaimed existentialist. They grappled with the dilemma that human beings must use their free will to make decisions—and assume responsibility for those decisions—without knowing conclusively what is true or false, right or wrong, good or bad. In other words, there is no way of knowing absolutely what the correct choices are, and yet individuals must make choices all the time, and be held accountable for them. Sartre described this as a "terrifying freedom." However, theologians such as American Paul Tillich (1886-1965) reconsidered the human condition in light of Christianity, arriving at far less pessimistic conclusions than did Sartre. For example, Tillich asserted that "divine answers" exist. Similarly, Jewish philosopher Martin Buber (1878-1965), who was also influenced by Kierkegaard, proposed that a personal and direct dialogue between the individual and God yields truths.

What was Nietzsche's philosophy about the "will to power"?

The German philosopher Friedrich Nietzsche (1844-1900) developed many theories of human behavior, and the will to power was one of these. While other philosophers (including the ancient Greek Epicurus) argued that humans are motivated by a desire to experience pleasure, Nietzsche asserted that it was neither pleasure nor the avoidance of pain that inspires humankind, but rather the desire for strength and power. He argued that in order to gain power, humans would even be willing to embrace pain. However, it's critical to note that he did not view this will to power strictly as a will to dominate others: Nietzsche glorified a superman or "overman" (*ubermensch*), an individual who could assert power over himself (or herself). He viewed artists as one example of an overman—since that person successfully harnesses his or her instincts through creativity and in so doing has actually achieved a higher form of power than would the person who only wishes to dominate others. A notable exception to Nietzsche's esteem for artists was the composer Richard Wagner (1813-1883), whom the philosopher opposed. Since Wagner led an immoral lifestyle, unlike the ubermensch, Nietzsche maintained that the composer had not gained power over his own instincts.

Nietzsche was a professor of classics at the University of Basel in Switzerland from 1868 to 1878. Retiring due to poor health, he turned to his writing, which included poetry. In 1889 he suffered a mental breakdown and died the next year. After his death, his sister, Elisabeth Förster-Nietzsche (1846-1935), altered her brother's works in editing, changing their meaning. In 1895 she married an anti-Semitic agitator, Bernhard Förster (1843-1889), who, with his wife, attempted to establish a pure Aryan (a non-Jewish Caucasian) colony in Paraguay. The effort failed, and Förster took his own life. These events and, more importantly, the changes to the philosopher's own words resulted in the popular misconception that Nietzsche's philosophies had given rise to Nazism.

What is natural law?

Natural law is the theory that some laws are fundamental to human nature, and as such they can only be known through human reason—without reference to manmade law. Roman orator and philosopher Cicero (106-43 B.C.) insisted that natural law is universal, meaning it is binding to governments and people everywhere.

Why are Thomas Paine's philosophies important to democratic thought?

English political philosopher and author Thomas Paine (1737-1809) believed that a democracy is the only form of government that can guarantee natural rights. Paine arrived in the

American colonies in 1774. Two years later he wrote Common Sense, a pamphlet that galvanized public support for the American Revolution (1775-83), which was already underway. During the struggle for independence, Paine wrote and distributed a series of 16 papers, called *Crisis*, upholding the rebels' cause in their fight. Paine penned his words in the language of common speech, which helped his message reach a mass audience in America and elsewhere. He soon became known as an advocate of individual freedom. The fight for freedom was one that he waged in letters: In 1791 and 1792 Paine, now back in England, released *The Rights of Man* (in two parts), a work in which he defended the cause of the French Revolution (1789-99) and appealed to the British people to overthrow their monarchy. For this he was tried and convicted of treason in his

Political philosopher and author Thomas Paine believed that a democracy is the only form of government that can guarantee natural rights. (Original painting by George Romney.)

homeland. Escaping to Paris, the philosopher became a member of the revolutionary National Convention. But during the Reign of Terror (1793-94) of revolutionary leader Maximilien Robespierre (1758-1794), Paine was imprisoned for being English. An American minister interceded on Paine's behalf, insisting that Paine was actually an American. Paine was released on this technicality. He remained in Paris until 1802, and then returned to the United States. Though he played an important role in the American Revolution by boosting the morale of the colonists, he nevertheless lived his final years as an outcast and in poverty.

What is Marxism?

Marxism is an economic and political theory named for its originator, Karl Marx (1818-1883). Marx was a German social philosopher and revolutionary who in 1844 in Paris met another German philosopher, Friedrich Engels (1820- 1895), beginning a long collaboration. Four years later they wrote the *Communist Manifesto,* laying the foundation for socialism and communism. The cornerstone of Marxism, to which Engels greatly contributed, is the belief that history is determined by economics. Based on this premise, Marx asserted that economic crises will result in increased poverty, which in turn, will inspire the working class (proletariat) to revolt, ousting the capitalists (bourgeoisie). According to Marx, once the working class has seized control, it will institute a system of economic cooperation and a classless society. In his most influential work, *Das Kapital* (The Capital), an exhaustive analysis of capitalism published in three volumes (1867, 1885, and 1894), Marx predicted the failure of the capitalist system, based on his belief that the history of society is "the history of class struggle." He and Engels viewed an international revolution as inevitable.

While Marxism still has followers in the late twentieth century, most scholars have discredited Marx's predictions, citing improved conditions for workers in industrialized nations, which has been brought about by the evolution of capitalism.

What are some other important philosophies?

- *Absurdism*, a philosophy strongly associated with the fiction of Albert Camus (1913-1960), as well as the writings of Soren Kierkegaard (1813–1855), states that it is pointless for people to try to find a meaning in life because there either is no such meaning or because there is a meaning but it does not pertain to human existence.

- *Determinism* asserts that the future has only one possible outcome because everything has been predestined by previous actions and decisions. What, exactly, determined the outcome could be anything from God to environmental conditions and geography.

- *Epicurianism* is based upon the teachings of the Greek Epicurus (341-270 B.C.E.), who believed that the main goal of life was to eliminate pain and fear and have a pleasurable existence by enjoying everything from food and sex to the pursuit of knowledge and satisfying personal relationships. It is closesly associated with hedonism, for this reason.

- *Nihilism* is the grim belief that there is absolutely no meaning, purpose, or truth in our lives. There is no God, and life is pointless.

- *Objectivism* is the idea put forth by author Ayn Rand (1905-1982) that meaning in life can be found by pursuing rational self-interests; that is, by making oneself happy. This is best done when human beings live in a laissez-faire, capitalistic society.

- First proposed by Auguste Comte (1798-1857), *Positivism* stresses that knowledge, real knowledge, only comes from science and by testing ideas using the scientific method.

- *Secular Humanism* holds that the only real values in life are based upon human concepts of justice, ethics, and reasoning. Furthermore, there is no absolute truth; instead, meaning and morality can vary from person to person.

- Proposed by the Greek philosopher Gorgias, *Solipsism* states that the only thing one can know for certain is that one exists; everything that exists outside the mind is uncertain and cannot be truly known.

- *Utilitarianism* a theory put forth by Jeremy Bentham (1748-1832)and expanded upon by John Stuart Mill (1806-1873), says, essentially, that the ends justify the means. Something is "good" if it brings happiness to the greatest number of people.

THE ARTS

WRITING AND LITERATURE

What was the first book?

It was *The Diamond Sutra*, published in the year A.D. 868. Archaeologists discovered it in the Caves of the Thousand Buddhas, at Kansu (Ganzu), China.

Who developed printing?

If printing is defined as the process of transferring repeatable designs onto a surface, then the first known printing was done by the Mesopotamians, who as early as 3000 B.C. used stamps to impress designs onto wet clay.

Printing on paper developed much later; Chinese inventor Ts'ai Lun (A.D. c. 50–c. 118) is credited with producing the first paper in A.D. 105. During the T'ang dynasty (618–906) Chinese books were printed with inked wood blocks, and it was the Chinese—not German printer Johannes Gutenberg (c. 1390-1468), as is widely believed—who developed movable type, allowing printers to compose a master page from permanent, raised characters. However, movable-type printing did not catch on in medieval China because the Chinese language has some 80,000 characters; printers found it more convenient to use carved blocks.

Why is Gutenberg considered the pioneer of modern printing?

Johannes Gutenberg (c. 1390-1468), a German who built his first printing press around 1440 to 1450, is considered the inventor of a lasting system of movable-type printing. Printing technology had only a brief existence in Europe before Gutenberg, whose process, culminating in the publication of the Gutenberg Bible (1452-1456), made printed material available to everyone, not just the clergy or the privileged class. Gutenberg is credited with helping spread the ideals of the Renaissance (1350-1600) throughout Europe.

How old are *Aesop's Fables*?

They date back to the sixth century B.C. However, it was not until the late 1600s that English-language versions appeared: In 1692 a complete translation of the stories, which are believed to have been written by a Greek slave, were published in London by Sir Roger L'Estrange (1616-1704). The short, moralistic tales, which were handed down through the oral tradition, include the well-known story of the tortoise and the hare (which teaches the lesson slow and steady wins the race) and the one about a wolf in sheep's clothing (people are not always what they seem). Since some of the timeless fables have been traced to earlier literature, many believe it is almost certain that Aesop is a legendary figure.

Who were the Brothers Grimm?

The German brothers Jacob (1785-1863) and Wilhelm (1786-1859), best known for their fairytales, were actually librarians and professors who studied law, together wrote a dictionary of the German language, and lectured at universities.

In 1805 Jacob traveled to Paris to conduct research on Roman law, and in a library there he found medieval German manuscripts of old stories that were slowly disintegrating; he decided the tales were too valuable to lose, and he vowed to collect them. The brothers' interest in fairytales also led them to search for old traditions, legends, and tales, especially those meant for children. They traveled the German countryside, interviewing villagers in an effort to gather stories—most of which were from the oral tradition and had never been written down. The brothers were diligent in their efforts, recording everything faithfully so that nothing was added and nothing was left out. When the first volume of *Kinderund Hausmärchen* (literally, the Children's Household Tales, but known better as *Grimm's Fairy Tales*) was published in 1812, children loved it. Subsequent volumes were published in German through 1815. The fairytales collected in the multivolume work included such classics as "The History of Tom Thumb," "Little Red Riding-Hood," "Bluebeard," "Puss in Boots," "Snow White and the Seven Dwarfs," "Goldilocks and the Three Bears," "The Princess and the Pea," "The Sleeping Beauty in the Wood," and "Cinderella."

What is "the Homeric question"?

During the eighteenth and nineteenth centuries, scholars became involved in a debate, referred to as "the Homeric question," about whether the *Iliad* and the *Odyssey* were written by the same author, or even if any one author can be credited with the entire composition of either poem, and what kind of an author Homer was. The dispute continues today. Scholars believe the *Iliad* was probably written much earlier than the *Odyssey*, though there is not enough evidence to prove that the Greek poet Homer (c. 850-? B.C.) did not write both epics. Further, it was suggested that Homer was a bard (oral poet) who was unable to read or write and who sang the great stories of the *Iliad*c and *Odyssey* to the accompaniment of a lyre. According to this theory, the tales would have been dictated by Homer to a scribe late in the poet's life. However, some have left open the possibility that the human histories told in the *Iliad* and the *Odyssey* were in fact the composite result of the storytelling of numerous bards.

Several other poems, including the *Margites* and the *Batrachomyomachia*, have also been attributed to Homer, but they were most likely written by his successors.

What is known about Homer?

It is most likely that Homer was an oral poet and performer. Though little is known about Homer, it's believed that he was an Ionian Greek who lived circa the eighth or ninth century B.C. In the 1920s scholar Milman Parry proved that Homer's poems were "formulaic in nature, relying on generic epithets (such as 'wine-dark sea' and 'rosy-fingered dawn'), repetition of stock lines, and descriptions and themes typical of oral folk poetry." All of this suggested that Homer was most likely a bard or rhapsode—an itinerant professional reciter—who improvised pieces to be sung at Greek festivals.

Why is the *Iliad* studied today?

Greek poet Homer's (c. 850-? B.C.) *Iliad* and *Odyssey* (both works credited to him) are considered to be among the greatest works of literature and have had a profound influence on western poetry, serving as the primary models for subsequent works, including the *Aeneid* (Virgil) and the *Divine Comedy* (Dante).

The *Iliad* in particular can be seen as both the beginning of western literature as we know it and the culmination of a long tradition of oral epic poetry that may date as far back as the thirteenth century B.C. The *Iliad* has been a part of western education for nearly 3,000 years. The epic poem, telling the story of a 10-year Trojan War, reveals the author's keen understanding of human nature.

What innovations are credited to Virgil?

Scholars acclaim Virgil (70-19 B.C.) for transforming the Greek literary traditions, which had long provided Roman writers with material, themes, and styles. Virgil populated his pastoral settings (always idealized by other writers) with contemporary figures; he combined observation with inquiry; employed a more complex syntax than had been in use previously; and developed realistic characters. These technical innovations informed all subsequent literature.

However, writing was not supposed to have been Virgil's occupation: In his youth, he studied rhetoric and philosophy, and he planned to practice law, but proved too shy for public speaking. So he returned to the small family farm his mother and father operated, where he studied and wrote poetry.

Is Virgil's *Aeneid* an unfinished work?

Yes, the *Aeneid* was technically unfinished by its author, Virgil (70-19 b.c.), who is considered the greatest Roman poet. Virgil spent the last ten years of his life working on the Aeneid, and he planned to devote three more years making revisions to this epic when, during his travels to gather new material for the poem, he became ill with fever and died. On his deathbed, Virgil requested that his companions burn the *Aeneid*. However, Augustus (63 b.c.-A.D. 14), the emperor of Rome, countermanded the request, asking Virgil's friends to edit the manuscript. Augustus did specify that the writers not add, delete, or alter the text significantly. The *Aeneid*, Virgil's great epic about the role of Rome in world history, was first published in 17 b.c. The work consists of 12 books, each between 700 and 1,000 lines long.

In addition to the *Aeneid* Virgil wrote *Eclogues* (or *Bucolica*), a set of 10 pastoral poems written (from 42-37 B.C.) as a response to the confiscation of his family's lands; and *Georgics*, a four-volume work (written from 36-29 B.C.) glorifying the Italian countryside. Within 50 years of his death in 19 B.C., Virgil's poems became part of the standard curriculum in Roman schools, ensuring the production of numerous copies. Virgil's works have remained accessible to scholars and students ever since.

Why is *Beowulf* considered an important work?

Beowulf, the earliest manuscript of which dates to about A.D. 1000, is the oldest surviving epic poem in English or any other European vernacular. It was written in Old English (the language of the Anglo-Saxons in England; used c. A.D. 500-1100); its author is unknown. Categorized as a folk-epic, *Beowulf* tells the story of a Scandinavian warrior hero who, on behalf of the Danish king, fights and kills the fearsome monster Grendel, then slays the monster's mother, and finally engages a fire-breathing dragon in mortal combat. Because of its combination of Christian and pagan themes, scholars believe the epic may have been written as early as 700 or 750.

Why is *The Divine Comedy* widely studied?

Simply put, *The Divine Comedy*, which consists of 100 cantos arranged in three books (*Inferno*, *Purgatorio*, and *Paradiso*), is studied not only for the beauty of its verse, but for its timeless message.

In a letter to his benefactor, Dante Alighieri (1265-1321) explained that by writing *The Divine Comedy* (*Divina Commedia* begun c. 1308) he would attempt "to remove those living in this life from the state of misery and lead them to the state of felicity." While the subject of the poem, according to Dante, is "the state of souls after death," allegorically, the poem is about humankind, who can exercise free will to bring "rewarding or punishing justice" upon themselves.

Dante's masterpiece is considered the seminal work of Italian literature: At the time that he wrote *The Divine Comedy*, Latin was the undisputed language of science and literature. Italian, on the other hand, was considered vulgar. By skillfully writing this poem in the vernacular (Tuscan Italian) rather than Latin, Dante parted from tradition, marking a critical development for vernacular writing. In its translations *The Divine Comedy* has become a point of reference for writers in any language. Scholars and students agree that Dante expresses universal truths in this work, which is also a finely crafted piece of literature.

Why is Chaucer's *Canterbury Tales* important to literature?

The unfinished work, which was begun about 1486 and written during the last 14 years of its author's life, is considered a masterpiece of Middle English, the language spoken by Anglo-Saxons in England from c. 1200 into the late 1400s. In the *Canterbury Tales*, Geoffrey Chaucer (1340-1400), who was the son of a wealthy wine merchant, weaves together stories told by 28 pilgrims whom the storyteller (the poet himself) met at an inn. The pilgrims, along with the innkeeper who joins them and the poet, represent all facets of English social life—aristocracy, clergy, commoners, and even a middle class, which was not officially recognized by the social structure of the day, but which, in fact, existed.

To connect the tales, Chaucer uses the framing device of a journey to the shrine of Thomas Becket (c.1118-1170), the archbishop of Canterbury who in 1170 was killed by overzealous knights in the service of England's King Henry II. In his prologue, Chaucer indicates that each traveler was to tell two tales out and two tales back from Canterbury Cathedral, for a total of 120 stories, which were intended to entertain the pilgrims during their trip. But Chaucer wrote only 24 tales, two of which are incomplete. The tales include bawdy humor, fables, and lessons. While the pilgrims reach the shrine, they do not return—a device some scholars have interpreted as deliberate on the author's part, as it suggests the human journey from earth to heaven. Whatever the intention, *The Canterbury Tales* reveal the author's ability

It is thought that William Shakespeare is widely studied because his words express universal and unchanging human concerns.

as a storyteller, as the editors of the *Norton Anthology of English Literature* assert, rivaling Shakespeare "in the art of providing entertainment on the most primitive level, and at the same time, of significantly increasing the reader's ability to comprehend reality."

The tales were extremely popular in late medieval England, printed and reprinted numerous times, particularly during the 1400s. Chaucer's rendering of details reveal both story and storyteller (pilgrim) at once, giving the reader a remarkable insight into the characters and revealing basic human paradoxes—which transcend time.

Why is Shakespeare widely studied?

English dramatist Ben Jonson (1572-1637) said it best when he proclaimed that Shakespeare "was not of an age, but for all time." Most teachers and students, not to mention critics and theatergoers down through the ages, likely agree with Jonson's remark: Shakespeare's canon (consisting of 37 plays, divided into comedies, tragedies, or histories, plus poems and sonnets) expresses universal and unchanging human concerns as no other works have. Shakespeare's words are familiar even to those who have not studied them, not simply because of the many contemporary adaptations of his works, but because Shakespearean phrases and variations thereof have, through the years, fallen into common usage. Consider these few examples from *Hamlet* alone: "Neither a borrower nor a lender be"; "To thine own self be true"; and "The play's the thing." No other writer's plays have been produced so often or read so widely in so many countries.

What is a poet laureate?

A poet laureate is someone who is recognized by his or her country or state as its most eminent and representative poet. Officially, a poet laureate is appointed or named by the government. England's first, if unofficially titled, poet laureate was Ben Jonson (1572-1637), a contemporary of Shakespeare. (Shakespeare acted a leading role in the first of Jonson's great plays, *Every Man in His Humour,* 1598.) In 1605 Jonson began writing a series of masques (short, allegorical dramas that were performed by actors wearing masks) for the court. Years later, in 1616, he was appointed poet laureate and in that capacity received a "substantial pension." Among Jonson's works are *Volpone* (1605), *Works* (a collection of poetry published in 1616, and which includes the oft-quoted line, "Drink to me only with thine eyes"), and *Pleasure Reconciled to Virtue* (1618).

Some sources trace the first British poet laureate back to Edmund Spenser (1552 or 1553-1599), who is called the "Poet's Poet." However, the title of poet laureate was not officially conferred on an English writer until 1638, when poet and dramatist William Davenant (1606-1668), who was reputed to be the godson or even the illegitimate son of Shakespeare, was given the honor. Other poet laureates of England include John Dryden (1631-1700), William Wordsworth (1770-1850), and Lord Alfred Tennyson (1809-1892).

How did the word "Machiavellian" get its meaning?

Machiavellian is defined as "characterized by cunning, duplicity, or bad faith." It's based on the theory of Italian diplomat Niccolò Machiavelli (1469-1527), who developed a code of political conduct that operates independent of ethics, thus disregarding moral authorities such as classical philosophy and Christian theology.

In 1513, after having been exiled from Florence, Italy, by the powerful Medici family, Machiavelli abruptly turned his attention to writing *The Prince,* which puts forth a calm and uncompromising analysis of techniques and methods that the successful ruler must use in order to gain—and keep—power. Written in the form of advice to the ruler, Machiavelli advises the Prince that only one consideration should govern his decisions: the effectiveness of a particular course of action, regardless of its ethical character. The book had little immediate impact in Italy, although it soon became legendary throughout Europe, and its major ideas—the power of politics—are familiar today even to people who have never read the book.

Why is Milton important to English literature?

Except for Shakespeare, the works of John Milton (1608-1674) have been the subject of more commentary than those of any other English writer. Milton is considered one of only a few writers to take their place in "the small circle of great epic writers." According to *Norton Anthology of English Literature,* in Milton's writings "two tremendous intellectual and social movements come to a head." The movements referred to are the Renaissance and the Reformation. Scholars point to Milton's use of classical references and the rich tapestry of his works as being Renaissance in nature, while his "earnest and individually minded Christianity" are resonant of the Reformation. For example, in his masterpiece *Paradise Lost* (1667), Milton, like poets Homer and Virgil before him, takes on humankind's entire experience: war, love, religion, hell, heaven, and the cosmos. But rather than having Adam triumph over evil through an act of heroism, he "accepts the burden of worldly existence, and triumphs over his guilt by admitting it and repenting it."

In addition to his famous epics, Milton wrote sonnets and other short poems, including "On Shakespeare," "L'Allegro," "Il Penseroso," and "Lycidas." His writings also include political discourse, chief of which is the essay *Areopagitica* (1644). Among the ideas that Milton championed were the limitation of the monarchy, dethroning of bishops, freedom of speech, and the institution of divorce. One commentator mused that "the guarantees of freedom in the United States Constitution owe more to Milton's *Areopagitica* than to John Locke."

What were Voltaire's beliefs?

The prolific French writer's corpus of 52 works were produced as part of his lifelong effort to expose injustices. Voltaire's famous words, *"Ecrasez l'infame"* (squash that which is evil), encapsulate his tenets: He believed in God, but abhorred priestly (high church) traditions; he spread the doctrines of rational skepticism to the world; he strongly advocated religious and political tolerance; and he held great faith in humankind's ability to strive for perfection. To the European literary world, he embodied the highest ideal of the Age of Reason (also called the Enlightenment). But victims of his wit feared and denigrated him. Celebrated by some during his lifetime, he has certainly been celebrated since. His masterpiece, *Candide* (1759), a satirical tale exploring the nature of good and evil, has been translated into more than 100 languages.

What was Goethe's contribution to world literature?

Johann Wolfgang Goethe (1749-1832) is considered Germany's greatest writer. He also was a scientist, artist, musician, and philosopher. As a writer, Goethe experimented with many genres and literary styles, and his works became a shaping force of the major German literary movements of the late eighteenth and early nineteenth centuries. His masterwork, the poetic drama *Faust* (1808; rewritten 1832), embodies the author's humanistic ideal of a world literature—one that transcends the boundaries of nations and historical periods. Indeed, the story of Faust, a German astrologer, magician, and soothsayer (c. 1480-1540), remains one of universal interest, and has been treated often in both literature and music: the legendary figure was believed to have sold his soul to the devil in exchange for the opportunity to experience all of life's pleasures.

Who was Alexis de Tocqueville?

Aristocrat Alexis de Tocqueville (1805-1859) was only 26 years old when he traveled to New York with his colleague and friend, Gustave de Beaumont (1802-1866), to study and observe American democracy.

Though Tocqueville set out with the pretext of studying the American penal system on behalf of the French government (both he and Beaumont were magistrates at the time), he had the deliberate and personal goal of conducting an onsite investigation of the world's first and then only completely democratic society: the United States. Tocqueville and Beaumont traveled for nine months through New England, eastern Canada, and numerous American cities, including New York; Philadelphia, Pennsylvania; Baltimore, Maryland; Washington, D.C.; Cincinnati, Ohio; and New Orleans, Louisiana.

The pair returned to France in 1832 and the following year published their study, *On the Penitentiary System in the United States and Its Application in France.* Once this official obligation was behind him, Tocqueville left his post as magistrate and moved into a modest Paris apartment. There he devoted two years to writing *Democracy in America* (1835, 1840). The work was soon proclaimed the classic treatment of its subject throughout the Western world and secured Tocqueville's fame as political observer, philosopher, and, later, sociologist.

241

Tocqueville proclaimed that during his travels, "Nothing struck me more forcibly than the general equality of conditions.... All classes meet continually and no haughtiness at all results from the differences in social position. Everyone shakes hands...." But he also foresaw the possibility that the principles of economic equality could be undermined by the American passion for equality, which not only "tends to elevate the humble to the rank of the great," but also "impels the weak to attempt to lower the powerful to their own level." While he warned against the possible "tyranny of the majority" as a hazard of democracy, he also added that law, religion, and the press provide safeguards against democratic despotism.

Who was the first to write a modern novel?

While there are differing opinions on the answer to this question, it is generally accepted that the credit for the novel as we know it belongs to Spanish writer Miguel de Cervantes (1547-1616). Cervantes wrote *Don Quixote* (in two parts, 1605 and 1615): It was the first extended prose narrative in European literature in which characters and events are depicted in what came to be called the modern realistic tradition. Considered an epic masterpiece, *Don Quixote* had an undeniable influence on early novelists, including English novelist and playwright Henry Fielding (who wrote the realistic novel *Tom Jones,* 1749). *Don Quixote* is also said to have anticipated later fictional masterpieces, including French novelist Gustave Flaubert's *Madame Bovary* (1857), Russian novelist Fyodor Dostoevsky's *The Idiot* (1868-69), and American writer Mark Twain's *The Adventures of Tom Sawyer* (1876) and *The Adventures of Huckleberry Finn* (1884).

Why is Jane Austen widely read today?

Austen is considered one of the greatest novelists in English. She wrote just six books during her lifetime, including her best-known works *Sense and Sensibility* (published 1811), *Pride and Prejudice* (1813), and *Emma* (1816), but in so doing she created the novel of manners, which continues to delight readers today. The daughter of a clergyman, Jane Austen (1775-1817) rejected the literary movement of the day, romanticism, opting instead to portray life as she knew it. As such, she was the first realist in the English novel. Austen's works are ripe with shrewd observation, wit, and an appreciation for the charms of everyday life, making her an engaging storyteller for all time.

Why is *Moby Dick* considered the greatest American novel?

The 1851 novel by Herman Melville (1819-1891), which opens with the familiar line "Call me Ishmael," has been acclaimed as one of the greatest novels of all time; many regard it as the best American novel. Of course, determining the best is a purely subjective matter, and Melville's work has many worthy rivals for the distinction, but *Moby Dick* remains a compelling and finely wrought work—in spite of the fact that it was not appreciated in its day. The story of a whaling captain's obsessive search for the whale that ripped off his leg, *Moby Dick* is both an exciting tale of the high seas and an interesting allegory, interpreted as the human quest to understand the ultimately unknowable ways of God. The work first received notoriety some 30 years after Melville's death.

Why was James Joyce's *Ulysses* banned in the United States?

Irish writer James Joyce's (1882-1941) masterpiece was originally published in 1922 (it had been serialized prior to then) by the Paris bookstore Shakespeare and Company. By 1928 it was officially listed as obscene by the U.S. Customs Court. The reason was twofold: the use of four-letter words and the stream-of-consciousness narrative of one of the characters, revealing her innermost thoughts. When the official stance on the book was challenged in U.S. court in 1933, the judge (John Woolsey) called it a "sincere and honest book," and after long reflection he ruled that it be openly admitted into the United States. Random House, the American publisher who had advocated the obscenity charge be challenged in court, promptly began typesetting the work in order to release a U.S. edition. But the court decision had important and lasting legal impact as well: it was a turning point in reducing government censorship. Prior to the case, laws that prohibited obscenity were not seen to be in conflict with the First Amendment of the U.S. Constitution (which is most often interpreted as a guarantee of freedom of speech), and the U.S. Post Office and the Customs Service alike both had the power to determine obscenity. The government appealed the decision to the U.S. Circuit Court of Appeals, but Judge Woolsey's decision held.

What is Proust's claim to literary fame?

Marcel Proust (1871-1922) is generally considered the greatest French novelist of the twentieth century and is credited with introducing to fiction the elements of psychological analysis, innovative treatment of time, and multiple themes. Proust is primarily known for his multivolume work *A la recherche du temps perdu* (1954), which was published in English as *Remembrance of Things Past*. Proust was an creative stylist as well as shrewd social observer.

In the mid-1890s Proust joined other prominent artists, including the great French novelist of the nineteenth century, Emile Zola (1840-1902), to form the protest group known as the Revisionists or Dreyfusards. The artists were staunch supporters of Alfred Dreyfus (1859-1935), and therefore vocal critics of the French military, who they accused of anti-Semitism for keeping the French army officer, wrongly accused of treason, imprisoned on Devil's Island.

When did American poetry begin?

As the self-described poet of democracy, Walt Whitman (1819-1892) was the first to compose a truly American verse—one that showed no references to European antecedents (throwing off both the narrative and ode forms of verse) and that clearly articulated the American experience.

His first published poetry was the self-published collection *Leaves of Grass* (1855). In an effort to gain recognition, Whitman promptly sent a copy to the preeminent man of American letters, Ralph Waldo Emerson (1803-82), who could count as his acquaintances and friends the great British poets William Wordsworth (1770-1850) and Samuel Taylor Coleridge (1772-1834), the renowned Scottish essayist Thomas Carlyle (1795-1881), and prominent American writers Henry David Thoreau (1817-1862) and Nathaniel Hawthorne (1804-1864). It was a bold move on Whitman's part, but it paid off: While *Leaves of Grass* had been unfavorably received by reviewers, Emerson composed a five-page tribute, expressing his enthusiasm for the poetry and remarking that Whitman was "at the beginning of a great career." Thoreau, too, praised the work. More than a century later, biographer Justin Kaplan acclaimed that in its time *Leaves of Grass* was "the most brilliant and original poetry yet written in the New World, at once the fulfillment of American literary romanticism and the beginnings of

American literary modernism." Whitman's well-known and frequently studied poems include "Song of Myself," "O Captain! My Captain!," "Song of the Open Road," and "I Sing the Body Electric."

While she was virtually unknown for her poetry during her lifetime, Emily Dickinson (1830-1886) was writing at about the same time as Whitman (the 1850s), publishing only a handful of poems before her death. Collections of Dickinson's works were published posthumously, and today she, too, is regarded as one of the great early poets of the United States. Had more of her work been brought out in print, perhaps she would have been recognized as the first truly American poet.

Zora Neale Hurston (pictured c. 1940) was the first black woman to be honored for creative writing with a prestigious Guggenheim Fellowship; she was one of the key figures of the Harlem Renaissance.

What were the lasting effects of the Harlem Renaissance?

The Harlem Renaissance (1925-35) marked the first time that white Americans (principally intellects and artists) gave serious attention to the culture of African Americans. The movement, which had by some accounts begun as early as 1917, was noted in a 1925 *New York Herald Tribune* article that announced, "We are on the edge, if not in the midst, of what might not improperly be called a Negro Renaissance." The first African American Rhodes scholar, Alain Locke (1886-1954), who was a professor of philosophy at Howard University, led and shaped the movement during which Upper Manhattan became a hotbed of creativity in the post-World War I (1914-18) era.

Not only was there a flurry activity, but there was a heightened sense of pride as well. The movement left the country with a legacy of literary works including those by Jean Toomer (his 1923 work *Cane* is generally considered the first work of the Harlem Renaissance), Langston Hughes ("The Negro Speaks of Rivers," 1921; *The Weary Blues,* 1926), Countee Cullen (*Color,* 1925; *Copper Sun,* 1927), Jessie R. Fauset (novelist and editor of *The Crisis,* the journal of the National Association for the Advancement of Colored People, or NAACP), Claude McKay (whose 1928 novel *Home to Harlem* evoked strong criticism from W. E. B. Du Bois and Alain Locke for its portrayal of black life), and Zora Neale Hurston (the author of the highly acclaimed 1937 novel *Their Eyes Were Watching God,* who was the first black woman to be honored for her creative writing with a prestigious Guggenheim Fellowship).

The Harlem Renaissance was not only about literature: jazz and blues music also flourished during the prosperous times of the postwar era. During the 1920s and 1930s Louis Armstrong, "Jelly Roll" Morton, Duke Ellington, Bessie Smith, and Josephine Baker rose to prominence. Their contributions to music performance are still felt by artists and audiences, regardless of color, today.

FINE ART

What are the characteristics of Botticelli's paintings?

The works of Sandro Botticelli (1445-1510), one of the early painters of the Italian Renaissance, are known for their serene compositions, refined elegance, and spirituality. A student of Florentine painter Fra Filippo Lippi (1406-1469), Botticelli refined Lippi's method of drawing such that he is considered one of the great "masters of the line."

Botticelli's work was soon eclipsed by that of Leonardo da Vinci (1452-1519), who was just a few years younger than he, but whose range of talents made Botticelli's work seem dated. Nevertheless, late in the nineteenth century, Botticelli began to be revered again by artists and critics alike, who hailed his works for their simplicity and sincerity. English art critic John Ruskin (1819-1900) held Botticelli up as an example of an artist who presented nature as an expression of a divinely created world.

Why is Botticelli's *The Birth of Venus* famous?

This immediately recognizable painting (c. 1482) is most likely known for its elegant figures, use of pictorial space, and decorative detail, which give the painting a tapestry effect. At the time it was painted, the presentation of a nude Venus was an innovation since the use of unclothed figures in art had been prohibited during the Middle Ages (500-1350). Botticelli, however, felt free to render Venus in this way since the work was commissioned by Florence's

Botticelli's well-known painting *Birth of Venus* was commissioned by Florence's powerful Medici family.

powerful Medici family, who were his patrons. Under their protection, Botticelli could pursue the world of his imagination without fearing charges of paganism and infidelity.

Though *The Birth of Venus* is extremely well known, *The Magnificat* (1483), Botticelli's round picture of the Madonna with singing angels, is his most copied work.

Why was the Medici family important to Renaissance art?

The Medici family was powerful in Florence, Italy, between the fourteenth and sixteenth centuries. The founder of the family was Giovanni di Bicci de Medici (1360- 1429), who amassed a large fortune through his skill in trade and who virtually ruled Florence between 1421 and 1429.

Later, Lorenzo de Medici (1449-1492) ruled Florence between 1478 and 1492. Though he was tyrannical, he was a great patron of the arts and letters. Lorenzo (also called "the Magnificent") maintained Fiesole, a villa outside Florence, where he surrounded himself with the great talents and thinkers of Florence, including a young artist named Sandro Botticelli (1445-1510). Lorenzo was also a patron of Michelangelo.

Did Michelangelo study anatomy?

Yes: In 1492 Michelangelo Buonarroti (1475-1564), a master sculptor of the human form, undertook the study of anatomy based on the dissection of corpses from the Hospital of Santo Spirito.

Perhaps most well known for his sculptures of *David* (1501-04) and *Moses* (1515-15), as well as his frescoes on the ceiling and walls of the Sistine Chapel, Michelangelo was also an architect who believed that buildings should follow the form of the human body "to the extent of disposing units symmetrically around a central and unique axis, in a relationship like that of the arms to the body." He also wrote poetry; he was a true Renaissance man.

Michelangelo was totally absorbed in his work and was known to be impatient with himself and with others. He has been likened to German composer Ludwig van Beethoven (1770-1827) since the personal letters of both men reveal a "deep sympathy and concern for those close to them, and profound understanding of humanity informs their works" (*Gardner's Art through the Ages*).

Of the great trio of High Renaissance artists—Leonardo, Michelangelo, and Raphael—who is considered the master?

Most historians and critics agree that it was Raphael Sanzio (1483-1520) who most clearly stated the ideals of the High Renaissance. Though arch rivals Leonardo da Vinci (1452-1519) and Michelangelo Buonarroti (1475-1564) influenced the younger Raphael, he developed his own style. A prolific painter, he was also a great technician whose work is characterized by a seemingly effortless grace. His most well-known work is *The School of Athens* (1509-11), which has been called "a complete statement of the High Renaissance in its artistic form and spiritual meaning." The painting, which projects a stagelike space onto a two-dimensional surface, reconvenes the great minds of the ancient world—Plato, Aristotle, Pythagoras, Herakleitos, Diogenes, Euclid—for an exchange of ideas. Raphael even included himself in this gathering of greatness. But it seems only appropriate for the master to be in such company: In this work, Raphael has achieved the art of perspective, bringing the discipline of mathematics to pictorial space where human figures appear to move naturally.

Why is Titian thought of as the "father of modern painting"?

During Titian's time (1488 or 1490-1576), artists began painting on canvas rather than on wood panels. A master of color, the Venetian painter was both popular and prolific. His work was so sought after that even with the help of numerous assistants, he could not keep up with demand.

His body of works established oil color on canvas as the typical medium of western pictorial tradition. Among his most well-known paintings are *Sacred and Profane Love* (c. 1515) and *Venus of Urbino* (1538).

Why is Rembrandt considered the archetype of the modern artist?

To understand the similarities between Rembrandt van Rijn (1606-1669) and the modern artist, it's important to note that this master portrait-painter, who broke ground in his use of light and shadow, was in his own time criticized for his work: Some thought it too personal or too eccentric. An Italian biographer asserted that Rembrandt's works were concerned with the ugly, and he described the artist as a tasteless painter. Rembrandt's subjects included lower-class people, the events of everyday life and everyday business, as well as the humanity and humility of Christ (rather than the choirs, trumpets, and celestial triumph that were the subjects of other religious paintings at the time). His portraits reveal his interest in the effects of time on human features—including his own. In summary, the Dutch artist approached his work with "psychological insight and … profound sympathy for the human affliction." He was also known to use the butt end of his brush to apply paint. Thus, he strayed outside the accepted limits of great art at the time.

Art critics today recognize Rembrandt as not only one of the great portrait painters, but a master of realism. The Dutch painter, who also etched, drew, and made prints, is regarded as an example for the working artist; he showed that the subject is less important than what the artist does with his materials.

Among his most acclaimed works are *The Syndics of the Cloth Guild* (1662) and *The Return of the Prodigal Son* (c. 1665). The first painting shows a board of directors going over the books, and Rembrandt astutely captures the moment when the six businessmen are interrupted, thus showing a remarkably real everyday scene. *The Return of the Prodigal Son* is one of the most moving religious paintings of all time. Here Rembrandt has with great compassion rendered the reunion of father and son, capturing that moment of mercy when the contrite son kneels before his forgiving father. Through his series of self-portraits, Rembrandt documented his own history—from the confidence and optimism of his youth to the "worn resignation of his declining years."

What exactly is impressionism?

The term "impressionism" was derived by a rather mean-spirited art critic from the title of one of Claude Monet's (1840-1926) early paintings, *Impression, Fog* (*La Havre,* 1872). The French impressionist painters were interested in the experience of the natural world and in rendering it exactly as it is seen—not fixed and frozen with an absolute perspective, but rather as constantly changing and as it is glimpsed by a moving eye.

Georges Seurat (1859-1891) and Paul Signac (1863-1935) are also typically thought of as impressionists; however, they are more appropriately dubbed neoimpressionists since they, along with Camille Pisarro (1830-1903), advanced the work of the original group through more scientific theories of light and color, introducing deliberate optical effects to their works. Seurat and Signac are commonly referred to as pointillists for the technique, pioneered by Seurat, of using small brush strokes to create an intricate mosaic effect. The postimpressionists, artists representing a range of explorations but all having come out of the impressionist movement, included both Seurat and Signac, as well as Henri de Toulouse-Lautrec (1864-1901), Paul Gaugin (1848-1903), Vincent van Gogh (1853-1890), and Paul Cézanne (1839-1906, who was also associated with the original impressionists).

Together the impressionists paved the way for the art of the twentieth century, since as a group they "asserted the identity of a painting as a thing, a created object in its own right, with its own structure and its own laws beyond and different from … the world of man and nature" (*History of Modern Art*).

Was Monet the "father of French impressionism"?

Michelangelo's statue of *David* is housed at the dome of Florence's Accademia Gallery, Italy.

Though the movement was named for one of Claude Monet's (1840-1926) paintings and his *Water Lilies* (1905) are arguably the most well-known and highly acclaimed impressionist works, impressionism is actually rooted in the works of the group's spiritual leader, Édouard Manet (1832-1883), who first began experimenting with color and light to bring a more naturalistic quality to painting.

In 1863 Manet exhibited two highly controversial and groundbreaking works: *Déjeuner sur l'herbe* and *Olympia*. Both paintings were based on classic subjects, but Manet rendered these pastoral scenes according to his own experience, giving them a decidedly more earthy and blatantly erotic quality than the Parisian critics and academicians of the day could accept. He was roundly criticized for his scandalous exhibition. Nevertheless, Manet persevered, and in 1868, with his portrait of the French writer Emile Zola, he again challenged the art world and its values. A critic for *Le National* denounced the portrait and cited among his complaints that Zola's trousers were not made of cloth. This, the artists observed, was both truth and revelation: the pants were made of paint. A few years later, in 1870, Manet began experimenting with painting outside, in the brilliance of natural sunlight. Manet pioneered many of the ideas and techniques taken up by the impressionists.

How did American Mary Cassatt join the Paris art world of the impressionists?

Mary Cassatt (1844-1926), the daughter of a wealthy investment banker from Pittsburgh, Pennsylvania, traveled to Paris in 1866 in the company of her mother and some women friends; the young Cassatt was determined to join the city's community of artists. Since women were not allowed to enroll in classes at Paris's Institute of Beaux Arts (the policy was changed in 1897), Cassatt privately studied painting and traveled in Europe, pursuing her artistic interests. Returning to Paris in 1874, she became acquainted with Edgar Degas (1834-1917), who remarked that the American artist possessed an "infinite talent" and that she was "a person who feels as I do." He made these observations after viewing one of her paintings at the Salon d'Automne in Paris. Cassatt went on to exhibit with the impressionists in 1879, 1880, 1881, and 1886, gaining her first solo exhibit in 1891.

Judith Barter, curator of American arts at the Art Institute of Chicago and organizer of the traveling exhibit "Mary Cassatt: Modern Woman," describes Cassatt as "a very good businesswoman … who knew how to market her career." During three and a half years of research, which she conducted to launch the exhibit, Barter explored the prevailing social climate of the day: The late nineteenth century was a time when feminists, who organized to campaign for political and social reforms (eventually winning women the vote in 1920), focused on maternity, encouraging women to be involved in caring for their children. To Cassatt, observed Barter, maternity was "the highest expression of womanhood." Women and children were the subjects of Cassatt's body of works, which includes oil paintings, pastels, prints, and etchings.

Cassatt's place among the impressionists has often been overshadowed by her male colleagues, and her contributions to the art world are mentioned only in passing in many art books, but her talent, insights, and sheer determination combined to create an impressive legacy. As Gaugin quipped, "Mary Cassatt has charm but she also has force."

Why were Matisse's paintings considered so shocking when they were debuted?

Even if they seem commonplace to art today, the color and style of the paintings of French expressionist Henri Matisse (1869-1954) were revolutionary in their day.

In 1905 Matisse, along with several other artists, exhibited works at Paris's Salon d'Automne. The wildly colorful paintings on display there are said to have prompted an art critic to exclaim that they were *fauves*, or "wild beasts." The name stuck: Matisse and his contemporaries who were using brilliant colors in an arbitrary fashion became known as the fauves. His famous work *Madame Matisse,* or *Green Stripe* (1905), showed his wife with blue hair and a green stripe running down the middle of her face, which was colored pink on one side of her nose and yellow on the other. Matisse was at the forefront of a movement that was building new artistic values. The fauves were not using color in a scientific manner (as Georges Seurat had done), nor were they using it in the nondescriptive manner of Paul Gaugin (1848-1903) and Vincent Van Gogh (1853-1890). The fauves were developing the concept of abstraction.

Throughout his career, Matisse continued to experiment with various art forms—painting, paper cutouts, and sculptures. All of his works indicate a progressive elimination of detail and simplification of line and color. So influential was his style on modern art that some 70 years later one art critic commented that it was as if Matisse belonged to a later generation—and a different world.

How is Picasso's work characterized?

It's impossible to characterize or classify the work of Spaniard Pablo Picasso (1881- 1973) since his career as an artist spanned his entire life and he experimented with many disciplines. Picasso often claimed that he could draw before he could speak, and by all accounts he spent much of his childhood engaged in drawing. He was only 15 years old when he submitted his first works for exhibition. And by the turn of the century, when he was still a young man, he began exploring the blossoming modern art movement. The rest of his career breaks into several periods. His Blue period (1901- 04) was named for the monochromatic use of the color for its subjects, and was likely the result of a despair brought on by the suicide of a friend. Next came his Rose period (beginning 1905), when images of harlequins and jesters appear in his works—all to a somewhat melancholic effect. He soon began to incorporate aspects of primitive art, and later experimented with geometric line and form in his works, which were constructions—or deconstructions—sometimes only identifiable by their title.

Many of Picasso's works fall into the category of cubism, exemplified by this 1948 painting, *Woman in an Armchair.*

In the spring of 1912 cubism exploded, and Picasso was on its forefront. In 1923 he broke new ground with surrealism. The key masterpiece in his body of works came in 1937 when he painted *Guernica,* his rendering of the horror of the German attack (supported by Spanish fascists) on the small Basque town (of Guernica) in Spain. His career reached its height during the 1940s, during which he lived in Nazi-occupied Paris.

Biographer Pierre Cabbane summed up the last period (1944-73) of Picasso's work: "He invented a second classicism: autobiographical classicism…. His final 30 years were to be a dizzying, breakneck race toward creation." During this time, Picasso did not chart any new artistic territory, but simply created art at an amazing rate. After his death in 1973, his estate yielded an inventory of 35,000 remaining works—paintings, drawings, sculptures, ceramics, prints, and woodcuts.

He left an enormous—even mind-boggling—legacy to the art world. In a 1991 article in *Vanity Fair,* Picasso's friend and biographer John Richardson observed, "Almost every artist of any interest who's worked in the last 50 years is indebted to Picasso … whether he's reacting against him knowingly or is unwittingly influenced by him. Picasso sowed the seeds whose fruits we are continuing to reap.

What is pop art?

Pop art began in the 1950s in Britain (the term itself was invented by English art critic Lawrence Alloway) and became one of the most influential art movements of the mid-twentieth century, particularly in Britain and the United States. Pop artists challenged the status of fine art by relying on mass media images, such as those from advertisements and popular culture, to create artworks. Key pop artists include Allen Jones (1937–), Eduardo Paolozzi (1924–2005), Peter Blake (1930–), and Richard Hamilton (1922–2011), all of whom worked primarily in the UK. American pop artists include Roy Lichtenstein (1923–2007), Robert Rauschenberg (1925–2008), Jasper Johns (1930–), and most notably, Andy Warhol (1928–1987).

Early pop art shows were held in London and New York City, including the "This is Tomorrow" show at the Whitechapel Art Gallery and a number of shows at New York's Sidney Janis Gallery. Critics were mixed in their reviews, with many critics shocked at the use of "low art" to create works of "fine art." For example, Robert Rauschenberg, who studied painting under Bauhaus artist Josef Albers, created a series of works incorporating the "Coca-Cola" logo and Roy Lichtenstein's large paintings mimicked the look and style of comic book art. Pop art questioned the difference between good and bad taste, and broadened the scope of possible fine art subject matter to include everyday objects and culture.

Who was Andy Warhol?

Andy Warhol (1928–1987) was an iconic artist-celebrity whose pop art images of Campbell's soup cans and film celebrities continue to be highly recognizable and immensely valuable. Popularly known for his bleach-blond hair, dark sunglasses, and turtle-neck sweaters, Andy Warhol was interested in stripping mass media images of their symbolic value, thus rendering them anew. Born in Pittsburgh, Pennsylvania, Warhol studied at the Carnegie Institute and moved New York City in 1949, where he began a career in commercial art. He also worked in painting, printmaking, sculpture, and film.

Warhol's New York studio, dubbed, "The Factory," was where Warhol and his team of assistants used silk screen machines to mass produce images. His goal was to mechanically produce familiar images until they no longer held any meaning, like saying the same word over and over until it sounds like nonsense. This explains paintings such as *Fragile– Handle with Care*, which depicts the word "fragile" repeatedly, until the words become nearly abstract. Similarly, Warhol made an eight-hour-long film of the Empire State Building, created using a single, drawn-out shot. Warhol's work dominated the 1960's art and fashion scene, and he continued to push boundaries into the 1980s, with celebrity portraits and continued exploitation of celebrity.

Why did Jasper Johns paint the American flag?

Jasper Johns (1930–) is an American contemporary artist known for his painting, printing, and sculpture. His paintings frequently feature familiar objects and symbols such as targets, numbers, and the American flag. In line with the themes and goals of pop art, Johns was in-

251

terested in using familiar objects in a new way. Rather than create new images, he wanted to depict "things the mind already knows" (as quoted in the Met Museum Timeline of Art History). He said that his decision to paint flags was inspired by a dream, and his realistic works serve to highlight the artificiality of the symbols he represents.

Who is David Hockney?

David Hockney (1937–) is considered an important early pop artist, though he dislikes that association and his work demonstrates a range of styles. A prominent contemporary artist whose career kick-started while he was still a student at the Royal College of Art in London, Hockney's early work frequently incorporated poetic fragments and personal themes. Paintings such as *We Two Boys Together Clinging* (1961) are reminiscent of the *art brut* of Jean Dubuffet with scrawled handwriting and child-like forms. Hockney's mid-career paintings are notably smooth and painted with acrylic, reflecting the artist's skill as a graphic artist as well as a painter. His most famous pop art work is arguably, *The Big Splash* (1967), a brightly painted scene of a California swimming pool in which a jarring and geometric diving board juts into the center of the scene. A swirled splash breaks the smooth monotony of the pool's blue water, creating a photo-like image. In the 1970s and 80s, he experimented with collage by incorporating Polaroid fragments into highly ordered paintings. His work with photography led to a prestigious award from the Royal Photographic Society in 2003. Hockney continues to paint and receive recognition for his work, including monumental landscapes such as *A Bigger Grand Canyon* (1998), which is composed of over sixty individual paintings.

Why did Roy Lichtenstein paint comic book images?

Roy Lichtenstein (1923–1997), whose early work reflected interest in Cubism and abstract expressionism, began to make his comic-book paintings in the 1960s. With paintings such as *Whaam!* (1963) and *Eddie Diptych* (1962), Lichtenstein transformed comic images into monumental works of fine art by enlarging them and rendering them with the so-called "Ben Day" dots used to print newspaper images. His approach has been described by some critics as a parody, but one in line with the goals of pop art. While Lichtenstein was able to transform the "low" art of comic books into fine art paintings, he also did the opposite. His *Yellow Brushstroke* (1965) depicts a single smear of yellow paint with so much detail it becomes nearly laughable, and completely banal. He also converted famous masterpieces, such as Vincent van Gogh's *Bedroom in Arles* (1888), into his iconic comic style. One of Lichtenstein's goals in creating these comic-like images was to encourage the viewer to question the way supposedly realistic paintings accurately depict reality.

What is op art?

The "op" in "op art" refers to optical illusion and op art paintings, such as Bridget Riley's *Metamorphosis* (1964), are composed of precise, geometric abstractions. Op art paintings pulse with an energy created by a strategic alignment of color and form, creating a blurring after-image, similar to the experience of looking at a bright light for too long, or looking into a funhouse mirror. Hungarian artist Victor Vasarely (1908–1997) was a pioneer of op art. His commercial paintings of zebras (and their repetitious black-and-white stripes) served as early optic experimentations while works such as the black-and-white *Supernovae* (1959–1961) are dynamic and restless. Vasarely linked these works to free-moving kinetic art by artists such as Alexander Calder. The viewer is an essential part of the op art experience because without the viewer—specifically the viewer's perception, there can be no optical illusion. Op art serves as an inquiry into the very nature of optical perception—the experience of seeing things.

What is minimalism?

Minimalism is a term that describes simple, geometric art that is often impersonal and made with a new set of materials, including aluminum, Plexiglas, plywood, and steel. Minimalist artists attempted to distill their work into a pure form, editing any reference to personality, feelings, symbolism, or story. The style became popular during the mid-1960s, though many art critics at the time accused minimalism of being too cold, and questioned whether art could, or should, be produced by industrial means. The term "minimalism" has been used to describe the art of many artists, from Ad Reinhardt to Yves Klein, Frank Stella to Robert Rauschenberg. The work of artist Donald Judd (1928–1994) is a good example of minimalism. Judd explored the difference between painting and sculpture with his series of wall structures. Judd's wall structures are composed of a series of machine-made rectangular forms that protrude from the wall, forms that he called "specific objects." The work of artist Anne Truitt (1921–2004) occasionally blurred the line between minimalism and color-field painting; however, her minimalist sculpture *Grant* (1963)—a long wooden beam, painted in acrylic—was a pure, impersonal, geometric form.

What is installation art?

Installation art is art that is more than three-dimensional—it creates a complete environment. Entire gallery spaces can be devoted to a single installation, usually—but not always—temporarily. Installation art became popular in the 1970s and continues to be an important art form today. Installations rely upon the interactions of the viewer/participant and can even be collected, which means they are not necessarily site-specific. Yves Klein created one of the first installations with his work *The Void* in 1958. For this work, Klein presented a completely empty, white-walled gallery. Other famous examples of installation art include British sculptor Rachel Whiteread's *Embankment* (2005), which she created for the Turbine Hall at the Tate Modern museum in London. The piece consisted of tower-like mountains made of thousands of white, plaster casts of boxes. Visitors to the gallery were able to move through the installation—allowing them to engage with a monumental art form on an intimate level.

Who is Jenny Holzer?

Jenny Holzer (1950–) is a conceptual artist known for text-based installations and public displays. Her earliest work was *Truisms* (1977–1979), which consisted of anonymous posters hung up around New York City with one-line phrases such as "Protect Me From What I Want," "Abuse of Power Comes As No Surprise," and "Expiring For Love Is Beautiful But Stupid." Along with displaying these truisms on posters, Holzer carved words into public benches, created t-shirts, hats, and more. Later in her career, she began to work with LED (light emitting diode) displays, which has garnered her much critical and popular success. For example, she created a sixty-five-foot-wide, permanent LED display in the lobby of 7 World Trade Center, in which text slowly scrolls. Holzer writes many of her own texts, and

253

during her later career she began to appropriate language from international poets as well as text from unclassified U.S. documents, including interrogation transcripts from Abu Ghraib in Iraq. In this case, Holzer projects private words in a public space, emphasizing the difference between private and public communication.

When was photography established as an art form?

In the early 1900s. Alfred Stieglitz (1864-1946) is the acknowledged "father of modern photography." His interest in the medium began when he was just a toddler: at the age of two, he became obsessed with a photo of his cousin, carrying it with him at all times. When he was nine years old, he took exception to a professional photographer's practice of using pigment to color a black-and-white photo, complaining that this spoiled the quality of the print.

Between 1887 and 1911 Stieglitz worked to establish photography as a valid form of artistic expression, a pursuit for which he was sometimes publicly derided. He believed that photography should be separate from painting, but on an equal footing as an art form. He also strove to differentiate photography by instilling it with an American essence; the streets of New York City became his subject. By the time Stieglitz founded the Photo-Secession Group in 1902, he had developed a uniquely American art form. Stieglitz also published and edited photography magazines, most notably *Camera Work* (1903-17). After an unhappy first marriage, in 1924, Stieglitz married American artist Georgia O'Keeffe (1887-1986), who became the subject of one of his best-known series of works.

ARCHITECTURE

How old is the Great Wall of China?

The immense structure, built as a barricade of protection against invasion, was begun during the third century B.C. by Emperor Shih Huang Ti (Cheng; c. 259-210 B.C.) of the Ch'in dynasty, and was expanded over the course of succeeding centuries. The wall stretches 1,500 miles, ranges in height between 20 to 50 feet, and is between 15 and 25 feet thick. In the thirteenth century, the wall was penetrated when Mongols conquered China, expanding their empire across all of Asia.

How old is the Parthenon?

The ancient temple, originally built on the Acropolis, a hill overlooking the city of Athens, was constructed between 447 and 432 B.C. by Greeks. The white marble edifice, considered a prime example of Greek architecture, has an interesting history: About A.D. 500, it became a Christian church; in the mid-1400s, when the region was captured by Turkish Muslims, it was turned into a mosque; and in 1687, when Venetians tried to take the city, the Parthenon was severely damaged; only ruins remain today.

How was the Colosseum ruined?

The Roman structure, begun during the reign of Vespasian (ruled A.D. 69-79), was disassembled during the Middle Ages (500-1350) when its stones and brocks were removed and used to construct other buildings. The Colosseum, situated in the center of the city of Rome,

The Great Wall of China, originally built as a barricade against invasion, stretches 1,500 miles and is visible from space.

was a giant, outdoor theater. Between 80 and 404, it was an entertainment center where battles were staged, gladiators competed, and men fought wild animals. It could seat 50,000 spectators who were separated from the arena by a 15-foot wall.

When was London's Westminster Abbey built?

The famed national church of England was begun between 1042 and 1065 when Edward the Confessor (c. 1003-1066) built a church on the site of the Abbey. King Henry III (1207-1272) began work on the main part of Westminster in 1245. Since the time of William the Conqueror (1066), all of England's rulers, except Edward V and Edward VIII, have been crowned at the church. The Abbey is also a burial place of great English statesmen and literary giants (the latter are buried in the Poet's Corner).

Why does the Leaning Tower of Pisa lean?

The famous bell tower in Pisa (in northwestern Italy) leans because of the unstable soil on which it was built. Construction began in 1173 on the approximately 180-foot campanile; it began to lean as soon as the first three floors were completed. Nevertheless, building continued, and the seven-story structure was finished between 1360 and 1370. Leaning a bit more each year, by the time it was closed for repairs in 1990, the tower tilted 14.5 feet out of line when measured from the top story. Engineers on the project worked to stabilize the foundation and straighten it slightly (to prevent damage). The tower, which was built alongside a church and

255

a baptistery, would probably not be remarkable if it were not for its slant. But with its characteristic angle, it continues to attract tourists to the small town on the Arno River.

Why is the Cathedral of Notre-Dame famous?

The Paris cathedral was built using the first true flying buttresses (masonry bridges that transmit the thrust of a vault or a roof to an outer support). The device allowed the structure to achieve a great height—one of the first Gothic churches to do so. Gothic was a medieval architectural style that predominated in northern Europe from the early twelfth century until the sixteenth century; it was epitomized in elaborate churches with stained-glass windows—ornamentation meant to instill the building itself with transcendental qualities. One of the leading examples of Gothic architecture is the Amiens Cathedral (in Amiens, northern France), which was begun in 1220. Its soaring nave (the central area of a church) epitomizes the era's drive for height. The Amiens cathedral is France's largest.

Why is Spain's Alhambra historically important?

The elaborate palace, built east of the city of Granada, in southern Spain, was built by Moors, Muslim North Africans who occupied the Iberian Peninsula (Spain and Portugal) for hundreds of years during the Middle Ages (500-1350). The fortified structure, built between 1238 and 1354, is a monument of Islamic architecture in the Western world. Its name is derived from an Arabic word meaning "red"; the highly ornamental palace, with its decorative columns, walls, and ceilings, was constructed of red brick. Perched on a hilltop, the Alhambra was the last stronghold of the Moors in Spain. In 1492 the palace was captured by forces of Spain's King Ferdinand (1452-1516) and Queen Isabella (1451-1504).

When was the Brooklyn Bridge completed?

The bridge, which spans New York's East River to connect Manhattan and Brooklyn, was completed in 1883. Upon opening, it was celebrated as a feat of modern engineering and, with its twin gothic towers, as an architectural landmark of considerable grace and beauty. It is a high statement of the era—an expression of the optimism of the Industrial Revolution. It was designed by German American engineer John Augustus Roebling (1806-1869), who, upon his death, was succeeded on the project by his son Washington Augustus Roebling (1837-1926). When the Brooklyn Bridge was finished, it was the longest suspension bridge in the world: it measures 1,595 feet. The bridge hangs from steel cables that are almost 16 inches thick. The cables are suspended from stone and masonry towers that are 275 feet tall. Specially designed watertight chambers allowed for the construction of the two towers—whose bases are built on the floor of the East River. The project proved to be an enormous and dangerous undertaking. Underwater workers suffered from the bends, a serious and potentially fatal blood condition caused by the decrease in pressure that results from rising from the water's depth too quickly. But man prevailed against the elements and, following 14 laborious years, on May 24, 1883, the Brooklyn Bridge was inaugurated. Five years later, Brooklyn became a borough of New York City, and in 1964 the bridge was designated a national historic landmark.

When did modern architecture begin?

The term "modern architecture" is used to refer to the architecture that turned away from past historical designs in favor of designs that are expressive of their own time. As such, it

Upon completion in 1883 the Brooklyn Bridge was considered a feat of modern engineering. (Photo, c. 1900.)

had its beginnings in the late nineteenth century when architects began reacting to the eclecticism that was prevalent at the time. Two "schools" emerged: art nouveau and the Chicago school.

Art nouveau, which had begun about 1890, held sway in Europe for some 20 years and was evident not only in architecture and interiors, but in furniture, jewelry, typography, sculpture, painting, and other fine and applied arts. Its proponents included Belgian architects Victor Horta (1861-1947) and Henry Van de Velde (1863-1957), and Spaniard Antonio Gaudi (1852-1926).

But it was the Chicago school that, in the rebuilding days after the Great Chicago Fire (1871), created an entirely new form. American engineer and architect William Le Baron Jenney (1832-1907) led the way. Four of the five younger architects who followed him had at one time worked in Jenney's office: Louis Henry Sullivan (1856- 1924), Martin Roche (1855-1927), William Holabird (1854-1923), and Daniel Hudson Burnham (1846-1912). Burnham was joined by another architect, John Wellborn Root (1850-1891). Together these men established solid principles for the design of modern buildings and skyscrapers where "form followed function." Ornament was used sparingly, and the architects fully utilized iron, steel, and glass.

By the 1920s modern architecture had taken firm hold, and in the mid-twentieth century it was furthered by the works of Walter Adolf Gropius (1883-1969), Le Corbusier (Charles-Édouard Jeanneret; 1887-1965), Ludwig Mies van der Rohe (1886-1969), and Frank Lloyd Wright (1867-1959). For practical purposes, modern architecture ended in the 1960s with the deaths of the aforementioned masters.

Examples of modern architecture include Chicago's Monadnock Building (1891), Reliance Building (1895), Carson Pirie Scott store (1904), and Robie House (1909); New York City's Rockefeller Center (1940), Lever House (1952), and Seagram Building (1958); as well as Taliesin West (1938-59) in Arizona, Johnson Wax Company's Research Tower (1949) in Wisconsin, and the Lovell House (1929) in Los Angeles.

Who invented the skyscraper?

The credit is usually given to American architect William Jenney (1832-1907), who designed the 10-story Home Insurance Building, erected on the corner of LaSalle and Monroe Streets in Chicago in 1885. The building was the first in which the entire structure was of skeleton construction—of cast iron, wrought iron, and Bessemer steel. However, some experts believe the first skyscraper to have been designed was one by the American firm Holabird and Roche, also in Chicago. The firm, founded by two former students of Jenney, designed the skeleton-framed Tacoma Building, which was actually not completed until 1889. Both the Home Insurance Building and the Tacoma Building were demolished in 1931 and 1929, respectively.

It was the use of steel, the innovation of a safe elevator, and the use of central heating that combined to make possible the construction of tall buildings toward the end of the nineteenth century. Once the trend had started, it quickly took off: Another Chicago firm, Burnham and Root (Burnham, too, had been a student of Jenney), completed the 14-story Reliance Building in 1895; it had a steel skeleton frame. The further development of the skyscraper is visible in the Gage Buildings in Chicago—two of which were designed by Holabird and Roche, and one by Louis Henry Sullivan (1856-1924), the Chicago architect often credited for mastering the skyscraper. Other Chicago skyscrapers built by Holabird and Roche during the early days of modern architecture include the Marquette Building (1894) and the Tribune Building (1901).

What is the tallest man-made structure in the world?

The Burj Dubai skyscraper is currently the tallest structure. When completed, it will reach a height of over 2,064 feet (629 meters). It has surpassed the CN Tower in Toronto, Canada, which since 1976 was the world's tallest building at 1,815 feet (553.3 meters).

THEATER

How old is the dramatic form of tragedy?

Tragedy, a form of drama central to western literature, dates to ancient times—the fifth century B.C., when Greeks held a religious festival to honor the god Dionysus (god of fertility, wine, and, later, drama). Famous ancient tragedies include *Oresteia* by Aeschylus (who is credited with inventing tragedy), *Oedipus Rex* by Sophocles, and *Medea* and *Trojan Women* by Euripides. The philosopher Aristotle observed that tragedy's function is a cathartic one—by participating in the drama, the spectators are purged of their emotions of pity and fear. The well-known Renaissance tragedies of William Shakespeare (1564-1616) harken back to the works of Roman statesman and playwright Seneca (c. 4 B.C.-A.D. 65), who wrote during the first century. He is credited with creating dramatic conventions including unity of time and place, violence, bombastic language, revenge, and ghostly appearances.

How old is comedy?

Like tragedy, comedy as a form of drama dates back to ancient Greece. While tragedy was meant to engage human emotions, thereby cleansing spectators of their fears (according to Aristotle), comedy's intent was simply to entertain and amuse audiences. Athenian poet Aristophanes (who flourished circa the fifth century B.C.) is considered the greatest ancient writer of comedy. His plays, written for the festival of Dionysus (the god of fertility, wine, and, later, drama), were a mix of social, political, and literary satire. Performance vehicles included farce, parody, and fantasy. During the fourth century B.C., this old comedy evolved into a new comedy, which was less biting and more romantic and realistic in nature. New comedy, which was marked by strong character development and often subtle humor, includes the works of Greek playwright Menander (flourished during the fourth century B.C.) and those of Roman comic writers Plautus (flourished third century B.C.) and Terence (flourished second century B.C.), all of whom were influences on Ben Jonson, William Shakespeare, Jean Molière, and other writers of the sixteenth and seventeenth centuries.

What is No drama?

It is the oldest form of traditional Japanese drama, dating to A.D. 1383. It is rooted in the principles of Zen Buddhism, a religion emphasizing meditation, discipline, and the transition of truth from master to disciple. History and legend are the subjects of *No* plays, which are traditionally performed on a bare, wooden stage by masked male actors who performed the story using highly controlled movements. The drama is accompanied by a chorus, which chants lines from the play. The art form was pioneered by actor-dramatist Motokiyo Zeami (1363-1443) when he was 20 years old. Zeami had begun acting at age seven and went on to write more than half of the roughly 250 *No* dramas that are still performed today.

What are the elements of Japanese kabuki?

The most popular traditional form of Japanese drama, kabuki features dance, song, mime, colorful costumes, heavy makeup, and lively, exaggerated movements to tell stories about historical events. The drama had its beginnings in 1575 when Okuni, a woman, founded a kabuki company. In 1603 at Kyoto women danced at the Kitani shrine, playing men's roles as well as women's. In October 1629 kabuki became an all-male affair by order of the shogun Iemitsu, who de-

Japanese kabuki tells stories through dance, song, mime, colorful costumes, heavy makeup, and lively, exaggerated movements.

259

cided that it was immoral for women to dance in public. Just as in Elizabethan England, women's roles were then performed by men. The performing art became increasingly popular during the 1600s, eclipsing *bunraku* (puppet theater), in which a narrator recites a story, which is acted by large, lifelike puppets. Today kabuki remains a viable art form, borrowing from other forms of drama to adapt to changing times.

What is a passion play?

A passion play is a dramatization of the scenes connected with the passion and crucifixion of Jesus Christ. The roots of the passion play can be traced to ancient times: early Egyptians performed plays dedicated to the god Osiris (god of the underworld and judge of the dead), and the Greeks also acted out plays to honor their god Dionysus (the god of fertility, wine, and, later, drama). During the Middle Ages (500-1350) liturgical (religious ceremonial) dramas were performed. Toward the end of the tenth century, the Western church began to dramatize parts of the Latin mass, especially for holidays such as Easter. These plays were performed in Latin by the clergy, inside the church building. Eventually the performances became more secular, with laymen acting out the parts on the steps of the church or even in marketplaces.

The liturgical dramas developed into so-called miracle plays or mystery plays. As a symbol of gratitude or as a request for a favor, villagers would stage the life story of the Virgin Mary or of a patron saint. When the plague (also called the Black Death) ravaged Europe, the villagers at Oberammergau, Germany, in the Bavarian Alps, vowed to enact a passion play at regular intervals in the hope that by so doing they would be spared the Black Death. They first performed this folk drama in 1634 and have continued to stage it every 10 years, attracting numerous tourists to the small town in southern Germany.

Why is the Globe Theatre famous?

The Globe is known because of William Shakespeare's (1564-1616) involvement in it. In the 1590s an outbreak of the plague prompted authorities to close London theaters. At the time Shakespeare was a member of the Lord Chamberlain's Men, an acting company. With other members of the troupe, he helped finance the building of the Globe (on the banks of the Thames River), which opened in 1599 as a summer playhouse. Plays at the Globe, then outside of London proper, drew good crowds, and the Lord Chamberlain's Men also gave numerous command performances at court for King James. By the turn of the century, Shakespeare was considered London's most popular playwright, and by 1603 the acting group, whose summer home was the Globe Theatre, was known as the King's Men.

What was vaudeville?

Light, comical theatrical entertainment, vaudeville flourished at the end of the nineteenth century and beginning of the twentieth century. Programs combined a variety of music, theater, and comedy to appeal to a wide audience. Script writers attracted immigrant audiences by using ethnic humor, exaggerating dialects, and joking about the difficulties of daily immigrant life in America. (The word *vaudeville* is derived from an old French term for a satirical song, *vaudevire,* which is a reference to the Vire valley of France, where the songs originated.)

Vaudeville made its way to the American stage by the 1870s, when acts performed in theaters in New York, Chicago, and other cities. Troupes traveled a circuit of nearly 1,000 theaters around the country. As many as 2 million Americans a day flocked to the shows to see headliners such as comedians Eddie Cantor (1892-1964) and W. C. Fields (1880-1946), singer Eva Tanguay (1878-1947), and French actress Sarah Bernhardt (1844-1923).

During the first two decades of the twentieth century, vaudeville was the most popular form of entertainment in the country. In the 1930s, just as New York opened the doors of its famous Radio City Music Hall, which was intended to be a theater for vaudeville, the entertainment form began a quick decline. Motion pictures, radio, and, later, television took its place, with numerous vaudeville performers parlaying their success into these new media. Among those entertainers who had their origins in vaudeville acts were actors Rudolph Valentino, Cary Grant, Mae West, Jack Benny, George Burns, Gracie Allen, Ginger Rogers, Fred Astaire, Will Rogers, and Al Jolson.

MUSIC

When was our system for notating music developed?

The innovation came in the early eleventh century, when Guido of Arezzo (c. 991-1050), an Italian monk, devised a precise system for defining pitch. Guido was a leading music teacher and theorist in his day. As such, he was invited in about 1028 to Rome, where he presented a collection of religious anthems to Pope John XIX. Guido used a system of four horizontal lines (a staff) on which to chart pitch, and he used the syllables *ut* (later replaced with *do*), *re, mi, fa, sol,* and *la* to name the first six tones of the major scale. Before Guido developed his precise method for teaching music, singers had to learn melodies by memorizing them, a process that took many years. Using his notating system, singers were able to sight-read melodies. Guido's famous treatise, *Micrologus,* was one of the most widely used instruction books of the Middle Ages (500-1350).

How many musical Bachs were there?

Johann Sebastian Bach (1685-1750) was only one of a long and extended line of competent musicians—some 14 of them. The Bach family was a musical dynasty. J. S.'s father, Ambrosius Bach (1645-1695), was a court musician for the Duke of Eisenach, and several of J. S. Bach's close relatives were organists in churches. His eldest brother, Johann Christoph Bach (1671-1721), was apprenticed to the famous German composer Johann Pachelbel (1653-1706).

J. S. Bach left a musical legacy even beyond the vast body of church, vocal, and instrumental music that he composed: Four of his sons and one grandson were also accomplished musicians. "The English Bach" refers to J. S.'s son Johann Christian Bach (1735-1782), who composed operas, oratorios, arias, cantatas, symphonies, concertos, and chamber music. A proponent of Rococo style music, J. C. Bach influenced Wolfgang Amadeus Mozart (1756-1791).

Why do music historians talk about "before Bach" and "after Bach"?

Some scholars use these terms to classify music history since the life work of Johann Sebastian Bach (1685-1750) was so substantial, consisting of some 1,100 works, and has had

261

lasting and profound influence on music composition. While he was not famous during his lifetime and had disagreements with employers throughout his career, J. S. Bach's works and innovations in many ways defined music as people now know it. The tempered scale is among his inventions, and he initiated a keyboard technique that is considered standard today. Chronologically, J. S. Bach marks the end of the "prolific and variegated" baroque era, which began about 1600 and ended the year of his death, 1750.

A devout Christian, J. S. Bach believed that all music was to "the glory of God and the re-creation of the human spirit." As a spiritual person and true believer in eternal life, he left behind an impressive body of church music, including 300 cantatas (or musical sermons) as well as passions and oratorios. As a devoted family man who believed all his children were born musicians (and therefore, the Bachs could stage drawing-room music at any time), J. S. Bach also wrote chamber music, including instrumental concertos, suites, and overtures. Among his most well-known and beloved works are *The Saint Matthew Passion; Jesu, Joy of Man's Desiring; Sheep May Safely Graze;* and his *Christmas Oratorio.*

How old was Mozart when he composed his first work?

A child prodigy, Wolfgang Amadeus Mozart (1756-1791) was composing at the age of five. He had been playing the harpsichord since the age of three. His father, Leopold (1719-1787), was a composer and violinist who recognized his son's unusual music ability and encouraged and taught young Mozart. In 1762 Leopold took his son and daughter, Maria Anna (nicknamed "Nannerl"; 1751-1829), on tour to Paris. While there, young Wolfgang Mozart composed his first published violin sonatas and improvisations.

However, the image of the effortless and "artless child of nature" is not altogether true. Contrary to the reports that the gifted composer never revised first-and-only drafts, he did work at his craft. In a letter to his father, he wrote, "It is a mistake to think that the practice of my art has become easy to me—no one has given so much care to the study of composition as I have. There is scarcely a famous master in music whose works I have not frequently and diligently studied." The fact is that he did make revisions to his works, though it is also true that he composed at a rapid pace. The result is an impressive body of works, unequaled in beauty and diversity. The complete output—some 600 works in every form (symphonies, sonatas, operas, operettas, cantatas, arias, duets, and others)—would be enough to fill almost 200 CDs. Among his most cherished works are *The Marriage of Figaro* (1786), *Don Giovanni* (1787), *Così fan tutte* (1790), and *The Magic Flute* (1791).

Was Beethoven really deaf for much of his life?

Yes, Ludwig van Beethoven (1770-1827) suffered a gradual hearing loss during his twenties, and eventually lost his hearing altogether (in his early thirties). The loss was devastating to the German composer. In a letter to his brother he wrote, "But how humbled I feel when someone near me hears the distant sound of a flute, and I hear nothing; when someone hears a shepherd singing, and I hear nothing!" At one point he even contemplated suicide but instead continued his work.

He had studied briefly with Mozart (in 1787) and Joseph Haydn (in 1792), and appeared for the first time in his own concert in 1800. While the loss of his hearing later prevented him from playing the piano properly, it did nothing to hold back his creativity. Between 1800 and 1824, Beethoven wrote nine symphonies, and many believe that he developed the form to perfection. His other works include five piano concertos and 32 piano sonatas, as well as string quartets, sonatas for piano and violin, opera, and vocal music, including oratorios. It was about the time that he completed his work on his third symphony, the *Eroica* (1804), that he went completely deaf. Though he was himself a classicist, music critics often refer to a turning point marked by the *Eroica,* which shows the complexity of the romantic age of music.

A true genius, Beethoven's innovations include expanding the length of both the symphony and the piano concerto, increasing the number of movements in the string quartet (from four to seven), and adding instruments—including the trombone, contrabassoon, and the piccolo—to the orchestra, giving it a broader range. Through his adventurous piano compositions, Beethoven also

Ludwig van Beethoven, considered a genius of musical composition, was deaf for much of his life.

heightened the status of the instrument, which was a relatively new invention (1710). Among his most well-known and most-often-performed works are his third (*Eroica*), fifth, sixth (*Pastoral*), and ninth (*Choral*) symphonies, as well as the fourth and fifth piano concertos.

It is remarkable—even unfathomable—that these works, so familiar to so many, were never heard by their composer. A poignant anecdote tells of Beethoven sitting on stage to give tempo cues to the conductor during the first public performance of his ninth symphony. When the performance had ended, Beethoven—his back to the audience—was unaware of the standing ovation his work had received until a member of the choir turned Beethoven's chair around so he could see the tremendous response.

Why is Brahms's first symphony sometimes called "Beethoven's tenth"?

In many ways, Johannes Brahms (1833-1897) was the inheritor of Beethoven's genius, prompting some music historians to refer to Brahms's first symphony as "Beethoven's tenth." This is not to diminish the work of the great nineteenth-century composer, who left an enduring corpus of works. Brahms demonstrated that classicism continued to have artistic validity—and was not incompatible with—the romanticism of the late nineteenth century.

What does Wagnerian mean?

It is a reference to anything that is in the style of German composer Richard Wagner (1813-1883). Wagner was an enormously creative composer, conductor, and artistic manager who is credited with no less than originating the music drama. His interest in theater began in his boyhood, and by his teens he was writing plays. So that he could put music to these works, he sought out composition teachers. It is no surprise then that Wagner later conceived of the idea of the "total work of art," where music, poetry, and the visual arts are brought together in one stunning performance piece.

As an adult, Wagner led a scandalous life—even today challenging the music-listening public to separate his life from his art. He was someone modern audiences would recognize as a truly gifted and charismatic—if amoral—artist, working on a grand scale. Were he alive now, Wagner might well be creating blockbusters. In fact his musical compositions are heard in movies (including Francis Ford Coppola's *Apocalypse Now*) and are familiar to even the youngest audience today—or at least those who watch Bugs Bunny cartoons.

But this is not to take away from Wagner's serious accomplishments: His most widely recognized operatic works include *Lohengrin* (1848), the *Ring* cycle (1848-74), and *Tristan und Isolde* (1859). In the decades after his death, Wagner's reputation grew to the point that through the end of the nineteenth century his influence was felt by most every composer, who often referred to Wagner's works in measuring the value of their own.

Why did Schoenberg face sharp criticism in his day?

The Vienna-born American composer Arnold Schoenberg (1874-1951), now considered one of the great masters of the twentieth century, was derided for having thrown out the rules of composition—for working outside the confines of traditional harmony.

In his youth, he was a fan of Wagner's compositions, seeing each of his major operas repeatedly. A series of Schoenberg's early works reflect the Wagnerian influence. But just after the turn of the century, Schoenberg set out on his own path. The result was the 1909 composition *Three Pieces* for piano, which some music historians argue is the single most important composition of the twentieth century. The work is atonal, which is to say it is organized without reference to key. Schoenberg abandoned the techniques of musical expression as they had been understood for hundreds of years. This was no small moment for the music world, and many reacted with vocal and vehement criticism. (Of the outcry Schoenberg remarked in 1947 that it was as if "I had fallen into an ocean of boiling water.")

But he had his followers, too, among them his students. Though he was essentially self-taught as a composer, he became one of the most influential teachers of his time. It's interesting to note, however, that his teaching approach was grounded in the traditional practices of tonal harmony. He later brought order to the chaos of atonalism by developing a 12-tone serialism, showing how entire compositions could be organized around an ordained sequence of 12 notes. However, he never taught the method and rarely lectured or wrote about it.

Why does the music of Bartók figure prominently in concert programs today?

Béla Bartók (1881-1945) is revered today not only for his ability as a pianist (his teacher compared him to Franz Liszt [1811-1886], who was perhaps the greatest pianist of the nineteenth century), but for his compositions, which are steeped in the tradition of Hungarian folk music. Bartók studied and analyzed Hungarian, Romanian, and Arabian folk tunes, publishing thousands of collections of them in his lifetime. While ethnic music had influenced the works of other composers, Bartók was the first to make it an integral part of art music composition. His works were unique in that the folk music provided the sheer essence and substance of the music, lending the compositions a primitive quality. Among his masterpieces are his three stage works: the ballets *The Wooden Prince* and *The Miraculous Mandarin,* and the one-act opera *Duke Bluebeard's Castle.*

The introduction of folk music as the core of a musical composition has had far-reaching influence, which must have been felt by American composer Aaron Copland (1900-1990), whose *Appalachian Spring* (1944) features a simple Shaker tune, front and center.

Is Stravinsky the twentieth century's foremost composer?

The Russian-born American composer Igor Stravinsky (1882-1971) is certainly one of the greatest composers of the twentieth century. Stravinsky wrote concerts, chamber music, piano pieces, and operas, as well as ballets, for which he may be most well known.

Between 1903 and 1906 Stravinsky studied under the great Russian composer Nikolay Rimsky-Korsakov (1844-1908). In 1908 Stravinsky wrote his first work of note, the orchestral fantasy *Fireworks,* which was in honor of the marriage of Rimsky-Korsakov's daughter. The piece caught the attention of Sergey Diaghilev (1872-1929) of the Ballets Russes, who invited the young composer to participate in the ballet company's 1910 season (Ballets Russes had dazzled audiences the year before, bringing new energy to the art form). In collaboration with Diaghilev, Stravinsky went on to create masterpieces—*The Firebird* (1910), *Petrushka* (1911), and *Rite of Spring* (1913) among them. The partnership served to elevate the role of the ballet composer in the art world.

Rite of Spring is either Stravinsky's most famous or most infamous work. It was first performed by the Ballets Russes in the third week of its 1913 season. The choreography was arranged by the famous dancer Vaslav Nijinsky (1890-1950). But the performance stunned both the music and dance worlds. So extreme was the audience's reaction to this premier work that a riot nearly broke out inside the theater. Stravinsky had composed his music not to express spring's idyllic qualities but rather its turmoil and dissonance—similar to childbirth. Nijinsky paired Stravinsky's composition with complicated and visually frenzied dance movements, later characterized by the composer as a jumping competition. Though many thought it a disastrous performance, when the Ballets Russes continued to London, *Rite of Spring* was more widely accepted there—largely because the audience had been duly prepared for it.

The following year, *Rite of Spring* was performed in concert in Russia, but the reaction was mixed. The young composer Sergei Prokofiev (1891-1953) was in the audience and later wrote that he had been so moved by the work that he could not recover from the effects. Listeners today are still moved by the elevated rhythm of *Rite of Spring,* which makes an entire orchestra into a kind of sustained percussion instrument. Ultimately, most musicians and critics came to regard the watershed work as one of the finest compositions of the twentieth century.

Who invented jazz?

Ferdinand "Jelly Roll" Morton (1885-1941), a New Orleans pianist, claimed credit for having invented jazz. And to some degree, it was fair of him to think so—after all, his recordings with the group the Red Hot Peppers (1926-30) are among the earliest examples of disciplined jazz ensemble work. But in truth, the evolution of jazz from ragtime and blues was something that many musicians, in several cities, took part in. Most regard Morton as *one* of the founders

265

of jazz, the other founders include Bennie Moten (1894-1935), Eubie Blake (1883-1983), Duke Ellington (1899-1974), and Thomas "Fats" Waller (1904-1943).

Some would go back even farther to trace the roots of jazz: From 1899 to 1914 Scott Joplin (1868-1917) popularized ragtime, which was based on African folk music. Even astute music critics may not be able to draw a clear-cut distinction between ragtime and early jazz. Both musical forms rely on syncopation (the stressing of the weak beats), and either style can be applied to an existing melody and transform it. The definitions and boundaries of the two terms have always been subject to debate, which is further complicated by the fact that some musicians of the time considered ragtime to be more or less a synonym for early jazz.

Jazz greats Duke Ellington (piano) and Louis Armstrong (trumpet) rehearse in New York City in January 1946.

But there are important, albeit not strict, differences between the two genres as well: Rags were composed and written down in the European style of notation, while early jazz was learned by ear (players would simply show one another how a song went by playing it); jazz encourages and expects improvisation, whereas ragtime, for the most part, did not; and the basic rhythms are also markedly different, with jazz having a swing or "hot" rhythm that ragtime does not.

Whatever its origins, jazz became part of the musical mainstream by the 1930s and influenced other musical genres as well—including classical. American composer George Gershwin (1898- 1937) was both a songwriter and composer of rags as well as a composer of symphonic works. Many of his works, including *Rhapsody in Blue* (1924) and his piano preludes, contain ragtime and jazz elements.

Perhaps more than any other composer and musician, Miles Davis (1926-1991) expanded the genre: Through decades of prolific work, Davis constantly pushed the boundaries of what defines jazz and in so doing set standards for other musicians.

Is blues music older than jazz?

Only slightly (and only if your definition of jazz doesn't include ragtime). Really, the two musical traditions developed side by side, with blues emerging about the first decade of the 1900s and hitting the height of its early popularity in 1920s Harlem, where the songs were seen as an expression of African American life. Great blues singers like Ma Rainey (1886-1939) and Bessie Smith (1894 or 1898-1937) sang of the black reality—determined but weary. During the Harlem Renaissance the music was a symbol for African American people who were struggling to be accepted for who they were. Poet Langston Hughes (1902-1967) saw the blues as a distinctly black musical genre, and as helping to free blacks from American standardization.

As the first person to codify and publish blues songs, American musician and composer W. C. Handy (1873-1958) is considered the "father of the blues." The Florence, Alabama, native produced a number of well-known works, including "Memphis Blues," "St. Louis Blues" (which is one of the most frequently recorded songs in popular music), "Beale Street Blues," and "Careless Love."

When did the Big Band era begin?

On December 1, 1934, Benny Goodman's *Let's Dance* was broadcast on network radio, which effectively launched the swing era, in which Big Band music achieved huge popularity. Goodman (1909-1986) was a virtuoso clarinetist and bandleader. His jazz-influenced dance band took the lead in making swing the most popular style of the time.

How old is country music?

Old-time music or "hillbilly music," both early names for country music, emerged in the early decades of the 1900s. By 1920 the first country music radio stations had opened, and healthy record sales in rural areas caused music industry executives to take notice. But it was an event in 1925, in the middle of the American Jazz Age, that put country music on the map: On November 28, WSM Radio broadcast *The WSM Barn Dance,* which soon became known as *The Grand Ole Opry* when the master of ceremonies, George D. Hay, took to introducing the program that way—since it was aired immediately after an opera program. The show's first performer was Uncle Jimmy Thompson (1848-1931). Early favorites included Uncle Dave Macon (1870-1952), who played the banjo and sang, and Roy Acuff (1903-1992), who was the Opry's first singing star. Millions tuned in and soon the Nashville-based show had turned Tennessee's capital city into Music City U.S.A. In the 1960s and again in the late 1980s and 1990s, country music reached the height of popularity, while holding on to its small-town, rural-based audience who were the show's first fans.

Is bluegrass music a distinctly American genre?

Yes, the style of music developed out of country music during the late 1930s and throughout the 1940s. Bill Monroe (1911-1996), a country and bluegrass singer-songwriter, altered the tempo, key, pitch, and instrumentation of traditional country music to create a new style—named for the band that originated it, Bill Monroe and the Blue Grass Boys (Monroe's home state was Kentucky). Bluegrass was first heard by a wide audience when in October 1939, Monroe and his band appeared on the popular country music radio program *The Grand Ole Opry*.

Although bluegrass evolved through several stages and involved a host of contributors, through it all Bill Monroe remained the guiding and inspirational force, and therefore merits the distinction of being the "father of bluegrass."

Who was more important to rock and roll—Elvis Presley or the Beatles?

While music historians—and fans of either or both—may be willing to offer an opinion, the question cannot be definitively answered. The fact is that popular music today would not be what it is had it not been for both Elvis Presley and the Beatles. And the influences of both are still felt.

Elvis Presley (1935-1977) brought to music an exciting and fresh combination of country, gospel, blues, and rhythm and blues music, and topped it all off with a style and sense of showmanship that dazzled young audiences. His first commercial recording was "That's All Right, Mama" in 1954, which was followed in 1956 by the success of "Heartbreak Hotel." Between 1956 and 1969 he had 17 number-one records. Presley defined a new musical style—and an era.

Among those the American Presley had influenced were four English musicians who called themselves the Beatles. Originally founded as the Quarrymen by John Lennon (1940-1980) in 1956, the group became the most popular rock-and-roll band of the 1960s. Their first single was "Love Me Do," released on October 5, 1962, and producer George Martin was encouraged that the Beatles could produce a number-one record. In 1963 they did: "Please Please Me" was released in Britain on January 12 and was an immediate hit. Other hits off their first

Elvis Presley (shown in 1956) brought to music an exciting and fresh combination of country, gospel, blues, and rhythm and blues.

album included "She Loves You" and "I Want to Hold Your Hand." The follow-up album, *With the Beatles,* was released in 1964 and established them as Britain's favorite group.

Already popular in their homeland, "Beatlemania" began in the United States on February 7, 1964, when the mop-topped "Fab Four" (Lennon along with Paul McCartney, b. 1942, George Harrison, 1943-2001, and Ringo Starr, b. 1940) arrived at New York's Kennedy International Airport and were met by a mob of more than 10,000 screaming fans and 110 police officers. Two days later, on February 9, the Beatles made their legendary appearance on *The Ed Sullivan Show.* By April the group held onto the top five positions on the U.S. singles charts. The British Invasion had begun.

In their early years, the Beatles brought a new energy to rock and roll and picked up where Presley, Buddy Holly, and Little Richard had left off. The instrumentation and orchestration of Beatles songs (for which their producer George Martin deserves at least some of the credit) were innovative at the time, and are common for rock music today. Their rock movies, *A Hard Day's Night* (1964) and *Help!* (1965), were a precursor to the music videos of today. When the band decided to break up, the April 10, 1970, announcement proved to be the end of an era.

DANCE

Why is the Ballets Russes famous?

he notoriety of the Ballets Russes began on a May night in 1909. It was then that the company, created by Russian impresario Sergey Diaghilev (1872-1929), performed innovative ballet choreographed by Michel Fokine (1880-1942). The Parisian audience, made up of the city's elite, was wowed by the choreography, set design, and musical scores, as well as the performances of the lead dancers—the athletic vigor of Vaslav Nijinsky, the delicate beauty of Tamara Karsavina, the expressiveness of Anna Pavlova, and the exotic quality of Ida Rubinstein. Ballet had been freed of the constraints and conventions that had held it captive. The art form was reawakened.

The reforms were on every level: choreography, performance, costuming, and design. The company's chief set designer was Léon Bakst (1866-1924), whose sense of color had influenced not only stage designs but even women's fashions. Soon Diaghilev and the Ballets Russes were at the center of the art world: Major twentieth-century painters, including Robert Edmond Jones, Pablo Picasso, André Derain, Henri Matisse, and Joan Miró, created set and costume designs for the dance company. And Diaghilev commissioned music that could match the spectacular dancing, choreography, and decor of his ballets. History's most celebrated composers, including Maurice Ravel, Claude Debussy, Richard Strauss, Sergei Prokofiev, and Igor Stravinsky, provided the scores for the dances performed by Ballets Russes. The company, under Diaghilev's direction, had created a completely different kind of dance drama, bringing ballet out of the shadows of opera and asserting it as an art form unto itself.

The ballet companies of today are the lasting legacy of the Ballets Russes. Diaghilev illustrated that through a collaborative process, excellent art could be created outside the traditional academy. The Ballets Russes provided twentieth-century dance with the model of the touring ballet company and seasonal repertory.

Who was Balanchine?

The name of the Russian-born choreographer is synonymous with modern American ballet: George Balanchine (1904-1983) was one of the most influential choreographers of the twentieth century, creating more than 200 ballets in his lifetime and choreographing 19 Broadway musicals as well as four Hollywood films. He co-founded three of the country's foremost dance institutions: the School of American Ballet (in 1934); the American Ballet Company (1935); and the New York City Ballet (1948), the first American ballet company to become a public institution.

His entrance into the world of dance was entirely accidental: In August 1914 Balanchine accompanied his sister to an audition at the Imperial School of Ballet and was invited to audition as well. Though his sister failed, he passed and, against his own wishes, was promptly enrolled. However, Balanchine remained uninterested in the art form, even running away from school shortly after starting. The turning point for the young dancer came with a performance of Tchaikovsky's ballet *The Sleeping Beauty* (1890). He was dazzled by the experience and chose to stay with the school's rigorous training program.

Serenade (1935; music by Tchaikovsky) is considered by many to be Balanchine's signature work. His other well-known works include *Apollo* (1928), *The Prodigal Son* (1929), *The Nutcracker* (1954), and *Don Quixote* (1965), as well as *Jewels*, the first full-length ballet without a plot.

Remembering the opportunity he had been given as a child, Balanchine was known for choreographing children's roles into many of his ballets. His outreach did not end there: He organized lecture-demonstration tours for schools, gave free ballet performances for underprivileged children, conducted free annual seminars for dance teachers, and gave free advice and use of his ballets to other ballet companies. Balanchine's unparalleled body of work was instrumental in establishing the vibrant style and content of contemporary ballet in America, where he brought ballet to the forefront of the performing arts.

Who was Dame Margot Fonteyn?

Fonteyn (1919-1991) has been called an "international ambassador of dance." The British-trained ballerina achieved worldwide fame and recognition during more than 34 years with the Royal Ballet, expanding the company's female repertoire and becoming the model for the modern ballerina. In 1962, at the age of 43, Fonteyn formed a dance partnership with Soviet defector Rudolf Nureyev (1938-1993), challenging traditional assumptions about the ability of mature dancers to continue vigorous performance careers. In her later years, she continued to be active in the world of dance, helping set up dance scholarships, fostering international artistic relations, and encouraging the growth of dance institutions around the world.

How did modern dance begin?

American dancer and choreographer Martha Graham (1894-1991) is the acknowledged creator of modern dance. She was 35 years old when the Martha Graham Dance Group made its debut on April 14, 1929, ushering in a new era in dance performance. The new form of dance dissolved the separation between mind and body and relied on technique that was built from within.

Graham's interest in dance had begun in her youth, and as an astute observer and manipulator of light and space, she came to be regarded later in life as one of the masters of the modernist movement—on a par with artist Pablo Picasso (1881-1973). She is credited with revolutionizing dance as an art form; in her hands it had become nonlinear and nonrepresentational theater. Choreographing some 180 works in her lifetime, she also taught many students who rose to prominence as accomplished and masterful dancers, including Merce Cunningham and Paul Taylor.

Who founded the Dance Theater of Harlem?

The Dance Theater of Harlem, the first world-renowned African American ballet company, was founded by Arthur Mitchell (1934-), a principal dancer with the New York City Ballet, along with Karel Shook (1920-1985), a dance teacher and former director of the Netherlands Ballet. The impetus for the creation of the company came on April 4, 1968, while Mitchell was waiting to board a plane from New York City to Brazil (where he was establishing that country's first national ballet company) and he heard that Martin Luther King Jr. (1929-1968) had been assassinated. Mitchell later said that as he sat thinking about the tragic news, he wondered to himself, "Here I am running around the world doing all these things, why not do them at home?" Mitchell had spent his youth in Harlem, and he felt he should return there to establish a school to pass on his knowledge to others and to give black dancers the opportunity to perform. The primary purpose of the school was "to promote interest in and teach young black people the art of classical ballet, modern and ethnic dance, thereby creating a much-needed self-awareness and better self-image of the students themselves."

The idea was a success: During the 1970s and 1980s the company toured nationally and internationally, often performing to sell-out crowds and participating in prestigious events including international art festivals, a state dinner at the White House, and the closing ceremonies of the 1984 Olympic Games.

Today, the Dance Theater of Harlem is acknowledged as one of the world's finest ballet companies. Not only did Mitchell succeed in giving black dancers the opportunity to learn and to perform, he effectively erased color barriers in the world of dance, testimony to the universality of classical ballet.

How long has the waltz been danced?

Considered the quintessential ballroom dance, the waltz first became popular in Europe in 1813. But it dates as far back as the mid-1700s (the first written occurrence of the word *waltz* was in 1781). In the 1850s the dance captivated Vienna, and the prolific Johann Strauss (1825-1899), also known as the "Waltz King," produced scores of new waltzes to meet the increasing demand. Many of the compositions were named for professional associations and societies.

One of the most well-known waltzes is "The Blue Danube," first performed by Strauss on February 15, 1867, in Vienna. The lyrics, from a poem by Karl Beck, were sung by the Viennese Male Singing Society. The new waltz created an immediate sensation. It is an Austrian tradition whenever "The Blue Danube" is played that the opening strain is played first, followed by a pause before the work is played by the full orchestra. The pause is so that the audience may applause.

MOVIES

When was the first movie shown?

On March 22, 1895, the first in-theater showing of a motion picture took place in Paris, when the members of the Société d'Encouragement à l'Industrie Nationale (National Society for the Promotion of Industry) gathered to see a film of workers leaving the Lumière factory at Lyons for their dinner hour. The cinematography of inventors Louis (1864-1948) and Auguste (1862-1954) Lumière, ages 31 and 33 respectively, was a vast improvement over the kinetoscope, introduced in 1894 by Thomas Edison, whose film could only be viewed by one person at a time. The 16-frame-per-second mechanism developed by the Lumière brothers became the standard for films for decades. The following year, on April 20,

Thomas Edison and George Eastman stand with a motion picture camera, c. 1925. Both inventors contributed to the innovation of movies.

271

1896, the first motion picture showing in the United States took place in New York; the film was shown using Thomas Edison's vitascope, which was an improvement on his kinetoscope, and a projector made by Thomas Armat.

What are the milestones in the motion picture industry?

Motion pictures continue to develop as new, sophisticated technologies are introduced to improve the moviegoing experience for audiences. In the decades following their rudimentary beginnings, there were many early milestones, including not only advancements in technology but improvements in conditions for those working in the then-fledgling industry:

1903: Edwin S. Porter's *The Great Train Robbery* was the first motion picture to tell a complete story. Produced by Edison Studios, the 12-minute epic established a pattern of suspense drama that was followed by subsequent movie makers.

1907: Bell & Howell Co. was founded by Chicago movie projectionist Donald H. Bell and camera repairman Albert S. Howell with $5,000 in capital. The firm went on to improve motion picture photography and projection equipment.

1910: *Brooklyn Eagle* newspaper cartoonist John Randolph Bray pioneered animated motion picture cartoons, using a "cel" system he invented and which was subsequently used by all animators.

1912: *Queen Elizabeth,* starring Sarah Bernhardt, was shown July 12 at New York's Lyceum Theater and was the first feature-length motion picture seen in America.

1915: D. W. Griffith's *The Birth of a Nation* provided the blueprint for narrative films.

1925: The new editing technique used in *Potemkin* revolutionized the making of motion pictures around the world. Soviet film director Sergei Eisenstein created his masterpiece by splicing film shot at many locations, an approach subsequently adopted by most film directors.

1926: The first motion picture with sound ("talkie") was demonstrated.

1927: The Academy of Motion Picture Arts and Sciences was founded by Louis B. Mayer of MGM Studios. The first president of the academy was Douglas Fairbanks.

1927: The first full-length talking picture, *The Jazz Singer,* starring vaudevillian Al Jolson, was released. By 1932 all movies talked.

1929: The first Academy Awards (for 1928 films) were held: Winners were William Wellman for *Wings,* Emil Jannings for best actor (in *Last Command*), and Janet Gaynor for best actress (in *Sunrise*). Movie columnist Sidney Skolsky dubbed the awards "the Oscars."

1928: Hollywood's major film studios signed an agreement with the American Telephone & Telegraph Corporation (AT&T) to use their technology to produce films with sound, leading to an explosion in the popularity of motion pictures.

1929: Eastman Kodak introduced 16-millimeter film for motion picture cameras.

1933: The Screen Actors Guild (SAG) was formed when six actors met in Hollywood to establish a self-governing organization of actors. The first organizing meeting yielded 18 founding members.

1935: The first full-length Technicolor movie was released, *Becky Sharpe*. The technology, however, was still in development, and the colors appeared garish.

1939: *Gone with the Wind* was released in Technicolor, which had come along way since its 1935 debut.

THE GOLDEN AGE AND CLASSIC HOLLYWOOD

Who created United Artists?

That was a partnership between D. W. Griffith, Charlie Chaplin, Mary Pickford, and Douglas Fairbanks Sr., who formed the movie production company in 1919.

When was Metro-Goldwyn-Mayer Pictures formed?

MGM Pictures was formed in 1924 when three other studios—Metro Pictures, Goldwyn Pictures, and the Louis B. Mayer Company—merged.

What were some other prominent studios that became powerful in the early decades?

Other big studios that had an influence on Hollywood were 20th Century Fox, Paramount Pictures, and Warner Brothers. Together with MGM and RKO, these were the "Big Five" (RKO was actually based in New York, however). The "Little Three" included United Artists, Columbia Pictures, and Universal Pictures.

How did the advent of sound in motion pictures change the industry?

Audiences loved them, but it spelled the doom for a number of actors, some of whom had a hard time remembering lines or had, well, funny-sounding voices. In silent films, too, a different style of acting was used than in "talkies." For example, slapstick was more effective without sound (Harold Lloyd's career came crashing down, for example), and in drama one would gesticulate wildly and exaggerate facial expressions to get the point across, but when people could hear dialogue such techniques came off as ludicrous.

Which film had the first sound?

It was not actually *The Jazz Singer* (1927), as most people think. A few shorts with sound and music were released the previous year, and, also in 1926, the feature film *Don Juan* had music. However, *The Jazz Singer* with Al Jolson (1886–1950) was the first with actual talking. A funny fact is that the filmmakers weren't looking for talking in the movie. They just wanted Jolson to sing, but they couldn't keep him from talking before his numbers and left it in the movie.

Silent films were still made for a few years, but by 1933 the era was at an end.

Why were so many musical made in early Hollywood films?

Everyone was enamored with the advent of sound in movies, and singing about it just seemed natural! Hollywood was making hundreds of them each year, and they were hugely popular.

273

One of the big early hits was 1929's *The Broadway Melody,* which won an Academy Award for best picture.

Who were some important figures in Westerns?

The Western genre was one of the most popular in both film and television through the 1970s. Actors such as John Wayne, Gary Cooper, Glenn Ford, Henry Fonda, and Jimmy Stewart and directors like John Ford and Sergio Leone dominated the big screen. TV shows such as *Gunsmoke, Bonanza, Wagon Train, The Rifleman, The Virginian,* and *Rawhide* were among the most popular series in the 1950s through the 1970s. Many of these were shot in California deserts close to Hollywood (a notable exception being the "Spaghetti Westerns" of Leone, who was famous for making Clint Eastwood movies in Spain).

How did horror movies get produced despite Hollywood censorship?

Because of the Hays Code, the largest studios were not able to get away with the scary flicks akin to those already being made in Germany and France. However, smaller studios such as

Buster Crabbe, who was born in Oakland, California, by the way, played Flash Gordon in the old movie serials. In this still from 1940s *Flash Gordon Conquers the Universe*, pictured are (left to right) actors Frank Shannon, Buster Crabbe, Carol Hughes, and Roland Drew.

Universal Pictures and United Artists could. This is why the early silent horror movies such as *The Hunchback of Notre Dame* (1923) and *The Phantom of the Opera* (1925), both starring make up acting wizard Lon Chaney Sr. (1883–1930) were produced by Universal. *Dracula* (1931), starring Hungarian actor Bela Lugosi (1882–1956) was similarly produced by Universal.

The genre was popular for years, but after a while it began to become a satire of itself with movies such as *Frankenstein Meets the Wolfman* (1943) and *Abbott and Costello Meet Frankenstein* (1948). It would not be seriously revived until the 1970s, when "scaryæ got a new definition with the movie *The Exorcist* (1973) and *The Shining* (1980). By then, the Hays Code was a distant memory.

How did science fiction movies get their start?

As with Westerns, science fiction in the movie theaters started with serials such as the "Buck Rogers" and "Flash Gordon" series of the 1930s. *Buck Rogers* was inspired by a novella by Philip Francis Nolan (1888–1940), and *Flash Gordon* by a comic strip by Alex Raymond (1909–1956). Pulp fiction books, however, really inspired many of the 1950s-era science fiction. These usually were outrageous tales of alien monsters battling humans, either on Earth or on other planets. A few, such as *The Day the Earth Stood Still* (1951) were more cerebral, but the best sci-fi written by the likes of Isaac Asimov, Robert Heinlein, Robert Silverberg, and their like remained in print novels.

The genre saw a decline in the 1960s and early 1970s until it was revived by George Lucas's (1944–) breakthrough *Star Wars* (1977) and Steven Spielberg's (1946–) *Close Encounters of the Third Kind* (1977). Lucas's special effects company, Industrial Light and Magic, sparked a special effects revolution that has culminated in advanced CGI evident in such modern films as *Avatar* (2009).

Why did the Golden Age of Hollywood come to an end?

The beginning of the end came with the an anti-trust case in 1938 concerning block booking, but World War II took attention away from enforcing the decision making the practice against the law. The nail in the coffin came in 1948 with the Supreme Court case *United States v. Paramount Pictures*. With this decision, big studios could no longer force theaters to buy movies in bulk, nor could the studios own their own theater franchises. The result was it permitted smaller studios and independents more freedom to sell their movies. With more competition, the quality of the movies went up, too, while quantity of production went down. This, in turn, also ended the period where actors were overworked making numerous films each year.

SPORTS

When were the first Olympic Games?

The Olympics date back to about 900 B.C.E., when, in ancient Greece, tens of thousands of sandal-wearing spectators descended on Olympia to cheer the runners, wrestlers, and bare-skinned boxers competing there. The games at Olympia were one of four athletic festivals in Greece, the others being the Isthmian games at Corinth, the Nemean games, and the Pythian games at Delphi, all of which alternated to form the periodos, or circuits, which guaranteed sports fans the opportunity to attend an athletic festival every year.

Winning was everything then: Athletes were required to register in order to compete, and rumors of Herculean opponents sometimes prompted competitors to withdraw. Victors were awarded crowns of olive leaves, and the second- and third-place finishers returned home undecorated.

The modern Olympic Games, begun by diminutive Frenchman Baron Pierre de Coubertin (1862–1937) possess a decidedly different spirit than did their ancient counterpart, where the only rules were that participants were not allowed to gouge, bite, put a knee to the groin, strangle, or throw sand at their opponent. The modern Olympic Games, publicly proposed by Coubertin on November 25, 1892, in Paris, and first held in Athens, Greece, in 1896, are based on their initiator's vision of the Olympic competition as an occasion to promote peace, harmony, and internationalism.

In April 1896, some 40,000 spectators pressed into the Panathenean Stadium, which had been constructed on the site of an ancient stadium in Athens, to witness the athletic feats of the first modern Olympic heroes. Thirteen nations participated: Only male athletes (just more than 300 of them) competed and Greece received the most medals (forty-seven). The second Olympic Games were held in 1900 in Paris.

When were the first Winter Games held?

The Winter Olympic Games had a slow birth, making their first official appearance almost three decades after the first modern Games were held in Athens (1896). In 1901 Nordic

An ancient Greek stadium in Messini.

Games were held in Sweden. However, only Scandinavian countries participated in the events, which organizers intended to hold every four years.

The Nordic Games constituted the first organized international competition involving winter sports. Then, as part of the Summer Olympic Games in 1908, host-city London held a figure skating competition that October. Three years later, an Italian member of the International Olympic Committee (IOC) encouraged Sweden, the next host of the Summer Games, to include winter sports in 1912 or hold a separate event for them. Since Sweden already played host to the Nordic Games, they declined to pursue the IOC suggestion.

The sixth Olympiad was slated to be held in 1916 in Berlin, and Germany vowed to stage winter sports competition as part of the event. But in 1914 World War I began, and the Berlin Games were canceled altogether.

After an eight-year hiatus, the Olympics resumed in 1920: Antwerp, Belgium, played host to athletes, which included figure skaters and ice hockey players along with the usual contingency of gymnasts, runners, fencers, and other summer sports competitors. The first IOC-sanctioned competition of winter sports was held in Chamonix, France, from January 25 to February 4, 1924. When the Games were staged next, in St. Moritz, Switzerland, in 1928, they were formally designated the second Winter Olympics.

From that year, the Winter Games were held every four years in the same calendar year as the Summer Games—until 1994. In 1986 IOC officials voted to change the schedule. The result was that the 1992 Winter Olympics in Albertville, France, were followed only two years later by the Summer Olympics in Lillehammer, Norway. The Winter and Summer Games are now each held every four years, alternating in even-numbered years.

Have the Olympic Games been held regularly since 1896?

No. In spite of the fact that international harmony ("Truce of God") is one of the hallmarks of the modern Olympic movement, the Games have been canceled by the governing body, the International Olympic Committee (IOC), due to world events: In 1916 the Games were canceled because of World War I (1914–1918); the 1940 and 1944 Games were called off due to World War II (1939–1945).

The Games have been affected by international politics, occasional boycotts, and demonstrations as well. Though the 1980 Summer Games continued as planned, the United States and as many as sixty-two other non-Communist countries (including Japan and the Federal Republic of Germany) boycotted them in protest of the 1979 Soviet invasion of neighboring Afghanistan. The following Summer Games, held in Los Angeles in 1984, were boycotted by the Soviets. The official reason was cited as "fear," though some skeptics believed the reason to be more specific: A fear of drug testing.

In 1968, in Mexico City, two African American track medalists—sprinters Tommie Smith and John Carlos—conducted a protest on the medal ceremony. Smith had won a gold medal in the 200 meter dash, while Carlos had captured the bronze medal. While on the medal stands, the two sprinters gave the so-called "Black Power" salute by raising their fists with black gloves to protest racial discrimination in the United States. This action earned them suspension and expulsion from the Olympic Village.

Olympic history turned dark at the 1972 Summer Games in Munich, when eleven Israeli athletes were killed in the Olympic Village by the Arab terrorist group Black September. A 1996 bombing at Olympic Park in Atlanta, Georgia, also cast a shadow over the Games.

Why is Jesse Owens considered so significant in Olympic history?

Jesse Owens, an American sprinter, is considered significant because he shattered German leader Adolf Hitler's creed of Aryan superiority at the 1936 Berlin Olympics. An African American, Owens won gold medals in the 100 meters, 200 meters, a sprint relay, and the long jump. Jesse Owens exploded the Nazi myth of Aryan superiority and became a world hero in the process.

How old is baseball?

Baseball, America's pastime, is more than 200 years old. According to legend, the sport's originator was U.S. Army officer Abner Doubleday (1819–1893), who was credited with inventing and naming the game in 1839, while he was attending school in Cooperstown, New York (the site of the Baseball Hall of Fame and Museum). But in 2004 a document was uncovered in Pittsfield, Massachusetts, citing a 1791 bylaw prohibiting the playing of baseball too close to (within eighty yards of) the town's meeting hall.

Historians verified the authenticity of the document and its date. This is believed to be the earliest written record of the game—and it establishes that the stick-and-ball sport was being played forty-two years before Doubleday's involvement. Baseball historians have long acknowledged that the sport, which is similar to the English games of cricket and rounders, had not one father, but thousands. Although the 2004 discovery indicates that the game was already in existence in 1791, and popular enough to be the subject of a town ordinance, it was in the 1800s that baseball developed into the game Americans still love today.

The first baseball club, the Knickerbocker Base Ball Club, was organized by American sportsman Alexander Cartwright (1820–1892) in 1842 in New York City. By 1845 the team had developed a set of twenty rules, which included specifications for where the bases are positioned and how runners can be tagged as out. The rules also defined a field of play, outside of which balls are foul. The so-called New York game spread in popularity after a famous 1846 match in Hoboken, New Jersey. By 1860 there were at least fifty organized ball clubs in the country. Union soldiers helped spread the game during the American Civil War (1861–1865), and the popularity of the sport greatly increased during the last three and a half decades of the nineteenth century.

The first professional baseball team was the Cincinnati Red Stockings, which began play in 1869. In 1876 the National League (NL) was founded: It included teams in Boston; Chicago; Cincinnati, Ohio; Hartford, Connecticut; Louisville, Kentucky; New York; Philadelphia; and St. Louis, Missouri. By the 1880s the sport had evolved into big business. An 1887 championship series between St. Louis and Detroit drew 51,000 paying spectators. The American League (AL) was formed in 1901, and two years later the two leagues staged a championship between their teams: In 1903, the Boston Americans (who became the Red Socks in 1908) beat the Pittsburgh Pirates in the first World Series.

An overall increase in American leisure time, created by the innovation of labor-saving household devices as well as a reduction in the average laborer's workweek, helped baseball become the national sport and its favorite pastime. Played on an open field, the game harkened back to the nation's agrarian roots; but with its standardized rules and reliance on statistics, it looked forward to a modern, industrialized future.

Who was George Herman Ruth?

George Herman "Babe" Ruth (1895– 1948) may be the most popular baseball player of all time—a larger-than-life character known for clubbing monstrous home runs. Known as "the Bambino" or "the Sultan of Swat," Ruth actually began his major league baseball career as a pitcher for the Boston Red Sox.

He was traded to the New York Yankees—the Sox's dreaded rivals—in one of the most lopsided deals in baseball history. Ruth led the Yankees to numerous championships in the 1920s. He clubbed more than 700 home runs in his career—a record that stood until Hank Aaron broke it in 1974.

Ruth became one of society's first great larger-than-life sports heroes. Along with heavyweight boxing champion Jack Dempsey, he symbolized the "Roaring Twenties," a time of optimism in the United States.

When did Major League Baseball become integrated?

Major League baseball became integrated when Branch Rickey, the manager of the Brooklyn Dodgers, signed African American Jackie Robinson to a contract. Robinson played a year for the Dodgers' minor league team and then in 1947 played for the Dodgers in a Hall of Fame career. Robin-

Babe Ruth in 1941.

How have steroids impacted baseball?

Steroids have had a deleterious impact on "America's pastime," with many referring to the recent period as the "steroids era." It may be too early to assess the long-term impact, but it certainly has impacted how fans and others assess record-breaking performances in the 1990s and 2000s. Both Mark McGwire and Sammy Sosa—two powerful sluggers who engaged in an exciting home run record chase in 1998—were linked to steroid use.

In 2005, eleven major league baseball players, including McGwire, appeared before the U.S. House of Representatives to answer questions about steroid use. McGwire declined to answer questions under oath. He later admitted to steroid use and said that he wished he never played in the "steroid era."

Barry Bonds, who hit seventy-three home runs in the 2001 season, and Roger Clemens—the most dominant pitcher in baseball for years—have also been linked to steroids. Both have faced criminal trials related to steroid investigations.

son—a former football and track and field star at UCLA—overcame insults and racial prejudice, paving the way for countless other players to follow in his footsteps.

In the nineteenth century, Moses Fleetwood Walker—an African American who had played college baseball at the University of Michigan—played in the American Association, an early professional baseball team in 1884. But, the United States Supreme Court approved of segregation in its infamous decision in *Plessy v. Ferguson* (1896), upholding a Louisiana law providing for separate railway transportation for blacks and whites. The *Plessy* decision upheld the so-called "separate but equal" doctrine, providing that separate facilities for different races were constitutional as long as they were roughly equal.

Robinson's breaking of the color barrier in major league baseball is considered one of the historic breakthroughs in civil rights and contributed greatly to breaking down the walls of prejudice in American society. Less than a decade after Robinson's integration of major league baseball, the U.S. Supreme Court ruled in *Brown v. Board of Education* (1954) that segregated public schools violated the Equal Protection Clause of the Fourteenth Amendment, overruling *Plessy v. Ferguson* and the "separate but equal" doctrine.

What happened to Pete Rose?

Pete Rose (1941–) was banned from baseball in 1989 after it was determined by new base-

Pete Rose

281

ball Commissioner Bart Giamatti that Rose had bet on Cincinnati Reds' baseball games while he served as the team's manager. The ban means that Rose is not eligible for the Baseball Hall of Fame in Cooperstown, New York.

The Pete Rose story is sad, because his accomplishments on the baseball field should ensure him a place in the highest pantheons of the Hall of Fame. He retired as baseball's all-time leader in hits with more than 4,250—a record that still exists. He also played in seventeen all-star games at five different positions.

Who invented basketball?

The ball-and-hoop game was invented by Canadian American James Naismith (1861–1939) in December 1891. An instructor at the YMCA College, in Springfield, Massachusetts, Naismith was asked by the head of the physical education department to come up with a game to keep students active indoors during the winter months. It had to fit inside the confines of a gym, have no physical contact, use a soft ball, and give everyone who participated a chance to handle the ball. Naismith nailed two peach baskets, which he found in the storeroom, to balcony railings at each end of the school's gym, found a soccer ball, divided his class of eighteen men into two teams, and introduced them—and as it would turn out, the rest of the world—to the game, which was later dubbed basket ball (two words). Improvements to the game came over the next two decades as it spread in popularity. In 1910 the important change of allowing ball handlers to move by dribbling was made. In 1916 the rules were changed to allow dribblers to shoot the ball.

Who was the greatest professional basketball player in history?

It depends on which basketball historian that you ask. Some would say that Michael Jordan, who led the Chicago Bulls to six championships in the National Basketball Association (NBA), was the greatest player of all time. Jordan combined uncanny athleticism with an indomitable will to win. He routinely led the NBA in scoring and became a cultural icon worldwide.

Others might point to Wilton Norman Chamberlain—"Wilt the Stilt." Standing more than seven feet tall, Wilt Chamberlain literally dominated the basketball game, once scoring more than one hundred points in a single NBA game. He averaged more than fifty points per game in a season and often led the NBA in rebounds. His physical talents were imposing and awe-inspiring.

However, critics of Chamberlain often point to his rival Bill Russell of the Boston Celtics as the greatest player in basketball history. Russell certainly was the greatest winner, as he led the Celtics to eleven championships in his thirteen NBA seasons. Russell played incredible defense and was the only player in the league who could present problems for Chamberlain.

When did football begin?

In ancient Greece and Rome, a game was played in which the object was to move a ball across a goal line by throwing, kicking, or running with it. Several modern games were derived from this, including rugby and soccer, from which American football directly evolved (in much of the world "football" refers to soccer, in which players are allowed to advance the ball only with their feet or heads).

Historians generally agree that the first game of American football was played on November 6, 1869, in New Brunswick, New Jersey, when Rutgers defeated the College of New

Jersey (present-day Princeton University), 6–4. They played on a field 120 yards long and 75 yards wide and used a round, soccer-like ball. Other eastern colleges, including Columbia, Harvard, and Yale, soon added the sport to their athletic programs. In 1876 a set of official rules were compiled. In the 1880s Yale coach Walter Camp (1859–1925) revised the rules, giving the world the game played today. He limited teams to eleven players, established the scrimmage system for putting the ball into play, introduced the concept of requiring a team to advance the ball a certain number of yards within a given number of downs, and came up with the idea of marking the field with yard lines.

Cam Newton of Auburn University accepts the Heisman Trophy in a 2010 ceremony.

What is the Heisman Trophy?

The Heisman Trophy is the premier award given in college football to the most outstanding player. Named after former Georgia Tech coach and athletic director John Heisman, the award has been given since 1935. The award contains a who's who list of great players, including: Roger Staubach from the Naval Academy (1963), O.J. Simpson from the University of Southern California (1968), Earl Campbell from the University of Texas (1977), Herschel Walker from the University of Georgia (1982), Barry Sanders from Oklahoma State University (1988), Tim Tebow from the University of Florida (2007), and Cam Newton from Auburn University (2010).

The only person to win the Heisman Trophy more than once was Ohio State running back Archie Griffin who won in 1974 and 1975. The award is dominated by running backs and quarterbacks. Only one defensive player (or predominately defensive player) has ever captured the award—Charles Woodson from the University of Michigan in 1997.

What is the Super Bowl?

The Super Bowl is arguably the biggest sporting event—at least in the United States and one of the most widely watched sporting events in the world. It crowns the champion of the National Football League (NFL). The winner of the American Football Conference (AFC) squares off against the winner of the National Football Conference (NFC) after surviving early playoff games.

The first Super Bowl took place on January 15, 1967, between the Green Bay Packers of the NFC and the Kansas City Chiefs of the AFC. The mighty Packers, coached by the legendary Vince Lombardi (1913–1970) won the game handily 35–10.

How old is golf?

Some historians trace golf back to a Roman game called paganica. When they occupied Great Britain from roughly 43 to 410 c.e. Romans played the game in the streets, using a stick and a leather ball. But there are other possible predecessors as well, including an English game (called cambuca), a Dutch game (kolf), a French and Belgian game called (chole), and a French game (jeu de mail).

But the game as we know it, the rules, equipment, and 18-hole course, certainly developed in Scotland, where it was played as far back as the early 1400s. The rules of the game were also codified there: *The Rules of Golf* was published in 1754 by the St. Andrews Golfers, later called the Royal & Ancient Golf Club. The first golf club (formed 1744) was the Honourable Company of Edinburgh Golfers in Edinburgh, Scotland. And it was none other than Mary, Queen of Scots (1542–1587), who is credited with being both the first woman golfer and the originator of the term "caddie." (The term is derived from the French term for the royal pages, cadets, who carried the queen's clubs.)

Tiger Woods

Where does golf sensation Tiger Woods rank among the greats?

Eldrick "Tiger" Woods (1975–) ranks among the best players of all time. Most experts consider him either the greatest or second only to the great Jack Nicklaus. Golfing historians and the public often focus on major championship wins in (1) the Masters; (2) the U.S. Open; (3) the British Open; and (4) the PGA Championship.

As of July 2012, Woods has won fourteen major championships, trailing only Nicklaus' eighteen career major titles. He has also won seventy-four career PGA titles—second all-time behind only Nicklaus.

Many assumed that Woods would not only break Nicklaus' record, but crush it. However, Woods suffered a high-profile dissolution of his marriage with revelations that he had carried on an assortment of affairs. The marital discord seemed to impact Woods' golf game, as he has not won a major championship since the U.S. Open in 2008.

He publicly admitted to numerous affairs in December 2009, and his golf game has plummeted. Routinely ranked the number one player in the world, he has dropped in the rankings, though part of this can be explained by injuries. In 2012 he started a comeback of sorts, winning three PGA tournaments by July.

How old is tennis?

The game is believed to have originated in France, where it was called jeu de paume (meaning "game of the palm"), in the 1100s or 1200s: Players hit a small ball back and forth over a net using the palms of their hands. The "father of modern tennis" is English soldier and sportsman Walter Clopton Wingfield (known as Major Wingfield [1833–1912]), who in 1873 published a rule book for lawn tennis and in 1874 patented equipment for the game.

Who competed in the famous (or infamous) "Battle of the Sexes" tennis match in 1973?

Billie Jean King (1943–), the top female tennis player in the world, defeated former male #1 player Bobby Riggs (1918–1995) at the Houston Astrodome in 1973. More than fifty million people watched this match live from thirty-seven different countries. There was a significant age difference between the two competitors, as King was about thirty years

Billie Jean King

old at the time and Riggs was fifty-five. Still many expected that Riggs would win the match, as he formerly held the number one ranking in men's tennis for part of the 1940s. Some had doubts about King prevailing, because earlier in the year Riggs had managed to defeat Margaret Court with an assortment of drop shots and junk balls.

King accepted Riggs' challenge. Always a believer in gender equality and women's rights, King took the match very seriously, believing that a loss would be devastating for women in sports and society. She defeated Riggs 6–4, 6–3, 6–3.

When did soccer originate?

There was an early Chinese game called cuju, which some see as a progenitor of modern soccer. However, modern soccer—called "football" in many parts of the world—developed in the nineteenth century in Great Britain. The first international match featured England and Scotland in 1872. Now, soccer is arguably the most popular sport in the world and international competitions dominate the sporting world. It first became an Olympic sport in 1900 and the first World Cup competition—the most widely watched sporting event in the world—began in 1930.

When did boxing originate and how did it develop?

Historians don't agree on when boxing began, but the sport certainly can be traced to the early Olympic Games. The Greeks had boxing in the Games as early as 688 b.c.e. There are carvings from the third and second millennium that show figures punching each other in Sumerian and Egyptian cultures.

Bare-knuckle boxing grew in popularity in Great Britain in the sixteenth and seventeenth centuries. In the eighteenth century, Jack Broughton—a top fighter in his day—drafted the first set of rules called "Broughton's Rules." He drafted these rules after one of his opponents, George Stevenson, died from their bout. Broughton introduced the first set of gloves called "mufflers." Under Broughton's Rules, a pugilist could not hit his opponent while the opponent was down. Boxers also had thirty seconds to get back to their feet after getting knocked down.

The next major set of boxing rules—which really modernized the sport—were drafted in 1867 by John Graham Chambers under the sponsorship of the Marquis of Queensbury. Called the "Queensbury Rules," these rules provided for three-minute rounds with one-minute periods of rest—what professional boxers use today.

Boxing became even more popular in the United States during the late nineteenth century, particularly with the emergence of a popular Irish puncher named John L. Sullivan, the last bare-knuckle heavyweight champion. Sullivan also was one of America's first genuine sport heroes with his gargantuan punch and even larger sized ego. After Sullivan lost his title in a gloved match, to "Gentleman" James J. Corbett, boxing moved into the modern era.

How did mixed martial arts originate and develop?

Mixed martial arts is the fastest growing sport in the world. Mixed martial arts, or MMA, is generally traced back to the Greek sport of pankration—a mix of boxing and wrestling that was featured in the Olympics in 648 B.C.E. The modern development of MMA comes in part from the Brazilian sport "Vale Tudo" which is roughly translated into "anything goes."

It is difficult to trace MMA because modern MMA incorporates so many different fighting disciplines and martial arts—judo, karate, wrestling, boxing, Muay Thai kickboxing, and Brazilian jiu-jitsu to name a few.

The sport of MMA took off in the United States with the emergence of an MMA tournament organized by the Ultimate Fighting Championships or UFC. It featured a tournament of different fighters who fought to the finish (until kayo or submission). UFC 1, which was held in Colorado, introduced much of the world to the power of Brazilian jiu-jitsu, as a relatively small man named Royce Gracie—from the legendary Brazilian fighting family—defeated an assortment of larger men to capture the tournament. Now, the UFC is the most popular and powerful brand and promotional force in mixed martial arts in the world.

ECONOMICS AND BUSINESS

What is capitalism?

The cornerstones of capitalism are private ownership of property (capital goods); property and capital create income for those who own the property or capital; individuals and firms openly compete with one another, with each seeking its own economic gain (so that competition determines prices, production, and distribution of goods); and participants in the system are profit-driven (in other words, earning a profit is the main goal). Capitalism is the antithesis of socialism, a theory by which government owns most, if not all, of a nation's capital. There is no pure capitalist system; national governments become involved in the regulation of business to some degree. But the economy of the United States is highly capitalistic in nature, as are the economies of many other industrialized nations, including Great Britain.

What does laissez-faire mean?

From the French, *laissez-faire* literally means "to let (people) do (as they choose)." As an economic doctrine, laissez-faire opposes government interference in economic and business matters, or at least desires to keep government's role to an absolute minimum. Laissez-faire favors a free market (a market characterized by open competition). The theory was popularized during the late eighteenth century as a reaction to mercantilism. Noted Scottish economist Adam Smith (1723-1790) was among the advocates of a laissez-faire market.

What is mercantilism?

An economic system that developed as feudalism was dissolving (at the end of the Middle Ages [500-1350]), mercantilism advocates strict government control of the national economy. Its adherents believe a healthy economy can only be achieved through state regulation. The goals were to accumulate bullion (gold or silver bars), establish a favorable balance of trade with other countries, develop the nation's agricultural concerns as well as its manufacturing concerns, and establish foreign trading policies.

287

What is Keynesian economics?

Keynesian economics are the collected theories of British economist and monetary expert John Maynard Keynes (1883-1946), who in 1935 published his landmark work, *The General Theory of Employment, Interest and Money.* A macroeconomist (he studied a nation's economy as a whole), Keynes departed from many of the concepts of a free-market economy. In order to ensure growth and stability, he argued that government needs to be involved in certain aspects of the nation's economic life. He believed in state intervention in fiscal policies, and during recessionary times he favored deficit spending, the loosening of monetary policies, and government public works programs (such as those of President Franklin D. Roosevelt's New Deal) to promote employment. Keynes's theories are considered the most influential economic formulation of the twentieth century.

Having played a central role in British war financing during World War II (1939-45), Keynes participated in the Bretton Woods Conference of 1944, where he helped win support for the creation of the World Bank, which was established in 1945 as a specialized agency of the United Nations. The body aims to further economic development by guaranteeing loans to nations, extending easy credit terms to developing nations, and providing risk capital to promote private enterprise in less-developed nations. It's interesting to note that Keynes was a key representative at the Paris Peace Conference of 1919, where the Treaty of Versailles was drawn up, officially ending World War I (1914-18). He quit the proceedings in Paris, returned to private life in London, and in 1919 published *The Economic Consequences of Peace,* in which he argued against the excessive war reparations that the treaty required of Germany. Keynes foresaw that the extreme punishment of Germany at the end of World War I would pave the way for future conflict in Europe.

Who was Adam Smith?

Scottish economist Adam Smith (1723-1790) is popular with conservative economists today because of his work titled *The Wealth of Nations* (written in 1776), which proposes a system of natural liberty in trade and commerce; in other words, a free-market economy. Smith, who was teaching at the University of Glasgow at the time, wrote, "Consumption is the sole end and purpose of all production, and the interest of the producer ought to be attended to, only so far as it may be necessary for promoting that of the consumer."

The Wealth of Nations established the classical school of political economy but has been faulted for showing no awareness of the developing Industrial Revolution. While Smith advocated both free-market competition and limited government intervention, he also viewed unemployment as a necessary evil to keep costs—and therefore prices—in check.

MONEY

When was money introduced?

The use of money dates back some 4,000 years, when people began using something of recognized value, such as precious metals including gold and silver, to purchase goods and services. In the absence of money, all transactions were made on the barter system, which is an exchange of goods and services negotiated by the parties involved. The introduction of money simplified the acquisition of products and services. The ancient country of Lydia, in the western part of Asia Minor (modern-day Turkey), is credited with the first use of standardized coins, made of gold and silver, in the seventh century b.c.

When was paper money first used?

Paper money first appeared in China during the Middle Ages (500-1350). In the ninth century a.d., paper notes were used by Chinese merchants as certificates of exchange and, later, for paying taxes to the government. It was not until the eleventh century, also in China, that the notes were backed by deposits of silver and gold (called "hard money").

What was the National Bank Act?

The National Bank Act of 1863 was designed to create a national banking system, float federal war loans, and establish a national currency. Congress passed the act to help resolve the financial crisis that emerged during the early days of the American Civil War (1861-65); the fight with the South was expensive, and no effective tax program had been drawn up to finance it. In December 1861 banks suspended specie payments (payments in gold or silver coins for paper currency)—people could not convert bank notes into coins. The government responded by passing the Legal Tender Act (1862), issuing $150 million in national notes called greenbacks. But bank notes (paper bills issued by state banks) accounted for most of the currency in circulation.

To bring financial stability to the nation and fund the war effort, the National Bank Act of 1863 was introduced in the Senate in January of that year. Secretary of the Treasury Salmon Chase (1808-1873), aided by Senator John Sherman (1823-1900) of Ohio, promoted it to the legislators. The bill was approved in the Senate by a close vote of 23 to 21. The House passed the legislation in February. National banks organized under the act were required to purchase government bonds as a condition of start-up. As soon as those bonds were deposited with the federal government, the bank could issue its own notes up to 90 percent of the market value of the bonds on deposit.

The National Bank Act improved but did not solve the nation's financial problems: Some of the 1,500 state banks, which had all been issuing bank notes, were converted to national banks by additional legislation (passed June 1864 to amend the original bank act). Other state banks were driven out of business or ceased to issue notes because of the 1865 passage of a 10 percent federal tax on notes they issued, making it unprofitable for them to print their own money. The legislation created $300 million in national currency—in the form of notes issued by the national banks. But since most of this money was distributed in the East, the money supply in other parts of the country remained precarious. The West demanded more money—an issue that would dominate American politics in the years after the American Civil War (1861-65). Nevertheless, the nation's banking system stayed largely the same—despite the Panic of 1873—until passage of the Federal Reserve Act in 1913.

What is the Federal Reserve?

It is the central banking system in the United States, created by a 1913 act of Congress, the Federal Reserve Act (sometimes called the Glass-Owens Bill). The legislation provided for a stable central banking system after the system set up by the National Bank Act of 1863 proved ineffective in managing the nation's currency, in responding to economic growth, or in exerting a controlling influence on the economy.

The Federal Reserve Act created 12 regional federal reserve banks: in Boston, Massachusetts; New York; Philadelphia, Pennsylvania; Cleveland, Ohio; Richmond, Virginia; Atlanta, Georgia; Chicago; St. Louis, Missouri; Minneapolis, Minnesota; Kansas City, Missouri; Dallas, Texas; and San Francisco, California. These institutions operate as "bankers' banks": member banks (commercial institutions) use their accounts with the Federal Reserve in the same way that consumers use their accounts on deposit at commercial banks. All national banks must be members of the Federal Reserve system; state banks may join the system upon meeting certain requirements. The Federal Reserve Act also established a Federal Reserve Board, now called the Board of Governors, to supervise the system. The board consists of seven members who are appointed by the president of the United States and are approved by the Senate. To reduce the possibility of nearsighted political influence, members serve staggered 14-year terms (one of the 14 terms expires every other year).

The duties of the Federal Reserve include lending money to commercial (member) banks, directing the reserve banks' purchase and sale of U.S. government securities on the open market, setting reserve requirements (for how much money needs to be in the U.S. Treasury), and regulating the discount rate (the interest rate the Federal Reserve charges commercial banks for loans), which is one of the system's principal influences on the economy. In performing these duties, the Federal Reserve (often called "the Fed" in financial circles) can expand (loosen) or contract (tighten) the supply of money in circulation. The Federal Reserve also issues the national currency and supervises and regulates the activities of banks and their holding companies. It began operation in November 1914.

The central bank systems of other developed nations include the Bank of Canada, Banque de France, and the Deutsche Bundesbank (of Germany).

When was the euro introduced?

The euro, the currency of the 12 European Union nations—Belgium, Germany, Greece, Spain, France, Ireland, Italy, Luxembourg, the Netherlands, Austria, Portugal, and Finland—went into circulation January 1, 2002, becoming part of daily life for more than 300 million people. The banknotes and coins replaced national currencies, making the franc, deutschmark, peseta, and lira, among others, history in the participating nations.

The euro's origins can be traced to a series of international agreements, beginning in 1978, which were made among the members of what was then called the European Community, or EC. In February 1986 the framework for the unified monetary system was agreed upon by nations who signed the Single European Act, creating "an area without internal frontiers in which the free movement of goods, persons, services, and capital is ensured." The 1989 Delors Report outlined a plan to introduce the currency in three phases. The final phase of that plan began on January 1, 1999, when the 11 countries (later to become 12) belonging to the European Union established the conversion rates between their respective national currencies and the euro, creating a monetary union with a single currency. A three-year transition phase followed, during which monetary transactions could be made in euro, but there was no requirement to do so. On January 1, 2002, the central banks of the 12 participating countries put into circulation about 7.8 billion euro notes and 40.4 billion euro coins, together worth 144 billion euros. Simultaneously each country began to withdraw its own currency from circulation. By February 28, 2002, the changeover was complete, meaning the national currencies were completely withdrawn and only the euro was in circulation.

When 10 new nations (Cyprus, Czech Republic, Estonia, Hungary, Latvia, Lithuania, Malta, Poland, Slovakia, and Slovenia) joined the EU on May 1, 2004, there was no timetable for their adoption of the euro. Previously, in 2003, Sweden voted against joining the euro area.

NATURAL RESOURCES

What was the biggest gold rush?

The greatest American gold rush began on January 24, 1848, when James Marshall discovered gold at Sutter's Mill in Coloma, California. Within a year, a large-scale gold rush was on. As the nearest port, the small town of San Francisco grew into a bustling city as fortune seekers arrived from around the world. Due to the influx, by 1850 California had enough people to qualify it for statehood. This pattern repeated itself elsewhere in the American West, including the Pikes Peak gold rush in 1859, which effectively launched the city of Denver, Colorado. The gold rush led to the discovery of copper, lead, silver, and other useful minerals. It also spawned related industry. One of the success stories is that of Levi Strauss (1829-1902), a Bavarian immigrant who in 1853 began making and selling sturdy clothing to miners in San Francisco.

In other countries, gold rushes had the same effect on the growth and development of regions: After the precious metal was discovered in Australia in 1851, the country's population almost tripled over the course of the next decade. The effect of an 1861 gold rush in nearby New Zealand was to double the country's population in six years' time. An 1886 discovery in South Africa led to the development of the city of Johannesburg. Just over a decade later, the infamous Yukon gold rush (in the Klondike region of Canada) spurred development there.

What is "black gold"?

Black gold is a term for oil or petroleum—*black* because of its appearance when it comes out of the ground, and *gold* because it made prospectors, drillers, and oil industry men rich. The oil industry in the United States began in 1859 when retired railroad conductor Edwin L. Drake (1819-1880) drilled a well near Titusville, Pennsylvania. His drill, powered by an old steam engine, struck oil. Oil from animal tallow and whales, had been used as a lubricant since colonial times. The discovery of a process for deriving kerosene, a clean-burning and easy-lighting fuel, from coal oil had been patented in 1854. After Drake's Titusville well produced shale oil, the substance was analyzed for its properties and it, too, was determined to be an excellent source of kerosene. Soon others began prospecting for "rock oil." Western Pennsylvania became an important oil-producing region. Wagons and river barges transported barrels to market; later, the railroad reached into the region; and by 1875 a pipeline was built to carry the oil directly to Pittsburgh. Petroleum products soon replaced whale oil as a fluid for illumination. During the 1880s, Ohio, Kentucky, Illinois, and Indiana also pro-

Miners in Colorado, 1880. Gold rushes led to a mass migration of prospectors to the American West and spurred the growth of such cities as San Francisco and Denver.

duced oil. In 1901 the famous Spindletop Field in eastern Texas produced the nation's first "gusher"—oil literally sprang out of the earth. During the next decade, California and Oklahoma joined Texas to lead the nation's oil production. Between 1859 and 1900, U.S. oil production boomed: Just 2,000 barrels were produced the year it was discovered in Pennsylvania; more than 64 million barrels were produced annually by the turn of the century.

The second half of the 1800s saw the oil industry boom: The fuel was used for lighting, heating, and lubrication (principally of machinery and tools). But the advent of the automobile and its central role in the life of twentieth-century America made the oil industry richer yet. Demand soon exceeded the nation's supply of petroleum, prompting the United States to increasingly rely on imported oil for fuel.

When did diamond mining begin in Africa?

An 1867 discovery of a "pretty pebble" along the banks of the Orange River in South Africa led to the finding of a rich diamond field near present-day Kimberley (the city was founded as a result of the mining, in 1871). Similar to the California gold rush roughly a decade and a half earlier, the finding in central South Africa prompted people from Britain and other countries to flock to the area. However, the ultimate outcome was conflict: Since both the British and the Boers (who were Dutch descendants living in South Africa) claimed the Kimberley area, the first Boer War ensued in 1880.

INDUSTRIAL REVOLUTION

How were finished goods produced before the Industrial Revolution?

Before the factory and machine age ushered in by the Industrial Revolution, people made many of their own finished goods, bought them from small-scale producers (who manufactured the goods largely by hand), or bought them from merchants who contracted homeworkers to produce goods. The putting-out system was a production method that was used in New England from the mid-1700s to the early 1800s. It worked this way: Merchants supplied raw materials (cotton, for example) to families, especially women and young girls, who would make partially finished goods (thread) or fully finished goods (cloth) for the merchant. These manufactured goods were then sold by the merchant. Homeworkers, who "put out" goods, provided the needed manufacturing labor of the day.

How did the textile industry begin?

The large-scale factory production of textiles began in the late 1700s, becoming established first in Great Britain, where a cotton-spinning machine was invented in 1783 by Richard Arkwright (1732-1792). Spinning mills were introduced to the United States in 1790 by English-born mechanist and businessman Samuel Slater (1768-1835). The 21-year-old had worked as a textile laborer for more than six years in an English mill where he learned the

Young girls work in a basket factory, 1908. Child labor was rampant in the United States until the Fair Labor Standards Act of 1938 brought reforms.

workings of Arkwright's machine, which the British considered the cornerstone of their booming textiles industry; laws prevented anyone with knowledge of the mill from leaving the country. In 1789 Slater, determined he could recreate the spinning mill and eager to seek his own fortune, disguised himself to evade the authorities and leave the country, sailing from England for American shores. Arriving in Providence, Rhode Island, he formed a partnership with the textiles firm Almy and Brown. Slater began building a spinning mill based on the Arkwright machine. This he did from memory. The spinning mill was debuted December 20, 1790, in the village of Pawtucket, Rhode Island, where the wheels of the mill were turned by the waters of the Blackstone River. The machine was a success and soon revolutionized the American textiles industry, which previously relied on cottage workers (the putting-out system) to manufacture thread and yarn.

Slater's innovation, which would earn him the title Father of the American Textiles Industry, spawned the factory system in the United States. By 1815 there were 165 cotton mills in New England, all working to capacity. The early mills were not large-scale, however, and for a time after Slaters's introductions, New England mills and merchants continued to rely on homeworkers to weave threads (now produced by the mills) into cloth.

In 1813 the Boston Manufacturing Company opened the first textile factory, where laborers ran spinning and weaving machines to produce woven cloth from start to finish. The advent of machinery had given rise to the factory system. And laborers were shifted from working in their homes to working in factories. While native New Englanders continued to provide the labor for the textile industry for the next two decades, an influx of immigrants in the mid-1800s provided the hungry manufacturers with a steady supply of laborers who were willing to work for less money and longer hours. Within the first three decades of the 1800s, New England became the center of the nation's textiles industry. The region's ample rivers and streams provided the necessary water power, and the commercial centers of Boston and New York City readily received the finished products. Labor proved to be in ample supply as well: Since the mill machinery was not complicated, children could operate it and did. Slater hired children ages 7 to 14 to run the mill, a practice that other New England textile factories also adopted. The Jefferson Embargo of 1807, which prohibited importing textiles, also aided the industry. New England's mills provided the model for the American factory system. Slater had brought the Industrial Revolution to America.

How did Eli Whitney invent the cotton gin?

American inventor Eli Whitney (1765-1825) is credited with developing the cotton gin, a machine that removes cottonseeds from cotton fibers. A simple cotton gin (called the *churka*) dates back to ancient India (300 b.c.). But Whitney's gin would prove to be far superior. In 1792 Whitney, who had recently graduated from Yale University, was visiting the Georgia plantation owned by Catharine Littlefield Greene, widow of American Revolution (1775-83) hero General Nathanael Greene (1742- 1786). Whitney observed that short-staple (or upland) cotton, which has green seeds that are difficult to separate from the fiber, differs from long-staple (also called Sea Island) cotton, which has black seeds that are easily separated. The latter was the staple of American commerce at the time. In 1793 Whitney, who is described as a mechanical genius, completed an invention that could be used to clean bolls of short-staple cotton of their seeds; he patented it the next year.

The machine worked by turning a crank, which caused a cylinder covered with wire teeth to revolve; the teeth pulled the cotton fiber, carrying it through slots in the cylinder as it revolved; since the slots were too small for the seeds, they were left behind; a roller with brushes then removed the fibers from the wire teeth. The cotton gin revolutionized the American textiles industry, which was then but a fledgling concern. The increase in cotton production was as much as fiftyfold: One large gin could process 50 times the cotton that a (slave) laborer could in a day. Soon plantations and farms were supplying huge amounts of cotton to textile mills in the Northeast, where in 1790 another inventor, British-born industrialist Samuel Slater (1768-1835), had built the first successful water-powered machines for spinning cotton. Together the inventions founded the American cotton industry. Whitney struggled to protect his patent, but imitations of his invention were already in production, prompting the U.S. government to allow his patent to expire. Though he did not profit from his cotton gin, he went on to devise a system of interchangeable parts, which introduced the idea of mass production and revolutionized manufacturing.

Why was the introduction of canning important?

The advent of canned foods not only created an industry, but it altered the average American diet, helped usher in the consumer age, and saved time. Canning, a process for preserving food (vegetables, fruits, meats, and fish) by heating and sealing it in airtight containers, was developed by French candymaker Nicolas-François Appert (c. 1750-1841) in 1809, though he did not understand why the process worked. Some 50 years later, the pioneering work of French chemist and microbiologist Louis Pasteur (1822-1895) explained that heating is necessary to the canning process since it kills bacteria (microorganisms) that would otherwise spoil the food. Canning was introduced to American consumers in stages. In 1821 the William Underwood Company began a canning operation in Boston, Massachusetts; in the 1840s oyster canning began in Baltimore, Maryland; in 1853 American inventor Gail Borden (1801-1874) developed a way to condense and preserve milk in a can, founding the Borden Company four years later; and in 1858 American inventor John Landis Mason (1832-1902) developed a glass jar and lid suited to home canning.

Though early commercial canning methods did not ensure a safe product and many American women avoided the convenience foods, the canning industry grew rapidly, at least in part due to the male market, which included cowboys in the West. Between 1860 and 1870 the U.S. canning industry increased output from 5 million to 30 million cans. Improvements in the process during the 1870s helped eliminate the chance that cans would burst (a problem early on). And though the canning process changes food flavor, color, and texture, the convenience and long shelf life of canned foods helped them catch on: By the end of the 1800s a wide variety of canned foods, which had also come down in price, were common to the urban American diet. Companies such as Franco-American advertised in women's magazines, promoting their "delicacies in tins." An outbreak of botulism in the 1920s prompted the American canning industry to make further improvements to its process.

When did chain stores begin?

The innovation of the chain store, technically defined as two or more retail outlets operated by the same company and which sell the same kind of merchandise, was made by American

295

businessmen George Gilman (c. 1830-1901) and George Huntington Hartford (1833-1917), who in 1859 set up the Great Atlantic & Pacific Tea Company in New York City. Better known as A&P, the stores proliferated rapidly, and other chain stores, such as W. P. Woolworth (established 1879) and J. C. Penney (1902) opened their doors for business. The early twentieth century saw tremendous growth of the chain stores: Between 1910 and 1931, the number of A&P stores grew from 200 to more than 15,000. While the department stores, also a byproduct of the late 1800s, catered to middle- and upper-class customers, the chain stores, including Woolworth's "five-and-dimes" (which sold many items at such low price points), served lower-income consumers.

Chain stores, which operate within all major retailing categories (including grocery stores, department stores, and drugstores, as well as apparel and food outlets), offer consumers many advantages. Their system of centralized and mass buying allow them to acquire merchandise from manufacturers and wholesalers at reduced costs; this savings is passed along to the consumer, who pays less for the item. Further, they experience economies of advertising: A single ad placement promotes all the stores within the chain. In the 1920s independent retailers rallied against the chain stores, citing they had unfair advantages. This argument has resurfaced off and on throughout the twentieth century, as chain stores entered into more and more retailing sectors, including hardware, jewelry, furniture, music, and books. But the only federal legislation that constructively attempted to regulate the chain stores came in 1936: The Robinson-Patman Act tried to control competition. Today chain stores account for roughly one-third of all American retail sales.

Shoppers in a crowded Woolworth's. Department stores emerged in the mid-1800s.

When did department stores begin?

Department stores, which offer a wide variety of goods for sale in various departments, emerged in the mid-1800s. Many evolved out of general stores (which offered a variety of goods but not divided into departments), while others evolved out of dry-goods stores (which sold textiles and related merchandise). The first bona fide department store was established in Paris: the Bon Marché (French meaning "good bargain") opened its doors in 1838. Between the 1850s and 1880s, numerous department stores opened in American cities—including Jordan Marsh, founded 1851 in Boston, Massachusetts; R. H. Macy's, founded 1858 in New York City (the store was known for its creative advertisements); Wanamaker's, founded 1861 in Philadelphia, Pennsylvania (it successfully implemented fixed pricing so that customers no longer haggled over price); and Marshall Field, founded 1881 in Chicago (within 25 years it became the world's largest wholesale and retail dry goods store). These pioneer department stores, multistoried enterprises located in downtown areas, introduced many innovations to merchandising, including the policy of returnable or exchangeable goods, ready-made apparel, clearly marked prices, and window displays. By the early 1900s department stores could be found throughout the country. The timing was right for their emergence. Urban centers grew rapidly at the end of the century, giving department stores a ready clientele; the advent of the telephone, electric lighting, and billing machines helped retailers conduct business efficiently; transportation improvements allowed for the shipment of large quantities of goods; and a variety of finished goods were mass-produced, increasing supply and lowering cost of production as well as the price to the consumer. By the 1910s the stores were part of a new mass culture, which centered in American cities. During the twentieth century, department store sales typically ranged between 6 and 12 percent of total annual retail sales.

What was the first mail-order company?

The mail-order business was pioneered by retailer Montgomery Ward & Company, founded in 1872 in Chicago when American merchant Aaron Montgomery Ward (1843-1913) set up shop over a livery stable and printed a one-sheet "catalog" of bargains. Midwestern farmers, hurt by low farm prices and rising costs, were a ready market for the value-priced goods, which were shipped by rail to rural customers. Originally called "The Original Grange Supply House," Montgomery Ward offered 30 dry goods priced at $1 or less and provided special terms of sale for Grange members (the Grange is an association of farmers). Ward bought merchandise directly from wholesalers and, since he did not maintain a store building, overhead was low. By 1876 Ward's catalog had grown to 150 pages; in 1884 it was 240 pages and offered nearly 10,000 products, including household items (such as furniture, cutlery, and writing paper), farm implements (such as harnesses and tools), and fashions (such as ready-made apparel and parasols). Ward offered customers "satisfaction or your money back." In 1886 American Richard W. Sears (1863-1914) entered the mail-order business, opening operations in Minneapolis, Minnesota. He moved the business to Chicago the following year and sold it in 1889. In 1893 he joined with Alvah C. Roebuck (1864-1948) to found Sears, Roebuck and Company. The Sears catalog, which soon consisted of hundreds of pages and thousands of items, became popularly known as the "Wish Book."

Montgomery Ward and Sears Roebuck were aided by the U.S. Postal Service's expansion into remote areas: Beginning in 1896 mail could be delivered via the RFD, Rural Free Delivery. In 1913 parcel post was added to the postal service's offerings, further benefiting the mail-order houses and their growing lists of customers. Montgomery Ward and Sears Roebuck offered rural America more than merchandise; the mail-order houses were farm families' link to the greater consumer society that was emerging at the turn of the century. Regardless of geography, rural Americans could purchase "store-bought" goods, manufactured goods that were mass-produced in factories. The mail-order houses offered customers convenience (since customer purchases no longer had to be deferred for the next trip to a town), variety (since catalogers catered to a nationwide customer base, on-hand inventory included a multitude of products), and low prices (the mail-order houses bought merchandise at reduced rates from the wholesalers). Fashions were no longer restricted to the middle- and upper-class city dwellers who had access to department stores; rural customers became aware of new styles each time the Montgomery Ward and Sears Roebuck catalogs were delivered, which, by the early 1900s, was twice a year.

Though both Montgomery Ward and Sears Roebuck exited the mail-order business to concentrate efforts on their chain store retail operations later in the century, they set the standard for modern mail-order houses through their early policies addressing merchandise returns, competitive pricing, flexible payment methods, and shipping terms.

Who were the "robber barons"?

They were the industrial and financial tycoons of the late nineteenth century, the early builders of American business. Some called them the captains of industry. The "robber barons"

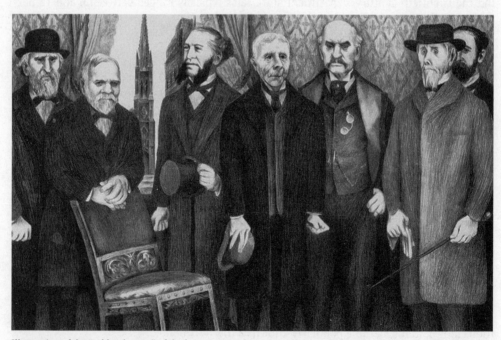

Illustration of the "robber barons" of the late nineteenth century: James J. Hill, Andrew Carnegie, Cornelius Vanderbilt, John D. Rockefeller, J. Pierpont Morgan, Edward H. Harriman, and Jay Gould. (Original lithograph by Bernarda Bryson.)

included bankers J. Pierpont Morgan (1837-1913) and Jay Cooke (1821- 1905); oil industrialist John D. Rockefeller (1839-1937); steel mogul Andrew Carnegie (1835-1919); financiers James J. Hill (1838-1916), James Fisk (1834-1872), Edward Harriman (1848-1909), and Jay Gould (1836-1892); and rail magnates Cornelius Vanderbilt (1794-1877) and Collis Huntington (1821-1900). These influential businessmen were hailed for expanding and modernizing the capitalist system and lauded for their philanthropic contributions to the arts and education. But they were also viewed as opportunistic, exploitative, and unethical.

Many factors converged to make the robber baron possible. The new nation was rich in natural resources, including iron, coal, and oil; technological advances steadily improved manufacturing machinery and processes; the population growth, fed by an influx of immigrants, provided a steady workforce, often willing to work for a low wage; the government turned over the building and operation of the nation's railways to private interests; and, adhering to the philosophy of laissez-faire (noninterference in the private sector), the government also provided a favorable environment in which to conduct business. Shrewd businessmen turned these factors to their advantage, amassing great empires. Reinvesting profits into their businesses, fortunes grew. The robber barons, especially the railroad men and the financiers who gained control of rail companies through stock buy-outs, hired lobbyists who worked on their behalf to gain the corporations subsidies, land grants, and even tax relief at both the federal and state levels.

The robber barons converted their business prowess into political might. In Washington, politicians grew tired of the advantage-seeking representatives of the nation's business leaders. Reform-minded progressives complained that the robber barons lived in opulent luxury while their workers barely eked out a living, their families teetering on despair.

After dominating the American economy for decades, changes around the turn of the century worked to curb the influence of the robber barons. In 1890 the federal government passed the Sherman Anti-Trust Act, making trusts (combinations of firms or corporations formed to limit competition and monopolize a market) illegal; workers continued to organize in labor unions, with which corporations were increasingly compelled to negotiate; the Interstate Commerce Commission (ICC) was established in 1887 to prevent abusive practices; and in 1913 the Sixteenth Amendment was ratified, allowing the federal government to collect a graduated income tax. Though many American businessmen and women would make great fortunes in the twentieth century, by the end of the 1920s the era of the robber barons had drawn to a close.

MODERN INDUSTRY

When was the New York Stock Exchange founded?

The oldest and largest stock exchange in the United States, the New York Stock Exchange (NYSE) had its origins on May 17, 1792, when local brokers who had been buying and selling securities under a designated tree agreed to formalize their business transactions. The NYSE that most people would recognize today opened for business in 1825 at 11 Wall Street, New York City. At the time most shares traded were in canal, turnpike, mining, and gaslight companies. Though a few industrial securities were first traded on the New York Stock Exchange as early as 1831, it was another 40 years before the complexion of trading changed to a more industrial nature. As the nation became increasingly manufacturing oriented, the companies listed on the exchange reflected the economic shift. Today, if corporations wish to list their stocks on the NYSE, they must have a minimum of 2,000 shareholders, each of those original shareholders must have 100 or more shares, the corporation must be able to issue at least 1 million shares of stock, and it must also provide a record of earnings for the previous three-year period. The board of the stock exchange can make exceptions to these guidelines. Corporations may be listed with other stock exchanges (such as the American Stock Exchange) or they may allow stock in their company to be traded as unlisted stocks, which are bought and sold in over-the-counter (OTC) trading. Companies that do not allow shares to be publicly traded are called private corporations.

When was the *Wall Street Journal* first published?

The newspaper, considered one of the world's best and certainly the preeminent American financial periodical, was first published in 1889, seven years after the Dow, Jones and Company (the comma between the two names was later dropped) was founded by financial reporters Charles Henry Dow (1851-1902) and Edward Davis Jones (1856-1920). Since the founding of the New York Stock Exchange (NYSE) in 1792, business reporting had been largely based on rumor or speculation. Dow and Jones were determined to provide American businesspeople and investors with up-to-date and accurate reporting on the stock market. In its first seven years of business, their publishing company grew from six employees to a staff of 50. In 1889 Dow and Jones expanded their two-page daily newspaper, titled *Customers' Afternoon Letter*, into the *Wall Street Journal*. The paper's stated goal was to give full and fair information regarding fluctuations in the prices of stocks, bonds, and some commodities. Further, the focus was to be on news rather than opinion. The paper began publishing composite lists of major stocks in 1884. In the decades since, it has expanded coverage to include all facets of the business and economic world and now caters to the leisure interests of businesspeople by publishing reports on the arts, travel, sports, and other recreational activities.

What is the history of the Dow Jones Industrial Average?

A measure of stock prices of important industrial companies, the Dow Jones Industrial Average (DJIA) was first printed in the *Wall Street Journal* in 1897. The average is an indica-

Who invented the assembly line?

Ford Motor Company founder Henry Ford (1863-1947) is credited with the creation of the assembly line, an industrial innovation that allowed cars to be produced quickly and efficiently. In 1913, 10 years after founding Ford Motor Company, Henry Ford installed the first moving assembly line in one of his Model T manufacturing plants. The innovation proved to be the beginning of the consumer age: The assembly line allowed greater efficiencies in auto production, which, in turn, reduced the price of a quality car, putting it in reach of the ordinary person. Soon, manufactured goods of every variety would be mass produced.

tor of the market overall and is used, along with other indexes, by investors, stockbrokers, and analysts to make investment forecasts and decisions. "The Dow," as it has come to be called, was conceived of as a summary measure of the stock market, an index that could be used to analyze past trends, indicate current trends, and even predict future ones. The first DJIA averaged the prices of 12 major companies. The list had been expanded since: in 1916 it averaged the stock prices of 20 companies; in 1928, 30. Adjustments have been made as the result of company mergers and dissolutions. Though it is a measure only of the New York Stock Exchange, the Dow Jones Average has been called a barometer of the stock market. News of fluctuations in the DJIA can affect market prices around the world.

Why was Ford's Model T important?

The enormous success of the Model T, a Ford Motor Company car introduced in 1908 and manufactured until 1927, has been the source of extensive analysis and commentary by historians, sociologists, economists, business writers, and pop culture experts. The Model T has been credited with not only changing America but with defining it. When Ford Motor Company founder and president Henry Ford (1863-1947) unveiled the prize Model T in October 1908, he hailed it as "a motor car for the great multitude." The product lived up to the promise. The internal combustion vehicle had been in production in the United States only since the 1890s, but in the decade preceding the Model T's debut, manufacturers and consumers alike had come to regard the "horseless carriage" as a luxury item, custom made for wealthy Americans. Ford had conceived of a different and, as the company would advertise throughout the century, a better idea: A car that was simple to operate, easy to service, comfortable, *and* affordable.

A 1914 Ford Model T. The vehicle, which was nicknamed "Tin Lizzie," became the symbol of low-cost, reliable transportation.

In 1914 Ford implemented the moving assembly line. It used the principles of scientific management, where each job has one "best way" of being accomplished, to bring unprecedented efficiency to manufacturing. Assembly time per car dropped to just 90 minutes. That year the Ford plant in Highland Park, Michigan, produced almost 250,000 Model Ts. To keep up with ever-rising demand, operations were sped up and capacity increased to the point that one day in 1925, Ford produced one Model T every 10 seconds. That year the car retailed for just $295, making the so-called "Tin Lizzie" (or the "Flivver") accessible to working-class families. By 1927, when Ford retired the Model T so the company could respond to consumer demand for cars with better performance, power, and styling, the company had turned out 15 million Tin Lizzies. Ford's innovative Model T, a reliable, no-nonsense, mass-produced automobile, manufactured on a moving assembly line, brought mobility within the reach of the average American. It had changed consumer mind-set to view the car as a necessity.

What was Black Tuesday?

It was the day the stock market crashed—Tuesday, October 29, 1929, signaling the beginning of the worldwide economic downturn called the Great Depression (1929-39).

On Thursday, October 24, 1929, stock values declined rapidly following a five-year period in which the average price of common stocks on the New York Stock Exchange had more than doubled. The prosperity of the 1920s and the widespread sale and purchase of Liberty Bonds (U.S. government bonds) to help finance World War I (1914-18) had encouraged many Americans to invest in the stock market: With the market robust, timing seemed right for speculation and America's experience with Liberty Bonds had made many people comfortable with and interested in investments. So when the stock market dropped precipitously on that fateful October day in 1929, the effects were felt by many. On the following Monday prices again plummeted; on Tuesday, October 29, stockholders panicked, selling off more than 16.4 million shares, and prices nose-dived. Institutions were also affected: Banks, also investors, lost huge sums of money, forcing many to close their doors. News of the stock market failure and bank closures caused many Americans to try to withdraw their money from their deposit accounts, leading to the famous run on the banks. The late-October financial crises marked the beginning of a decade of hard times.

What was the New Deal?

While the Great Depression began with the stock market crash on Black Tuesday, October 29, 1929, many factors contributed to the financial crisis, including overproduction, limited foreign markets (due to war debts that prevented trading), and overexpansion of credit, as well as stock market speculation. Soon the country was in the grips of a severe economic downturn that affected most every American. Some were harder hit than others: many lost their jobs (16 million people were unemployed at the depth of the crisis, accounting for about a third of the workforce); families were unable to make their mortgage payments and lost their homes; hunger was widespread, since there was no money to buy food. The sight of people waiting in bread lines was a common one.

It was amidst this crisis, which was soon felt overseas, that Franklin D. Roosevelt (1882-1945) took office as president in 1933. In his inaugural address, he called for faith in America's future, saying, "The only thing we have to fear is fear itself." Roosevelt soon rolled out a program of domestic reforms called the New Deal. For the first time in American history,

Shacks serve as homes for men and women in a Seattle, Washington, "Hooverville." Such villages popped up during the Great Depression and were sarcastically named after President Herbert Hoover.

the federal government took a central role in organizing business and agriculture. Roosevelt initiated aid programs and directed relief in the form of public works programs that would put people back to work. The new government agencies that were set up included the Public Works Administration, Federal Deposit Insurance Corporation, Security and Exchange Commission, National Labor Relations Board, Tennessee Valley Association, the National Recovery Administration, and the Civilian Conservation Corps. These government organizations soon become known by their initials (PWA, FDIC, SEC, NLRB, TVA, NRA, CCC). Roosevelt's critics charged him with giving the federal government too much power and began calling his New Deal "alphabet soup." The president became widely known as FDR.

Though the New Deal measures alleviated the situation and did put some Americans back to work, the country did not pull out of the Depression until industry was called upon to step up production in order to provide arms, aircraft, vehicles, and supplies for the war effort. It was during the early days of World War II (1939-45), the economy buoyed by military spending, that the nation finally recovered. Many New Deal agencies are still part of the federal government today.

Why was the introduction of plastic important to industry?

Pioneered in the early 1900s, plastic—which is any synthetic organic material that can be molded under heat and pressure to retain a shape—affected every industry and every consumer. As a malleable material, plastic could quite literally be molded for countless uses,

303

both for the production of goods and as a material in finished goods. In 1909 Bakelite plastic was introduced, and over the next three decades the plastics industry grew, developing acrylic, nylon, polystyrene, and vinyl (polyvinyl chloride or PVC) in the 1930s, and polyesters in the 1940s. The applications seemed endless: from household items such as hosiery, clocks, radios, toys, flooring, food containers, bags, electric plugs, and garden hoses, to commercial uses such as automobile bodies and parts, airplane windows, boat hulls, packaging, and building materials. The space industry and medicine have also found critical uses for plastic products. Scientists have continued to find new applications for plastics—in products such as compact disks (CDs), computer diskettes, outdoor furniture, and personal computers (PCs). The material has become essential to modern life.

When did IBM enter the personal computer business?

IBM (International Business Machines, organized in 1924) had long been an industry leader in developing and producing computers for business and science, but in August 1981, the company jumped into the consumer business, competing with upstart Apple for a share in the personal computer (PC) business. The PC introduced by IBM used a Microsoft disk-operating system (MS-DOS) and soon captured 75 percent of the market. Observing the company's enormous success, other firms began producing IBM "clones," which could use the same software as the IBM PC.

When was Microsoft founded?

It wasn't all that long ago, 1975, that computer whiz Bill Gates (1955-) founded what is now the dominant manufacturer of computer software (so dominant that the company has faced antitrust allegations from the federal government). Gates was only 19 years old when he founded the business with his friend Paul Gardner Allen, and he had dropped out of Harvard to do so. It paid off: Gates was a billionaire by age 30. Though he's undoubtedly a math ace (he scored a perfect 800 in math on his SATs and began writing computer programs when he was all of 13), Gates has more than once credited the success of Microsoft to not his own programming skills—but to hiring the best programming talent for the Redmond, Washington-based company.

ECONOMIC LEGISLATION

What was the Embargo Act?

On December 22, 1807, President Thomas Jefferson (1743-1826) signed the Embargo Act, prohibiting ships that were destined for foreign ports from leaving the United States. The legislation had been drawn up in an effort to pressure France and Britain, which were then at war and had been seizing U.S. merchant ships to prevent each other from receiving American goods. The situation began after the French navy was crushed by the British under Admiral Horatio Nelson (1758-1805) at the Battle of Trafalgar (October 1805). French ruler Napoleon Bonaparte (1769-1821) turned to economic warfare in his long struggle with the British, directing all countries under French control not to trade with Britain. Its economy dependent on trade, Britain struck back by imposing a naval blockade on France, which soon interfered with U.S. shipping. Ever since the struggle between the two European powers had begun in 1793, the United States had tried to remain neutral. But the interruption of shipping to and from the Continent and the search and seizure of ships posed significant problems to the American export business. The Embargo Act was an attempt to solve these problems without getting involved in the conflict. But the effort failed. The embargo made sales of U.S. farm surpluses impossible. New England shippers protested the act and were joined by southern cotton and tobacco planters in their opposition. Nevertheless, the embargo remained in effect for 14 months, during which the American economy suffered and many ships resorted to smuggling. In 1809 Congress passed the Non-Intercourse Act, which limited the shipping embargo to France and Britain; all other foreign ports were again open to U.S. ships. Three years later, the United States was drawn into the conflict, fighting the British in the War of 1812 (1812-14).

What was the Tariff of Abominations?

In 1828 the U.S. Congress passed a bill putting high tariffs (government taxes) on imported goods. The measure was intended to protect the burgeoning industries of New England, where numerous factories had opened during the first three decades of the century and the manufacture of finished goods defined the region's economy. Congress figured that by placing high taxes on goods from other countries, Americans would buy American-made products. But southern farmers had come to rely on cheaper imported goods. Believing the 1828 legislation was overly protective of the nation's industrial interests, southerners dubbed it the "tariff of abominations." Vice President John C. Calhoun (1782-1850), from South Carolina, openly and strongly criticized the tax, pronouncing that any state could declare null a federal law it deemed unconstitutional. In response, Congress took measures to lower the tariffs, but not eliminate them. South Carolina remained dissatisfied with the legislation, and in 1832 the state declared the tariff act null and void. Further, it threatened secession from the Union. President Andrew Jackson (1767-1845), unwilling to tolerate such rebelliousness and determined to enforce the federal law at all costs, asked Congress to pass the Force Bill—legislation allowing the nation's armed forces to collect the tariffs. Jackson's move inspired tremendous opposition in Congress. The Senate leader of the anti-Jackson contingency was Henry Clay (1777-1852) of Kentucky. Clay, who had earned himself the nickname "Great Pacificator" for his work in crafting the Missouri Compromise (1820), presented another compromise in 1833. He proposed that duties on certain goods could remain high but others should be gradually reduced over time. The Compromise Tariff authored by Clay averted an all-out conflict in the nation. The measure was passed and thereafter tariffs were adjusted depending on the prevailing economic conditions. But the fury over the Tariff of Abominations further revealed the North-South differences and the federal-government-versus-states'-rights issues that would inspire the southern states—led by South Carolina—to secede from the Union in 1860 and 1861, bringing on the American Civil War (1861-65).

How old is the U.S. income tax?

It dates to 1913. Proposed in Congress on July 12, 1909, and ratified February 3, 1913, the Sixteenth Amendment to the U.S. Constitution gives the federal government (specifically, the U.S. Congress) authority to levy and collect income taxes. The language of the amendment states that incomes "from whatever sources derived" may be taxed—and without regard to a census. In other words, it is up to Congress to determine the level at which citizens of the country are taxed, and this may be done without apportionment among the individual states.

One hundred years before the Sixteenth Amendment was approved, Congress had begun eyeing income tax as a way to collect funds for government use. Lawmakers first considered levying an income tax to help pay for the War of 1812 (1812-14), which the new republic fought against Great Britain over shipping disputes. During the American Civil War (1861-65), Congress imposed an income tax for the first time, charging workers and businessmen between 3 and 5 percent of their earnings and establishing (in 1862) a Bureau of Internal Revenue to administer the tax program. Once the war was over, income taxes were phased out. In 1894, responding to increasing economic and political pressures, the legislature again passed an income tax law (2 percent on all incomes over $4,000), as part of the Wilson-Gorman Tariff Act. But it was struck down by the U.S. Supreme Court, which declared it unconstitutional in the case of *Pollock v. Farmers' Loan and Trust Company* (1898). In the early 1900s, the idea of an income tax received widespread political support for the first time. Progressive politicians could see that the nation's wealth was poorly distributed, the gap between rich and poor growing wider. Conservative politicians worried that the government would not be able to respond to a national emergency if it lacked resources. These political factions found a single voice in favor of a graduated income tax (a tax based on level of income: those who earn more pay higher taxes). To circumvent the U.S. Supreme Court, it was necessary for Congress to propose an amendment to the Constitution. In ratifying the amendment, the states gave Congress the authority to set rates and collect income tax.

Tax rates have fluctuated ever since the passage of the Sixteenth Amendment, reaching their highest mark during World War II (1939-45) when the rate soared to 91 percent. The war effort also brought the innovation of automatic withholdings: Taxes were deducted directly from paychecks. In 1953 the Bureau of Internal Revenue was dramatically reorganized to create the Internal Revenue Service (IRS). Over the decades, tax laws (collectively called the Tax Code) have become increasingly complex, prompting a recent movement in favor of a flat (versus the graduated) tax, where all taxpayers are charged at the same rate.

When was the Interstate Commerce Commission formed?

The Interstate Commerce Commission (ICC) was established by act of Congress in 1887. The agency is responsible for regulating the rates and services of specified carriers that transport freight (goods, whether raw or finished) and passengers between states. Its jurisdiction, expanded by subsequent acts of Congress, includes trucking, bus services, water carriers, expedited delivery services, and even oil pipelines. The regulatory agency, the nation's first such body, was borne out of necessity in the late 1800s, as farmers in particular charged the railroads with discriminatory freight practices. With rail lines crisscrossing the nation, the question of who would control rates and monitor practices had become an increasingly difficult one to answer. Many states, particularly in the Midwest, set up their own regulatory boards, but because the rail companies operated between states, enforcing state laws on them proved cumbersome and impractical. Meanwhile the railroads, operating without the purview of any effective regulatory body, set their own standards and practices, which resulted in many abuses.

In an 1877 U.S. Supreme Court ruling, in the case of *Munn v. Illinois*, the authority of the state boards to regulate the railroads was upheld. But less than a decade later, in the case of *Wabash, St. Louis and Pacific Railway Company v. Illinois,* the high court invalidated its earlier decision and proclaimed that only the U.S. Congress has the right to regulate interstate commerce. Citing Section 8 of Article 1 of the U.S. Constitution (1790), which states that "Congress shall have the power … to regulate commerce with foreign nations, and among the several states, and with the Indian tribes," the Interstate Commerce Act was passed in 1887, setting up the Interstate Commerce Commission to regulate the interstate railroads. The agency's purview was later expanded to include all ground and water carriers that operate on an interstate basis. In addition to controlling rates, the agency also enforces laws against discrimination. The ICC's authority was strengthened by congressional legislation including the Hepburn Act (1906) and the Mann-Elkins Act (1910).

What is the Sherman Anti-Trust Act?

Passed by Congress in 1890, the Sherman Anti-Trust Act was an attempt to break up corporate trusts (combinations of firms or corporations formed to limit competition and monopolize a market). The legislation stated that "every contract, combination in the form of trust or otherwise, or conspiracy in the restraint of trade" is illegal. While the act made clear that anyone found to be in violation of restraining trade would face fines, jail terms, and the payment of damages, the language lacked clear definitions of what exactly constituted restraint of trade. The nation's courts were left with the responsibility of interpreting the Sherman Anti-Trust Act, and the justices proved as reluctant to take on big business as Congress had been.

The legislation was introduced in Congress by Senator John Sherman (1823- 1900) of Ohio, in response to increasing outcry from state governments and the public for the passage of national antitrust laws. Many states had passed their own antitrust bills or had made constitutional provisions prohibiting trusts, but the statutes proved difficult to enforce and big business found ways around them. When the legislation proposed by Sherman reached the Senate, conservative congressmen rewrote it; many charged that the Senators had made it deliberately vague. In the decade after its passage, the federal government prosecuted only 18 antitrust cases and court decisions did little to break up monopolies. But after the turn of the century, a progressive spirit in the nation grew; among progressive reformers' demands was that government regulate business. In 1911 the U.S. Justice Department won key victories against monopolies, breaking up John D. Rockefeller's Standard Oil Company of New Jersey and James B. Duke's American Tobacco Company. The decisions set a precedent for how the Sherman Anti-Trust Act would be enforced and demonstrated a national intolerance toward monopolistic trade practices. In 1914 national antitrust legislation was strengthened by the passage of the Clayton Anti-Trust Act, which outlawed price fixing (the practice of pricing below cost to eliminate a competitive product), made it illegal for the same executives to manage two or more competing companies (a practice called interlocking directorates), and prohibited any corporation from owning stock in a competing corporation. The creation of the Federal Trade Commission (FTC) that same year provided further insurance that U.S. corporations engaging in unfair practices would be investigated by the government.

Between 1880 and the early 1900s corporate trusts proliferated in the United States, becoming powerful business forces. The vague language of the Sherman Anti-Trust legislation and the courts' reluctance to prosecute big business based on that act did little to break up the monopolistic giants. The tide turned against corporate trusts when Theodore Roosevelt (1858-1919) became president in September 1901, after President William McKinley (1843-

1901) was assassinated. Roosevelt launched a "trust-busting" campaign, initiating, through the attorney general's office, some 40 lawsuits against American corporations such as American Tobacco Company, Standard Oil Company, and American Telephone and Telegraph (AT&T). Government efforts to break up the monopolies were strengthened in 1914, during the presidency of Woodrow Wilson (1856-1924), when Congress passed the Clayton Anti-Trust legislation and created the Federal Trade Commission (FTC), which is responsible for keeping business competition free and fair. Trust-busting declined during the prosperity of the 1920s, but was again vigorously pursued in the 1930s, during the administration of Franklin D. Roosevelt (1882-1945).

What is NAFTA?

NAFTA is the North American Free Trade Agreement, signed on December 17, 1992, by U.S. president George H. W. Bush (1924-), Canadian prime minister Brian Mulroney (1939-), and Mexican president Carlos Salinas de Gortari (1948-). It went into effect January 1, 1994. Inspired by the success of the European Community's open-trade agreement, the architects of NAFTA aimed to create free trade among North America's three largest countries. A 1988 pact between the United States and Canada had already lifted numerous barriers to trade between the two nations; that agreement was expanded to include Mexico through a series of negotiations that were preliminarily approved in August 1992 and were concluded with the signing of NAFTA later that year. The agreement removes trade barriers, including customs duties and tariffs, over the course of 15 years, allowing commodities and manufactured goods to be freely traded among the three nations. NAFTA also includes provisions that allow American and Canadian service companies to expand their markets into Mexico.

What is the TPP?

TPP stands for Trans-Pacific Partnership. The trade deal, which has been agreed to but not ratified as of August 2016, would involve twelve nations: the United States, Japan, Australia, Canada, Mexico, New Zealand, Vietnam, Malaysia, Brunei, Singapore, Peru, and Chile. These member nations would enjoy slashed tariffs on traded goods and is intended to bring the countries closer together through shared economic regulations and policies similar to the European Union's practices. If ratified, it would affect forty percent of world trade. It's important to note the TPP excludes China, and it is therefore seen by many as a bid to counter China's growing economic dominance.

Critics of the TPP fear its potential to foster competition between labor forces between member nations and that it makes it possible for governments to sue each other for their economic policies.

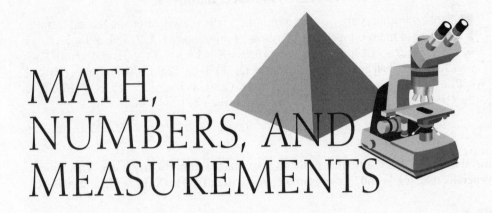

MATH, NUMBERS, AND MEASUREMENTS

NUMBERS

When and where did the concept of "numbers" and counting first develop?

The human adult (including some of the higher animals) can discern the numbers one through four without any training. After that people must learn to count. To count requires a system of number manipulation skills, a scheme to name the numbers, and some way to record the numbers. Early people began with fingers and toes, and progressed to shells and pebbles. In the fourth millennium B.C.E. in Elam (near what is today Iran along the Persian Gulf), accountants began using unbaked clay tokens instead of pebbles. Each represented one order in a numbering system: a stick shape for the number one, a pellet for ten, a ball for 100, and so on. During the same period, another clay-based civilization in Sumer in lower Mesopotamia invented the same system.

When was a symbol for the concept zero first used?

Surprisingly, the symbol for zero emerged later than the concept for the other numbers. The ancient Greeks, for instance, conceived of logic and geometry, concepts providing the foundation for all mathematics, yet they never had a symbol for zero. Hindu mathematicians are usually given credit for developing a symbol for the concept "zero"; it appears in an inscription at Gwalior dated 870 C.E. It is certainly older than that; it is found in inscriptions dating from the seventh century in Cambodia, Sumatra, and Bangka Island (off Sumatra). While there is no documented evidence for the zero in China before 1247, some historians believe that it originated there and arrived in India via Indochina.

What are Roman numerals?

Roman numerals are symbols that stand for numbers. They are written using seven basic symbols: I (1), V (5), × (10), L (50), C (100), D (500), and M (1,000). Sometimes a bar is place over a numeral to multiply it by 1,000. A smaller numeral appearing before a larger nu-

> ## What are Fibonacci numbers?
>
> **F**ibonacci numbers are a series of numbers where each, after the second term, is the sum of the two preceding numbers—for example, 1, 1, 2, 3, 5, 8, 13, 21 .... (1 + 1 = 2, 1 + 2 = 3, 2 + 3 = 5, 3 + 5 = 8, 5 + 8 = 13, 8 + 13 = 21, and so on). They were first described by Leonardo Fibonacci (ca. 1180-ca. 1250), also known as Leonard of Pisa, as part of a thesis on series in his most famous book Liber abaci (The Book of the Calculator), published in 1202 and later revised by him.

meral indicates that the smaller numeral is subtracted from the larger one. This notation is generally used for 4s and 9s; for example, 4 is written IV, 9 is IX, 40 is XL, and 90 is XC.

What is the largest prime number presently known?

A prime number is one that is evenly divisible only by itself and 1. The integers 1, 2, 3, 5, 7, 11, 13, 17, and 19 are prime numbers. Euclid (ca. 300 B.C.E.) proved that there is no "largest prime number," because any attempt to define the largest results in a paradox. If there is a largest prime number (P), adding 1 to the product of all primes up to and including P, 1 PLUS ($1 \times 2 \times 3 \times 5 \times ... \times P$), yields a number that is itself a prime number, because it cannot be divided evenly by any of the known primes. In 2008, the 45th and 46th prime numbers were discovered to be $2^{37156667-1}$ and $2^{43112609-1}$ respectively. They are both prime numbers that are part of a special class of prime numbers called Mersenne Primes (named after Marin Mersenne, 1588-1648, a French monk who did the first work in this area). Mersenne primes occur where 2n-1 is prime.

There is no apparent pattern to the sequence of primes. Mathematicians have been trying to find a formula since the days of Euclid, without success. The 39th prime was discovered on a personal computer as part of the GIMPS effort (the Great Internet Mersenne Prime Search), which was formed in January 1996 to discover new world-record-size prime numbers. GIMPS relies on the computing efforts of thousands of small, personal computers across the planet. Interested participants can become involved in the search for primes by pointing their browsers to: http://www. mersenne.org/prime.htm.

How are names for large and small quantities constructed in the metric system?

Each prefix listed below can be used in the metric system and with some customary units. For example, centi + meter = centimeter, meaning one-hundredth of a meter.

Prefix	Power	Numerals
Exa-	10^{18}	1,000,000,000,000,000,000
Peta-	10^{15}	1,000,000,000,000,000
Tera-	10^{12}	1,000,000,000,000
Giga-	10^{9}	1,000,000,000
Mega-	10^{6}	1,000,000
Myria-	10^{5}	100,000

Prefix	Power	Numerals
Kilo-	10^3	1,000
Hecto-	10^2	100
Deca-	10^1	10
Deci-	10^{-1}	0.1
Centi-	10^{-2}	0.01
Milli-	10^{-3}	0.001
Micro-	10^{-6}	0.000001
Nano-	10^{-9}	0.000000001
Pico-	10^{-12}	0.000000000001
Femto-	10^{-15}	0.000000000000001
Atto-	10^{-18}	0.000000000000000001

Why is the number ten considered important?

One reason is that the metric system is based on the number ten. The metric system emerged in the late-eighteenth century out of a need to bring standardization to measurement, which had up to then been fickle, depending upon the preference of the ruler of the day. But ten was important well before the metric system. Nicomachus of Gerasa, a second-century neo-Pythagorean from Judea, considered ten a "perfect" number, the figure of divinity present in creation with mankind's fingers and toes. Pythagoreans believed ten to be "the first-born of the numbers, the mother of them all, the one that never wavers and gives the key to all things." And shepherds of West Africa counted sheep in their flocks by colored shells based on ten, and ten had evolved as a "base" of most numbering schemes. Some scholars believe the reason ten developed as a base number had more to do with ease: ten is easily counted on fingers and the rules of addition, subtraction, multiplication, and division for the number ten are easily memorized.

What are some very large numbers?

Name	Value in powers of 10	Number of 0's	Number of groups of three 0's after 1,000
Billion	10^9	9	2
Trillion	10^{12}	12	3
Quadrillion	10^{15}	15	4
Quintillion	10^{18}	18	5
Sextillion	10^{21}	21	6
Septillion	10^{24}	24	7
Octillion	10^{27}	27	8
Nonillion	10^{30}	30	9
Decillion	10^{33}	33	10
Undecillion	10^{36}	36	11
Duodecillion	10^{39}	39	12
	Value in	Number	Number of groups

Name	powers of 10	of 0's	of three 0's after 1,000
Tredecillion	10^{42}	42	13
Quattuor-decillion	10^{45}	45	14
Quindecillion	10^{48}	48	15
Sexdecillion	10^{51}	51	16
Septen-decillion	10^{54}	54	17
Octodecillion	10^{57}	57	18
Novemdecillion	10^{60}	60	19
Vigintillion	10^{63}	63	20
Centillion	10^{303}	303	100

The British, French, and Germans use a different system for naming denominations above one million. The googol and googolplex are rarely used outside the United States.

How large is a googol?

A googol is 10^{100} (the number 1 followed by 100 zeros). Unlike most other names for numbers, it does not relate to any other numbering scale. The American mathematician Edward Kasner first used the term in 1938; when searching for a term for this large number, Kasner asked his nephew, Milton Sirotta, then about nine years old, to suggest a name. The googolplex is 10 followed by a googol of zeros, represented as 10^{googol}. The popular Web search engine Google.com is named after the concept of a googol.

What is an irrational number?

Numbers that cannot be expressed as an exact ratio are called irrational numbers; numbers that can be expressed as an exact ratio are called rational numbers. For instance, 1/2 (one half, or 50 percent of something) is rational. 1.61803 (θ), 3.14159 (π), 1.41421 ($\sqrt{2}$), are irrational. History claims that Pythagoras in the sixth century B.C.E. first used the term when he discovered that the square root of 2 could not be expressed as a fraction.

What is the value of pi out to 30 digits past the decimal point?

Pi (π) represents the ratio of the circumference of a circle to its diameter, used in calculating the area of a circle (πr^2) and the volume of a cylinder ($\pi r^2 h$) or cone. It is a "transcendental number," an irrational number with an exact value that can be measured to any degree of accuracy, but that can't be expressed as the ratio of two integers. In theory, the decimal extends into infinity, though it is generally rounded to 3.1416. The Welsh-born mathematician William Jones selected the Greek symbol (π) for Pi. Rounded to 30 digits past the decimal point, it equals 3.141592653589793238462643383279. In 1989, Gregory and David Chudnovsky at Columbia University in New York City calculated the value of pi to 1,011,961,691 decimal places. They performed the calculation twice on an IBM 3090 mainframe and on a CRAY-2 supercomputer with matching results. In 1991, they calculated pi to 2,260,321,336 decimal places. In 1999, Yasumasa Kanada and Daisuke Takahashi of the University of Tokyo calculated pi out to 206,158,430,000 digits. Mathematicians have also calculated pi in binary format (i.e. 0s and

What are imaginary numbers?

Imaginary numbers are the square roots of negative numbers. Since the square is the product of two equal numbers with like signs it is always positive. Therefore, no number multiplied by itself can give a negative real number. The symbol i is used to indicate an imaginary number.

1s). The five trillionth binary digit of pi was computed by Colin Percival and 25 others at Simon Fraser University. The computation took over 13,500 hours of computer time.

Why is seven considered a supernatural number?

In magical lore and mysticism, all numbers are ascribed certain properties and energies. Seven is a number of great power, a magical number, a lucky number, a number of psychic and mystical powers, of secrecy and the search for inner truth. The origin of belief in seven's power lies in the lunar cycle. Each of the moon's four phases lasts about seven days. The Sumerians, who based their calendar on the moon, gave the week seven days and declared the seventh and last day of each week to be uncanny. Life cycles on Earth also have phases demarcated by seven. Furthermore, there are said to be seven years to each stage of human growth; there are seven colors to the rainbow; and seven notes are in the musical scale. The seventh son of a seventh son is said to be born with formidable magical and psychic powers. The number seven is widely held to be a lucky number, especially in matters of love and money, and it also carries great prominence in the old and new testaments. Here are a few examples: the Lord rested on the seventh day; there were seven years of plenty and seven years of famine in Egypt in the story of Joseph; God commanded Joshua to have seven priests carry trumpets, and on the seventh day they were to march around Jericho seven times; Solomon built the temple in seven years; and there are seven petitions of the Lord's Prayer.

What are some examples of numbers and mathematical concepts in nature?

The world can be articulated with numbers and mathematics. Some numbers are especially prominent. The number six is ubiquitous: every normal snowflake has six sides; every honeybee colony's combs are six-sided hexagons. The curved, gradually decreasing chambers of a nautilus shell are propagating spirals of the Golden Section and the Fibonacci sequence of numbers. Pine cones also rely on the Fibonacci sequence, as do many plants and flowers in their seed and stem arrangements. Fractals are evident in shorelines, blood vessels, and mountains.

MATHEMATICS

How is arithmetic different from mathematics?

Arithmetic is the study of positive integers (i.e. 1, 2, 3, 4, 5, ...) manipulated with addition, subtraction, multiplication, and division, and the use of the results in daily life. Mathematics is the study of shape, arrangement, and quantity. It is traditionally viewed as consisting of three fields: algebra, analysis, and geometry. But any lines of division have evaporated because the fields are now so interrelated.

Who invented calculus?

The German mathematician Gottfried Wilhelm Leibniz published the first paper on calculus in 1684. Most historians agree that Isaac Newton invented calculus eight to ten years earlier, but he was typically very late in publishing his works. The invention of calculus marked the beginning of higher mathematics. It provided scientists and mathematicians with a tool to solve problems that had been too complicated to attempt previously.

Gottfried Wilhelm Leibniz made important contributions to the science of calculus and designed early manifestations of the computer.

What is the most enduring mathematical work of all time?

The *Elements of Euclid* (fl. about 300 B.C.E.) has been the most enduring and influential mathematical work of all time. In it, the ancient Greek mathematician presented the work of earlier mathematicians and included many of his own innovations. The *Elements* is divided into 13 books: the first six cover plane geometry; seven to nine address arithmetic and number theory; 10 treats irrational numbers; and 11 to 13 discuss solid geometry. In presenting his theorems, Euclid used the synthetic approach, in which one proceeds from the known to the unknown by logical steps. This method became the standard procedure for scientific investigation for many centuries, and the *Elements* probably had a greater influence on scientific thinking than any other work.

How long has the abacus been used? Is it still used?

The abacus grew out of early counting boards, with hollows in a board holding pebbles or beads used to calculate. It has been documented in Mesopotamia back to around 3500 B.C.E. The current form, with beads sliding on rods, dates back at least to 15th-century China. Before the use of decimal number systems, which allowed the familiar paper-and-pencil methods of calculation, the abacus was essential for almost all multiplication and division. The abacus is still used in many countries where modern calculators are not available. It is also still used in countries,

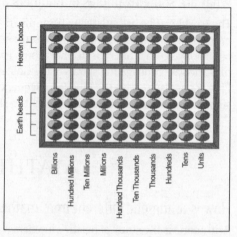

A Chinese abacus called a suan pan.

such as Japan and China, that have long traditions of abacus use. As recently as the mid-
1970s, most Japanese shopkeepers used abaci
for totaling customers' bills. While the cal-
culator is now more widely used, many people still prefer to check the results on an
abacus. At least one manufacturer offers calculators with small, built-in abaci.

What are Napier's bones?

In the 16th century, the Scottish mathematician John Napier (1550-1617), Baron of
Merchiston, developed a method of simplifying the processes of multiplication and division, using exponents of 10, which Napier
called logarithms (commonly abbreviated as
logs). Using this system, multiplication is reduced to addition and division to subtrac-

John Napier, the Scottish mathematician known for
a device called "Napier's bones," devised the use of
the decimal point when writing numbers.

tion. For example, the log of 100 (10^2) is 2; the log of 1000 (10^3) is 3; the multiplication of
100 by 1000, $100 \times 1000 = 100,000$, can be accomplished by adding their logs:
$\log[(100)(1000)] = \log(100) + \log(1000) = 2 + 3 = 5 = \log(100,000)$. Napier published his
methodology in *A Description of the Admirable Table of Logarithms* in 1614. In 1617 he
published a method of using a device, made up of a series of rods in a frame, marked with
the digits 1 through 9, to multiply and divide using the principles of logarithms. This device
was commonly called "Napier's bones" or "Napier's rods."

What is the difference between a median and a mean?

If a string of numbers is arranged in numerical order, the median is the middle value of the
string. If there is an even number of values in the string, the median is found by adding the
two middle values and dividing by two. The arithmetic mean, also known as the simple average, is found by taking the sum of the numbers in the string and dividing by the number
of items in the string. While easy to calculate for relatively short strings, the arithmetic
mean can be misleading, as very large or very small values in the string can distort it. For
example, the mean of the salaries of a professional football team would be skewed if one of
the players was a high-earning superstar; it could be well above the salaries of any of the
other players. The mode is the number in a string that appears most often.

For the string 111222234455667, for example, the median is the middle number of the
series: 3. The arithmetic mean is the sum of numbers divided by the number of numbers in
the series, $51 \div 15 = 3.4$. The mode is the number that occurs most often, 2.

When does $0 \times 0 = 1$?

Factorials are the product of a given number and all the factors less than that number. The
notation n! is used to express this idea. For example, 5! (five factorial) is $5 \times 4 \times 3 \times 2 \times 1$
$= 120$. For completeness, 0! is assigned the value 1, so $0 \times 0 = 1$.

When did the concept of square root originate?

A square root of a number is a number that, when multiplied by itself, equals the given number. For instance, the square root of 25 is 5 (5 × 5 = 25). The concept of the square root has been in existence for many thousands of years. Exactly how it was discovered is not known, but several different methods of exacting square roots were used by early mathematicians. Babylonian clay tablets from 1900 to 1600 B.C.E. contain the squares and cubes of integers 1-30. The early Egyptians used square roots around 1700 B.C.E., and during the Greek Classical Period (600 to 300 B.C.E.) better arithmetic methods im-

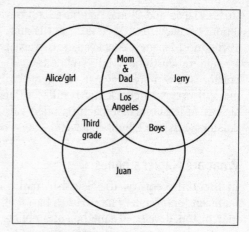

Example of a Venn diagram.

proved square root operations. In the 16th century, French mathematician René Descartes was the first to use the square root symbol, called "the radical sign," $\sqrt{}$.

What are Venn diagrams?

Venn diagrams are graphical representations of set theory, which use circles to show the logical relationships of the elements of different sets, using the logical operators (also called in computer parlance "Boolean Operators") *and, or,* and *not.* John Venn (1834-1923) first used them in his 1881 Symbolic Logic, in which he interpreted and corrected the work of George Boole (1815-1864) and Augustus de Morgan (1806- 1871). While his attempts to clarify perceived inconsistencies and ambiguities in Boole's work are not widely accepted, the new method of diagraming is considered to be an improvement. Venn used shading to better illustrate inclusion and exclusion. Charles Dodgson (1832-1898), better known as Lewis Carroll, refined Venn's system, in particular by enclosing the diagram to represent the universal set.

What are the common mathematical formulas for volume?

Volume of a sphere:

Volume = 4/3 times pi times the cube of the radius

$$V = 4/3 \times \pi r^3$$

Volume of a pyramid:

Volume = 1/3 times the area of the base times the height

$$V = 1/3bh$$

Volume of a cylinder:

Volume = area of the base times the height

$$V = Ah$$

Volume of a circular cylinder (with circular base):

Volume = pi times the square of the radius of the base times the height

$$V = \pi r^2 h$$

Volume of a cube:

Volume = the length of one side cubed

$$V = S^3$$

Volume of a cone:

Volume = 1/3 times pi times the square of the radius of the base times the height.

$$V = 1/3 \ \pi r^2 h$$

Volume of a rectangular solid:

Volume = length times width times height

$$V = lwh$$

How many feet are on each side of an acre that is square?

An acre that is square in shape has about 208.7 feet (64 meters) on each side.

What are the common mathematical formulas for area?

Area of a rectangle:

Area = length times width

$$A = lw$$

Area = altitude times base

$$A = ab$$

Area of a circle:

Area = pi times the radius squared

$$A = \pi r^2 \text{ or } A = 1/4\pi d^2$$

Area of a triangle:

Area = one half the altitude times the base

$$A = 1/2ab$$

Area of the surface of a sphere:

Area = four times pi times the radius squared

$$A = 4\pi r^2 \text{ or } A = \pi d^2$$

Area of a square:

Area = length times width, or length of one side squared

$$A = s^2$$

Area of a cube:

Area = square of the length of one side times 6

$$A = 6s^2$$

Area of an ellipse:

Area = long diameter times short diameter times 0.7854.

How is Pascal's triangle used?

Pascal's triangle is an array of numbers, arranged so that every number is equal to the sum of the two numbers above it on either side. It can be represented in several slightly different triangles, but this is the most common form:

$$
\begin{array}{ccccccccccc}
 & & & & & 1 & & & & & \\
 & & & & 1 & & 1 & & & & \\
 & & & 1 & & 2 & & 1 & & & \\
 & & 1 & & 3 & & 3 & & 1 & & \\
 & 1 & & 4 & & 6 & & 4 & & 1 & \\
1 & & 5 & & 10 & & 10 & & 5 & & 1
\end{array}
$$

French mathematician and scientist Blaise Pascal (1623–1662) uncovered a relationship between numbers in Pascal's triangle.

The triangle is used to determine the numerical coefficients resulting from the computation of higher powers of a binomial (two numbers added together). When a binomial is raised to a higher power, the result is expanded, using the numbers in that row of the triangle. For example, $(a + b)^1 = a^1 + b^1$, using the coefficients in the second line of the triangle. $(a + b)^2 = a^2 + 2ab + b^2$, using the coefficients in the next line of the triangle. (The first line of the triangle correlates to $(a + b)^0$.) While the calculation of coefficients is fairly straightforward, the triangle is useful in calculating them for the higher powers without needing to multiply them out. Binomial coefficients are useful in calculating probabilities; Blaise Pascal was one of the pioneers in developing laws of probability.

As with many other mathematical developments, there is some evidence of a previous appearance of the triangle in China. Around 1100 C.E., the Chinese mathematician Chia Hsien wrote about "the tabulation system for unlocking binomial coefficients"; the first publication of the triangle was probably in a book called *Piling-Up Powers and Unlocking Coefficients,* by Liu Ju-Hsieh.

Who discovered the formula for the area of a triangle?

Heron (or Hero) of Alexandria (first century B.C.E.) is best known in the history of mathematics for the formula that bears his name. This formula calculates the area of a triangle with sides a, b, and c, with s = half the perimeter: A = [s (2 - a)(s - b)(s - c)]. The Arab mathematicians who preserved and transmitted the mathematics of the Greeks reported that this formula was known earlier to Archimedes (ca. 287-212 B.C.E.), but the earliest proof now known is that appearing in Heron's *Metrica.*

What is the Pythagorean theorem?

In a right triangle (one where two of the sides meet in a 90-degree angle), the hypotenuse is the side opposite the right angle. The Pythagorean theorem, also known as the rule of Pythagoras, states that the square of the length of the hypotenuse is equal to the sum of the squares of the other two sides ($h^2 = a^2 + b^2$). If the lengths of the sides are: h = 5 inches, a = 4 inches, and b = 3 inches, then

$$h = \sqrt{a^2 + b^2} = \sqrt{4^2 + 3^2} = \sqrt{16 + 9} = \sqrt{25} = 5$$

The theorem is named for the Greek philosopher and mathematician Pythagoras (ca. 580–ca. 500 B.C.E.). Pythagoras is credited with the theory of the functional significance of numbers in the objective world and numerical theories of musical pitch. As he left no writings, the Pythagorean theorem may actually have been formulated by one of his disciples.

What are the Platonic solids?

The Platonic solids are the five regular polyhedra: the four-sided tetrahedron, the six-sided cube or hexahedron, the eight-sided octahedron, the twelve-sided dodecahedron, and the twenty-sided icosahedron. While they had been studied as long ago as the time of Pythagorus (around 500 B.C.E.), they are called the Platonic solids because they were first described in detail by Plato around 400 B.C.E. The ancient Greeks gave mystical significance to the Platonic solids: the tetrahedron represented fire, the icosahedron represented water, the stable cube represented the Earth, the octahedron represented the air. The twelve faces of the dodecahedron corresponded to the twelve signs of the zodiac, and this figure represented the entire universe.

What is a golden section?

Golden section, also called the divine proportion, is the division of a line segment so that the ratio of the whole segment to the larger part is equal to the ratio of the larger part to the smaller part. The ratio is approximately 1.61803 to 1. The number 1.61803 is called the Golden Number (also called Phi [with a capital P]). The golden number is the limit of the ratios of consecutive Fibonacci numbers, such as, for instance, 21/13, and 34/21. A golden rectangle is one whose length and width correspond to this ratio. The ancient Greeks thought this shape had the most pleasing proportions. Many famous painters have used the Golden Rectangle in their paintings, and architects have used it in their design of buildings, the most famous example being the Greek Parthenon.

What is a Möbius strip?

A Möbius strip is a surface with only one side, usually made by connecting the two ends of a rectangular strip of paper after putting a half-twist (180 degrees relative to the opposite side) in the strip. Cutting a Möbius strip in half down the center of the length of the strip results in a single band with four half-twists. Devised by the German mathematician August Ferdinand Möbius (1790–1868) to illustrate the properties of one-sided surfaces, it was presented in a paper that was not discovered or published until after his death. Another 19th-century German mathematician, Johann Benedict Listing, developed the idea independently at the same time.

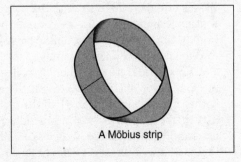

A Möbius strip

A Möbius strip.

What are fractals?

A fractal is a set of points that is too irregular to be described by traditional geometric terms, but that often have some degree of self-similarity; that is, they are made of parts that resemble the whole. They are used in image processing to compress data and to depict apparently chaotic objects in nature such as mountains or coastlines. Scientists also use fractals to better comprehend rainfall trends, patterns formed by clouds and waves, and the distribution of vegetation. Fractals are also used to create computer-generated art.

How is percent of increase calculated?

To find the percent of increase, divide the amount of increase by the base amount. Multiply the result by 100 percent. For example, a raise in salary from $10,000 to $12,000 would have percent of increase = (2,000 4 10,000) × 100% = 20%.

What is the difference between simple interest and compound interest?

Simple interest is calculated on the amount of principal only. Compound interest is calculated on the amount of principal plus any previous interest already earned. For example, $100 invested at a rate of 5 percent for 1 year will earn $5.00 after one year earning simple interest. The same $100 will earn $5.12 if compounded monthly.

If 30 people are chosen at random, what is the probability that at least two of them have their birthday on the same day?

The probability that at least two people in a group of 30 share the same birthday is about 70 percent.

What is the law of very large numbers?

Formulated by Persi Diaconis (1945-) and Frederick Mosteller (1916-) of Harvard University, this long-understood law of statistics states that "with a large enough sample, any outrageous thing is apt to happen." Therefore, seemingly amazing coincidences can actually be expected if given sufficient time or a large enough pool of subjects. For example, when a

---

How was the length of a meter originally determined?

It was originally intended that the meter should represent one ten-millionth of the distance along the meridian running from the North Pole to the equator through Dunkirk, France, and Barcelona, Spain. French scientists determined this distance, working nearly six years to complete the task in November 1798. They decided to use a platinum-iridium bar as the physical replica of the meter. Although the surveyors made an error of about two miles, the error was not discovered until much later. Rather than change the length of the meter to conform to the actual distance, scientists in 1889 chose the platinum-iridium bar as the international prototype. It was used until 1960. Numerous copies of it are in other parts of the world, including the United States National Bureau of Standards.

New Jersey woman won the lottery twice in four months, the media publicized it as an incredible long shot of 1 in 17 trillion. However, when statisticians looked beyond this individual's chances and asked what were the odds of the same happening to any person buying a lottery ticket in the United States over a six-month period, the number dropped dramatically to 1 in 30. According to researchers, coincidences arise often in statistical work, but some have hidden causes and therefore are not coincidences at all. Many are simply chance events reflecting the luck of the draw.

WEIGHTS, MEASURES, AND MEASUREMENT

What is the SI system of measurement?

French scientists as far back as the 17th and 18th centuries questioned the hodgepodge of the many illogical and imprecise standards used for measurement, and so began a crusade to make a comprehensive, logical, precise, and universal measurement system called Système Internationale d'Unités, or SI for short. It uses the metric system as its base. Since all the units are in multiples of 10, calculations are simplified. Today all countries except the United States, Burma, and Liberia use this system. However, some elements within American society do use SI—scientists, exporting/importing industries, and federal agencies (as of November 30, 1992).

The SI or metric system has seven fundamental standards: the meter (for length), the kilogram (for mass), the second (for time), the ampere (for electric current), the kelvin (for temperature), the candela (for luminous intensity), and the mole (for amount of substance). In addition, two supplementary units, the radian (plane angle) and steradian (solid angle), and a large number of derived units compose the current system, which is still evolving. Some derived units, which use special names, are the hertz, newton, pascal, joule, watt, coulomb, volt, farad, ohm, siemens, weber, tesla, henry, lumen, lux, becquerel, gray, and sievert. Its unit of volume or capacity is the cubic decimeter, but many still use "liter" in its place. Very large or very small dimensions are expressed through a series of prefixes, which increase or decrease in multiples of ten. For example, a decimeter is 1/10 of a meter; a centimeter is 1/100 of a meter, and a millimeter is 1/1000 of a meter. A dekameter is 10 meters, a hectometer is 100 meters, and a kilometer is 1,000 meters. The use of these prefixes enable the system to express these units in an orderly way and avoid inventing new names and new relationships.

How is the length of a meter presently determined?

The meter is equal to 39.37 inches. It is presently defined as the distance traveled by light in a vacuum during 1/299,792,458 of a second. From 1960 to 1983, the length of a meter had been defined as 1,650,763.73 times the wavelength of the orange light emitted when a gas consisting of the pure krypton isotope of mass number 86 is excited in an electrical discharge.

How did the yard as a unit of measurement originate?

In early times the natural way to measure lengths was to use various portions of the body (the foot, the thumb, the forearm, etc.). According to tradition, a yard measured on King

Henry I (1068-1135) of England became the standard yard still used today. It was the distance from his nose to the middle fingertip of his extended arm.

Other measures were derived from physical activity such as a pace, a league (distance that equaled an hour's walking), an acre (amount plowed in a day), a furlong (length of a plowed ditch), etc., but obviously these units were unreliable. The ell, based on the distance between the elbow and index fingertip, was used to measure out cloth. It ranged from 0.513 to 2.322 meters depending on the locality where it was used and even on the type of goods measured.

Below are listed some linear measurements that evolved from this old reckoning into U.S. customary measures:

U.S. customary linear measures

1 hand	=	4 inches
1 foot	=	12 inches
1 yard	=	3 feet
1 rod (pole or perch)	=	16.5 feet
1 fathom	=	6 feet
1 furlong	=	220 yards or 660 feet or 40 rods
1 (statute) mile	=	1,760 yards or 5,280 feet or 8 furlongs
1 league	=	5,280 yards or 15,840 feet or 3 miles
1 international nautical mile	=	6,076.1 feet

Conversion to metric

1 inch	=	2.54 centimeters
1 foot	=	0.304 meters
1 yard	=	0.9144 meters
1 fathom	=	1.83 meters
1 rod	=	5.029 meters
1 furlong	=	201.168 meters
1 league	=	4.828 kilometers

Conversion to metric

1 mile	=	1.609 kilometers
1 international nautical mile	=	1.852 kilometers

Why is a nautical mile different from a statute mile?

Queen Elizabeth I established the statute mile as 5,280 feet (1,609 meters). This measure, based on walking distance, originated with the Romans, who designated 1,000 paces as a land mile.

The nautical mile is not based on human locomotion, but on the circumference of the Earth. There was wide disagreement on the precise measurement, but by 1954 the United States adopted the international nautical mile of 1,852 meters (6,076 feet). It is the length on the Earth's surface of one minute of arc.

1 nautical mile (Int.) = 1.1508 statute miles

1 statute mile = 0.868976 nautical miles

How are U.S. customary measures converted to metric measures and vice versa?

Listed below is the conversion process for common units of measure:

To convert from	To	Multiply by
acres	meters, square	4,046.856
centimeters	inches	0.394
centimeters	feet	0.0328
centimeters, cubic	inches, cubic	0.06
centimeters, square	inches, square	0.155
feet	meters	0.305
feet, square	meters, square	0.093
gallons, U.S.	liters	3.785
grams	ounces (avoirdupois)	0.035
hectares	kilometers, square	0.01
hectares	miles, square	0.004
inches	centimeters	2.54
inches	millimeters	25.4
inches, cubic	centimeters, cubic	16.387
inches, cubic	liters	0.016387
inches, cubic	meters, cubic	0.0000164
inches, square	centimeters, square	6.4516
inches, square	meters, square	0.0006452
kilograms	ounces, troy	32.15075
kilograms	pounds (avoirdupois)	2.205
kilograms	tons, metric	0.001
kilometers	feet	3,280.8
kilometers	miles	0.621
kilometers, square	hectares	100
knots	miles per hour	1.151
liters	fluid ounces	33.815
liters	gallons	0.264
liters	pints	2.113
liters	quarts	1.057
meters	feet	3.281
meters	yards	1.094
meters, cubic	yards, cubic	1.308
meters, cubic	feet, cubic	35.315
meters, square	feet, square	10.764
meters, square	yards, square	1.196
miles, nautical	kilometers	1.852
miles, square	hectares	258.999
miles, square	kilometers, square	2.59
miles (statute)	meters	1,609.344
miles (statute)	kilometers	1.609344
ounces (avoirdupois)	grams	28.35
ounces (avoirdupois)	kilograms	0.0283495

To convert from	To	Multiply by
ounces, fluid	liters	0.03
pints, liquid	liters	0.473
pounds (avoirdupois)	grams	453.592
pounds (avoirdupois)	kilograms	0.454
quarts	liters	0.946
tons (short/U.S.)	tonne	0.907
ton, long	tonne	1.016
tonne	ton(short/U.S.)	1.102
tonne ton,	long	0.984
yards	meters	0.914
yards, square	meters, square	0.836
yards, cubic	meters, cubic	0.765

Which countries of the world have not formally begun converting to the metric system?

The United States, Burma, and Liberia are the only countries that have not formally converted to the metric system. As early as 1790, Thomas Jefferson, then Secretary of State, proposed adoption of the metric system. It was not implemented because Great Britain, America's major trading source, had not yet begun to use the system.

What are the equivalents for dry and liquid measures?

U.S. customary dry measures

1 pint	=	33.6 cubic inches
1 quart	=	2 pints or 67.2006 cubic inches
1 peck	=	8 quarts or 16 pints or 537.605 cubic inches
1 bushel	=	4 pecks or 2,150.42 cubic inches or 32 quarts
1 barrel	=	105 quarts or 7,056 cubic inches
1 pint, dry	=	0.551 liter
1 quart, dry	=	1.101 liters
1 bushel	=	35.239 liters

U.S. customary liquid measures

1 tablespoon	=	4 fluid drams or 0.5 fluid ounce
1 cup	=	0.5 pint or 8 fluid ounces
1 gill	=	4 fluid ounces
4 gills	=	1 pint or 28.875 cubic inches
1 pint	=	2 cups or 16 fluid ounces
2 pints	=	1 quart or 57.75 cubic ounces
1 quart	=	2 pints or 4 cups or 32 fluid ounces
4 quarts	=	1 gallon or 231 cubic inches or 8 pints or 32 gills or 0.833 British quart
1 gallon	=	16 cups or 231 cubic inches or 128 fluid ounces
1 bushel	=	8 gallons or 32 quarts

Conversion to metric

1 fluid ounce	=	29.57 milliliters or 0.029 liter
1 gill	=	0.118 liter
1 cup	=	0.236 liter
1 pint	=	0.473 liter
1 U.S. quart	=	0.833 British quart or 0.946 liter
1 U.S. gallon	=	0.833 British gallon or 3.785 liters

What is the difference between a short ton, a long ton, and a metric ton?

A short ton or U.S. ton or net ton (sometimes just "ton") equals 2,000 pounds; a long ton or an avoirdupois ton is 2,240 pounds; and a metric ton or tonne is 2,204.62 pounds. Other weights are compared below:

U.S. customary measure

1 ounce	=	16 drams or 437.5 grains
1 pound	=	16 ounces or 7,000 grains or 256 drams
1 (short) hundredweight	=	100 pounds
1 long hundredweight	=	112 pounds
1 (short) ton	=	20 hundredweights or 2,000 pounds
1 long ton	=	20 long hundredweights or 2,240 pounds

Conversion to metric

1 grain	=	65 milligrams
1 dram	=	1.77 grams
1 ounce	=	28.3 grams
1 pound	=	453.5 grams
1 metric ton (tonne)	=	2,204.6 pounds

What are the U.S. and metric units of measurement for area?

U.S. customary area measures

1 square foot	=	144 square inches
1 square yard	=	9 square feet or 1,296 square miles
1 square rod or pole or perch	=	30.25 square yards or 272.5 square feet
1 rood	=	40 square rods
1 acre	=	160 square rods or 4,840 square yards or 43,460 square feet
1 section	=	1 mile square or 640 acres
1 township	=	6 miles square or 36 square miles or 36 sections
1 square mile	=	640 acres or 4 roods, or 1 section

International area measures

1 square millimeter	=	1,000,000 square microns
1 square centimeter	=	100 square millimeters
1 square meter	=	10,000 square centimeters
1 are	=	100 square meters

1 hectare	=	100 ares or 10,000 square meters
1 square kilometer	=	100 hectares or 1,000,000 square meters

How much does water weigh?

U.S. customary measures

1 gallon	=	4 quarts

U.S. customary measures

1 gallon	=	231 cubic inches
1 gallon	=	8.34 pounds
1 gallon	=	0.134 cubic foot
1 cubic foot	=	7.48 gallons
1 cubic inch	=	.0360 pound
12 cubic inches	=	.433 pound

British measures

1 liter	=	1 kilogram
1 cubic meter	=	1 tonne (metric ton)
1 imperial gallon	=	10.022 pounds
1 imperial gallon salt water	=	10.3 pounds

How are avoirdupois measurements converted to troy measurements and how do the measures differ?

Troy weight is a system of mass units used primarily to measure gold and silver. A troy ounce is 480 grains or 31.1 grams. Avoirdupois weight is a system of units that is used to measure mass, except for precious metals, precious stones, and drugs. It is based on the pound, which is approximately 454 grams. In both systems, the weight of a grain is the same—65 milligrams. The two systems do not contain the same weights for other units, however, even though they use the same name for the unit.

What is a theodolite?

This optical surveying instrument used to measure angles and directions is mounted on an adjustable tripod and has a spirit level to show when it is horizontal. Similar to the more commonly used transit, the theodolite gives more precise readings; angles can be read to fractions of a degree. It is comprised of a telescope that sights the main target, a horizontal plate to provide readings around the horizon, and a vertical plate and scale for vertical readings. The surveyor uses the geometry of triangles to calculate the distance from the angles measured by the theodolite. Such triangulation is used in road- and tunnel-building and other civil engineering work. One of the earliest forms of this surveying instrument was described by Englishman Leonard Digges (d. 1571?) in his 1571 work, *Geometrical Treatise Named Pantometria*.

Troy

> 1 grain = 65 milligrams
> 1 ounce = 480 grains = 31.1 grams
> 1 pound = 12 ounce = 5760 grains = 373 grams

Avoirdupois

> 1 grain = 65 milligrams
> 1 ounce = 437.5 grains = 28.3 grams
> 1 pound = 16 ounces = 7000 grains = 454 grams

To convert from	To	Multiply by
pounds avdp	ounces troy	14.583
pounds avdp	pounds troy	1.215
pounds troy	ounces avdp	1.097
pounds troy	pounds avdp	0.069
ounces avdp	ounces troy	0.911
ounces troy	ounces avdp	1.097

How is the distance to the horizon measured?

Distance to the horizon depends on the height of the observer's eyes. To determine that, take the distance (in feet) from sea level to eye level and multiply by three, then divide by two and take the square root of the answer. The result is the number of miles to the horizon. For example, if eye level is at a height of six feet above sea level, the horizon is almost three miles away. If eye level were exactly at sea level, there would be no distance seen at all; the horizon would be directly in front of the viewer.

TIME

How is time measured?

The passage of time can be measured in three ways. Rotational time is based on the unit of the mean solar day (the average length of time it takes the Earth to complete one rotation on its axis). Dynamic time, the second way to measure time, uses the motion of the moon and planets to determine time and avoids the problem of the Earth's varying rotation. The first dynamic time scale was Ephemeris Time, proposed in 1896 and modified in 1960.

Atomic time is a third way to measure time. This method, using an atomic clock, is based on the extremely regular oscillations that occur within atoms. In 1967, the atomic second (the length of time in which 9,192,631,770 vibrations are emitted by a hot cesium atom) was adopted as the basic unit of time. Atomic clocks are now used as international time standards.

But time has also been measured in other less scientific terms. Listed below are some other "timely" expressions.

Twilight—The first soft glow of sunlight; the sun is still below the horizon; also the last glow of sunlight.

Midnight—12 A.M.; the point of time when one day becomes the next day and night becomes morning.

Daybreak—The first appearance of the sun.

Dawn—A gradual increase of sunlight.

Noon—12 P.M.; the point of time when morning becomes afternoon.

Dusk—The gradual dimming of sunlight.

Sunset—The last diffused glow of sunlight; the sun is below the horizon.

Evening—A term with wide meaning, evening is generally the period between sunset and bedtime.

Night—The period of darkness, lasting from sunset to midnight.

What is the basis for modern timekeeping?

Mankind has typically associated the durations of the year, month, week, and day on the earth and moon cycles. The modern clock, however, is based on the number 60. The Sumerians around 3000 B.C.E. employed a base ten counting system and also a base 60 counting system. The timekeeping system inherited this pattern with 60 seconds per minute and 60 minutes per hour. Ten and sixty fit together to form the notion of time: 10 hours is 600 minutes; 10 minutes is 600 seconds; one minute is 60 seconds. One second is not related to any of these factors; instead, scientists based the duration of one second on cesium-133, an isotope of the metal cesium. Officially, one second is the amount of time it takes for a cesium-133 atom to vibrate 9,192,631,770 times.

What is the exact length of a calendar year?

The calendar year is defined as the time between two successive crossings of the celestial equator by the sun at the vernal equinox. It is exactly 365 days, 5 hours, 48 minutes, 46 seconds. The fact that the year is not a whole number of days has affected the development of calendars, which over time generate an accumulative error. The current calendar used, the Gregorian calendar, named after Pope Gregory XIII (1502-1585), attempts to compensate by adding an extra day to the month of February every four years. A "leap year" is one with the extra day added.

When does a century begin?

A century has 100 consecutive calendar years. The first century consisted of years 1 through 100. The 20th century started with 1901 and ended with 2000. The 21st century began on January 1, 2001.

When did January 1 become the first day of the new year?

When Julius Caesar (100-44 B.C.E.) reorganized the Roman calendar and made it solar rather than lunar in the year 45 B.C.E., he moved the beginning of the year to January 1. When the Gregorian calendar was introduced in 1582, January 1 continued to be recognized as the first day of the year in most places. In England and the American colonies, however, March 25, intended to represent the spring equinox, was the beginning of the year. Under this system, March 24, 1700, was followed by March 25, 1701. In 1752, the British government changed the beginning date of the year to January 1.

Besides the Gregorian calendar, what other kinds of calendars have been used?

Babylonian calendar—A lunar calendar composed of alternating 29-day and 30-day months to equal roughly 354 lunar days. When the calendar became too misaligned with astronomical events, an extra month was added. In addition, three extra months were added every eight years to coordinate this calendar with the solar year.

Chinese calendar—A lunar month calendar of 12 periods having either 29 or 30 days (to compensate for the 29.5 days from new moon to new moon). The new year begins on the first new moon over China after the sun enters Aquarius (between January 21st and February 19th). Each year has both a number and a name (for example, the year 1992, or 4629 in the Chinese era, is the year of the monkey). The calendar is synchronized with the solar year by the addition of extra months at fixed intervals.

Muslim calendar—A lunar 12-month calendar with 30 and 29 days alternating every month for a total of 354 days. The calendar has a 30-year cycle with designated leap years of 355 days (one day added to the last month) in the 30-year period. The Islamic year does not attempt to relate to the solar year (the season). The dating of the beginning of the calendar is 622 c.e. (the date of Muhammad's flight from Mecca to Medina).

Jewish calendar—A blend of the solar and lunar calendar, this calendar adds an extra month (Adar Sheni, or the second Adar or Veadar) to keep the lunar and solar years in alignment. This occurs seven times during a 19-year cycle. When the extra 29-day month is inserted, the month Adar has 30 days instead of 29. In a usual year the 12 months alternately have 30, then 29 days.

Egyptian calendar—The ancient Egyptians were the first to use a solar calendar (about 4236 b.c.e. or 4242 b.c.e.), but their year started with the rising of Sirius, the brightest star in the sky. The year, composed of 365 days, was one-quarter day short of the true solar year, so eventually the Egyptian calendar did not coincide with the seasons. It used twelve 30-day months with five-day weeks and five dates of festival.

Coptic calendar—Still used in areas of Egypt and Ethiopia, it has a similar cycle to the Egyptian calendar: 12 months of 30 days followed by five complementary days. When a leap year occurs, usually preceding the Julian calendar leap year, the complementary days increase to six.

Roman calendar—Borrowing from the ancient Greek calendar, which had a four-year cycle based on the Olympic Games, the earliest Roman calendar (about 738 b.c.e.) had 304 days with 10 months. Every second year a short month of 22 or 23 days was added to coincide with the solar year. Eventually two more months were added at the end of the year (Januarius and Februarius) to increase the year to 354 days. The Roman republican calendar replaced this calendar during the reign of Tarquinius Priscus (616-579 b.c.e.). This new lunar calendar had 355 days, with the month of February having 28 days. The other months had either 29 or 31 days. To keep the calendar aligned with the seasons, an extra month was added every two years. By the time the Julian calendar replaced this one, the calendar was three months ahead of the season schedule.

Julian calendar—Julius Caesar, (100-44 B.C.E.) in 46 B.C.E., wishing to have one calendar in use for all the empire, had the astronomer Sosigenes develop a uniform solar calendar with a year of 365 days with one day ("leap day") added every fourth year to compensate for the true solar year of 365.25 days. The year had 12 months with 30 or 31 days except for February, which had 28 days (or 29 days in a leap year). The first of the year was moved from March 1 to January 1.

Gregorian calendar—Pope Gregory XIII (1502-1585) instituted calendrical reform in 1582 to realign the church celebration of Easter with the vernal equinox (the first day of spring). To better align this solar calendar with the seasons, the new calendar would not have leap year in the century years that were not divisible by 400. Because the solar year is shortening, today a one-second adjustment is made (usually on December 31 at midnight) when necessary to compensate.

Japanese calendar—It has the same structure as the Gregorian calendar in years, months, and weeks. But the years are enumerated in terms of the reigns of emperors as epochs. The last epoch (for Emperor Akihito) is Epoch Heisei, which started January 8, 1989.

Hindu calendars—The principal Indian calendars reckon their epochs from historical events, such as rulers' accessions or death dates, or a religious founder's dates. The Vikrama era (originally from Northern India and still used in western India) dates from February 23, 57 B.C.E., in the Gregorian calendar. The Saka era dates from March 3, 78 C.E., in the Gregorian calendar and is based on the solar year with 12 months of 365 days and 366 days in leap years. The first five months have 31 days; the last seven have 30 days. In leap years, the first six months have 31 days and the last six have 30. The Saka era is the national calendar of India (since 1957). The Buddhist era starts with 543 B.C.E. (believed to be the date of Buddha's death).

Three other secular calendars of note are the *Julian Day calendar* (a calendar astronomers use, which counts days within a 7,980-year period and must be used with a table), the *perpetual* calendar (which gives the days of the week for the Julian and Gregorian calendars as well), and the *world* calendar, which is similar to the perpetual calendar, having 12 months of 30 or 31 days, a year-day at the end of each year, and a leap-year-day before July 1 every four years.

There have been attempts to reform and simplify the calendar. One such example is the Thirteen-Month or International Fixed calendar, which would have 13 months of four weeks each. The month Sol would come before July; there would be a year-day at the end of each year and a leap-year-day every four years just before July 1. A radical reform was made in France when the French republican calendar (1793-1806) replaced the Gregorian calendar after the French Revolution. It had 12 months of 30 days and five supplementary days at the end of the year (six in a leap-year), and weeks were replaced with 10-day decades.

What is the Julian Day Count?

This system of counting days rather than years was developed by Joseph Justus Scaliger (1540-1609) in 1583. Still used by astronomers today, the Julian Day Count (named after Scaliger's father, Julius Caesar Scaliger) Julian Day (JD) 1 was January 1, 4113 B.C.E. On this date the

Julian calendar, the ancient Roman tax calendar, and the lunar calendar all coincided. This event would not occur again until 7,980 years later. Each day within this 7,980-year period is numbered. December 31, 1991, at noon is the beginning of JD 2,448,622. The figure reflects the number of days that have passed since its inception. To convert Gregorian calendar dates into Julian Day, simple JD conversion tables have been devised for astronomers.

Do all calendars other than the Gregorian calendar use a twelve-month cycle?

No. Some calendars have a varying cycle of months, with their first month falling at a different time. Listed below are some variations with the beginning month of the year in italics:

Months of the year

Gregorian	Hebrew	Hindu
January	Shebat	Magha
February	Adar	Phalguna
March	Nisan	Caitra
April	Iyar	Vaisakha

Gregorian	Hebrew	Hindu
May	Sivan	Jyaistha
June	Tammuz	Asadhe
July	Ab	Sravana
August	Elul	Bhadrapada
September	Tishri	Asvina
October	Heshvan	Karttika
November	Kislev	Margasivsa
December	Tebet	Pansa
	Ve-Adar (13th month every three years)	

Muslim	Chinese	
Muharram	Li Chun	Li Qui
Safar	Yu Shui	Chu Shu
Rabi I	Jing Zhe	Bai Lu
Rabi II	Chun Fen	Qui Fen
Jumada I	Qing Ming	Han Lu
Jumada II	Gu Yu	Shuang Jiang
Rajab	Li Xia	Li Dong
Sha'ban	Xiao Man	Xiao Xue
Ramadan	Mang Zhong	Da Xue
Shawwal	Xia Zhi	Dong Zhi
Dhu'l-Qa'da	Xiao Shu	Xiao Han
Dhu'l-hijja	Da Shu	Da Han

Which animal designations have been given to the Chinese years?

There are 12 different names, always used in the same sequence: Rat, Ox, Tiger, Hare (Rabbit), Dragon, Snake, Horse, Sheep (Goat), Monkey, Rooster, Dog, and Pig. The following table shows this sequence.

Chinese year cycle

Rat	Ox	Tiger	Hare (Rabbit)	Dragon	Snake
1996	1997	1998	1999	2000	2001
2008	2009	2010	2011	2012	2013
2020	2021	2022	2023	2024	2025

Horse	Sheep (Goat)	Monkey	Rooster	Dog	Pig
2002	2003	2004	2005	2006	2007
2014	2015	2016	2017	2018	2019
2026	2027	2028	2029	2030	2031

The Chinese year of 354 days begins three to seven weeks into the western 365-day year, so the animal designation changes at that time, rather than on January 1.

When does leap year occur?

A leap year occurs when the year is exactly divisible by four, except for centenary years. A centenary year must be divisible by 400 to be a leap year. There was no February 29 in 1900, which was not a leap year. The year 2000 was a centenary leap year, and the next one will be 2400.

What is a leap second?

The Earth's rotation is slowing down, and to compensate for this lagging motion a leap second is added to a specified day. One leap second was used in 1992 to keep the calendar in close alignment with international atomic time. To complete this change, 23h 59m 59s universal time on June 30, 1992 was followed by 23h 59m 60s and this in turn was followed by 0h 0m 0s on July 1.

Where do the names of the days of the week come from?

The English days of the week are named for a mixture of figures in Anglo-Saxon and Roman mythology.

Day	Named after
Sunday	The sun
Monday	The moon

Day	Named after
Tuesday	Tiu (the Anglo-Saxon god of war, equivalent to the Norse Tyr or the Roman Mars)
Wednesday	Woden (the Anglo-Saxon equivalent of Odin, the chief Norse god)
Thursday	Thor (the Norse god of thunder)
Friday	Frigg (the Norse god of love and fertility, the equivalent of the Roman Venus)
Saturday	Saturn (the Roman god of agriculture)

What is the origin of the week?

The week originated in the Babylonian calendar, where one day out of seven was devoted to rest.

How were the months of the year named?

The English names of the months of the current (Gregorian) calendar come from the Romans, who tended to honor their gods and commemorate specific events by designating them as month names:

January (*Januarius* in Latin), named after Janus, a Roman two-faced god, one face looking into the past, the other into the future.

February (*Februarium*) is from the Latin word *Februare*, meaning "to cleanse." At the time of year corresponding to our February, the Romans performed religious rites to purge themselves of sin.

March (*Martius*) is named in honor of Mars, the god of war.

April (*Aprilis*), after the Latin word *Aperio*, meaning "to open," because plants begin to grow in this month.

May (*Maius*), after the Roman goddess Maia, as well as from the Latin word *Maiores* meaning "elders," who were celebrated during this month.

June (*Junius*), after the goddess Juno and Latin word *iuniores*, meaning "young people."

July (*Iulius*) was, at first, known as *Quintilis* from the Latin word meaning five, since it was the fifth month in the early Roman calendar. Its name was changed to July, in honor of Julius Caesar (100-44 B.C.E.).

August (*Augustus*) is named in honor of the Emperor Octavian (63-14 B.C.E.), first Roman emperor, known as Augustus Caesar. Originally the month was known as *Sextilis* (sixth month of early Roman calendar).

September (*September*) was once the seventh month and accordingly took its name from *septem*, meaning "seven."

October (*October*) takes its name from *octo* (eight); at one time it was the eighth month.

November (*November*) from *novem*, meaning "nine," once the ninth month of the early Roman calendar.

December (*December*) from *decem*, meaning "ten," once the tenth month of the early Roman calendar.

Why are the lengths of the seasons not equal?

The lengths of the seasons are not exactly equal because the orbit of the Earth around the sun is elliptic rather than a circular. When the Earth is closest to the sun in January, gravitational forces cause the planet to move faster than it does in the summer months when it is far away from the sun. As a result, the autumn and winter seasons in the Northern Hemisphere are slightly shorter than spring and summer. The duration of the northern seasons are:

spring   92.76 days
summer 93.65 days
autumn 89.84 days
winter   88.99 days

How is the date for Easter determined?

The rule for establishing the date in the Christian Churches is that Easter always falls on the first Sunday after the first full moon that occurs on or just after the vernal equinox. The vernal equinox is the first day of spring in the Northern Hemisphere. Because the full moon can occur on any one of many dates after the vernal equinox, the date of Easter can be as early as March 22 and as late as April 25.

How is the date for Passover determined?

Passover (Pesah) begins at sundown on the evening before the 15th day of the Hebrew month of Nisan, which falls in March or April. Celebrated as a public holiday in Israel, the Passover commemorates the exodus of the Israelites from Egypt in 1290 B.C.E. The term "Passover" is a reference to the last of the 10 plagues that "passed over" the Israelite homes at the end of their captivity in Egypt.

How is "local noon" calculated?

Local noon, also called "the time of solar meridian passage," is the time of day when the sun is at its highest point in the sky. This is different from noon on clocks. To calculate local noon, first find the sunrise and sunset (readily available in larger newspapers), add the total amount of sunlight, divide this number by two, and add that to the sunrise. For instance, if sunrise is at 7:30 A.M. and sunset is at 8:40 P.M., the total sunlight is 13 hours and ten minutes, divided by two is 6 hours and 40 minutes (13 hours/2 = 6.5 hours plus 10 minutes), added to 7:30 A.M. equals a local noon of 1:40 P.M.

When is Daylight Savings Time observed in the United States?

In 1967, all states and possessions of the United States were to begin observing Daylight Savings Time at 2 A.M. on the first Sunday in April of every year. The clock would advance one hour at that time until 2 A.M. of the last Sunday of October, when the clock would be turned

Occasionally one sees a date expressed as "B.P. 6500" instead of "B.C. 6500". What does this signify?

Archaeologists use the B.P. or BP as an abbreviation for years before the present. This date is a rough generalization of the number of years before 1950, and is a date not necessarily based on radiocarbon dating methods.

back one hour. In the intervening years, the length of this time period changed, but on July 8, 1986, the original starting and ending dates were reinstated. A 1972 amendment allowed some areas to be exempt. In 2005, the U.S. Congress established a law that took effect in 2007 and changed the dates for Daylight Savings Time. It now begins on the second Sunday of March (at 2:00 A.M. clocks are moved ahead one hour) and ends on the first Sunday in November (clocks are moved back an hour, again at 2:00 P.M.).

Which states and territories of the United States are exempt from Daylight Savings Time?

Arizona, Hawaii, Puerto Rico, the U.S. Virgin Islands, American Samoa, and most of Indiana are exempt from Daylight Savings Time.

How many time zones are there in the world?

There are 24 standard time zones that serially cover the Earth's surface at coincident intervals of 15 degrees longitude and 60 minutes Universal Time (UT), as agreed at the Washington Meridian Conference of 1884, thus accounting, respectively, for each of the 24 hours in a calendar day.

When traveling from Tokyo to Seattle and crossing the International Date Line, what day is it?

Traveling from west to east (Tokyo to Seattle), the calendar day is set back (e.g., Sunday becomes Saturday). Traveling east to west, the calendar day is advanced (e.g., Tuesday becomes Wednesday). The International Date Line is a zigzag line at approximately the 180th meridian, where the calendar days are separated.

What is meant by Universal Time?

On January 1, 1972, Universal Time (UT) replaced Greenwich Mean Time (GMT) as the time reference coordinate for scientific work. Universal Time is measured by an atomic clock and is seen as the logical development of the adoption of the atomic second in 1968. An advantage of UT is that the time at which an event takes place can be determined very readily without recourse to the time-consuming astronomical observations and calculations that were necessary before the advent of atomic clocks. Universal Time is also referred to as International Atomic Time. GMT is measured according to when the sun crosses the Greenwich Meridian (zero degrees longitude, which passes through the Greenwich Observatory).

Who establishes the correct time in the United States?

The United States National Institute of Standards and Technology (NIST) uses a cesium beam clock as its NIST atomic frequency standard to determine atomic time. It is possible to check the time by accessing the NIST Web site at http://www. nist.gov and selecting "check time" from the options. The clock is accurate to plus or minus one second. The atomic second was officially defined in 1967 by the 13th General Conference of Weights and Measures as 9,192,631,770 oscillations of the atom of cesium-133. This cesium-beam clock of the NIST is referred to as a primary clock because, independently of any other reference, it provides highly precise and accurate time.

What is the United States Time Standard signal?

Universal Time is announced in International Morse Code each five minutes by radio stations WWV (Fort Collins, Colorado) and WWVH (Puuene, Maui, Hawaii). These stations are under the direction of the U.S. National Institute of Standards and Technology (formerly called National Bureau of Standards). They transmit 24 hours a day on 2.5, 5, 10, 15, and 20 megahertz. The first radio station to transmit time signals regularly was the Eiffel Tower Radio Station in Paris in 1913.

What do the initials A.M. and P.M. mean?

The initials A.M. stand for *ante meridian*, Latin for "before noon." The initials P.M. stand for *post meridian*, Latin for "after noon."

How does a sundial work?

The sundial, one of the first instruments used in the measurement of time, works by simulating the movement of the sun. A gnomon is affixed to a time (or hour) scale and the time is read by observing the shadow of the gnomon on the scale. Sundials generally use the altitude of the sun to give the time, so certain modifications and interpretations must be made for seasonal variance.

How is time denoted at sea?

The day is divided into watches and bells. A watch equals four hours except for the time period between 4 P.M. and 8 P.M., which has two short watches. Within each watch there are eight bells—one stroke for each half hour, so that each watch ends on eight bells except the dog watches, which end at four bells. New Year's Day is marked with 16 bells.

Bell	Time equivalent		
1 bell	12:30 or 4:30		or 8:30 A.M. or P.M.
2 bells	1:00	5:00	9:00
3 bells	1:30	5:30	9:30
4 bells	2:00	6:00	10:00
5 bells	2:30	6:30	10:30
6 bells	3:00	7:00	11:00
7 bells	3:30	7:30	11:30
8 bells	4:00	8:00	12:00

What is the difference between a quartz watch and a mechanical watch?

Quartz watches and mechanical watches use the same gear mechanism for turning the hour and minute gear wheels. Mechanical watches are powered by a coiled spring known as the mainspring and regulated by a system called a lever escarpment. As the watch runs, the mainspring unwinds. Quartz watches are powered by a battery-powered electronic integrated circuit on a tiny piece of silicon chip and regulated by quartz crystals that vibrate and produce electric pulses at a fixed rate.

Who invented the alarm clock?

Levi Hutchins of Concord, New Hampshire, invented an alarm clock in 1787. His alarm clock, however, rang at only one time—4 A.M. He invented this device so that he would never sleep past his usual waking time. He never patented or manufactured it. The first modern alarm clock was made by Antoine Redier (1817-1892) in 1847. It was a mechanical device; the electric alarm clock was not invented until around 1890. The earliest mechanical clock was made in 725 C.E. in China by Yi Xing and Liang Lingzan.

What is military time?

Military time divides the day into one set of 24 hours, counting from midnight (0000) to midnight of the next day (2400). This is expressed without punctuation.

Midnight becomes 0000 (or 2400 of the next day)
1:00 A.M. becomes 0100 (pronounced oh-one hundred)
2:10 A.M. becomes 0210
Noon becomes 1200
6:00 P.M. becomes 1800
9:45 P.M. becomes 2145

To translate 24-hour time into familiar time, the A.M. times are obvious. For P.M. times, subtract 1200 from numbers larger than 1200; e.g., 1900 - 1200 is 7 P.M.

Who set a doomsday clock for nuclear annihilation?

The clock first appeared on the cover of the magazine *Bulletin of the Atomic Scientists* in 1947 and was set at 11:53 P.M. The clock, created by the magazine's board of directors, represents the threat of nuclear annihilation, with midnight as the time of destruction. The clock has been reset eighteen times in fifty-five years. In 1953, just after the United States tested the hydrogen bomb, it was set at 11:58 P.M., the closest to midnight ever. In 1991, following the collapse of the Soviet Union, it was moved back to 11:43 P.M., the farthest from midnight the clock has ever been. However, in 1995, the clock was shifted forward to 11:47, reflecting the instability of the post-Cold-War world. The clock was set at seven minutes to midnight (11:53 P.M.) in 2002 because little progress is being made on global nuclear disarmament, and because terrorists are seeking to acquire and use nuclear and biological weapons.

TECHNOLOGY

RADIO AND TELEVISION

Who invented radio?

Guglielmo Marconi (1874-1937), of Bologna, Italy, was the first to prove that radio signals could be sent over long distances. Radio is the radiation and detection of signals propagated through space as electromagnetic waves to convey information. It was first called wireless telegraphy because it duplicated the effect of telegraphy without using wires. On December 12, 1901, Marconi successfully sent Morse code signals from Newfoundland to England.

In 1906, the American inventor Lee de Forest (1873-1961) built what he called "the Audion," which became the basis for the radio amplifying vacuum tube. This device made voice radio practical, because it magnified the weak signals without distorting them. The next year, de Forest began regular radio broadcasts from Manhattan, New York. As there were still no home radio receivers, de Forest's only audience was ship wireless operators in New York City Harbor.

What was the first radio broadcasting station?

The identity of the "first" broadcasting station is a matter of debate since some pioneer AM broadcast stations developed from experimental operations begun before the institution of formal licensing practices. According to records of the Department of Commerce, which then supervised radio, WBZ in Springfield, Massachusetts, received the first regular broadcasting license on September 15, 1921. However, credit for the first radio broadcasting station has customarily gone to Westinghouse station KDKA in Pittsburgh for its broadcast of the Harding-Cox presidential election returns on November 2, 1920. Unlike most other earlier radio transmissions, KDKA used electron tube technology to generate the transmitted signal and hence to have what could be described as broadcast quality. It was the first corporate-sponsored radio station and the first to have a well-defined commercial purpose—it was not a hobby or a publicity stunt. It was the first broadcast station to be licensed on a frequency outside the amateur bands. Altogether, it was the direct ancestor of modern broadcasting.

How are the call letters beginning with "K" or "W" assigned to radio stations?

These beginning call letters are assigned on a geographical basis. For the majority of radio stations located east of the Mississippi River, their call letters begin with the letter "W"; if the stations are west of the Mississippi, their first call letter is "K." There are exceptions to this rule. Stations founded before this rule went into effect kept their old letters. So, for example, KDKA in Pittsburgh has retained the first letter "K"; likewise, some western pioneer stations have retained the letter "W." Since many AM licensees also operate FM and TV stations, a common practice is to use the AM call letters followed by "-FM" or "-TV."

In 1901 Italian electrical engineer Guglielmo Marconi proved that radio signals could transmit messages over long distances. He won the Nobel Prize in Physics in 1909 for his work.

Why do FM radio stations have a limited broadcast range?

Usually radio waves higher in frequency than approximately 50 to 60 megahertz are not reflected by the Earth's ionosphere, but are lost in space. Television, FM radio, and high frequency communications systems are therefore limited to approximately line-of-sight ranges. The line-of-sight distance depends on the terrain and antenna height, but is usually limited to from 50 to 100 miles (80 to 161 kilometers). FM (frequency-modulation) radio uses a wider band than AM (amplitude-modulation) radio to give broadcasts high fidelity, especially noticeable in music—crystal clarity to high frequencies and rich resonance to base notes, all with a minimum of static and distortion. Invented by Edwin Howard Armstrong (1891-1954) in 1933, FM receivers became available in 1939.

Why do AM stations have a wider broadcast range at night?

This variation is caused by the nature of the ionosphere of the Earth. The ionosphere consists of several different layers of rarefied gases in the upper atmosphere that have become conductive through the bombardment of the atoms of the atmosphere by solar radiation, by electrons and protons emitted by the sun, and by cosmic rays. These layers, sometimes called the Kennelly-Heaviside layer, reflect AM radio signals, enabling AM broadcasts to be received by radios that are great distances from the transmitting antenna. With the coming of night, the ionosphere layers partially dissipate and become an excellent reflector of the short waveband AM radio waves. This causes distant AM stations to be heard more clearly at night.

Can radio transmissions between space shuttles and ground control be picked up by shortwave radio?

Amateur radio operators at Goddard Space Flight Center, Greenbelt, Maryland, retransmit shuttle space-to-ground radio conversations on shortwave frequencies. These retransmissions can be heard freely around the world. To hear astronauts talking with ground controllers during liftoff, flight, and landing, a shortwave radio capable of receiving single-sideband signals should be tuned to frequencies of 3.860, 7.185, 14.295, and 21.395 megahertz. British physics teacher Geoffrey Perry, at the Kettering Boys School, has taught his students how to obtain telemetry from orbiting Russian satellites. Since the early 1960s Perry's students have been monitoring Russian space signals using a simple taxicab radio, and using the data to calculate position and orbits of the spacecraft.

What is HD Radio® Technology?

HD Radio® Technology upgrades traditional analog AM and FM radio broadcasts to digital broadcasts. In 2002, the Federal Communications Commission (FCC) authorized iBiquity Corporation to begin digital broadcasting. Radio stations are able to broadcast in analog and digital simultaneously. The digital format is transmitted as a continuous digital data stream, in which the digital signal is compressed using iBiquity's compression technology. It is broadcast by a transmitter designed specifically for HD Radio broadcasting. Radio listeners with an HD Radio receiver hear high-quality digital broadcasts without static and hiss. In addition, broadcasters can create extra channels, known as HD2, HD3, and HD4, adjacent to the original channel with other listening options such as sports, talk, and other music options. HD Radio® technology can also display text, such as song titles and album covers.

How does satellite digital radio differ from traditional AM and FM radio?

Unlike traditional AM and FM radio stations, satellite radio is broadcast via satellites placed in orbit over the Earth similar to satellite TV. Although the FCC assigned certain frequencies in the 2.3-GHz microwave S-band in 1992, commercial satellite radio service did not begin until 2001 (XM Satellite Radio) and 2002 (Sirius Satellite Radio). XM Radio launched two geostationary Earth orbits in 2001. It launched two newer satellites in 2005 and 2006. The ground station transmits a signal to the two GEO satellites, which bounce the signals back to radio receivers on the ground. Ground transmitters and repeaters provide service where the satellite signal is blocked. There are more than 170 channels of digital radio. Satellite radio displays the song title, artist, and genre of music on the radio.

Sirius Radio also uses a system of satellites, but instead of GEO satellites, it uses a system of three SS/L-1300 satellites that form an inclined elliptical satellite constellation. The elliptical orbit path of each satellite positions them over the United States for sixteen hours per day, with at least one satellite over the country at all times. In 2007 Sirius Radio merged with XM Radio to form SiriusXM Radio. Unlike traditional AM and FM radio stations that rely on advertising revenue for their operations and is free to listeners, satellite radio is only available to subscribers for a monthly fee.

How do submerged submarines communicate?

Using frequencies from very high to extremely low, submarines can communicate by radio when submerged if certain conditions are met and depending on whether or not avoiding detection is important. Submarines seldom transmit on long-range, high-radio frequencies if detection is important, as in war. However, Super (SHF), Ultra (UHF), or Very High Frequency (VHF) two-way links with cooperating aircraft, surface ships, via satellite, or with the shore are fairly safe with high data rate, though they all require that the boat show an antenna above the water or send a buoy to the surface.

What technology is being developed that could potentially replace UPC codes and/or magnetic strips to identify and track information?

Radio frequency identification systems (RFID) are gaining popularity to identify and track information. There are two parts to an RFID system: a tag or a card that can store and modify information and a transmitter with an antenna to communicate the information. There are passive and active RFID tags. Passive tags do not have a power supply. The reading signal induces the power to transmit the response. They tend to be small and lightweight but can only be read from distances of a few inches to a few yards. Passive tags are often attached to merchandise to reduce store loss. They are often used in "smart cards" for transit systems. Active RFID tags have their own battery to supply power so they can initiate communication with the reader. The signal is much stronger and may be read over greater distances. Active RFID tags have been used to track cattle and on shipping containers.

What are some uses of RFID tags?

RFID tags are used in a wide variety of applications, including:

• automatic fare payment systems for transit systems

Which actress received a patent for a system that reduced the risk of detection of radio-controlled torpedoes?

Hedy Lamarr (1914–2000) received U.S. Patent #2,292,387 for frequency shifting or hopping as a way to reduce the risk of detection or jamming of radio-controlled torpedoes in 1942. Since radio signals were broadcast on a specific frequency, they could easily be jammed by enemy transmitters. Lamarr, along with composer George Antheil (1900–1959), devised a system of rapidly switching frequencies at split-second intervals in seemingly random order. When senders and receivers switched ("hopped") frequencies at the same time, the signal was clear. Lamarr and Antheil were inducted into the National Inventors Hall of Fame in 2014 for their secret communication system. Although the technology was never used during World War II, it was used during the Cuban Missile Crisis in 1962. Frequency shifting is used in cellular telephones and Bluetooth systems, enabling computers to communicate with peripheral devices.

- automatic toll payments for highways and bridges
- student ID cards
- U.S. passports
- tracking cattle
- identification chips placed beneath the skin of pets to help identify lost pets and return them to their owners
- tracking goods from shipment to inventory
- smart cards for locks

Who was the founder of television?

The idea of television (or "seeing by electricity," as it was called in 1880) was offered by several people over the years, and several individuals contributed a multiplicity of partial inventions. For example, in 1897 Ferdinand Braun (1850-1918) constructed the first

RFID tags like these are attached to items in stores and help track product information and sales.

cathode ray oscilloscope, a fundamental component to all television receivers. In 1907, Boris Rosing proposed using Braun's tube to receive images, and in the following year Alan Campbell-Swinton likewise suggested using the tube, now called the cathode-ray tube, for both transmission and receiving. The figure most frequently called the father of television, however, was a Russian-born American named Vladimir K. Zworykin (1889-1982). A former pupil of Rosing, he produced a practical method of amplifying the electron beam so that the

light/dark pattern would produce a good image. In 1923, he patented the iconoscope (which would become the television camera), and in 1924 he patented the kinoscope (television tube). Both inventions rely on streams of electrons for both scanning and creating the image on a fluorescent screen. By 1938, after adding new and more sensitive photo cells, Zworykin demonstrated his first practical model.

Another "father" of television is the American Philo T. Farnsworth (1906-1971). He was the first person to propose that pictures could be televised electronically. He came up with the basic design for an apparatus in 1922 and discussed his ideas with his high school teacher. This documented his ideas one year before Zworykin and was critical in settling a patent dispute between

Vladimir Zworykin demonstrates a cathode ray television set to Westinghouse employee Mildred Birt in this 1934 photo.

Farnsworth and his competitor at the Radio Corporation of America. Farnsworth eventually licensed his television patents to the growing industry and let others refine and develop his basic inventions.

During the early 20th century others worked on different approaches to television. The best-known is John Logie Baird (1888-1946), who in 1936 used a mechanized scanning device to transmit the first recognizable picture of a human face. Limitations in his designs made any further improvements in the picture quality impossible.

How do flat-panel displays differ from traditional screens?

Flat-panel screens are different because they do not use the cathode-ray tube. Cathode-ray tube monitors—the monitors that are nearly omnipresent around the world—work by bombarding a phosphorescent screen with a ray of electrons. The electrons illuminate "phosphors" on the screen into the reds, greens, and blues that form the picture. In contrast, flat-panel displays use a grid of electrodes, crystals, or vinyl polymers to create the small dots that make up the picture. Flat-panel screens are not a new idea: LCD (short for liquid crystal display) watches and calculators going back decades have relied on crystal-based flat-panel displays. The newest flat-panel screens found on laptop computers use plasma display panels (or "PDPs"). They can be very wide—over a meter—but only a few centimeters thick. A PDP screen is made of a layer of picture elements in the three primary colors. Electrodes from a grid behind produce a charge that create ultraviolet rays. These rays illuminate the various picture elements and form the picture.

What is high-definition television?

The amount of detail shown in a television picture is limited by the number of lines that make it up and by the number of picture elements on each line. The latter is mostly determined by the width of the electron beam. To obtain pictures closer to the quality associated with 35-millimeter photography, a new television system, HDTV (high-definition television), will have more than twice the number of scan lines with a much smaller picture element. Currently, American and Japanese television has 525 scanning lines, while Europe uses 625 scanning lines. The Japanese are generally given credit for being pioneers in HDTV, ever since the Japanese broadcasting company NHK began research in 1968. In fact, the original pioneer was RCA's Otto Schade, who began his research after the end of World War II. Schade was ahead of his time, and decades passed before television pickup tubes and other components became available to take full advantage of his research.

HDTV cannot be used in the commercial broadcast bands until technical standards are approved by the United States Federal Communications Commission (FCC) or the various foreign regulating agencies. The more immediate problem, however, has been a technological one—HDTV needs to transmit five times more data than is currently assigned to each television channel. One approach is signal compression—squeezing the 30-megahertz bandwidth signal that HDTV requires into the six-megahertz bandwidth currently used for television broadcasting. The Japanese and Europeans have explored analog systems that use wavelike transmission, while the Americans based their HDTV development on digital transmission systems. In 1994, the television industry cleared this hurdle when it accepted a digital signal transmission system developed by Zenith.

The public can now enjoy HDTV: programming and television sets are available, albeit in limited broadcast areas and at a high cost. The programming is available through digital service for about 450 stations in 130 markets (almost every large city). Where digital HDTV service is not yet available, customers can order satellite service, but it requires a specialized dish and receiver. Television sets are also available, but as with any new technology prices are still high, starting at about $2,000 for an entry-level set with wide-screen models approaching $5,000.

TELECOMMUNICATIONS AND RECORDINGS

When was the first commercial communications satellite used?

In 1960 *Echo 1,* the first communications satellite, was launched. Two years later, on July 10, 1962, the first commercially funded satellite, *Telstar 1* (paid for by American Telephone and Telegraph), was launched into low Earth orbit. It was also the first true communications satellite, being able to relay not only data and voice, but television as well. The first broadcast, which was relayed from the United States to England, showed an American flag flapping in the breeze. The first commercial satellite (in which its operations are conducted like a business) was *Early Bird,* which went into regular service on June 10, 1965, with 240 telephone circuits. *Early Bird* was the first satellite launched for Intelsat (International Telecommunications Satellite Organization). Still in existence, the system is owned by member nations—each nation's contribution to the operating funds are based on its share of the system's annual traffic.

How does a fiber-optic cable work?

A fiber-optic cable is composed of many very thin strands of coated glass or plastic fibers that transmit light through the process of "cladding," in which total internal reflection of light is achieved by using material that has a lower refractive index. Once light enters the fiber, the cladding layer inside it prevents light loss as the beam of light zigzags inside the glass core. Glass fibers can transmit messages or images by directing beams of light inside itself over very short or very long distances up to 13,000 miles (20,917 kilometers) without significant distortion. The pattern of light waves forms a code that carries a message. At the receiving end, the light beams are converted back into electric current and decoded. Uses include telecommunications medical fiber-optic viewers, such as endoscopes and fiberscopes, to see internal organs; fiber-optic message devices in aircraft and space vehicles; and fiber-optic connections in automotive lighting systems.

Fiber-optic cables have greater "bandwidth": they can carry much more data than metal cable. Because fiber optics is based on light beams, the transmissions are more impervious to electrical noise and can also be carried greater distances before fading. The cables are thinner than metal wires. Fiber-optic cable delivers data in digital code instead of an analog signal, the delivery method of metal cables; computers are structured for digital, so there is a natural symbiosis. The main disadvantage is cost: fiber optics are much more expensive than traditional metal cable.

What is the difference between "analog" and "digital"?

The word analog is derived from "analogous," meaning something corresponds to something else. A picture of a mountain is a representation of the mountain. If the picture is on traditional color film it is called an analog picture and is characterized by different colors and range of color on the paper. However, if the photographer took the picture with a digital camera, the image is digital: it is stored as a series of numbers in the camera's memory. Its colors are discrete. In communications and computers, a range of continuous variables characterizes analog. Digital, in contrast, is characterized by measurements that happen at discrete intervals. Digital representations are, therefore, more precise. Common examples of analog media include records (music) and VCR tapes (movies). Counterpart examples of digital media include CD-ROM discs and DVD movies.

How does a fax machine work?

Telefacsimile (also telefax or facsimile or fax) transmits graphic and textual information from one location to another through telephone lines. A transmitting machine uses either a digital or analog scanner to convert the black-and-white representations of the image into electrical signals that are transmitted through the telephone lines to a designated receiving machine. The receiving unit converts the transmission back to an image of the original and prints it. In its broadest definition, a facsimile terminal is simply a copier equipped to transmit and receive graphics images.

The fax was invented by Alexander Bain of Scotland in 1842. His crude device, along with scanning systems invented by Frederick Bakewell in 1848, evolved into several modern versions. In 1924, faxes were first used to transmit wire photos from Cleveland to New York, a boon to the newspaper industry.

How does OLED technology differ from LCD technology?

Organic light-emitting diodes (OLED) are thin panels made from organic materials that emit light when electricity is applied through them. The components of an OLED are:

- Substrate to support the OLED
- An anode layer, which removes electrons (adds electron "holes") when a current flows through the device
- Organic layers consisting of organic (carbon-based) polymers
- Conducting layer which transports the electron "holes" from the anode
- Emissive layer where the light is made when electrons are transported from the cathode
- Cathode, which injects electrons when a current flows through the device Unlike LCD displays, OLEDs emit light so they do not require a backlight. This allows

OLED (organic light-emitting diodes) technology makes the latest advance in televisions—curved screens—possible.

them to be very thin. An OLED device is usually just 100 to 500 nanometers thick—about 200 times smaller than a single human hair. A major use of OLED technology is for television. The advantages of OLED versus LCD technology include better image quality, quick response time, and reduced consumption of electricity. The first working OLED displays were developed in 1987 by Ching W. Tang (1947–) and Steven Van Slyke at Eastman Kodak.

This 1960 video tape recorder (called an Ampex VR-2000) is on exhibit at the National Czech Technical Museum in Prague.

What is the Dolby noise reduction system?

The magnetic action of a tape produces a background hiss—a drawback in sound reproduction on tape. A noise reduction system known as Dolby—named after Ray M. Dolby (1933–2013), its American inventor—is widely used to deal with the hiss. In quiet passages, electronic circuits automatically boost the signals before they reach the recording head, drowning out the hiss. On playback, the signals are reduced to their correct levels. The hiss is reduced at the same time, becoming inaudible. Dolby received the National Medal of Technology and Innovation in 1997 and was inducted into the National Inventors Hall of Fame in 2004 for inventing technologies to improve sound quality in recordings.

Who developed the first video tape recorder?

The first video tape recorder (VTR) was developed by Charles Ginsburg (1920–1992). Ginsburg led the research team at Ampex Corporation that developed a machine that consisted of recording heads rotating at high speed that applied high-frequency signals on magnetic tape to record live television images. The Ampex VRX-1000 (later renamed the Mark IV) was introduced in April 1956. Ampex won an Emmy Award for the invention of the VTR in 1957. Ginsburg was inducted into the National Inventors Hall of Fame in 1990 for the development of the VTR, which led to significant technological advances in broadcasting and television program production.

How are compact discs (CDs) made?

The master disc for a CD is an optically flat glass disc coated with a resist. The resist is a chemical that is impervious to an etchant that dissolves glass. The master is placed on a turntable. The digital signal to be recorded is fed to the laser, turning the laser off and on in response to the binary on-off signal. When the laser is on, it burns away a small amount of the resist on the disc. While the disc turns, the recording head moves across the disc, leaving a spiral track of elongated "burns" in the resist surface. After the recording is complete, the glass master is placed in the chemical etchant bath. This developing removes the glass only where the resist is burned away. The spiral track now contains a series of small pits of varying length and constant depth. To play a recorded CD, a laser beam scans the three miles (five kilometers) of playing track and converts the "pits" and "lands" of the CD into binary codes. A photodiode converts these into a coded string of electrical impulses. In October 1982, the first CDs were marketed; they were invented by Phillips (Netherlands) Company and Sony in Japan in 1978.

How does a DVD differ from a CD?

A DVD is much larger than a CD. A standard DVD can hold about seven times more data than a CD holds. The additional storage capacity provides enough storage for a full-length movie. DVD discs and players first became available in November 1996 in Japan and March 1997 in the United States.

What is virtual reality?

Virtual reality combines state-of-the-art imaging with computer technology to allow users to experience a simulated environment as reality. Several different technologies are integrated into a virtual reality system, including holography, which uses lasers to create three-dimensional images, liquid crystal displays, high-definition television, and multimedia techniques that combine various types of displays in a single computer terminal.

Wearing a headset that surrounds one's field of vision, this young woman enters a virtual reality world that can seem quite real.

What is Blue-ray?

Blue-ray discs are the next step up after DVDs. Whereas DVDs can store up to about 17 GB of data, Blue-ray discs story anywhere from 25 to 100 GB and offer higher resolution video. Another difference is that Blue-ray discs are read with a violet laser versus the longer-wavelength red laser used for CDs and DVDs.

What is digital video recording (DVR)?

A digital video recorder (DVR) consists of a hard drive connected to the outside world through various jacks (similar to the ones used to hook up other equipment, such as a cable box). The television signal is received by the built-in tuner through either antenna, cable, or satellite. Signals from antenna or cable go into an MPEG-2 encoder, which converts the data from analog to digital. The signal is then sent to the hard drive for storage and then to the MPEG-2 decoder, which converts the signal back from digital to analog and sends it to the television for viewing. Depending on the system, it is possible to record up to three hundred hours of programming. Unlike VCR devices, a DVR is tapeless. It is also possible to begin watching a recording prior to the completion of the recording. Some systems have dual tuners that permit the recording of different programs on different channels at the same time. It is also possible to access a system remotely. TiVo introduced the first DVR in March 1999.

Who invented the telephone?

Alexander Graham Bell (1847–1922) was the first person to receive a patent for the telephone. He filed for a patent on February 14, 1876, and received U.S. Patent #174,465 on March 7, 1876. The telephone consisted of a transmitter and receiver—each a thin disk in front of an electromagnet. Bell's telephone was based on the concept that a continuous, varying electric current could transmit and reconvert continuously varying sound waves. While Bell received the first patent, other inventors had also worked on inventing the telephone. Bell was inducted into the National Inventors Hall of Fame in 1974 for his contributions to improve telegraphy and the development of the of telephone. Elisha Gray (1835–1901) filed a caveat (an announcement of an invention) on the same day that Bell filed for his patent. According to the records at the patent office, Bell was the fifth entry and Gray was the thirty-ninth entry on February 14, 1876. Gray was inducted into the National Inventors Hall of Fame in 2007 for his improvements to the technology of telegraphy. Another person to design a talking telegraph was Antonio Meucci (1808–

Alexander Graham Bell patented the telephone in 1876.

1889). He filed a caveat for a talking telegraph or telephone on December 28, 1871. He renewed the caveat in 1872 and 1873. The U.S. House of Representatives passed House Resolution 269 on June 11, 2002, honoring Meucci's contributions and work in the development of the telephone.

When did caller ID first become available to the general public?

Caller ID first became available to the general public in April 1987 in New Jersey. In the mid-1980s, telephone companies implemented a new system to route calls based on the international standard Signaling System 7 (SS7). Information about the call setup, termination, and other data was handled on a different data circuit. Using the new SS7 system, it was possible to include the calling party's phone number and name to the telephone network's central office. New Jersey Bell was the first telephone company to realize the data could be sold to phone system subscribers. Since the telephones in use at the time did not have the capability to display the caller ID information, a special caller ID unit was necessary to see the calling party's information. The box was attached to the phone and for a monthly service fee to the local telephone company, the customer could see the name and number of the calling party. The first caller ID unit was sold at a Sears store in Jersey City, New Jersey, in April 1987.

How does VoIP differ from traditional telephone calls?

Voice over Internet Protocol (VoIP) is a technology that allows users to make voice calls using a broadband Internet connection. VoIP services convert the human voice into a digital signal, which can travel over the Internet. If calls are made to a traditional telephone, the signal is converted to a regular telephone signal before it reaches the destination. VoIP calls can also be made from one computer to another computer. Depending on the VoIP service provider, calls may be limited to people with the same service or to anyone with a telephone number, including local, long distance, mobile, and international phone numbers. Some service providers work over a computer or a special VoIP phone, while others work using a traditional phone connected to a VoIP adapter. An advantage of VoIP calling is that subscribers may not need to subscribe to and pay for a traditional telephone line. VoIP calls made from a computer with a broadband connection do not incur charges beyond those for the broadband service. A disadvantage of VoIP calling is that calling may not be available during a power outage. Also, most VoIP services do not connect directly to 9-1-1 emergency calling.

When were the first mobile telephones developed?

Mobile phones were first developed by AT&T in the 1940s. The earliest type of mobile phone was permanently attached to an automobile and was powered by the car's battery. It also had an antenna that had to be mounted outside the vehicle. The second type of mobile phone was a transportable, or bag, cellular phone. It had its own battery pack that allowed owners to detach it from the car and carry it in a pouch. However, most bag phones weighed about 5 pounds (2.25 kilograms) and were not very practical when used this way. The first hand-held portable cellular phone was developed in the early 1970s. It used 14 large-scale integration chips, weighed close to 2 pounds (0.9 kilograms), and talk time was measured in minutes.

When was the first cell phone call made using a portable, hand-held phone?

Martin Cooper (1928–), an employee of Motorola, first demonstrated the use of a portable cell phone on April 3, 1973, when he called Joel S. Engel (1936–) of AT&T Bell Labs. Engel received the National Medal of Technology and Innovation in 1994 for his contributions to the development of cellular phones. Cooper and Engel both received the Draper Prize for Engineering for their contributions developing the world's first cellular telephone systems and networks. The first cellular network, Advanced Mobile Phone System (AMPS), was tested in July 1978 in the Chicago suburbs. The system consisted of ten cells, each of which was approximately one mile across. Most of the phones in the network were car phones and not portable phones.

When did cell phones begin using digital technology in America?

Digital cell phones (2G technology) were introduced in 1995 and called PCS (personal communications services) phones. They are digital because they convert the speech into a chain of numbers, making the transmission much clearer, and enhances security by making eavesdropping more difficult. It also allows for computer integration. Users can send and receive email and browse the Web. They are cellular because antennas on metal towers—visible on the horizon of nearly every reasonably developed location in America—send and receive all calls within a geographical area. Transmissions are carried over microwave radiation. Wireless companies can use the same frequency over again in different cells (except for cells that are nearby) because each cell is small and therefore requires only a limited range signal. When users move across cells, the signal is "handed off" to the next cell tower.

How does a smartphone differ from a cell phone?

There is no precise definition of a smartphone, but generally, it is a cell phone with built-in applications and Internet access. The earliest smartphones essentially combined features of a cell phone with those of a personal digital assistant (PDA). IBM designed the first smartphone in 1992 called the Simon personal communicator. Today, smartphones are generally equipped with an operating system that allows them to send emails (often syncing with a computer), browse the Web, view spreadsheets and documents, send and receive text messages, operate as an MP3 player, play games, and have a camera for taking digital pictures or videos. More than cell phones, smartphones are comparable to private miniature computers.

What is 4G LTE?

The designation 4G stands for fourth-generation technology for data access over cellular networks. Data includes everything except phone calls and simple text messages (SMS). It includes everything else that is done on smartphones and tablets, such as accessing the Internet and web browsing, checking email, downloading apps, watching videos, and downloading pictures. It is essential for Internet use when a hard-wired or Wi-Fi network is not available. The advantage of 4G over 3G technology is the speed. It is almost as fast to download and upload using 4G technology as on home and office computers using Wi-Fi. Many companies offer a 4G network, but they are not all the same. LTE stands for Long Term Evolution. It was developed by the 3rd Generation Partnership Project (3GPP), a group focused on telecommunications standard development. Most technical experts consider 4G LTE to be the fastest version of 4G and the one that adheres most closely to the official technical standard.

When was the first text message sent?

Neil Papworth (1969–) sent the first text message to Richard Jarvis at Vodafone in December 1992. Since mobile phones did not have keyboards in 1992, he typed the message on a computer keyboard. The message was "Merry Christmas." According to recent data, 1.91 trillion texts were sent in 2013.

COMPUTERS, THE INTERNET, AND ROBOTICS

Who invented the computer?

Computers developed from calculating machines. One of the earliest mechanical devices for calculating, still widely used today, is the abacus—a frame carrying parallel rods on which beads or counters are strung. The abacus originated in Egypt in 2000 B.C.E.; it reached the Orient about a thousand years later, and arrived in Europe in about the year 300 C.E. In 1617, John Napier (1550-1617) invented "Napier's Bones"—marked pieces of ivory for multiples of numbers. In the middle of the same century, Blaise Pascal (1623- 1662) produced a simple mechanism for adding and subtracting. Multiplication by repeated addition was a feature of a stepped drum or wheel machine of 1694 invented by Gottfried Wilhelm Leibniz (1646-1716). In 1823, the English visionary Charles Babbage (1792-1871) persuaded the British government to finance an "analytical engine." This would have been a machine that could undertake any kind of calculation. It would have been driven by steam, but the most important innovation was that the entire program of operations was stored on a punched tape. Babbage's machine was not completed in his lifetime because the technology available to him was not sufficient to support his design. However, in 1991 a team led by Doron Swade at London's Science Museum built the "analytical engine" (sometimes called the "difference engine") based on Babbage's work. Measuring 10 feet (3 meters) wide by 6.5 feet (2 meters) tall, it weighed three tons and could calculate equations down to 31 digits. The feat proved that Babbage was way ahead of his time, even though the device was impractical because one had to turn a crank hundreds of times in order to generate a single calculation. Modern computers use electrons, which travel at nearly the speed of light.

Based on the concepts of British mathematician Alan M. Turing (1912-1954), the earliest programmable electronic computer was the 1,500-valve "Colossus," formulated by Max Newman (1897-1985), built by T. H. Flowers, and used by the British government in 1943 to crack the German codes generated by the coding machine "Enigma."

What is meant by fifth-generation computers? What are the other four generations?

The evolution of computers has advanced so much in the past few decades that "generations" are used to describe these important advances:

First-generation computer—a mammoth computer using vacuum tubes, drum memories, and programming in machine code as its basic technology. Univax 1, used in 1951, was one of the earliest of these vacuum-tube based electronic computers. The generation starts at the end of World War II and ends about 1957.

Second-generation computer—a computer using discrete transistors as its basic technology. Solid-state components replaced the vacuum tubes during this period from 1958 to 1963. Magnetic core memories store information. This era includes the development of high-level computer languages.

Third-generation computer—a computer having integrated circuits, semiconductor memories, and magnetic disk storage. New operating systems, minicomputer systems, virtual memory, and timesharing are the advancements of this period from 1963 to 1971.

Fourth-generation computer—a computer using microprocessors and large-scale integrated chips as its basic technology, which made computers accessible to a large segment of the population. Networking, improved memory, database management systems, and advanced languages mark the period from 1971 to the end of the 1980s.

Fifth-generation computer—a computer that uses inference to draw reasoned conclusions from a knowledge base and interacts with its users via an intelligent user interface to perform such functions as speech recognition, machine translation of natural languages, and robotic operations. These computers using artificial intelligence have been under development since the early 1980s, especially in Japan, as well as in the United States and Europe. In 1991, however, Japan began a new 10-year initiative to investigate neural networks, which will probably divert resources from development of the fifth generation as traditionally defined.

With just two digital paddles and a little white square representing a ball, Pong was a simple, but popular, tennis-style computer game that first appeared on store shelves in 1972.

What is an algorithm?

An algorithm is a set of clearly defined rules and instructions for the solution of a problem. It is not necessarily applied only in computers, but can be a step-by-step procedure for solving any particular kind of problem. A nearly 4,000-year-old Babylonian banking calculation inscribed on a tablet is an algorithm, as is a computer program that consists of step-by-step procedures for solving a problem.

The term is derived from the name of Muhammad ibn Musa al Kharizmi (ca. 780-ca. 850), a Baghdad mathematician who introduced Hindu numerals (including 0) and decimal calculation to the West. When his treatise was translated into Latin in the 12th century, the art of computation with Arabic (Hindu) numerals became known as algorism.

What was the first computer game?

Despite that computers were not invented for playing games, the idea that they could be used for games did not take long to emerge. Alan Turing proposed a famous game called "Imitation Game" in 1950. In 1952, Rand Air Defense Lab in Santa Monica created the first military simulation games. In 1953, Arthur Samuel created a checkers program on the new IBM 701. From these beginnings computer games have today become a multi-billion-dollar industry.

What was the first successful video-arcade game?

Pong, a simple electronic version of a tennis game, was the first successful video-arcade game. Although it was first marketed in 1972, Pong was actually invented 14 years earlier in 1958 by William Higinbotham, who headed instrumentation design at Brookhaven National Laboratory at the time. Invented to amuse visitors touring the laboratory, the game was so popular that visitors would stand in line for hours to play it. Higinbotham dismantled the system two years later, and, considering it a trifle, did not patent it. In 1972, Atari released Pong, an arcade version of Higinbotham's game, and Magnavox released Odyssey, a version that could be played on home televisions.

What is a silicon chip?

A silicon chip is an almost pure piece of silicon, usually less than one centimeter square and about half a millimeter thick. It contains hundreds of thousands of microminiature electronic circuit components, mainly transistors, packed and interconnected in layers beneath the surface. These components can perform control, logic, and memory functions. There is a grid of thin metallic strips on the surface of the chip; these wires are used for electrical connections to other devices. The silicon chip was developed independently by two researchers: Jack Kilby of Texas Instruments in 1958, and Robert Noyce (b. 1927) of Fairchild Semiconductor in 1959.

While silicon chips are essential to most computer operation today, a myriad of other devices depend on them as well, including calculators, microwave ovens, automobile diagnostic equipment, and VCRs.

Are any devices being developed to replace silicon chips?

When transistors were introduced in 1948, they demanded less power than fragile, high-temperature vacuum tubes; allowed electronic equipment to become smaller, faster, and more dependable; and generated less heat. These developments made computers much more economical and accessible; they also made portable radios practical. However, the smaller components were harder to wire together, and hand wiring was both expensive and error-prone.

In the early 1960s, circuits on silicon chips allowed manufacturers to build increased power, speed, and memory storage into smaller packages, which required less electricity to operate and generated even less heat. While through most of the 1970s manufacturers could count on doubling the components on a chip every year without increasing the size of the chip, the size limitations of silicon chips are becoming more restrictive. Though components continue to grow smaller, the same rate of shrinking cannot be maintained.

Researchers are investigating different materials to use in making circuit chips. Gallium arsenide is harder to handle in manufacturing, but it has potential for greatly increased switching speed. Organic polymers are potentially cheaper to manufacture and could be used for liquid-crystal and other flat-screen displays, which need to have their electronic circuits spread over a wide area. Unfortunately, organic polymers do not allow electricity to pass through as well as the silicons do. Several researchers are working on hybrid chips, which could combine the benefits of organic polymers with those of silicon. Researchers are also in the initial stages of developing integrated optical chips, which would use light rather than electric current. Optical chips would generate little or no heat, would allow faster switching, and would be immune to electrical noise.

What are carbon nanotubes?

Carbon nanotubes are structures of microscopic cylinders that scientists can create when electricity arcs between two carbon electrodes. The carbon atoms become arranged in a lattice that forms a tiny tube a few nanometers long (a nanometer is a billionth of a meter). Scientists can then position them to act as transmitters. The benefit of such a structure is that they are a hundred times smaller than transistors now used on computer chips. Carbon nanotubes may eventually replace the standard silicon computer chip, allowing increased performance in a smaller size.

What is Moore's Law?

Gordon Moore, cofounder of Intel, a top microchip manufacturer, observed in 1965 that the number of transistors per microchip—and hence a chip's processing power—would double about every year and a half. The press dubbed this Moore's Law. Despite claims that this ever-increasing trend cannot perpetuate, history has shown that microchip advances are, indeed, keeping pace with Moore's prediction.

Who invented the computer mouse?

A computer "mouse" is a hand-held input device that, when rolled across a flat surface,

This prototype mouse that was invented by Douglas C. Engelbart in 1968 was made out of wood and had a simple button at the top.

causes a cursor to move in a corresponding way on a display screen. A prototype mouse was part of an input console demonstrated by Douglas C. Englehart in 1968 at the Fall Joint Computer Conference in San Francisco. Popularized in 1984 by the Macintosh from Apple Computer, the mouse was the result of 15 years devoted to exploring ways to make communicating with computers simpler and more flexible.

The physical appearance of the small box with the dangling, tail-like wire suggested the name of "mouse."

What are the generations of programming languages?

Computer scientists use the following abbreviations to grade computer languages in steps or evolutions:

1GL—A first-generation language is called a "machine language," the set of instructions that the programmer writes for the processor to perform. It appears in binary form. It is written in 0s and 1s.

2GL—A second-generation language is termed an "assembly" language, because an assembler converts it into machine language for the processor.

3GL—A third-generation language is called a "high-level" programming language. Java and C++ are 3GL languages. A compiler then converts it into machine language, typically written like this:

```
if (chLetter ≥ 'B')
Console.WriteLine ("Usage: one argument");
return 1; // sample code
```

4GL—A fourth-generation language resembles plain language. Relational databases use this language. An example is the following:

FIND All Titles FROM Books WHERE Title begins with "Handy"

5GL—A fifth-generation language uses a graphical design interface that allows a 3GL or 4GL compiler to translate the language. This is similar to HTML text editors because it allows drag and drop of icons and visual display of hierarchies.

What does it mean to "boot" a computer?

Booting a computer is starting it, in the sense of turning control over to the operating system. The term comes from bootstrap, because bootstraps allow an individual to pull on boots without help from anyone else. Some people prefer to think of the process in terms of using bootstraps to lift oneself off the ground, impossible in the physical sense, but a reasonable image for representing the process of searching for the operating system, loading it, and passing control to it. The commands to do this are embedded in a read-only memory (ROM) chip that is automatically executed when a microcomputer is turned on or reset. In mainframe or minicomputers, the process usually involves a great deal of operator input. A cold boot powers on the computer and passes control to the operating system; a warm boot resets the operating system without powering off the computer.

What is the difference between operating system software and application software?

Operating system software tells the computer how to run the hardware resources and software applications. Application software provides the directions and instructions that allow computers to create documents and images, solve calculations, maintain files, and operate games. Examples of application software are word processing, databases, spreadsheets, graphics for desktop publishing, media, and games.

What are the tasks of an operating system?

An operating system is found in all computers and other electronic devices, such as cell phones. The operating system manages all the hardware and software resources of the computer. Operating systems manage data and devices, such as printers, in the computer. Operating systems have the ability to multitask, allowing the user to keep several different applications open at the same time. Popular operating systems for computers are Windows (Microsoft), OS X (Macintosh), and Linux.

Which computer was the first to have a graphical user interface?

The earliest operating systems were text-based, meaning they only allowed for text input. As computer usage changed, it became clear there was a need to develop a graphical user interface (GUI) that would allow graphics, including icons and a drag-and-drop feature of text and icons. The Apple Macintosh personal computer was the first real operating system to have a GUI. Microsoft Windows followed, but instead of the operating systems having a GUI interface, it had a GUI interface on a text-based operating system. The user's mouse movements would be translated into text commands. Windows 95 was the first version to have a GUI.

What is the Android operating system?

The Android operating system, based on Linux, is used mostly for smartphones and tablets. It was developed by a startup company in 2003 with backing from Google. Google bought the company in 2005. Each version of Android is named after a dessert since, according to Google, the devices that use Android "make our lives so sweet." The current version, 5.0, is the Lollipop. Other versions have been named the Kit Kat, Jelly Bean, Ice Cream Sandwich, Honeycomb, Gingerbread, Froyo, Éclair, and Donut.

Where did the term bug originate?

The slang term bug is used to describe problems and errors occurring in computer programs. The term may have originated during the early 1940s at Harvard University, when computer pioneer Grace Murray Hopper (1906-1992) discovered that a dead moth had caused the breakdown of a machine on which she was working. When asked what she was doing while removing the corpse with tweezers, she replied, "I'm debugging the machine." The moth's carcass, taped to a page of notes, is preserved with the trouble log notebook at the Virginia Naval Museum.

What does DOS stand for?

DOS stands for "disk operating system," a program that controls the computer's transfer of data to and from a hard or floppy disk. Frequently, it is combined with the main operating system. The operating system was originally developed at Seattle Computer Products as SCP-DOS. When IBM decided to build a personal computer and needed an operating system, it chose the SCP-DOS after reaching an agreement with the Microsoft Corporation to produce the actual operating system. Under Microsoft, SCP-DOS became MS-DOS, which IBM referred to as PC-DOS (personal computer), and which everyone eventually simply called DOS.

What is a computer virus and how is it spread?

Taken from the obvious analogy with biological viruses, a computer "virus" is a program that searches out other programs and "infects" them by replicating itself in them. When the programs are executed, the embedded virus is executed too, thus propagating the "infection." This normally happens invisibly to the user. A virus cannot infect other computers, however, without assistance. It is spread when users communicate by computer, often when they trade programs. The virus might do nothing but propagate itself and then allow the program to run normally. Usually, however, after propagating silently for a while, it starts doing other things—possibly inserting "cute" messages or destroying all of the user's files. Computer "worms" and "logic bombs" are similar to viruses, but they do not replicate themselves within programs as viruses do. A logic bomb does its damage immediately—destroying data, inserting garbage into data files, or reformatting the hard disk; a worm can alter the program and database either immediately or over a period of time.

In the 1990s, viruses, worms, and logic bombs have become such a serious problem, especially among IBM PC and Macintosh users, that the production of special detection and "inoculation" software has become an industry.

What was the name of the personal computer introduced by Apple in the early 1980s?

Lisa was the name of the personal computer that Apple introduced. The forerunner of the Macintosh personal computer, Lisa had a graphical user interface and a mouse.

When did the first portable computer become available?

Perhaps the earliest portable computer was the Osborne 1, which was first available in April 1981. Created by Adam Osborne (1939–2003), the Osborne 1 is better described as a "luggable" computer than a portable computer. It weighed 24 pounds (10.9 kilograms), had two 5.25-inch floppy disk drives, a five-inch screen, 64K RAM, and a processor that ran on 4 Mhz, but it did not have a battery. It included a word processing program and a spreadsheet program. It was approximately the size of a sewing machine and fit under the seat of a commercial airliner. The cost was $1,795.

What is 3-D printing?

Charles Hull (1939–) invented stereolithography, commonly referred to as 3-D printing, in 1984 as a way to build models in plastic layer by layer. The method uses UV light to cure and bond one polymer layer on top of the next layer. Although 3-D printing techniques were first used in research and development labs, it quickly became a tool to create models and prototypes in industry and manufacturing. It is now used to create automobile and aircraft components, artificial limbs, artwork, musical instruments, and endless other products. It is one of the products that has spurned the maker movement. Hull was awarded U.S Patent #4,575,330 in 1986 for his invention and was inducted into the National Inventors Hall of Fame in 2014.

What is a pixel?

A pixel (from the words pix, for picture, and element) is the smallest element on a video display screen. A screen contains thousands of pixels, each of which can be made up of one or more dots or a cluster of dots. On a simple monochrome screen, a pixel is one dot; the two colors of image and background are created when the pixel is switched either on or off. Some monochrome screen pixels can be energized to create different light intensities to allow a range of shades from light to dark. On color screens, three dot colors are included in each pixel—red, green, and blue. The simplest screens have just one dot

A 3-D printer replicates a wrench in this photograph. Such printers are getting more sophisticated, building such things as car parts and aircraft components.

of each color, but more elaborate screens have pixels with clusters of each color. These more elaborate displays can show a large number of colors and intensities. On color screens, black is created by leaving all three colors off; white by all three colors on; and a range of grays by equal intensities of all the colors. The resolution of a computer monitor is expressed as the number of pixels on the horizontal axis and the number of pixels on the vertical axis. For example, a monitor described as 800 × 600 has 800 pixels on the horizontal axis and 600 pixels on the vertical axis. The higher the numbers, e.g., 1600 × 1200, the better the resolution.

What is the technology of a touch screen?

Touch screen technology relies on physical touch of the screen by the user using a finger or stylus for input. Instead of using a computer mouse to activate the cursor, merely touching the screen identifies the location and allows the user to modify the information on the screen. The basic underlying principle is that there is an electrical current running through a sensor on the screen. Touching the screen causes a voltage change, which indicates the location of the physical contact. Specialized hardware converts the voltage changes on the sensors into signals the computer can receive. Finally, software relates to the computer or other device, e.g., smartphone, what is happening on the sensor. The computer or device reacts to the inputted information accordingly.

Who is considered the inventor of touch screen technology?

The technology for touch screens is traced to the digitizing tablet developed by George Samuel Hurst (1927–2010) in the 1970s. As early as 1971, scientists used a "touch sensor" to record data from graphs by placing the graph on the digitizing tablet and pressing the paper against the tablet with a stylus. Although not a transparent screen, it was the forerunner of the modern touch screen. The first commercial producer of digitizing tablets was Elographics (later known as Elo Touch Solutions). Elographics and Siemens Corporation developed a transparent version of the tablet on curved glass that could fit over a cathode ray tube (CRT) screen.

What devices or applications use touch screens?

Touch screens are commonly used for automated teller machines (ATMs), hand-held devices, including PDAs, tablets, and smartphones, information kiosks, and public computers, such as for ticket sales at airports, theaters, museums, and other public venues. They have been helpful for users with special needs that rely on assistive technology. The iPhone, introduced in 2007, uses only touch screen technology.

What is the information highway?

A term originally coined by former Vice President Al Gore (1948-), the information highway is envisioned as an electronic communications network of the near future that would easily connect all users to one another and provide every type of electronic service possible, including shopping, electronic banking, education, medical diagnosis, video conferencing, and game playing. Initially implemented on a national scale, it would eventually become a global network.

The exact form of the information superhighway is a matter of some debate. Two principle views currently exist. One visualizes the superhighway as a more elaborate form of the Internet, the principle purpose of which would be to gather and exchange written information via a global electronic mail network. The other possibility centers around plans to create an enhanced interactive television network that would provide video services on demand.

What is the Internet?

The Internet is the world's largest computer network. It links computer terminals together via wires or telephone lines in a web of networks and shared software. With the proper equipment, an individual can access vast amounts of information and search databases on various

Which technology holds the most promise for keeping information sent over the Internet secure?

Public-key cryptography is a means for authenticating information sent over the Internet. The system works by encrypting and decrypting information through the use of a combination of "keys." One key is a published "public key"; the second is a "private key," which is kept secret. An algorithm is used to decipher each of the keys. The method is for the sender to encrypt the information using the public key, and the recipient to decrypt the information using the secret private key.

The strength of the system depends on the size of the key: a 128-bit encryption is about $3 \times 1,026$ times stronger than 40-bit encryption. No matter how complex the encryption, as with any code, keeping the secret aspects secret is the important part to safeguarding the information.

computers connected to the Internet, or communicate with someone located anywhere in the world as long as he or she has the proper equipment.

Originally created in the late 1960s by the U.S. Department of Defense Advanced Research Projects Agency to share information with other researchers, the Internet mushroomed when scientists and academics using the network discovered its great value. Despite its origin, however, the Internet is not owned or funded by the U.S. government or any other organization or institution. A group of volunteers, the Internet Society, addresses such issues as daily operations and technical standards.

What is email?

Electronic mail, also known as E mail or email, uses communication facilities to transmit messages. Many systems use computers as transmitting and receiving interfaces, but fax communication is also a form of E mail. A user can send a message to a single recipient, or to many. Different systems offer different options for sending, receiving, manipulating text, and addressing. For example, a message can be "registered," so that the sender is notified when the recipient looks at the message (though there is no way to tell if the recipient has actually read the message). Many systems allow messages to be forwarded. Usually messages are stored in a simulated "mailbox" in the network server or host computer; some systems announce incoming mail if the recipient is logged onto the system. An organization (such as a corporation, university, or professional organization) can provide electronic mail facilities; national and international networks can provide them as well. In order to use email, both sender and receiver must have accounts on the same system or on systems connected by a network.

What is spam?

Spam, also called junk email, is unsolicited email. Spam is an annoyance to the recipient and may contain computer viruses or spyware. It often advertises products that are usually not of interest to the recipient and are oftentimes vulgar in content. Some estimate that as many as one billion spam messages are sent daily. Many email programs have spam filters or blockers to detect spam messages and either delete them or send them to the "junk" mailbox.

What is a hacker?

A hacker is a skilled computer user. The term originally denoted a skilled programmer, particularly one skilled in machine code and with a good knowledge of the machine and its operating system. The name arose from the fact that a good programmer could always hack an unsatisfactory system around until it worked.

The term later came to denote a user whose main interest is in defeating password systems. The term has thus acquired a pejorative sense, with the meaning of one who deliberately and sometimes criminally interferes with data available through telephone lines. The activities of such hackers have led to considerable efforts to tighten security of transmitted data. The "hacker ethic" is that information-sharing is the proper way of human dealing, and, indeed, it is the responsibility of hackers to liberally impart their wisdom to the software world by distributing information. Nefarious hacker attacks by people outside the company costs companies on average about $56,000 per attack.

Who coined the term technobabble?

John A. Barry used the term "technobabble" to mean the pervasive and indiscriminate use of computer terminology, especially as it is applied to situations that have nothing at all to do with technology. He first used it in the early 1980s.

How did the Linux operating system get its name?

The name Linux is combination of the first name of its principal programmer, Finland's Linus Torvalds (1970-), and the UNIX operating system. Linux (pronounced with a short "i") is an open source computer operating system that is comparable to more powerful, expansive, and usually costly UNIX systems, of which it resembles in form and function. Linux allows users to run an amalgam of reliable and hearty open-source software tools and interfaces, including powerful Web utilities such as the popular Apache server, on their home computers. Anyone can download Linux for free or can obtain it on disk for only a marginal fee. Torvalds created the kernel—or heart of the system—"just for fun," and released it freely to the world, where other programmers helped further its development. The world, in turn, has embraced Linux and made Torvalds into a folk hero.

What is the idea behind "open-source software"?

Open-source software is computer software where the code (the rules governing its operation) is available for users to modify. This is in contrast to proprietary code, where the software vendor veils the code so users cannot view and, hence, manipulate (or steal) it. The software termed open source is not necessarily free—that is, without charge; authors can charge for its use, and some do, albeit nominal fees. According to the Free Software Foundation, "Free software" is a matter of liberty, not price. To understand the concept, you should think of "free" as in "free speech," not as in "free beer." Free software is a matter of the users' freedom to run, copy, distribute, study, change, and improve the software." Despite this statement, most of it is available without charge. Open-source software is usually protected under the notion of "copyleft," instead of "copyright" law. Copyleft does not mean releasing material to the public domain, nor does it mean near absolute prohibition from copying, like the federal copyright law. Instead, according to the Free Software Foundation, copyleft is a form of protection guaranteeing that whoever redistributes software, whether modified or not, "must pass along the freedom to further copy and share it." Open source has evolved into a movement of sharing, cooperation, and mutual innovation, ideas that many believe are necessary in today's cutthroat corporatization of software.

Who invented the World Wide Web?

Tim Berners-Lee (1955-) is considered the creator of the World Wide Web (WWW). The WWW is a massive collection of interlinked hypertext documents that travel over the Internet and are viewed through a browser. The Internet is a global network of computers developed in the 1960s and 1970s by the U.S. Department of Defense's Advanced Research Project Agency (hence the term "Arpanet"). The idea of the Internet was to provide redundancy of communications in case of a catastrophic event (like a nuclear blast), which might destroy a single connection or computer but not the entire network. The browser is used to translate the hypertext, usually written in Hypertext Markup Language (HTML), so it is human-readable on a computer screen. Along with Gutenberg's invention of the printing press, the inception of the WWW in 1990 and 1991, when Berners-Lee released the tools and protocols onto the Internet, is considered one of humanity's greatest communications achievements.

What is Wi-Fi?

Wi-Fi is a wireless local area network. The Wi-Fi Alliance certifies that network devices comply with the appropriate standard, IEEE 802.11. A Wi-Fi hotspot is the geographic boundary covered by a Wi-Fi access point. One research study reported there were 5.69 million public hotspots in 2015 and projected there would be over 13 million public wifi hotspots in 2020.

What is the client/server principle and how does it apply to the Internet?

The client/server principle refers to the two components of a centralized computer network: client and server machines. Clients request information and servers send them the requested information. For example, when an individual uses his computer to look at a Web page, his computer acts as the client, and the computer hosting the web page is the server. Browsers enable the connection between clients and servers. During the 1990s, Netscape, an outgrowth of the early browser Mosaic, and Internet Explorer were the dominant browsers. Eventually, Microsoft's Internet Explorer became the dominant browser. Other frequently used browsers are Mozilla Firefox, Safari, and Google Chrome.

What is a Uniform Resource Locator, or URL?

A Uniform Resource Locator (URL) can be thought of as the "address" for a given computer on the Internet. A URL consists of two parts: 1) the protocol identifier and 2) the resource name. The protocol identifier indicates which protocol to use, e.g., "http" for Hypertext Transfer Protocol or "ftp" for File Transfer Protocol. Most browsers default to "http" as the protocol identifier, so it is not necessary to include that part of the URL when entering an Internet address in the browser's toolbar. The resource identifier specifies the IP (Internet Protocol) address or domain name where the Web page is located. An IP address is a string of numbers separated by periods. More familiar and easier to remember than the IP address is a domain name. Domain names are comprised of a name with a top-level domain (TLD) suffix. The IP address and domain name both point to the same place; typing "192.0.32.10" in the address bar of a web browser will bring up the same page as entering the more user-friendly "example.com."

What are some common top-level domain (TLD) suffixes?

Common top-level domain suffixes are:

Top-Level Domain (TLD)	Meaning of the Suffix
.com	Commercial organization, business, or company
.edu	Educational institution
.org	Nonprofit organization (sometimes used by other sites)
.gov	U.S. government agency
.mil	U.S. military agency
.net	Network organizations

How does a search engine work?

Internet search engines are akin to computerized card catalogs at libraries. Viewed through a web browser with an Internet connection, they provide a hyperlinked listing of locations on the World Wide Web according to the requested keyword or pattern of words submitted by the searcher. A Web directory service provides the same service, but uses different methods to gather its source information. A Web directory service employs humans to "surf" Web sites and organize them into a hierarchical index by subject or some other category. A search engine, however, uses computer software called "spiders" or "bots" to search out, inventory, and index Web pages automatically. The spiders scan each Web page's content for words and the frequency of the words, then stores that information in a database. When the user submits words or terms, the search engine returns a list of sites from the database and ranks them according to the relevancy of the search terms.

When was Google founded?

In 1996 Stanford University graduate students Larry Page (1973–) and Sergey Brin (1973–) began collaborating on a search engine called BackRub. BackRub operated on the Stanford servers for more than a year until it began to take up too much bandwidth. In 1997, Page and Brin decided they needed a new name for the search engine and decided upon Google as a play on the mathematical term "googol." (A googol is the numeral 1 followed by 100 zeros.) Their goal was to organize the seemingly infinite amount of information on the Web. Google first incorporated as a company in September 1998, and the corporation went public in 2004.

How has computer gaming changed since the 1970s?

The computer game industry has grown to a multi-billion-dollar industry since the 1970s. The introduction of physically interactive computer games, such as Microsoft Xbox and Nintendo Wii, allowed game players to play virtual games, such as tennis, basketball, and baseball. Furthermore, games are no longer available just on consoles but are available on the Internet, where large groups of players can play simultaneously.

What are some examples of user-generated content on the World Wide Web?

Blogs (short for web logs) are akin to modern-day diaries (or logs) of thoughts and activities of the author. In the late 1990s, software became available to create blogs using templates that made them accessible to a wide audience as a publishing tool. Blogs may be created by single individuals or by groups of contributors. Blog entries are organized in reverse chronological order with the most recent entries being seen first. Entries may include text, audio, images, video, and links to other sites. Blog authors may invite reader feedback via comments, which allow for dialogue between blog authors and readers. Wikis, from the Hawaiian word *wikiwiki*, which means "fast," are Web pages that allow users to add and edit material in a collaborative fashion. The first wikis were developed in the mid-1990s by Ward Cunningham (1949–) as a way for users to quickly add content to Web pages. The advantage of this software was that the users did not need to know complicated languages to add material to the Web. One of the best known wikis is Wikipedia, an online, collaborative encyclopedia. Although entries to Wikipedia need to come from published sources and be based on fact, rather than the writer's opinion, there is no overall editorial authority on the site. Podcasts are broadcast media that may be created by anyone and are available on demand. Unlike traditional broadcast media (radio and television), podcasts are easily created with a microphone, video camera, computer, and connection to the Web. Podcasting does not require sophisticated recording or transmitting equipment. Most podcasts are broadcast on a weekly, biweekly, or monthly schedule. While traditional broadcast media follow a set schedule, podcasts may be downloaded onto a computer or a portable device such as an MP3 player and listened to whenever it is convenient.

What is Web 2.0?

Web 2.0 is not a new version of the World Wide Web but rather a collection of new technologies that changes the way users interact with the Web. When Tim Berners-Lee (1955–) created the World Wide Web, it was a repository of information with static content, and users were generally unable to easily change or add to the content they were viewing. Newer technologies allow users to contribute to the Internet with blogs, wikis, and social networking sites. A further distinction of Web 2.0 is "cloud computing," where data and applications ("apps") are stored on Web servers, rather than on individual computers, allowing users to access their documents, files, and data from any computer with a Web browser. Apps include many products, such as word processing and spreadsheets, that were traditionally found in software packages. For example, Google Drive allows users to access documents and files from any computer. Users are able to collaborate and edit documents in "real" time without having to send documents back and forth through email.

When were chat rooms a popular way to communicate?

Chat rooms were a popular way to communicate in "real-time" via an Internet connection in the 1990s. Users were able to send messages to each other directly. Although CompuServe had launched a CB Simulator service in the 1980s and bulletin board server (BBS) systems were available in the late 1980s, America Online (AOL) chat rooms were not available until 1993. In 1996, AOL introduced a monthly flat rate instead of an hourly rate for chat room usage. The number of users increased dramatically, despite the fact that users relied on dial-up service at much slower speeds than today's Internet connections. AOL introduced Instant Messenger (AIM) in 1997. However, with the introduction of Friendster, MySpace, and Facebook, chat room usage declined. AOL discontinued chat rooms in 2010, and Yahoo Messenger ceased to exist in 2012.

Who coined the term "social networking"?

One of the first individuals to use the term "social network" was John Arundel Barnes (1918–2010), a British sociologist/anthropologist. He developed the concept of a social network in a 1954 paper, *Class and Committees in a Norwegian Island Parish,* to describe the social ties or network of relations in a Norwegian fishing village. The first use of "social networking" and "social media" in the electronic age is hard to pinpoint. Tina Sharkey (1964–), formerly of iVillage, believes she began using the term in 1994, while Ted Leonsis (1957–), formerly of AOL, believes it was coined sometime around 1997 by AOL executives. It was popularized in the early twenty-first century.

Who founded Facebook?

Facebook was founded by Mark Zuckerberg (1984–) while a student at Harvard as a social networking site for Harvard students. While membership was initially limited to Harvard

365

students, it soon expanded to include all college students, then a version for high school students, and then to anyone with an email address. There are now over one billion Facebook users, making it the most popular social media website. Facebook users are able to stay connected with family, friends, and business associates.

Who developed Twitter?

Twitter was developed by Jack Dorsey (1976–) in 2006. He sent his first tweet on March 21, 2006. The tweet was: "just setting up my twttr." There are now 284 million monthly active Twitter users, and 500 million tweets are sent each day. When the US Airways plane crashed in the Hudson River in 2009, it was shared via Twitter (including a photo of the plane) before the traditional news media reported the story.

How many characters are allowed in a tweet?

Tweets are expressions of ideas or thoughts of a moment. Tweets can contain text, photos, and videos. Tweets are made up of 140-character messages. Users can both follow or read Twitter accounts and send messages.

In which industries are robots being used?

A robot is a device that can execute a wide range of maneuvers under the direction of a computer. Reacting to feedback from sensors or by reprogramming, a robot can alter its maneuvers to fit a changed task or situation. The worldwide population of robots is about 250,000, with approximately 65 percent being used in Japan and 14 percent being used in the United States (the second largest user).

Robots are used to do welding, painting, drilling, sanding, cutting, and moving tasks in manufacturing plants. Automobile factories account for more than 50 percent of robot use in the United States. Robots can work in environments that are extremely threatening to humans or in difficult physical environments. They clean up radioactive areas, extinguish fires, disarm bombs, and load and unload explosives and toxic chemicals. Robots can process light-sensitive materials, such as photographic films that require near darkness—a difficult task for human workers. They can perform a variety of tasks in underwater exploration and in mines (a hazardous, low-light environment). There are only 100 robots in mines, but they produce about one-third of the coal coming from these mines. In the military and security fields, robots are used to sense targets or as surveillance devices. In the printing industry, robots perform miscellaneous tasks, such as sorting and tying bundles of output material, delivering paper to the presses, and applying book covers. In research laboratories, small desktop robots prepare samples and mix compounds.

What film was the first to feature a robot?

In 1886, the French movie *L'Ève future* had a Thomas Edison-like mad scientist building a robot in the likeness of a woman. A British lord falls in love with her in a variation on the Pygmalion theme. True working robots, in contrast to these entertainment devices, are strictly functional in appearance, looking more like machines rather than human beings or animals. However, one early exception to this is the very human-looking "Scribe" built in 1773 by two French inventors, Pierre and Henri-Louis Jacquel-Droz, a father and son team, who produced "The Automaton" to dip a quill pen into an inkwell and write a text of 40 characters maximum.

Who was the founder of cybernetics?

Norbert Wiener (1894-1964) is considered the creator of cybernetics. Derived from the Greek word kubernetes, meaning steerman or helmsman, cybernetics is concerned with the common factors of control and communication in living organisms, automatic machines, or organizations. These factors are exemplified by the skill used in steering a boat, in which the helmsman uses continual judgment to maintain control. The principles of cybernetics are used today in control theory, automation theory, and computer programs to reduce many time-consuming computations and decision-making processes formerly done by people.

PHYSICS AND CHEMISTRY

What is physics?

Physics is the study of the structure of the natural world. It seeks to explain natural phenomena in terms of a comprehensive theoretical structure in mathematical form. Physics depends on accurate instrumentation, precise measurements, and the expression of results in mathematical terms. It describes and explains the motion of objects that are subject to forces. Physics forms the basis of chemistry, biology, geology, and astronomy. Although these sciences involve the study of systems much more complex than those that physicists study, the fundamental aspects are all based on physics.

Physics is also applied to engineering and technology. Therefore a knowledge of physics is vital in today's technical world. For these reasons physics is often called the fundamental science.

What are the subfields of physics?

The word *physics* comes from the Greek *physis*, meaning nature. Aristotle (384–322 B.C.E.) wrote the first known book entitled *Physics*, which consisted of a set of eight books that was a detailed study of motion and its causes. The ancient Greek title of the book is best translated as *Natural Philosophy*, or writings about nature. For that reason, those who studied the workings of nature were called "Natural Philosophers." They were educated in philosophy and called themselves philosophers. One of the early modern textbooks that used physics in its title was published in 1732. It was not until the 1800s that those who studied physics were called physicists. In the nineteenth, twentieth, and twenty-first centuries physics has proven to be a very large and important field of study. Due to the huge breadth of physics, physicists today must concentrate their work in one or two of the subfields of physics. The most important of these fields are listed below.

- *Quantum mechanics and relativity*—Both of these fields study the descriptions and explanations of the way small particles interact (quantum physics), the motion of objects moving near the speed of light (special relativity), and the causes and effects of gravity (general relativity).

369

- *Elementary particles and fields*—The study of the particles that are the basis of all matter. Both their properties and their interactions are included.

- *Nuclear physics*—The study of the properties of the nuclei of atoms and the protons and neutrons of which they are composed.

- *Atomic and molecular physics*—The study of single atoms and molecules that are made up of these atoms. Studies include interactions with each other and with light.

- *Condensed matter physics*—Otherwise known as solid-state physics, condensed matter is a study of the physical and electrical properties of solid materials. An exciting new study is that of nano materials, leading to nanotechnology.

The Greek philosopher Aristotle wrote the first known book about physics.

- *Electromagnetism and optics*—Studies how electric and magnetic forces interact with matter. Light is a type of electromagnetic wave and so is a part of electromagnetism.

- *Thermodynamics and statistical mechanics*—Studies how temperature affects matter and how heat is transferred. Thermodynamics deals with macroscopic objects; statistical mechanics concerns the atomic and molecular motions of very large numbers of particles, including how they are affected by heat transfer.

- *Mechanics*—Deals with the effect of forces on the motion and energy of physical objects. Modern mechanics studies mostly involve fluids (fluid dynamics) and granular particles (like sand), as well as the motions of stars and galaxies.

- *Plasma physics*—Plasmas are composed of electrically charged atoms. Plasmas studied include those in fluorescent lamps, in large-screen televisions, in Earth's atmosphere, and in stars and material between stars. Plasma physicists are also working to create controlled nuclear fusion reactors to produce electricity.

- *Physics education research*—Investigates how people learn physics and how best to teach them.

Applications of Physics

- *Acoustics*—Musical acoustics studies the ways musical instruments produce sounds. Applied acoustics includes the study of how concert halls can best be designed. Ultrasound acoustics uses sound to image the interior of metals, fluids, and the human body.

- *Astrophysics*—Studies how astronomical bodies, such as planets, stars, and galaxies, interact with one another. A subfield is cosmology, which investigates the formation of the universe, galaxies, and stars.

- *Atmospheric physics*—Studies the atmosphere of Earth and other planets. Today most activity involves the causes and effects of global warming and climate change.

- *Biophysics*—Studies the physical interactions of biological molecules and the use of physics in biology.
- *Chemical physics*—Investigates the physical causes of chemical reactions between atoms and molecules and how light can be used to understand and cause these reactions.
- *Geophysics*—Geophysics is the physics of Earth. It deals with the forces and energy found within Earth itself. Geophysicists study tectonic plates, earthquakes, volcanic activity, and oceanography.
- *Medical physics*—Investigates how physical processes can be used to produce images of the inside of humans, as well as the use of radiation and high-energy particles in treating diseases such as cancer.

How is "absolute zero" defined?

Absolute zero is the theoretical temperature at which all substances have zero thermal energy. Originally conceived as the temperature at which an ideal gas at constant pressure would contract to zero volume, absolute zero is of great significance in thermodynamics and is used as the fixed point for absolute temperature scales. Absolute zero is equivalent to 0 K, -459.67°F, or -273.15°C.

The velocity of a substance's molecules determines its temperature; the faster the molecules move, the more volume they require, and the higher the temperature becomes. The lowest actual temperature ever reached was two-billionth of a degree above absolute zero (2×10^{-9} K) by a team at the Low Temperature Laboratory in the Helsinki University of Technology, Finland, in October 1989.

What is superconductivity?

Superconductivity is a condition in which many metals, alloys, organic compounds, and ceramics conduct electricity without resistance, usually at low temperatures. Heike Kamerlingh Onnes, a Dutch physicist, discovered superconductivity in 1911. The modern theory regarding the phenomenon was developed by three American physicists—John Bardeen, Leon N. Cooper, and John Robert Schrieffer. Known as the BCS theory after the three scientists, it postulates that superconductivity occurs in certain materials because the electrons in them, rather than remaining free to collide with imperfections and scatter, form pairs that can flow easily around imperfections and do not lose their energy. Bardeen, Cooper, and Schrieffer received the Nobel Prize in Physics for their work in 1972. A further breakthrough in superconductivity was made in 1986 by J. Georg Bednorz and K. Alex Müller. Bednorz and Müller discovered a ceramic material consisting of lanthanum, barium, copper and oxygen which became superconductive at 35 K (-238°C)—much higher than any other material. Bednorz and Müller won the Nobel Prize in Physics in 1987. This was a significant accomplishment since in most situations the Nobel Prize is awarded for discoveries made as many as 20 to 40 years earlier.

What is the string theory?

A relatively recent theory in particle physics, the string theory conceives elementary particles not as points but as lines or loops. The idea of these "strings" is purely theoretical since no string has ever been detected experimentally. The ultimate expression of string theory may potentially require a new kind of geometry—perhaps one involving an infinity of dimensions.

What is inertia?

Inertia is a tendency of all objects and matter in the universe to stay still, or, if moving, to continue moving in the same direction, unless acted on by some outside force. This forms the first law of motion formulated by Isaac Newton (1642-1727). To move a body at rest, enough external force must be used to overcome the object's inertia; the larger the object is, the more force is required to move it. In his *Philosophae Naturalis Principia Mathematica*, published in 1687, Newton sets forth all three laws of motion. Newton's second law is that the force to move a body is equal to its mass times its acceleration (F = MA), and the third law states that for every action there is an equal and opposite reaction.

In 1687, Isaac Newton published his *Philosophae Naturalis Principia Mathematica,* laying the foundation for the science of mechanics.

What is a Leyden jar?

A Leyden jar, the earliest form of capacitor, is a device for storing an electrical charge. First described in 1745 by E. Georg von Kleist (c. 1700-1748), it was also used by Pieter van Musschenbroek (1692-1761), a professor of physics at the University of Leyden. The device came to be known as a Leyden jar and was the first device that could store large amounts of electric charge. The jars contained an inner wire electrode in contact with water, mercury, or wire. The outer electrode was a human hand holding the jar. An improved version coated the jar inside and outside with separate metal foils with the inner foil connected to a conducting rod and terminated in a conducting sphere. This eliminated the need for the liquid electrolyte. In use, the jar was normally charged from an electrostatic generator. The Leyden jar is still used for classroom demonstrations of static electricity.

What is a wave?

A wave is a traveling disturbance that moves energy from one location to another without transferring matter. Oscillations in a medium or material create mechanical waves that propagate away from the location of the oscillation. For example, a pebble dropped into a pool of water creates vertical oscillations in the water, while the wave propagates outward horizontally along the surface of the water.

ELECTROMAGNETIC WAVES

What is an electromagnetic wave?

Electromagnetic waves consist of two transverse waves: one an oscillating electric field, the other a corresponding magnetic field perpendicular to it. Light, infrared, ultraviolet, radio, and X rays are all examples of electromagnetic waves.

All electromagnetic waves travel at the speed of light when they are in a vacuum. Electromagnetic waves are characterized by their frequency or wavelength and amplitude. Electromagnetic waves differ from other waves in that they do not need a medium such as air, water, or steel through which to travel.

How is an electromagnetic wave created and detected?

Electromagnetic waves are created by accelerating electrons that create an oscillating electric field. This field in turn creates an oscillating magnetic field, which creates another oscillating electric field, and so on. The energy carried by the waves radiates into the area around the moving charges. When it strikes a material whose electrons can move freely, it causes these particles to oscillate.

What is the electromagnetic spectrum?

The electromagnetic spectrum is the wide range of electromagnetic (EM) waves from low to high frequency. The spectrum ranges from low-frequency radio waves, all the way to gamma rays, which have a very high frequency. In the middle of the spectrum is a small region containing the frequencies of light.

Who predicted electromagnetic waves?

In 1861, James Clerk Maxwell (1831–1879) demonstrated the mathematical relationship between oscillating electric and magnetic fields. In his *Treatise on Electricity and Magnetism*, written in 1873, Maxwell described the nature of electric and magnetic fields using four differential equations, known to physicists today as "Maxwell's Equations." Putting the four equations together predicted the existence of the electromagnetic wave.

Maxwell was a professor at Cambridge University in England from 1871 until his death in 1879. He published other works on thermodynamics and the motion of matter as well. He also developed the kinetic theory of gases, and performed research in the field of color vision. Although Maxwell is not widely known to the lay audience, he is revered in the scientific community, and rates in the pantheon of physics greats with Newton and Einstein.

Who demonstrated that electromagnetic waves exist?

Heinrich Hertz (1857–1894) was a German physicist who was the first person to demonstrate that electromagnetic waves existed. He designed a transmitter and receiver that produced waves with a 4-meter wavelength. He used standing waves to measure their wavelength. He showed that they could be reflected, refracted, polarized, and could produce interference. It was Hertz's breakthroughs in electromagnetic waves that paved the way for

373

the development of radio. In 1930 Hertz was honored by having the unit of frequency, which was cycles per second, replaced by the hertz (Hz).

What is the speed of light?

The figure is 186,282 miles (299,792 kilometers) per second.

What are the primary colors in light?

Color is determined by the wavelength of visible light (the distance between one crest of the light wave and the next). Those colors that blend to form "white light" are, from shortest wave length to longest: red, orange, yellow, green, blue, indigo, and violet. All these monochromatic colors, except indigo, occupy large areas of the spectrum (the entire range of wavelengths produced when a beam of electromagnetic radiation is broken up). These colors can be seen when a light beam is refracted through a prism. Some consider the primary colors to be six monochromatic colors that occupy large areas of the spectrum: red, orange, yellow, green, blue, and violet. Many physicists recognize three primary colors: red, yellow, and blue; or red, green, and blue. All other colors can be made from these by adding two primary colors in various proportions. Within the spectrum, scientists have discovered 55 distinct hues. Infra-red and ultraviolet rays at each end of the spectrum are invisible to the human eye.

How is light emitted?

You undoubtedly have seen the light emitted by hot objects. Whether it is the dull red glow of the heating coil on an electric range or the orange glow of the element in an electric oven or the bright yellow-white of the glowing filament of an incandescent lamp, you have seen light emitted by hot objects. Even the yellow glow of a fire comes from light emitted by hot carbon particles. Energy, usually from stored chemical energy, is converted into thermal energy. That energy is transferred to the surroundings by radiation, including light. Unfortunately, producing light in this way is very inefficient because about 97% of the energy goes into infrared radiation that warms the environment rather than light that can be seen. Because of their large energy use, many countries will be banning incandescent lamps in the next few years.

Light can also be emitted by gases and solids. Neon signs are one example of a gas that glows because electrical energy is converted into light energy. High-intensity lamps use either sodium or mercury vapor to produce intense light. Fluorescent tubes and compact fluorescent lamps (CFLs) use electrical energy to excite mercury atoms. The ultraviolet emitted by these atoms causes compounds deposited on the inside surfaces of the lamps to glow. The

How do polarized sunglasses reduce glare?

Sunlight reflected from the horizontal surface of water, glass, and snow is partially polarized, with the direction of polarization chiefly in the horizontal plane. Such reflected light may be so intense as to cause glare. The Polaroid material in sunglasses will block light that is polarized in a direction perpendicular to the transmission axes; Polaroid sunglasses are made with the transmission axes of the lenses oriented vertically.

colors can be chosen to emulate incandescent lamps or daylight. CFLs convert up to 15% of the electrical energy into light.

Lasers, mostly used today in CD and DVD players and supermarket bar-code scanners and pointers, usually consist of a small crystal composed of a mixture of elements like gallium, arsenic, and aluminum. The lasers produce single-color, intense light that is emitted as a compact ray. The LED lights that are often used as on/off indicators, traffic lights, car taillights, stop, and turning lights also use electrical energy and the same kind of materials used in laser pointers to produce light that is radiated into many directions. White LEDs that are beginning to be used in home lighting are costly to produce, but are much more efficient and last much longer than incandescent lamps.

What is a light-year?

A year is a unit of time, but a light-year is a unit of distance. Specifically, it is the distance that light travels in one year. Since light travels at 299,792 km/s and a year consists of 31.557×10^6 s, a light-year is 9.4605×10^{12} km or about 6 trillion miles.

The light-year is used to express distances to stars and galaxies.

What is the Doppler effect?

The Austrian physicist Christian Doppler (1803-1853) in 1842 explained the phenomenon of the apparent change in wavelength of radiation—such as sound or light—emitted either by a moving body (source) or by the moving receiver. The frequency of the wavelengths increases and the wavelength becomes shorter as the moving source approaches, producing high-pitched sounds and bluish light (called blue shift). Likewise, as the source recedes from the receiver the frequency of the wavelengths decreases, the sound is pitched lower, and light appears reddish (called red shift). This Doppler effect is commonly demonstrated by the whistle of an approaching train or the roar of a jet aircraft.

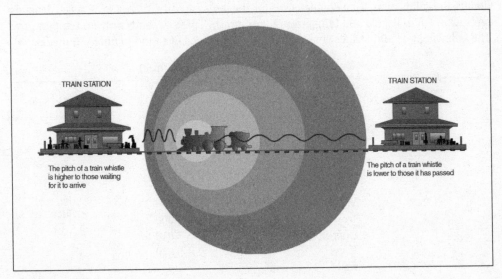

TRAIN STATION

TRAIN STATION

The pitch of a train whistle is higher to those waiting for it to arrive

The pitch of a train whistle is lower to those it has passed

The Doppler effect.

There are three differences between acoustical (sound) and optical (light) Doppler effects: The optical frequency change is not dependent on which is moving—the source or observer—nor is it affected by the medium through which the waves are moving, but acoustical frequency is affected by such conditions. Optical frequency changes are affected if the source or observer moves at right angles to the line connecting the source and observer. Observed acoustical changes are not affected in such a situation. Applications of the Doppler phenomenon include the Doppler radar and the measurement by astronomers of the motion and direction of celestial bodies.

How fast does sound travel?

Light travels almost one million times faster than sound—specifically, 880,000 times the speed of sound. Light and all electromagnetic waves travel at a speed of 3×10^8 meters per second, while the speed of sound is only about 340 meters per second or 760 miles per hour on a typical spring day.

The speed of sound compared to the speed of light can be observed at a baseball game. A spectator sitting in the outfield bleachers sees the batter hit a ball before she hears the crack of the bat.

How fast does sound travel in different media?

A simple model that explains the main factors affecting the speed of sound is a collection of balls (molecules) connected to each other by springs (bonds between molecules). Vibration from one ball will be transferred by the springs to neighboring balls, and in succession throughout the collection. The stiffer the springs and the lighter the balls, the faster the vibrations will be transferred. The springs are a model of the *bulk elasticity* (how the volume changes when the pressure on it changes) of the material, the balls and their spacing model the density of the material. In general, the speed is slowest in gases, fastest in solids. Even though liquids and solids are about 1,000 times denser than gases, the greater elasticity of liquids and solids more than compensates for the larger density. In gases the speed depends on the kind of molecule and temperature. For air, the speed depends only on temperature. The following table illustrates some examples of the speed of sound in different media.

Medium	Speed (m/s)
Air (0°C)	331
Air (20°C)	343
Air (100°C)	366
Helium (0°C)	965
Mercury	1,452
Water (20°C)	1,482
Lead	1,960
Wood (oak)	3,850
Iron	5,000
Copper	5,010
Glass	5,640
Steel	5,960

What is the sound barrier?

The sound barrier is the speed that an object must travel to exceed the speed of sound. The speed of sound is often used as a reference with which to measure the velocity of an aircraft. The speed of sound, 331 meters per second at 0°C, is Mach 1. Twice the speed of sound is Mach 2, three times the speed of sound is Mach 3, and so on.

What is a sonic boom?

A sonic boom occurs when an object travels faster than the speed of sound. The boom itself is caused by an object, such as a supersonic airplane, traveling faster than the sound waves themselves can travel. The sound waves pile up on one another, creating a shock wave that travels through the atmosphere, resulting in a "boom" when it strikes a person's

Supersonic planes, such as this F-15 fighter jet, can go beyond Mach 1. When they do, they generate a "sonic boom" caused by sound waves piling up and creating a shock wave.

ears. A sonic boom is not a momentary event that occurs as the plane breaks the sound barrier; rather, it is a continuous sound caused by a plane as it travels at such a speed, but the shock wave travels with the plane, so we hear it only when the plane is in one location.

All objects that exceed the speed of sound create sonic booms. For example, missiles and bullets, which travel faster than the sound barrier, produce sonic booms as they move through the atmosphere. The shockwave created by an F-15 fighter plane, for instance, is visible.

What are the characteristics of alpha, beta, and gamma radiation?

Radiation is a term that describes all the ways energy is emitted by the atom as X-rays, gamma rays, neutrons, or as charged particles. Most atoms, being stable, are nonradioactive; others are unstable and give off either particles or gamma radiation. Substances bombarded by radioactive particles can become radioactive and yield alpha particles, beta particles, and gamma rays.

Alpha particles, first identified by Antoine-Henri Becquerel (1852-1908), have a positive electrical charge and consist of two protons and two neutrons. Because of their great mass, alpha particles can travel only a short distance, around two inches (five centimeters) in air, and can be stopped by a sheet of paper.

Beta particles, identified by Ernest Rutherford (1871-1937), are extremely high-speed electrons that move at the speed of light. They can travel far in air and can pass through solid matter several millimeters thick.

Gamma rays, identified by Marie (1867-1934) and Pierre Curie (1859-1906), are similar to X-rays, but they usually have a shorter wave length. These rays, which are bursts of photons, or very short-wave electromagnetic radiation, travel at the speed of light. They are much more penetrating than either the alpha or beta particles and can go through seven inches (18 centimeters) of lead.

MATTER

Who proposed the theory of the atom?

The modern theory of atomic structure was first proposed by the Japanese physicist Hantaro Nagaoka (1865-1950) in 1904. In his model, electrons rotated in rings around a small central nucleus. In 1911, Ernest Rutherford (1871-1937) discovered further evidence to prove that the nucleus of the atom is extremely small and dense and is surrounded by a much larger and less dense cloud of electrons. In 1913, the Danish physicist Niels Bohr (1885-1962) suggested that electrons orbit the nucleus in concentric quantum shells that correspond to the electron's energy levels.

What is the fourth state of matter?

Plasma, a mixture of free electrons and ions or atomic nuclei, is sometimes referred to as a "fourth state of matter." Plasmas occur in thermonuclear reactions as in the sun, in fluorescent lights, and in stars. When the temperature of gas is raised high enough, the collision of atoms becomes so violent that electrons are knocked loose from their nuclei. The result of a gas having loose, negatively charged electrons and heavier, positively charged nuclei is called a plasma.

All matter is made up of atoms. Animals and plants are organic matter; minerals and water are inorganic matter. Whether matter appears as a solid, liquid, or gas depends on how the molecules are held together in their chemical bonds. Solids have a rigid structure in the atoms of the molecules; in liquids the molecules are close together but not packed; in a gas, the molecules are widely spaced and move around, occasionally colliding but usually not interacting. These states—solid, liquid, and gas—are the first three states of matter.

What is the difference between nuclear fission and nuclear fusion?

Nuclear fission is the splitting of an atomic nucleus into at least two fragments. Nuclear fusion is a nuclear reaction in which the nuclei of atoms of low atomic number, such as hydrogen and helium, fuse to form a heavier nucleus. In both nuclear fission and nuclear fusion substantial amounts of energy are produced.

Who is generally regarded as the discoverer of the electron, the proton, and the neutron?

The British physicist Sir Joseph John Thomson (1856-1940) in 1897 researched electrical conduction in gases, which led to the important discovery that cathode rays consist of negatively charged particles called electrons. The discovery of the electron inaugurated the electrical theory of the atom, and this, along with other work, entitled Thomson to be regarded as the founder of modern atomic physics.

Ernest Rutherford (1871-1937) discovered the proton in 1919. He also predicted the existence of the neutron, later discovered by his colleague, James Chadwick (1891- 1974). Chadwick was awarded the 1935 Nobel Prize for physics for this discovery.

How did a total solar eclipse confirm Einstein's theory of general relativity?

When formulating his theory of general relativity, Albert Einstein (1879-1955) proposed that the curvature of space near a massive object like the sun would bend light that passed close by. For example, a star seen near the edge of the sun during an eclipse would appear to have shifted by 1.75 arc seconds from its usual place. The British astronomer Arthur Eddington (1882-1944) confirmed Einstein's hypothesis during an eclipse on May 29, 1919. The subsequent attention given Eddington's findings helped establish Einstein's reputation as one of science's greatest figures.

Murray Gell-Mann theorized the existence of fundamental particles he called "quarks."

How did the quark get its name?

This theoretical particle, considered to be the fundamental unit of matter, was named by Murray Gell-Mann (b. 1929) an American theoretical physicist and Nobel Prize winner. Its name was initially a playful tag that Gell-Mann invented, sounding something like "kwork." Later, Gell-Mann came across the line "Three quarks for Master Marks" in James Joyce's *Finnegan's Wake*, and the tag became known as a quark. There are six kinds or "flavors" (up, down, strange, charm, bottom, and top) of quarks, and each "flavor" has three varieties or "colors" (red, blue, and green). All eighteen types have different electric charges (a basic characteristic of all elementary particles). Three quarks form a proton (having one unit of positive electric charge) or a neutron (zero charge), and two quarks (a quark and an antiquark) form a meson. Like all known particles, a quark has its anti-matter opposite, known as an antiquark (having the same mass but opposite charge).

What was Richard Feynman's contribution to physics?

Richard Feynman (1918-1988) developed a theory of quantum electrodynamics that described the interaction of electrons, positrons, and photons, providing physicists a new way to work with electrons. He reconstructed quantum mechanics and electrodynamics in his own terms, formulating a matrix of measurable quantities visually represented by a series of graphs knows as the Feynman diagrams. Feynman was awarded the Nobel Prize in Physics in 1965.

What are the subatomic particles?

Subatomic particles are particles that are smaller than atoms. Historically, subatomic particles were considered to be electrons, protons, and neutrons. However, the definition of subatomic particles has now been expanded to include elementary particles, which are the particles so small that they do not appear to be made of more minute units. The physical study of such particles became possible only during the twentieth century with the development of increasingly sophisticated apparatus. Many new particles have been discovered in the last half of the twentieth century.

A number of proposals have been made to organize the particles by their spin, their mass, or their common properties. One system is now commonly known as the Standard Model. This system recognizes two basic types of fundamental particles: quarks and leptons. Other force-carrying particles are called bosons. Photons, gluons, and weakons are bosons. Leptons include electrons, muons, taus, and three kinds of neutrinos. Quarks never occur alone in nature. They always combine to form particles called hadrons. According to the Standard Model, all other subatomic particles consist of some combination of quarks and their antiparticles. A proton consists of three quarks.

What are colligative properties?

Colligative properties are properties of solutions that depend on the number of particles present in the solution and not on characteristics of the particles themselves. Colligative properties include depression of freezing point and elevation of boiling point. For living systems, perhaps the most important colligative property is osmotic pressure.

What substance, other than water, is less dense as a solid than as a liquid?

Only bismuth and water share this characteristic. Density (the mass per unit volume or mass/volume) refers to how compact or crowded a substance is. For instance, the density of water is 1 g/cm^3 (gram per cubic centimeter) or 1 kg/l (kilogram per liter); the density of a rock is 3.3 g/cm^3; pure iron is 7.9 g/cm^3; and the Earth (as a whole) is 5.5 g/cm^3 (average). Water as a solid (i.e., ice) floats, which is a good thing; otherwise, ice would sink to the bottom of every lake or stream.

Why is liquid water more dense than ice?

Pure liquid water is most dense at 39.2°F (3.98°C) and decreases in density as it freezes. The water molecules in ice are held in a relatively rigid geometric pattern by their hydrogen bonds, producing an open, porous structure. Liquid water has fewer bonds; therefore, more molecules can occupy the same space, making liquid water more dense than ice.

What does half-life mean?

Half-life is the time it takes for the number of radioactive nuclei originally present in a sample to decrease to one-half of their original number. Thus, if a sample has a half-life of one year, its radioactivity will be reduced to half its original amount at the end of a year and to one quarter at the end of two years. The half-life of a particular radionuclide is always the same, independent of temperature, chemical combination, or any other condition. Natural radiation was discovered in 1896 by the French physicist Antoine Henri Becquerel (1852-1908). His discovery initiated the science of nuclear physics.

Who made the first organic compound to be synthesized from inorganic ingredients?

In 1828, Friedrich Wöhler (1800-1882) synthesized urea from ammonia and cyanic acid. This synthesis dealt a deathblow to the vital-force theory, which held that definite and fundamental differences existed between organic and inorganic compounds. The Swedish chemist Jöns Jakob Berzelius (1779-1848) proposed that the two classes of compounds were produced from their elements by entirely different laws. Organic compounds were produced under the influence of a vital force and so were incapable of being prepared artificially. This distinction ended with Wöhler's synthesis.

Who is known as the founder of crystallography?

The French priest and mineralogist René-Just Haüy (1743-1822) is called the father of crystallography. In 1781 Haüy had a fortunate accident when he dropped a piece of calcite and it broke into small fragments. He noticed that the fragments broke along straight planes that met at constant angles. Haüy hypothesized that each crystal was built from successive additions of what is now called a unit cell to form a simple geometric shape with constant angles. An identity or difference in crystalline form implied an identity or difference in chemical composition. This was the beginning of the science of crystallography.

By the early 1800s many physicists were experimenting with crystals; in particular, they were fascinated by their ability to bend light and separate it into its component colors. An important member of the emerging field of optical mineralogy was the British scientist David Brewster (1871-1868), who succeeded in classifying most known crystals according to their optical properties.

The work of French chemist Louis Pasteur (1822-1895) during the mid 1800s became the foundation for crystal polarimetry—a method by which light is polarized, or aligned to a single plane. Pierre Curie (1859-1906) and his brother Jacques (1855-1941) discovered another phenomenon displayed by certain crystals called piezoelectricity. It is the creation of an electrical potential by squeezing certain crystals.

Perhaps the most important application of crystals is in the science of X-ray crystallography. Experiments in this field were first conducted by the German physicist Max von Laue (1879-1960). This work was perfected by William Henry Bragg (1862-1942) and William Lawrence Bragg (1890-1971), who were awarded the Nobel Prize in physics for their work. The synthesis of penicillin and insulin were made possible by the use of X-ray crystallography.

CHEMICAL ELEMENTS, ETC.

Who are some of the founders of modern chemistry?

Several contenders share this honor:

Swedish chemist Jöns Jakob Berzelius (1779-1848) devised chemical symbols, determined atomic weights, contributed to the atomic theory, and discovered several new elements. Between 1810 and 1816, he described the preparation, purification, and analysis of 2,000 chemical compounds. Then he determined atomic weights for 40 elements. He simplified chemical symbols, introducing a notation—letters with numbers—that replaced the pictorial symbols his predecessors used, and that is still used today. He discovered cerium (in 1803, with Wilhelm Hisinger), selenium (1818), silicon (1824), and thorium (1829).

Robert Boyle (1627-1691), a British natural philosopher, is considered one of the founders of modern chemistry. Best known for his discovery of Boyle's Law (volume of a gas is inversely proportional to its pressure at constant temperature), he was a pioneer in the use of experiments and the scientific method. A founder of the Royal Society, he worked to remove the mystique of alchemy from chemistry to make it a pure science.

The French chemist Antoine-Laurent Lavoisier (1743-1794) is regarded as another founder of modern chemistry. His wide-ranging contributions include the discrediting of the phlogiston theory of combustion, which had been for so long a stumbling block to a true understanding of chemistry. He established modern terminology for chemical substances and did the first experiments in quantitative organic analysis. He is sometimes credited with having discovered or established the law of conservation of mass in chemical reactions.

John Dalton (1766-1844), an English chemist, proposed an atomic theory of matter that became a basic theory of modern chemistry. His theory, first proposed in 1803, states that each chemical element is composed of its own kind of atoms, all with the same relative weight.

Dmitry Ivanovich Mendeleyev, the Russian chemist renowned for developing the periodic table of elements.

Who developed the periodic table?

Dmitry Ivanovich Mendeleyev (1834-1907) was a Russian chemist whose name will always be linked with the development of the periodic table. He was the first chemist really to understand that all elements are related members of a single ordered system. He changed what had been a highly fragmented and speculative branch of chemistry into a true, logical science. His nomination for the 1906 Nobel Prize for chemistry failed by one vote, but his name became recorded in perpetuity 50 years later when element 101 was called mendelevium.

According to Mendeleyev, the properties of the elements, as well as those of their compounds, are periodic functions of their atomic weights (in the 1920s, it was discovered that atomic number was the key rather than weight). Mendeleyev compiled the first true periodic table listing all the 63 (then-known) elements. In order to make the table work, Mendeleyev had to leave gaps, and he predicted that further elements would eventually be discovered to fill them. Three were discovered in Mendeleyev's lifetime: gallium, scandium, and germanium.

There are 95 naturally occurring elements; of the remaining elements (elements 96 to 109), 10 are undisputed. There are approximately 17 million chemical compounds registered with *Chemical Abstracts* that have been produced from these elements.

What was the first element to be discovered?

Phosphorus was first discovered by German chemist Hennig Brand in 1669 when he extracted a waxy white substance from urine that glowed in the dark. But Brand did not publish his findings. In 1680, phosphorus was rediscovered by the English chemist Robert Boyle.

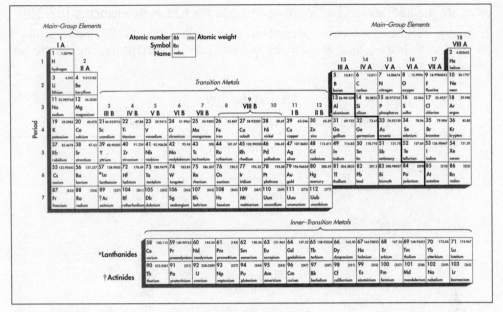

The periodic table.

What are the alkali metals?

These are the elements at the left of the periodic table: lithium (Li, element 3), potassium (K, element 19), rubidium (Rb, element 37), cesium (Cs, element 55), francium (Fr, element 87), and sodium (Na, element 11). The alkali metals are sometimes called the sodium family of elements, or Group I elements. Because of their great chemical reactivity (they easily form positive ions), none exist in nature in the elemental state.

What are the alkaline Earth metals?

These are beryllium (Be, element 4), magnesium (Mg, element 12), calcium (Ca, element 20), strontium (Sr, element 38), barium (Ba, element 56), and radium (Ra, element 88). The alkaline Earth metals are also called Group II elements. Like the alkali metals, they are never found as free elements in nature and are moderately reactive metals. Harder and less volatile than the alkali metals, these elements all burn in air.

What are the transition elements?

The transition elements are the 10 subgroups of elements between Group II and Group XIII, starting with period 4. They include gold (Au, element 79), silver (Ag, element 47), platinum (Pt, element 78), iron (Fe, element 26), copper (Cu, element 29), and other metals. All transition elements are metals. Compared to alkali and alkaline Earth metals, they are usually harder and more brittle and have higher melting points. Transition metals are also good conductors of heat and electricity. They have variable valences, and compounds of transition elements are often colored. Transition elements are so named because they comprise a gradual shift from the strongly electropositive elements of Groups I and II to the electronegative elements of Groups VI and VII.

What are the transuranic chemical elements and the names for elements 102-109?

Transuranic elements are those elements in the periodic system with atomic numbers greater than 92. Many of these elements are ephemeral, do not exist naturally outside the laboratory, and are not stable.

Elements 93-109

Element Number	Name	Symbol
93	Neptunium	Np
94	Plutonium	Pu
95	Americum	Am
96	Curium	Cm
97	Berkelium	Bk
98	Californium	Cf
99	Einsteinium	Es
100	Fermium	Fm
101	Mendelevium	Md
102	Nobelium	No
103	Lawrencium	Lr
104	Rutherfordium	Rf
105	Dubnium	Db
106	Seaborgium	Sg
107	Bohrium	Bh
108	Hassium	Hs
109	Meitnerium	Mt

The names for elements 110-116 are under review by the International Union of Pure and Applied Chemistry.

Which are the only two elements in the periodic table named after women?

Curium, atomic number 96, was named after the pioneers of radioactive research Marie (1867-1934) and Pierre Curie (1859-1906). Meitnerium, atomic number 109, was named after Lise Meitner (1878-1968), one of the founders of nuclear fission.

Which elements are the "noble metals"?

The noble metals are gold (Au, element 79), silver (Ag, element 47), mercury (Hg, element 80), and the platinum group, which includes platinum (Pt, element 78), palladium (Pd, element 46), iridium (Ir, element 77), rhodium (Rh, element 45), ruthenium (Ru, element 44), and osmium (Os, element 76). The term refers to those metals highly resistant to chemical reaction or oxidation (resistant to corrosion) and is contrasted to "base" metals, which are not so resistant. The term has its origins in ancient alchemy whose goals of transformation and perfection were pursued through the different properties of metals and chemicals. The term is not synonymous with "precious metals," although a metal, like platinum, may be both.

The platinum group metals have a variety of uses. In the United States more than 95 percent of all platinum group metals are used for industrial purposes. While platinum is a coveted material for jewelry making, it is also used in the catalytic converters of automobiles to control exhaust emissions, as are rhodium and palladium. Rhodium can also be alloyed with platinum and palladium for use in furnace windings, thermocouple elements, and in aircraft spark-plug electrodes. Osmium is used in the manufacture of pharmaceuticals and in alloys for instrument pivots and long-life phonograph needles.

What is Harkin's rule?

Atoms having even atomic numbers are more abundant in the universe than are atoms having odd atomic numbers. Chemical properties of an element are determined by its atomic number, which is the number of protons in the atom's nucleus.

Which elements are liquid at room temperature?

Mercury ("liquid silver," Hg, element 80) and bromine (Br, element 35) are liquid at room temperature 68° to 70°F (20° to 21°C). Gallium (Ga, element 31) with a melting point of 85.6°F (29.8°C) and cesium (Cs, element 55) with a melting point of 83°F (28.4°C), are liquid at slightly above room temperature and pressure.

What are some chemical elements whose symbols are not derived from their English names?

Modern Name	Symbol	Older Name
antimony	Sb	stibium
copper	Cu	cuprum
gold	Au	aurum
iron	Fe	ferrum
lead	Pb	plumbum
mercury	Hg	hydrargyrum
potassium	K	kalium
silver	Ag	argentum
sodium	Na	natrium
tin	Sn	stannum
tungsten	W	wolfram

Which chemical element is the most abundant in the universe?

Hydrogen (H, element 1) makes up about 75 percent of the mass of the universe. It is estimated that more than 90 percent of all atoms in the universe are hydrogen atoms. Most of the rest are helium (He, element 2) atoms.

Which chemical elements are the most abundant on Earth?

Oxygen (O, element 8) is the most abundant element in the Earth's crust, waters, and atmosphere. It composes 49.5 percent of the total mass of these compounds. Silicon (Si, element 14) is the second most abundant element. Silicon dioxide and silicates make up about 87 percent of the materials in the Earth's crust.

Which elements are the best and worst conductors of electricity?

The element with the lowest electrical resistance (and thus the highest electrical conductivity) under standard conditions is silver, followed by copper, gold, and aluminum. The poorest conductors of electricity among the metals are manganese, gadolinium, and terbium.

How do lead-acid batteries work?

Lead-acid batteries consist of positive and negative lead plates suspended in a diluted sulfuric acid solution called an electrolyte. Everything is contained in a chemically and electrically inert case. As the cell discharges, sulfur molecules from the electrolyte bond with the lead plates, releasing excess electrons. The flow of electrons is called electricity.

Which elements have the most isotopes?

The elements with the most isotopes, with 36 each, are xenon (Xe) with nine stable isotopes (identified from 1920 to 1922) and 27 radioactive isotopes (identified from 1939 to 1981), and cesium (Cs) with one stable isotope (identified in 1921) and 35 radioactive isotopes (identified from 1935 to 1983).

The element with the fewest number of isotopes is hydrogen (H), with three isotopes, including two stable ones—protium (identified in 1920) and deuterium (identified in 1931)—and one radioactive isotope—tritium (first identified in 1934, but later considered a radioactive isotope in 1939).

Which element has the highest density?

Either osmium or iridium is the element with the highest density; however, scientists have yet to gather enough conclusive data to choose between the two. When traditional methods of measurement are employed, osmium generally appears to be the densest element. Yet, when calculations are made based upon the space lattice, which may be a more reliable method given the nature of these elements, the density of iridium is 22.65 compared to 22.61 for osmium.

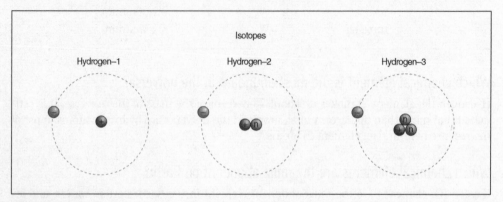

Isotopes

Hydrogen–1   Hydrogen–2   Hydrogen–3

Hydrogen isotopes.

Which elements have the highest and lowest boiling points?

Helium has the lowest boiling point of all the elements at -452.074°F (-268.93°C) followed by hydrogen -423.16°F (-252.87°C). The highest boiling point for an element is that of rhenium 10,104.8°F (5,596°C) followed by tungsten 10,031°F (5,555°C).

Which elements are the hardest and softest?

Carbon is both the hardest and softest element occurring in two different forms as graphite and diamond. A single crystal of diamond scores the absolute maximum value on the Knoop hardness scale of 90. Based on the somewhat less informative abrasive hardness scale of Mohs, diamond has a hardness of 10. Graphite is an extremely soft material with a Mohs hardness of only 0.5 and a Knoop hardness of 0.12.

What are isomers?

Isomers are compounds with the same molecular formula but different structures due to the different arrangement of the atoms within the molecules. Structural isomers have atoms connected in different ways. Geometric isomers differ in their symmetry about a double bond. Optical isomers are mirror images of each other.

What are the gas laws?

The gas laws are physical laws concerning the behavior of gases. They include Boyle's law, which states that the volume of a given mass of gas at a constant temperature is inversely proportional to its pressure; and Charles's law, which states that the volume of a given mass of gas at constant pressure is directly proportional to its absolute temperature. These two laws can be combined to give the General or Universal gas law, which may be expressed as:

$$(pressure \times volume)/temperature = constant$$

Avogadro's law states that equal volumes of all gases contain the same number of particles if they all have the same pressure and temperature.

The laws are not obeyed exactly by any real gas, but many common gases obey them under certain conditions, particularly at high temperatures and low pressures.

What is heavy water?

Heavy water, also called deuterium oxide (D20), is composed of oxygen and two hydrogen atoms in the form of deuterium, which has about twice the mass of normal hydrogen. As a result, heavy water has a molecular weight of about 20, while ordinary water has a molecular weight of about 18. Approximately one part heavy water can be found in 6,500 parts of ordinary water, and it may be extracted by fractional distillation. It is used in thermonuclear weapons and nuclear reactors and as an isotopic tracer in studies of chemical and biochemical processes. Heavy water was discovered by Harold C. Urey in 1931.

What is a Lewis acid?

Named after the American chemist Gilbert Newton Lewis (1875-1946), the Lewis theory defines an acid as a species that can accept an electron pair from another atom, and a base as a species that can donate an electron pair to complete the valence shell of another atom.

387

Hydrogen ion (proton) is the simplest substance that will do this, but Lewis acids include many compounds—such as boron trifluoride (BF_3) and aluminum chloride ($AlCl_3$)—that can react with ammonia, for example, to form an addition compound or Lewis salt.

Which chemical is used in greater quantities than any other?

Sodium chloride (NaCl), or salt, has over 14,000 uses, and is probably used in greater quantities and for more applications than any other chemical.

MEASUREMENT, METHODOLOGY, ETC.

What was the first national physics society organized in the United States?

The first national physics society in the United States was the American Physical Society, organized on May 20, 1899, at Columbia University in New York City. The first president was Henry Augustus Rowland.

What was the first national chemical society organized in the United States?

The first national chemical society in the United States was the American Chemical Society, organized in New York City on April 20, 1876. The first president was John William Draper (1811-1882).

What are the four major divisions of chemistry?

Chemistry has traditionally been divided into organic, inorganic, analytical, and physical chemistry. Organic chemistry is the study of compounds that contain carbon. More than 90 percent of all known chemicals are organic. Inorganic chemistry is the study of compounds of all elements except carbon. Analytical chemists determine the structure and composition of compounds and mixtures. They also develop and operate instruments and techniques for carrying out the analyses. Physical chemists use the principles of physics to understand chemical phenomena.

What were some of the leading contributions of Albert Einstein?

Albert Einstein (1879-1955) was the principal founder of modern theoretical physics; his theory of relativity (speed of light is a constant and not relative to the observer or source of light), and the relationship of mass and energy ($e = mc^2$), fundamentally changed human understanding of the physical world.

During a single year in 1905, he produced three landmark papers. These papers

Albert Einstein revolutionized twentieth-century human understanding of the physical world.

To convert Celsius to Kelvin: Add 273.15 to the temperature(K = C + 273.15). To convert Fahrenheit to Celsius: Subtract 32 from the temperature and multiply the difference by 5; then divide the product by 9 (C = $\frac{9}{5}$[F − 32]). To convert Celsius to Fahrenheit: Multiply the temperature by 1.8, then add 32 (F = $\frac{9}{5}$C + 32 or F = 1.8C + 32).

How are Celsius temperatures converted into Fahrenheit temperatures?

The formulas for converting Celsius temperatures into Fahrenheit (and the reverse) are as follows:

$$F = (C \times \tfrac{9}{5}) + 32$$
$$C = (F - 32) \times \tfrac{5}{9}$$

Some useful comparisons of the two scales:

Temperature	Fahrenheit	Celsius
Absolute zero	-459.67	-273.15
Point of equality	-40.0	-40.0
Zero Fahrenheit	0.0	-17.8
Freezing point of water	32.0	0.0
Normal human blood temperature	98.4	36.9
100 degrees F	100.0	37.8
Boiling point of water (at standard pressure)	212.0	100.0

Who invented chromatography?

Chromatography was invented by the Russian botanist Mikhail Tswett (1872-1919) in the early 1900s. The technique was first used to separate different plant pigments from one another. Chromatography has developed into a widely used method to separate various components of a substance from one another. Three types of chromatography are high-performance liquid chromatography (HPLC), gas chromatography, and paper chromatography. Different chromatography techniques are used in forensic science and analytical laboratories.

What is nuclear magnetic resonance?

Nuclear magnetic resonance (NMR) is a process in which the nuclei of certain atoms absorb energy from an external magnetic field. Analytical chemists use NMR spectroscopy to identify unknown compounds, check for impurities, and study the shapes of molecules. They use the knowledge that different atoms will absorb electromagnetic energy at slightly different frequencies.

What is STP?

The abbreviation STP is often used for standard temperature and pressure. As a matter of convenience, scientists have chosen a specific temperature and pressure as standards for comparing gas volumes. The standard temperature is 0°C (273 K) and the standard pressure is 760 torr (one atmosphere).

How did the electrical term ampere originate?

It was named for André Marie Ampère (1775-1836), the physicist who formulated the basic laws of the science of electrodynamics. The ampere (symbol A), often abbreviated as "amp," is the unit of electric current, defined at the constant current, that, maintained in two straight parallel infinite conductors placed one meter apart in a vacuum, would produce a force between the conductors of 2×10^{-7} newton per meter. For example, the amount of current flowing through a 100-watt light bulb is 1 amp; through a toaster, 10 amps; a TV set, 3 amps; a car battery, 50 amps (while cranking). A newton (symbol N) is defined as a unit of force needed to accelerate one kilogram by one meter second^{-2}, or $1 N = +Kg^{MS-2}$.

How did the electrical unit volt originate?

The unit of voltage is the volt, named after Alessandro Volta (1745-1827), the Italian scientist who built the first modern battery. (A battery, operating with a lead rod and vinegar, was also manufactured in ancient Egypt.) Voltage measures the force or "oomph" with which electrical charges are pushed through a material. Some common voltages are 1.5 volts for a flashlight battery; 12 volts for a car battery; 115 volts for ordinary household receptacles; and 230 volts for a heavy-duty household receptacle.

How did the electrical unit watt originate?

Named for the Scottish engineer and inventor James Watt (1736-1819), the watt is used to measure electric power. An electric device uses one watt when one volt of electric current drives one ampere of current through it.

What is a mole in chemistry?

A mole (symbol mol), a fundamental measuring unit for the amount of a substance, refers to either a gram atomic weight or a gram molecular weight of a substance. It is the quantity of a substance that contains 6.02×1023 atoms, molecules, or formula units of that substance. This number is called Avogadro's number or constant after Amadeo Avogadro (1776-1856), who is considered to be one of the founders of physical science.

How does gram atomic weight differ from gram formula weight?

Gram atomic weight is the amount of an element (substance made up of atoms having the same atomic number) equal to its atomic weight in grams. Gram formula weight is an amount of a compound (a combination of elements) equal to its formula weight in grams.

SPACE

THE UNIVERSE

What is astronomy?

Astronomy is the scientific study of the universe and everything in it. This includes, but is not limited to, the study of motion, matter, and energy; the study of planets, moons, asteroids, comets, stars, galaxies, and all the gas and dust between them; and even the study of the universe itself, including its origin, aging processes, and final fate.

What is astrophysics?

Astrophysics is the application of the science of physics to the universe and everything in it. The most important way astronomers gain information about the universe is by gathering and interpreting light energy from other parts of the universe (and even the universe itself). Since physics is the most relevant science in the study of space, time, light, and objects that produce or interact with light, the majority of astronomy today is conducted using physics.

What is astrochemistry?

Astrochemistry is the application of the science of chemistry to the universe and everything in it. Modern chemistry—the study of complex molecules and their interactions—has developed almost exclusively at or near Earth's surface, with its temperature, gravity, and pressure conditions. Its application to the rest of the universe, then, is not quite as direct or ubiquitous as with physics. Even so, astrochemistry is extremely important to cosmic studies: The interactions of chemicals in planetary atmospheres and surfaces is vital to understanding the planets and other bodies in the solar system. Many chemicals have been detected in interstellar gas clouds throughout the Milky Way and other galaxies, including water, carbon monoxide, methane, ammonia, formaldehyde, acetone (which we use in nail polish remover), ethylene glycol (which we use in antifreeze), and even 1,3-dihydroxyacetone (which is found in sunless tanning lotion).

What is astrobiology?

Astrobiology is the application of the science of biology to the universe and everything in it. This branch of astronomy is very new. The serious use of biology to study the cosmos has blossomed in recent years, however, and has become very important in the field as a whole. With modern astronomical methods and technology, it has become scientifically feasible to search for extraterrestrial life, look for environments where such life could exist, and study how such life could develop.

What is cosmology?

Cosmology is the part of astronomy that specifically examines the origin of the universe. Until the advent of modern astronomy, cosmology was relegated to the domain of religion or abstract philosophy. Today, cosmology is a vibrant part of science and is not limited to gazing out into the cosmos. Current scientific theories have shown that the universe was once far smaller than an atomic nucleus. This means that modern particle physics and high-energy physics, which can be studied on Earth, are absolutely necessary to decipher the mysteries of the very early universe and, ultimately, the very beginning of everything.

What is space?

Most people think of space as merely the absence of anything else—the "nothing" that surrounds objects in the universe. Actually, space is the fabric in which everything in the universe is embedded and through which all things travel. Imagine, for example, a gelatin dessert with pieces of fruit suspended within it. The fruit represents the objects in the universe, while the gelatin represents space. Space is not "nothing"; rather, it surrounds everything, holds everything, and contains everything in the universe.

Space has three dimensions, usually thought of as length (forward-and-backward), width (left-and-right), and height (up-and-down). It is possible to curve space, though, so that a dimension might not represent a straight line.

What is time?

Time is actually a dimension, a direction that things in the universe can travel in and occupy. Just as objects in the universe can move up and down; forward and backward; or side to side, objects can also move through time. Unlike the three spatial dimensions, however, different kinds of objects in our universe move through time in only specific directions. Mathematically, it is correct to say that matter—galaxies, stars, planets, and people—only move forward in time. Meanwhile, particles made of antimatter only move backward in time; and particles of energy—such as photons, which have no mass—do not move in time.

How do space and time relate to one another?

The three dimensions of space and one dimension of time are linked together as a four-dimensional fabric called spacetime. In the early twentieth century scientists such as Alexander Friedmann (1888–1925), Howard Percy Robertson (1903–1961), and Arthur Geoffrey Walker (1909–2001) presented the modern mathematical representation of how the four dimensions are linked together; this equation is called the metric of the universe.

What is spacetime?

Imagine a big sheet of flexible, stretchable fabric like rubber or spandex. This sheet is like a two-dimensional surface, which can be dimpled, bent, twisted, or poked, depending on what objects are placed on it. Spacetime can be thought of as a flexible, bendable structure just like this rubber sheet, except that it is four-dimensional and its lengths and distances are related mathematically by the Friedmann-Robertson-Walker metric.

Who first explained the relationship between space and time?

The famous German American scientist Albert Einstein (1879–1955) first realized that, in order to explain the results of the Michelson-Morley experiment, travel through space and travel through time must be intimately linked. His special theory of relativity, published in 1905, showed that objects can move through time at different speeds in the same way that they can move through space at different speeds. Einstein thought there must be a very strong connection between space and time and that this connection was essential to describe the shape and structure of the universe. He did not have the mathematical expertise, however, to show how the connection might work.

Einstein consulted his friends and colleagues to figure out the best way to proceed in his research. Aided by the discoveries of the German mathematician Georg Riemann (1826–1866), the Russian-German-Swiss mathematician Herman Minkowski (1864–1909), and the tutelage of Hungarian-Swiss mathematician Marcel Grossmann (1878–1936), Einstein learned the mathematical formulations of non-Euclidean elliptical geometry and tensors. In 1914 Einstein and Grossmann published the beginnings of a general theory of relativity and gravitation; Einstein went on to complete the formation of the theory over the next few years.

How do we know that the general theory of relativity is true?

No scientific idea can be correctly called a proven scientific theory until it is confirmed by experiments or observations. The general relativistic formulation of gravity predicts that light, as well as matter, will follow the path of space that is bent by massive objects. If general relativity was correct, then the light from distant stars would follow a curved path through space caused by the gravity of the Sun. The apparent positions of the stars in the part of the sky near the Sun's location, therefore, should be different from their apparent positions when the Sun is not in that place.

To test this prediction, British astrophysicist Arthur Eddington (1882–1944) organized a major scientific expedition in 1919 to observe the sky during a solar eclipse. With the Moon shading the Sun's bright light, astronomers measured the relative positions of distant stars near the Sun's position at that time. Then they compared them to those positions measured at night, when the Sun was not in the field of view. The apparent positions were indeed different, and the discrepancies were consistent with the results predicted by Einstein's theory. This observational confirmation of the general theory of relativity changed the field of physics forever. The discovery made news headlines, and Albert Einstein became an international celebrity.

What is Einstein's General Theory of Relativity?

The main ideas in the general theory of relativity are that space and time are knit together in a four-dimensional fabric called spacetime, and that spacetime can be bent by mass. Massive objects cause spacetime to "dimple" toward the object (think of the way that a bowling ball set on a trampoline causes the trampoline to dimple).

In the four-dimensional spacetime of the universe, if a less massive object approaches a more massive object (for example, a planet approaches a star), the less massive object will follow the lines of curved space and be drawn toward the more massive one. Thinking of the bowling ball on the trampoline, if a marble rolls past the bowling ball and into the dimpled part of the trampoline, then the marble will fall in toward the bowling ball. According to the general theory of relativity, this is how gravity works. Newton's theory of universal gravitation, according to Einstein, is almost completely correct in describing *how* gravity works, but it was not quite complete in explaining *why* it works.

What is Einstein's Special Theory of Relativity?

According to the special theory of relativity, the speed of a beam of light is the same no matter how the light source is moving. It doesn't matter who observes the light beam, or how the observers are moving. This means that the speed of light is the fastest speed at which anything can travel in the universe.

Furthermore, if the speed of a light beam is constant, that means that other properties of motion must change. Since speed is defined as the distance traveled divided by the elapsed time, this means that the distances and times experienced by any object will change depending on how fast it is moving. When you are moving, you experience time more slowly than someone else who is standing still.

Finally, since mass can be thought of as the amount of resistance that an object has to motion, any object that has mass cannot travel at the speed of light. Only energy in the form of electromagnetic radiation—that is, light—can travel at that speed; and matter is not energy, but can be converted into energy. This is represented by the famous equation $E = mc^2$.

CHARACTERISTICS OF THE UNIVERSE

What is the universe?

The universe is all of space, time, matter, and energy that exist. Most people think of the universe as just space, but space is just the framework, the "scaffolding" in which the universe exists. Furthermore, space and time are intimately connected in a four-dimensional fabric called spacetime.

Amazingly, some hypotheses suggest that the universe we live in is not all there is. In this case, there is more than just space, time, matter, and energy. Other dimensions exist, and possibly other universes. None of those models, however, have yet been confirmed.

How old is the universe?

The universe is not infinitely old. According to modern astronomical measurements, the universe began to exist about 13.7 billion years ago.

Is the universe infinite?

It has not yet been scientifically determined exactly how large the universe is. It may indeed be infinitely large, but we have no way yet to confirm this possibility scientifically.

What is the structure of the universe?

The structure of the universe—as opposed to the structure of matter in the universe—is determined by the shape of space. The shape of space is, surprisingly, curved. On a very large scale—millions or even billions of light-years across—space has a three-dimensional "saddle shape" that mathematicians refer to as "negative curvature." In our daily lives, however, it is such a tiny effect that we do not notice it.

On smaller scales—that of planets, stars, and galaxies—the structure of the universe can be altered by massive objects. This alteration manifests itself as the curvature of space and time, as explained by the general theory of relativity.

How big is the universe?

Here on Earth, in the Milky Way galaxy, there is a limit to how far out into the universe humans can observe, regardless of what technology is used. Imagine, for example, being on a ship in the middle of the ocean. If you look in all directions, all you see is water, out to a certain distance. But Earth's surface extends far beyond that horizon limit. The farthest limit to our viewing is called the cosmic horizon. Everything within that cosmic horizon is called the observable universe. In many cases, for the sake of brevity, astronomers refer to the "observable universe" as merely the "universe."

The size of the observable universe is determined by a combination of the age and the expansion rate of the universe. Taking both these effects into account, the current distance to the cosmic horizon can be computed at any point in time. However, since the cosmic horizon is always getting farther away, astronomers usually prefer to describe cosmic sizes using the distance that light must travel from one point to another in our expanding universe. This distance is based on the age of the universe and the speed of light. Thus, since the universe is 13.7 billion years old, we usually say that the cosmic horizon is 13.7 billion light-years away, or about eighty billion trillion miles, in every direction.

How did the universe begin?

The scientific theory that describes the origin of the universe is called the Big Bang. According to the Big Bang theory, the universe began to exist as a single point of spacetime, and it has been expanding ever since. As that expansion has occurred, the conditions in the universe have changed—from small to big, from hot to cold, and from young to old—resulting in the universe we observe today.

Who were the first scientists to formulate the Big Bang theory?

In 1917 Dutch astronomer Willem de Sitter (1872–1934) showed how Albert Einstein's general theory of relativity could be used to describe an expanding universe. In 1922, Russian mathematician Alexander Friedmann (1888–1925) derived an exact mathematical description of an expanding universe. In the late 1920s, the Belgian astronomer Georges-Henri

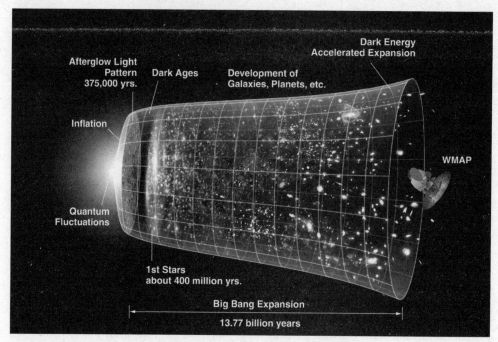

Astronomers have measured the age of the universe to be about 13.7 billion years old.

Lemaître (1894–1966) independently rediscovered Friedmann's mathematical formulation. Lemaître deduced that if the universe were indeed expanding, and has been doing so for its entire existence, then there would have to be a moment in the distant past when the whole universe occupied just a single point. That moment, and that point, would be the origin of the cosmos. Lemaître's work, and that of de Sitter and Friedmann, were eventually confirmed through observations. Since Lemaître was a Jesuit priest as well as an astronomer, he has sometimes been called "the father of the Big Bang."

According to the Big Bang theory, what happened when the universe began?

The Big Bang theory does not explain why the Big Bang actually happened. A well-established hypothesis is that the universe began in a "quantum foam"—a formless void where bubbles of matter, far smaller than atoms, were fluctuating in and out of existence on timescales far shorter than a trillionth of a trillionth of a trillionth of a second. In our universe today, such quantum fluctuations are thought to occur, but they happen so quickly that they never affect what happens in the cosmos. But if, 13.7 billion years ago, one particular fluctuation appeared but did not disappear, suddenly ballooning outward into a gigantic, explosive expansion, then it is possible that something like today's universe could have been the eventual result.

In another, more recently proposed hypothesis, the universe is a four-dimensional space-time that exists at the intersection of two five-dimensional structures called membranes. Picture two soap bubbles that come in contact with one another and stick together: The "skin" where the bubbles intersect is a two-dimensional result of the interaction between two three-dimensional structures. If the membrane hypothesis is correct, then the Big Bang

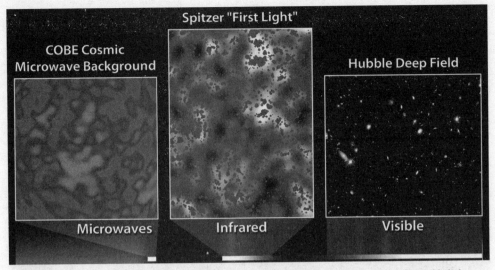

Spitzer "First Light"

COBE Cosmic
Microwave Background

Hubble Deep Field

Microwaves

Infrared

Visible

Three views of the universe from observatories show the stars and galaxies as they appear in the visible light spectrum, in infrared, and how the microwave background appears. This microwave background provides evidence of the Big Bang, according to astronomers.

event marked the moment the two membranes made contact. Neither of these models has any kind of experimental or observational confirmation yet.

What evidence is there for the Big Bang based on the nature of energy in the universe?

Perhaps the most convincing evidence confirming the Big Bang theory is the cosmic microwave background radiation: the leftover energy from the hot, early universe that still fills space and permeates the cosmos in every direction. Scientists had predicted that such background radiation would indicate that the temperature of space would be several degrees above absolute zero. The detection of the background radiation showed that the temperature was very close to three degrees Kelvin—a spectacular success of the scientific method.

BLACK HOLES

What objects in the universe have the strongest gravity?

The most massive objects in the universe exert the most gravity. However, the strength of a gravitational field near any given object also depends on the size of the object. The smaller an object is, the stronger its field can be. The ultimate combination of large mass and small size is the black hole.

What is a black hole?

One definition of a black hole is an object whose escape velocity equals or exceeds the speed of light. The idea was first proposed in the 1700s, when scientists hypothesized that Newton's

The blue highlights surrounding the object Abell 520 indicate high concentrations of dark matter.

law of universal gravitation allowed for the possibility of stars that were so small and massive that particles of light could not escape. Thus, the star would be black

Can anything escape a black hole?

According to British physicist Stephen Hawking (1948–), energy can slowly leak out of a black hole. This leakage, called Hawking radiation, occurs because the event horizon (boundary) of a black hole is not a perfectly smooth surface, but "shimmers" at a subatomic level due to quantum mechanical effects. At these quantum mechanical scales, space can be thought of as being filled with so-called virtual particles, which cannot be detected themselves but can be observed by their effects on other objects. Virtual particles come in two "halves," and if a virtual particle is produced just inside the event horizon, there is a tiny chance that one "half" might fall deeper into the black hole, while the other "half" would tunnel through the shimmering event horizon and leak back into the universe.

What is dark matter?

In the 1930s, astronomer Fritz Zwicky (1898–1974) noticed that, in the Coma cluster of galaxies, many of the individual galaxies were moving around so fast that there had to be a tremendous amount of gravitational pull toward the center of the cluster; otherwise, the galaxies would literally fling themselves out of the cluster. The amount of matter that needed to exist in the cluster to produce that much gravity far exceeded the amount of matter observed in all the galaxies in the cluster put together. This extra matter became known as "dark matter."

In 1970 astronomer Vera C. Rubin (1928–) and physicist W. Kent Ford (1931–)showed that stars in the Andromeda Galaxy were moving so fast that for the stars to stay in the galaxy there had to be a tremendous amount of matter surrounding and enveloping the entire galaxy like a giant cocoon. Since this matter is not visible to telescopes by the light it emits, but rather only by the gravity it exerts, this, too, is an example of evidence for dark matter.

After decades of further study, dark matter has now been confirmed as an important constituent of matter around galaxies, in clusters of galaxies, and throughout the universe as a whole. According to the latest measurements, about 85 percent of the matter in the universe is dark matter.

What is dark energy?

When Albert Einstein, Willem de Sitter, Alexander Friedmann, Georges-Henri Lemaître and others were working on the nature of the universe in the early twentieth century, Einstein introduced a mathematical term into his equations to keep a balance between cosmic expansion and gravitational attraction. This term became known as the "cosmological constant," and seemed to represent an unseen energy that emanated from space itself.

After Edwin Hubble and other astronomers showed that the universe was indeed expanding, the cosmological constant no longer appeared to be necessary, and so it was not seriously considered again for decades. Then, starting in the 1990s, a series of discoveries suggested that the "dark energy" represented by the cosmological constant does indeed exist. Current measurements indicate that the density of this dark energy throughout the universe is much greater than the density of matter—both luminous matter and dark matter combined.

Though astronomers have measured the presence of this dark energy, we still have no idea what causes this energy, nor do we have a clue what this energy is made of. The quest to understand the cosmological constant in general, and dark energy in particular, is one of the great unsolved questions in astronomy today.

What is dark matter made of?

Nobody has any real idea of what dark matter is. There exist some educated guesses, such as a new class of "weakly interacting massive particles" (WIMPs) or huge agglomerations of them ("WIMPzillas"); another class of "charged undifferentiated massive particles" (CHUMPs); or very light, neutral subatomic particles called neutralinos. No dark matter particle has ever been detected, however, so these possibilities are still nothing more than educated guesses.

How does dark matter affect the shape of the universe?

Dark matter in the universe exerts a gravitational pull in the expanding universe. The more dark matter there is in the universe, the more likely it would be that the universe would have a closed geometry, and that the universe would end in a Big Crunch.

How does dark energy affect the shape of the universe?

Dark energy apparently counteracts gravity by making space expand more energetically. If the amount of dark energy in the universe is, as astronomers think, proportional to the amount of space, then the continuing expansion of the universe means that the total amount of dark energy keeps increasing. Since the total amount of mass in the universe is not increasing, that means that the expansive effect of dark energy will ultimately overcome the contractive effect of dark matter. The more dark energy there is, the more open the geometry of the universe will tend to be, and the faster the expansion rate of the universe will increase over time.

GALAXY FUNDAMENTALS

What is a galaxy?

A galaxy is a vast collection of stars, gas, dust, other interstellar material, and dark matter that forms a cohesive gravitational unit in the universe. In a way, galaxies are to the universe what cells are to the human body: each galaxy has its own identity, and it ages and evolves on its own, but it also interacts with other galaxies in the cosmos. There are many, many different kinds of galaxies; Earth's galaxy is called the Milky Way.

How many galaxies are there in the universe?

Thanks to the finite speed of light and the finite age of the universe, we can only see the universe out to a boundary called the cosmic horizon, which is about 13.7 billion light-years in every direction. Within this observable universe alone, there exist an estimated fifty to one hundred billion galaxies.

What kinds of galaxies are there?

Galaxies are generally grouped by their appearance into three types: spiral, elliptical, and irregular. These groups are further subdivided into categories like barred spiral and grand design spiral, giant elliptical and dwarf spheroidal, and Magellanic irregular or peculiar.

What is a group of galaxies?

A group of galaxies usually contains two or more galaxies the size of the Milky Way or larger, plus a dozen or more smaller galaxies. The Milky Way and Andromeda galaxies are the two large galaxies in the Local Group. There are a few dozen smaller galaxies in the group, including the Magellanic Clouds, the dwarf elliptical Messier 32, the small spiral galaxy Messier 33, and many small dwarf galaxies. The Local Group of galaxies is a few million light-years across.

What is a cluster of galaxies?

A cluster of galaxies is a large collection of galaxies in a single gravitational field. Rich clusters of galaxies usually contain at least a dozen large galaxies as massive as the Milky Way, along with hundreds of smaller galaxies. At the center of large clusters of galaxies there is usually a group of elliptical galaxies called "cD" galaxies. Clusters of galaxies are usually about ten million light-years across. The Milky Way galaxy is near—but not in—the Virgo cluster, which itself is near the center of the Virgo supercluster

What is a supercluster of galaxies?

Superclusters of galaxies are the largest collections of massive structures. They occur at the nodes of large numbers of matter filaments in the cosmic web, and are up to a hundred mil-

What kind of galaxy is the Milky Way?

Figuring out the shape of the Milky Way is, for us, somewhat like a fish trying to figure out the shape of the ocean. Based on careful observations and calculations, though, it appears that the Milky Way is a barred spiral galaxy, probably classified as a SBb or SBc on the Hubble tuning fork diagram.

lion or more light-years across. There are usually many clusters of galaxies in a supercluster, or a single very large cluster at its center, along with many other groups and collections of galaxies that are collected in the supercluster's central gravitational field. Superclusters contain many thousands—and sometimes millions—of galaxies. The Milky Way galaxy is located on the outskirts of the Virgo supercluster.

What is the Milky Way galaxy?

The Milky Way is the galaxy we live in. It contains the Sun and at least one hundred billion other stars. Some modern measurements suggest there may be up to five hundred billion stars in the galaxy. The Milky Way also contains more than a billion solar masses' worth of free-floating clouds of interstellar gas sprinkled with dust, hundreds of star clusters that contain anywhere from a few hundred to a few million stars each, and probably millions or even billions of planets.

How large is the Milky Way?

Current measurements indicate that the stellar disk of the Milky Way is about 100,000 light-years across and one thousand light-years thick. If the Milky Way disk were the size of a large pizza, then the solar system might be a microscopic speck of oregano halfway out from the center to the edge of the crust. The bar-bulge structure of the Milky Way is about three thousand light-years high and maybe ten thousand light-years long.

If you take into account the dark matter in the Milky Way, its size increases dramatically. Based on current measurements, at least 90 percent of the mass in the Milky Way's gravitational field is made up of dark matter, so the luminous stars, gas, and dust of the galaxy are embedded at the center of a huge, roughly spherical dark matter halo more than a million light-years across.

What is a quasar?

The term "quasar" is short for "quasi-stellar radio source." The term came into general usage in the 1960s, when astronomers studying cosmic radio sources noticed that many of them looked like stars on photographs. Subsequent studies showed that they were not stars at all, but rather active galactic nuclei. Nowadays, the word "quasar" is often used to mean any quasi-stellar object (QSO), whether or not it emits radio waves.

When and how were quasars first found?

In the 1950s and 1960s, astronomers in Cambridge, England, began to use the most sensitive radio telescopes of the day to map the entire sky. There have been several "Cambridge catalogs," each deeper and more detailed than the last. The common practice in modern astronomy is that, when an object is detected using one band of electromagnetic radiation, the same object is searched for in other bands as well to get a more comprehensive understanding of the object through all of its different types of light emission.

The third Cambridge (3C) catalog contains hundreds of radio sources, and astronomers took visible-light photographs of these sources to see what they would look like to our eyes. The 273rd object in the 3C catalog looked like a star. But when astronomers subsequently studied its emitted light more carefully , it was discovered that 3C 273 was actually an active galaxy far away from the Milky Way. In fact, 3C 273 was the first quasar ever discovered and identified as a distant "active galactic nucleus" (AGN) galaxy

STAR BASICS

What is a star?

A star is a mass of incandescent, electrically charged gas that produces energy at its core by nuclear fusion. Most of the visible light in the universe is produced by stars. The Sun is a star.

How many stars are there in the sky?

Without the interference of light from ground sources, a person with good eyesight can see about two thousand stars on any given night. If both hemispheres are included, then about four thousand stars are visible. With the help of binoculars or telescopes, however, the number of visible stars increases dramatically. In our Milky Way galaxy alone, there are more than one hundred billion stars, and in our observable universe there are at least a billion times that number.

What is the closest star to Earth?

The Sun is the closest star to Earth. It is ninety-three million miles away from Earth on average.

Other than the Sun, what is the next closest star to Earth?

The closest star system to Earth is the multiple star system Alpha Centauri. The faintest star in that system, known as Proxima Centauri, has been measured to be about 4.2 light-years away from Earth. The main star in Alpha Centauri is about 4.4 light-years away. The table below lists other nearby stars.

Stars Closest to the Sun

Name	Spectral Type	Distance in Light-Years
Proxima Centauri*	M5V (red dwarf)	4.24
Alpha Centauri A*	G2V (sun-like)	4.37
Alpha Centauri B*	K0V (orange dwarf)	4.37
Barnard's Star	M4V (red dwarf)	5.96

Name	Spectral Type	Distance in Light-Years
Wolf 359	M6V (red dwarf)	7.78
Lalande 21185	M2V (red dwarf)	8.29
Sirius	A1V (blue dwarf)	8.58
Sirius B	DA2 (white dwarf)	8.58
Luyten 726-8A	M5V (red dwarf)	8.73
Luyten 726-8B	M6V (red dwarf)	8.73
Ross 154	M3V (red dwarf)	9.68
Ross 248	M5V (red dwarf)	10.32
Epsilon Eridani	K2V (orange dwarf)	10.52
Lacaille 9352	M1V (red dwarf)	10.74
Ross 128	M4V (red dwarf)	10.92
EZ Aquarii	M5V (red dwarf)	11.27
Procyon A	F5V (blue-green dwarf)	11.40
Procyon B	DA (white dwarf)	11.40
61 Cygni A	K5V (orange dwarf)	11.40
61 Cygni B	K7V (orange dwarf)	11.40
Struve 2398 A	M3V (red dwarf)	11.53
Struve 2398 B	M4V (red dwarf)	11.53
Groombridge 34 A	M1V (red dwarf)	11.62
Groombridge 34 B	M3V (red dwarf)	11.62

*These stars are in the Alpha Centauri system.

HOW STARS WORK

Why do stars shine?

Stars shine because nuclear fusion occurs in their core. Nuclear fusion changes lighter elements into heavier ones and can release tremendous amounts of energy in the process. The most powerful nuclear weapons on Earth are powered by nuclear fusion, but they are puny compared to the nuclear explosiveness of the Sun.

How does nuclear fusion work in stars like the Sun?

Atomic nuclei cannot just combine randomly. Rather, only a small number of specific fusion reactions can occur, and even then only under very extreme circumstances. In the Sun's core temperatures exceed 27 million degrees Fahrenheit (15 million degrees Celsius) and pressures exceed one hundred billion Earth atmospheres. In these circumstances, there is a minute chance—less than a billion to one!—that, in any given year, a proton will fuse with another nearby proton to form a deuteron, also known as a deuterium nucleus or "heavy hydrogen" nucleus. The deuteron then fuses quickly with another proton to produce a helium-3 nucleus. Finally, after waiting around on average for another million years or so, two nearby helium-3 nuclei can fuse to form a helium-4 nucleus and release two protons.

405

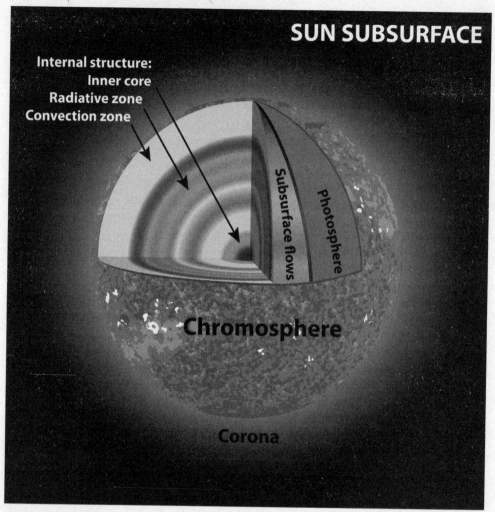

Internal structure:
Inner core
Radiative zone
Convection zone

Subsurface flows

Photosphere

Chromosphere

Corona

The layers of the Sun.

In this multi-step sequence, called the "proton-proton chain," hydrogen is transformed into helium-4, and a tiny bit of matter is converted into energy. Even though it is very hard for any given pair of protons to fuse into a deuteron, there are so many protons in the core of the Sun that more than one trillion trillion trillion such fusion reactions occur there each second. The amount of mass converted into energy is thus huge—about 4.5 million tons per second—and provides enough outward push to keep the Sun in a stable size and shape, and thus allow it to shine its stellar glow out into space.

What happens in the radiative zone of the Sun?

The energy produced by nuclear fusion at the core of the Sun travels outward as radiation—photons traveling through the solar plasma. Although the photons travel at the speed of light, the plasma in a star is so dense that the photons keep running into particles and bouncing away in an unpredictable pattern called a random walk. The bouncing around is so extreme, that it takes an average of one million years for the solar light to travel the 250,000 miles (400,000 kilometers) through the radiative zone. In the vacuum of space, light can travel that distance in less than two seconds

What happens in the convective zone of the Sun?

The convective zone begins at a depth of about 90,000 miles (150,000 kilometers) below the surface of the Sun. In the convective zone, the temperatures are cool enough—under 1,800,000 degrees Fahrenheit (1,000,000 degrees Kelvin)—that the atoms in the plasma there can absorb the photons coming outward from the Sun's radiative zone. The plasma gets very hot, and begins to rise upward out of the Sun. The motion of the plasma creates convection currents, like those that happen in Earth's atmosphere and oceans, which carry the Sun's energy to the photosphere on seething rivers of hot gases.

This is how the convection works. As the temperature of the gas that has absorbed energy at the bottom of the convection zone increases, the gas expands, becoming less dense than its surroundings. These bundles of hot gas, because they are less dense, float up toward the surface of the convection layer like hot air balloons rising up into the air on a cold morning. At the top of this layer, they radiate away their excess energy, becoming cooler and denser, and then they sink down again through the convection layer. The effect is a continuous cycle of "conveyor belts" of hot gas moving up and cooler gas moving down.

What happens in a star's photosphere?

The photosphere is the layer of a star's atmosphere that we see when viewing the Sun in visible light. It is sometimes referred to as the "surface" of a star. It is a few hundred miles thick, and it is made up of planet-sized cells of hot gas called granules. These gas cells are in constant motion, continuously changing size and shape as they carry heat and light through from the Sun's interior to its exterior. Sunspots, regions of intense magnetic activity, also occasionally appear in the photosphere and last from hours to weeks.

What happens in a star's chromosphere?

The chromosphere, the thin and usually transparent layer of the Sun's atmosphere between the photosphere and the corona, is a highly energetic plasma that is punctuated with flares—bright, hot jets of gas—and faculae consisting of bright hydrogen clouds called plages. The chromosphere is generally not visible except with ultraviolet or X-ray telescopes.

The chromosphere is around one thousand to two thousand miles thick and has some unexpected physical properties. For example, while the density of the gas decreases from the inner edge of the chromosphere to the outer edge, the temperature of the gas increases dramatically—from about 7,250 to 180,000 degrees Fahrenheit (4,000 to 100,000 degrees Celsius)—even though the distance to the Sun is actually increasing. At its outer limit, the chromosphere breaks up into narrow gas jets called spicules and merges into the Sun's corona.

What is a sunspot?

Sunspots, when viewed by visible light, appear as dark blemishes on the Sun. Most sunspots have two physical components: the umbra, which is a smaller, dark, featureless core, and the penumbra, which is a large, lighter surrounding region. Within the penumbra are delicate-looking filaments that extend outward like spokes on a bicycle wheel. Sunspots vary in size and tend to be clustered in groups; many of them far exceed the size of our planet and could easily swallow Earth whole.

Sunspots are the sites of incredibly powerful, magnetically driven phenomena. Even though they look calm and quiet in visible light, pictures of sunspots taken in ultraviolet light and in X rays clearly show the tremendous energy they produce and release, as well as the powerful magnetic fields that permeate and surround them.

How bright is the Sun compared to other stars?

The apparent magnitude of the Sun is a large negative number. As viewed in visible light, the Sun has $m = -26.7$ brightness because it is so close and, thus, has the lowest apparent magnitude of any celestial object. The Sun's absolute magnitude is 4.8 as viewed in visible light. This number, unlike the Sun's apparent magnitude, is roughly in the middle of the range of most stars.

How long has the Sun been shining?

The Sun has been shining for 4.6 billion years. We know this from a variety of scientific studies. The most convincing evidence comes from the study of meteorites. Using various dating methods, some of these meteorites have been shown to have formed at the time the Sun began to shine. They have been dated to be 4.6 billion years old, so the Sun is estimated to be that old as well.

How much longer will the Sun shine?

Based on the scientific understanding of how stars work, our Sun will continue to conduct nuclear fusion at its core for about another five to six billion years.

What is the size and structure of the Sun?

The Sun has a core at its center; a radiative zone surrounding the core; a convective zone surrounding the radiative zone; a thin photosphere at its surface; and a chromosphere and corona that extends beyond the photospheric surface. In all, the Sun is about 853,000 miles (1,372,500 kilometers) across, which is about 109 times the diameter of Earth.

The different zones and layers in and around the Sun exist because the physical conditions—mostly temperature and pressure—of the Sun change depending on the distance from the Sun's center. At the core, for example, temperatures exceed 15 million degrees Kelvin, whereas the inner part of the

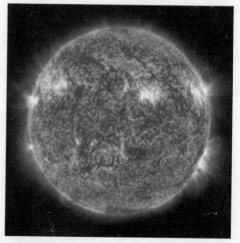

This image of the Sun was created from a collage of pictures provided by NASA.

convective zone is just under 1 million degrees Kelvin, and the photosphere is about 5,800 degrees Kelvin.

What is the Sun made of?

The Sun's mass is composed of 71 percent hydrogen, 27 percent helium, and 2 percent other elements. In terms of the number of atoms in the Sun, 91 percent are hydrogen atoms, 9 percent are helium atoms, and less than 0.1 percent are atoms of other elements. Most of the stars in the universe have a similar chemical composition.

How massive is the Sun?

The Sun has a mass of 4.39 million trillion trillion pounds (1.99 million trillion trillion kilograms). The most massive supergiant stars have about one hundred times more mass than the Sun. The least massive dwarf stars and brown dwarfs contain about one-hundredth the mass of the Sun.

How hot is the Sun?

The temperature at the center of the Sun is about 27 million degrees Fahrenheit (15 million degrees Kelvin). This is typical for stars that convert hydrogen into helium using the proton-proton chain, but it is hotter than some stars and much cooler than others. This is especially true if these other stars harbor fusion processes other than the proton-proton chain, such as the carbon-nitrogen-oxygen cycle or the triple-alpha reaction.

What is a brown dwarf?

A brown dwarf is another name for a very low-mass star or a "failed star." The existence of brown dwarfs—objects that formed like stars with so little mass that there is almost no nuclear fusion in them, yet with much more mass than any planet in our solar system—was not confirmed until the 1990s. The reason is that their photospheres are so cool that they are very dim, emit very little visible light, and can be found only using infrared telescope technology. Since their discovery, infrared telescopes and infrared astronomical cameras have advanced by leaps and bounds. One result is that a huge number of brown dwarfs have been discovered in recent years. In fact, so many have been identified that it is now hypothesized that the number of brown dwarfs may rival all the other stars in our galaxy put together

What is a red dwarf?

A red dwarf is another name for a low-mass, main-sequence star. They are cool compared to most other kinds of stars (their photospheric temperature is about 6,000 degrees Fahrenheit, or 3,000 degrees Kelvin), so they glow a dull red. Red dwarfs are small and faint compared to most other kinds of stars.

What is a red giant?

A red giant is a kind of star that represents an evolutionary phase of intermediate and high-mass stars that have surpassed their main sequence lifetimes. When a star like the Sun becomes a red giant, a sudden burst of energy is produced by new fusion processes at the core

In this artist's depiction, our solar system is compared to what a brown dwarf star system might look like.

of the star. This burst pushes the plasma in the star outward. When the equilibrium of the star's inward and outward forces are restored, the star has swelled to about one hundred times its original diameter. The swollen, bloated star is so large that its outer layers do not contain as much star-stuff, and the star's surface (photosphere) cools down to the temperatures of red dwarfs (about 6,000 degrees Fahrenheit or 3,000 Kelvin). The Sun is destined to become a red giant, and when it does, about five billion years from now, it will swallow the planets Mercury and Venus, and destroy Earth as well.

What is a white dwarf?

A white dwarf is one common kind of stellar "corpse." Stars of intermediate and low mass tend to end their lives as white dwarfs. As the energy produced by nuclear fusion dwindles and ends in the cores of these stars, they collapse under their own weight until the atoms in the stars' plasma bump up against one another. Any further collapse of the star is halted by the atoms' electrons interacting with one another: a condition called electron degeneracy. The collapse concentrates the remaining heat of the dying star into a tiny space, causing the white dwarf to glow white-hot. A white dwarf the mass of the Sun will only be as large as our planet Earth, a shrinkage of about one hundred times in diameter and a million times in volume. One teaspoon of white dwarf star material weighs several tons.

What is a blue giant?

A blue giant is the name for a star that is, as its name suggests, big and blue. Such stars are usually high-mass stars on the main sequence. Blue giants live for only a million years or so, glowing a million times brighter than the Sun before they blow apart in titanic supernova explosions.

What is a neutron star?

A neutron star is the collapsed core of a star that is left over after a supernova explosion. It is, so to speak, matter's last line of defense against gravity. In order to stay internally supported as an object and not be crushed into a singularity, the neutrons in the object press up against one another in a state known as neutron degeneracy. This state, which resembles the conditions within an atomic nucleus, is the densest known form of matter in the universe.

What is a pulsar?

When a neutron star spins, it sometimes spins incredibly fast—up to hundreds of times a second. A magnetic field billions of times stronger than Earth's can form as a result. If the field interacts with nearby electrically charged matter, it can result in a great deal of energy being radiated into space, a process called synchrotron radiation. In this scenario, the slightest unevenness or surface feature on the neutron star can cause a significant "blip" or "pulse" in the radiation being emitted. Each time the neutron star spins around once, a pulse of radiation comes out. Such an object is called a pulsar.

PLANETARY SYSTEMS

What is a planetary system?

A planetary system is a system of astronomical objects that populate the vicinity of a star. This includes objects like planets, asteroids, comets, and interplanetary dust. In a more general sense, this also includes the star itself, its magnetic field, its stellar wind, and the physical effects of those things, including ionization boundaries and shock fronts.

What is our own planetary system called?

The Sun is the gravitational anchor of the planetary system where we live. The term "solar" refers to anything having to do with the Sun; so we call our own planetary system the solar system. Often, astronomers will refer to other planetary systems as "solar systems" too, though that is not technically correct.

How large is our solar system?

Our solar system reaches well past the orbit of the most distant planet, Neptune, which is about three billion miles (five billion kilometers) away from the Sun. Beyond Neptune is the Kuiper Belt, a thick, doughnut-shaped cloud of small, icy bodies that extends to about eight billion miles (twelve billion kilometers). Far beyond that still is the Oort Cloud, which is a huge, thick, spherical shell thought to contain trillions of comets and comet-like bodies. The Oort Cloud may extend as far as a light-year, nearly six trillion miles, out from the Sun.

PLANET BASICS

What is a planet?

There have been many attempts to define the term "planet" over the centuries, but to date there is still no universally agreed-upon scientific definition of the term. Generally speaking, however, a planet usually refers to an object that is not a star (that is, has no nuclear fusion going on in its core); that moves in orbit around a star; and is mostly round because its own gravitational pull has shaped it into, more or less, a sphere.

What are the masses, orbital periods, and positions of the planets in our solar system?

The table below lists the basic information about the planets in our solar system.

The Planets of Our Solar System

Name	Mass (in Earth masses*)	Diameter (in Earth diameters**)	Distance to Sun (in AUs***)	Orbital Period (in Earth years)
Mercury	0.0553	0.383	0.387	0.241
Venus	0.815	0.949	0.723	0.615
Earth	1	1	1	1
Mars	0.107	0.532	1.52	1.88
Jupiter	317.8	11.21	5.20	11.9
Saturn	95.2	9.45	9.58	29.4
Uranus	14.5	4.01	19.20	83.7
Neptune	17.1	3.88	30.05	163.7

*One Earth Mass equals 5.98 X 10<+>24<+> kilograms.
**One Earth Diameter equals 12,756 kilometers.
***An astronomical unit (AU) is the distance from Earth to the Sun and is roughly 1.5×10^8 meters.

What are the general characteristics of the planets in our solar system?

All the planets in our solar system, by the current scientific classification system, must satisfy three basic criteria:

1. A planet must be in hydrostatic equilibrium—a balance between the inward pull of gravity and the outward push of the supporting structure. Objects in this kind of equilibrium are almost always spherical or very close to it.

2. A planet's primary orbit must be around the Sun. That means objects like the Moon, Titan, or Ganymede, are not planets, even though they are round due to hydrostatic equilibrium, because their primary orbit is around a planet.

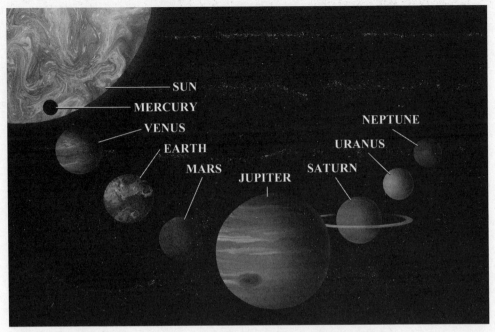

There are now officially only eight planets in our solar system after Pluto was downgraded.

3. A planet must have cleared out other, smaller objects in its orbital path, and thus must be by far the largest object in its orbital neighborhood. This means that Pluto is not a planet, even though it meets the other two criteria; there are thousands of Plutinos in the orbital path of Pluto, and it crosses the orbit of Neptune, which is a much larger and more massive object.

The eight objects in our solar system that meet all three criteria are Neptune, Uranus, Saturn, Jupiter, Mars, Earth, Venus, and Mercury.

What is the current official planetary classification system?

On August 24, 2006, the general assembly of the International Astronomical Union approved the current system of classifying planets in our solar system. This system added a specific scientific requirement for planethood: It must have cleared all other significantly sized bodies out of its orbital path or neighborhood, probably through collisions or gravitational interactions. This system also creates a new designation called a "dwarf planet," which describes an object that fulfills all the criteria of a planet except this one. This system, like every other classification that has come before it, has strengths and weaknesses; no matter what, though, it gives all people a starting point to learn about—and hopefully understand—what planets are all about.

This current classification system means that, officially, there are eight planets in the solar system—Mercury, Venus, Earth, Mars, Jupiter, Saturn, Uranus, and Neptune—and a number of dwarf planets, including Pluto, Ceres, Haumea, Makemake, and Eris.

What was the previous planetary classification system?

The previous classification system was based on historical knowledge and size. The eight planets in our solar system today, plus Pluto, were known to scientists and were believed to be large—at least, all larger than Earth's moon. Other objects that were known to orbit the Sun—but were smaller than about two thousand miles across—were called asteroids (or, more generally, minor planets). So until August 24, 2006, the International Astronomical Union officially recognized Pluto as the ninth planet. It does not anymore.

What planets are included in the inner solar system?

The planets that are collectively thought of as belonging to the inner solar system are Mercury, Venus, Earth, and Mars.

What is the terrestrial planet zone and what does it contain?

The terrestrial planet zone is generally considered to be the part of the solar system containing the planets Mercury, Venus, Earth and Mars. These four objects are called the terrestrial planets because they resemble one another (specifically, Earth) in their structure: a metallic core, surrounded by a rocky mantle and thin crust. There are three moons in the terrestrial zone as well: Earth's moon, and the two moons of Mars: Phobos and Deimos

What are the physical properties of Mercury?

Mercury's diameter is a little more than one-third that of Earth's, and it has just 5.5 percent of Earth's mass. On average, Mercury is fifty-eight million kilometers (thirty-six million miles) away from the Sun. That is so close to the Sun that Mercury's orbit is rather tilted and stretched into a long elliptical shape. Mercury orbits the Sun in just eighty-eight Earth days, but Mercury's day—the time it takes to rotate once around its polar axis—is about fifty-nine Earth days.

Mercury's surface is covered with deep craters, separated by plains and huge banks of cliffs. Mercury's most notable surface feature is an ancient crater called the Caloris Basin, which is about five times the size of New England—a huge pit for such a small planet! Mercury's very thin atmosphere is made primarily of sodium, potassium, helium, and hydrogen. On its day side (the side facing the Sun), temperatures reach 800 degrees Fahrenheit (430 degrees Celsius); on its night side, the heat escapes through the negligible atmosphere, and temperatures plunge to 280 degrees below zero Fahrenheit (–170 degrees Celsius).

What are the physical properties of Venus?

Venus is similar to Earth in many ways. The orbit of Venus is closer to that of Earth than any other planet, and it has a similar size and composition. However, the surface characteristics differ greatly.

A year on Venus is equal to 225 Earth days, compared to Earth's 365-day year. Venus, however, rotates on its polar axis backwards compared to Earth, so a Venus sunrise occurs in the west and sunset is in the east. Furthermore, a Venusian day is 243 Earth days long, which makes it even longer than a Venusian year.

The surface conditions of Venus are far different from that of our own planet. It is blanketed by a thick atmosphere nearly one hundred times denser than ours, and it is made mostly of carbon dioxide, along with some nitrogen and trace amounts of water vapor, acids, and heavy metals. Venus's clouds are laced with poisonous sulfur dioxide, and its surface temperature is a brutal 900 degrees Fahrenheit (500 degrees Celsius). Interestingly, this is even hotter than Mercury, which is much closer to the Sun. These hostile conditions came about because of a runaway greenhouse effect on Venus that persists to this day.

What are the physical properties of Mars?

Mars is the fourth planet from the Sun in our solar system. Its diameter is about half that of Earth, and its year is about 687 Earth days. That means that its seasons are about twice as long as ours here on Earth. However, a Martian day is very close in length to an Earth day—only about twenty minutes longer, in fact.

The Martian atmosphere is very thin—only about seven-thousandths the density of Earth's atmosphere. The atmosphere is mostly carbon dioxide, with tiny fractions of oxygen, nitrogen, and other gases. At the equator, during the warmest times of the Martian summer, the temperature can reach nearly zero degrees Fahrenheit (–18 degrees Celsius); at the poles, during the coldest times of the Martian winter, temperatures drop to 120 degrees below zero Fahrenheit (–85 degrees Celsius) and beyond.

Mars has fascinating geologic features on its surface; it is covered with all sorts of mountains, craters, channels, canyons, highlands, lowlands, and even polar ice caps. Scientific evidence strongly suggests that once, billions of years ago, Mars was much warmer than it is now, and was an active, dynamic planet.

What are some of the most interesting geological features of Mars?

Mars has a rich variety of geological features: huge craters, broad plains, tall mountains, deep canyons, and much more, all with colorful names. The tallest mountain in the solar system, the extinct volcano Olympus Mons, rises fifteen miles (twenty-four kilometers) above the Martian surface. A massive canyon called the Vallis Marineris (Mariner Valley) cuts across the northern hemisphere of Mars for more than 2,000 miles (3,200 kilometers); it is three times deeper than the Grand Canyon. On Earth, the Vallis Marineris would stretch from Arizona to New York. A noteworthy feature on the southern hemisphere of Mars is Hellas, an ancient canyon that was probably filled with lava long ago and is now a large, light area covered with dust.

What is a gas giant planet?

Gas giant planets are so named because they are much larger than the terrestrial planets, and they have atmospheres so thick that the gas is a dominant part of the planets' structures.

Which planets in our solar system are considered gas giants?

Jupiter, Saturn, Uranus, and Neptune are all categorized as gas giants.

What is the gas giant zone?

The gas giant zone is the part of the solar system roughly between the orbit of Jupiter and the orbit of Pluto. It contains the outer (gas giant) planets Jupiter, Saturn, Uranus, and Neptune. Each of the gas giant planets has a host of moons and rings or ringlets.

What are the physical properties of Jupiter?

Jupiter is by far the largest planet in our solar system. It is about twice as massive as all the other planets, moons, and asteroids in our solar system put together. However, its day is only ten hours long, less than half an Earth day. The fifth planet out from the Sun, Jupiter is 1,300 times Earth's volume and 320 times Earth's mass.

Most of Jupiter's mass consists of swirling gases, mostly hydrogen and helium; in this incredibly thick, dense atmosphere, storms of incredible magnitude rage and swirl. The largest of these storms is the Great Red Spot, which is often visible from Earth through even a small telescope.

Jupiter is the largest of the four gas giants in our solar system. In fact, if Jupiter, which is made up mostly of hydrogen and helium, had been very much larger when the solar system formed, it could have become a star and Earth would have been part of a binary star system.

Jupiter has a rocky core made of material thought to be similar to Earth's crust and mantle. However, this core may be the size of our entire planet, and its temperature may be as high as 18,000 degrees Fahrenheit (10,000 degrees Celsius), with pressures equal to two million Earth atmospheres. Around this core, in these extreme conditions, it is likely that a thick layer of liquid hydrogen is present; at least some of the hydrogen in this layer conducts electricity like metal, and is possibly the cause of Jupiter's intense magnetic field, which is five times greater than even that of the Sun.

At least sixty moons orbit Jupiter. Many of them are only a few miles across and are probably captured asteroids. However, four of them—Io, Europa, Ganymede, and Callisto—are about the size as Earth's Moon or larger

What do we know about Jupiter's Great Red Spot?

The Great Red Spot is a huge windstorm more than 8,500 miles (14,000 kilometers) wide and 16,000 miles (26,000 kilometers) long. You could easily place the planets Earth and Venus side-by-side inside the Great Red Spot! The storm that perpetuates the Spot is apparently powered by the upswell of hot, energetic gases from deep inside Jupiter's atmosphere, which produce winds that blow counterclockwise around the Spot at 250 miles (400 kilometers) per hour.

The Great Red Spot may derive its red color from sulfur or phosphorus, but this has not been conclusively shown. Beneath it are three white, oval areas; each is a storm about the size of the planet Mars. There are thousands of huge and powerful storms on Jupiter, and many of them can last for a very long time. However, the Great Red Spot, which has been going on for at least four hundred years, and which was first studied by Galileo Galilei, remains the biggest and most visible Jovian storm yet recorded.

What are the physical properties of Saturn?

Saturn is similar to Jupiter, though about one-third the mass. Still, it is about ninety-five times more massive than Earth. Saturn's average density is actually lower than that of water.

While only one-third the mass of Jupiter, Saturn is stunning with its spectacular ring display.

A day on Saturn is only ten hours and thirty-nine minutes long; it spins so fast that its diameter at the equator is 10 percent larger than its diameter from pole to pole.

Saturn has a solid core likely made of rock and ice, which is thought to be many times the mass of Earth. Covering this core is a layer of liquid metallic hydrogen, and on top of that are layers of liquid hydrogen and helium. These layers conduct strong electric currents that, in turn, generate Saturn's powerful magnetic field.

Saturn has dozens of moons, and its largest moon is Titan, which is larger than Earth's own moon and has a thick, opaque atmosphere. Perhaps the most spectacular part of Saturn is its magnificent system of planetary rings; the part which can be seen in visible light stretches some 170,000 miles (300,000 kilometers) across.

What is Saturn's atmosphere like?

Saturn has hazy, yellow cloud-tops made primarily of crystallized ammonia. The clouds are swept into bands by fierce, easterly winds that have been clocked at more than 1,100 miles (1,800 kilometers) per hour at the equator. Saturn's winds near its poles are much tamer. Also like Jupiter, powerful cyclonic storms appear on Saturn often. About every thirty years, for example, a massive storm forms that appears white. Known as the "Great White Spot"— even though it is not the same storm every time—it can be visible for up to a month, shining like a spotlight on the planet's face, before it dissipates and stretches around the planet as a thick white stripe. This recurring storm is thought to be a result of the warming of Saturn's atmosphere toward the end of the Saturnian summer, which causes ammonia deep inside the atmosphere to bubble up to the cloud-tops, only to be whipped around by the planet's powerful winds.

Why is there a giant hexagon at the north pole of Saturn?

In the 1980s NASA's *Voyager* spacecraft observed strange cloud formations near Saturn's north pole that looked like pieces of a giant six-sided figure. In the decades since, this huge hexagonal cloud formation has persisted, and the *Cassini* spacecraft mapped it in detail. The hexagon is about twice the diameter of Earth—and although it has formed

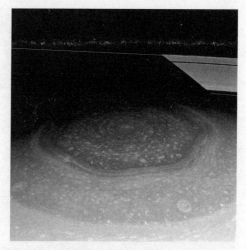

The unexpected cloud formations surrounding Saturn's north pole have attracted the attention—and speculations—of astronomers.

completely naturally, it looks eerily artificial. Astronomers are studying this mysterious formation very carefully, and they think that it might be caused by a high-speed jet stream moving within Saturn's dynamic atmosphere.

What are Saturn's rings like?

The main part of Saturn's ring system is divided into three components: the bright A and B rings and the dimmer C ring. (There are many other fainter rings as well.) The A and B rings are divided by a large gap called the Cassini Division, named after Gian Domenico Cassini (1625–1712). Within the A ring itself is another division, called the Encke Gap after Johann Encke (1791–1865), who first found it in 1837. Although these gaps appear to be completely empty, they are nonetheless filled with tiny particles, and, in the case of the Cassini Division, dozens of tiny ringlets.

Recently, several more rings around Saturn have been discovered which are large, fuzzy, and very faint. One of those, the E ring, is comprised of particles sprayed into space by geysers of ice crystals on Saturn's moon Enceladus. Another ring, which extends more than eleven million miles (seventeen million kilometers) outward from Saturn, rotates in the opposite direction as the main ring system and is currently visible only with infrared telescopes.

What are the physical properties of Uranus?

Uranus is the seventh major planet in our solar system, and the third of four gas giant planets. It is 31,800 miles (51,200 kilometers) in diameter, just under four times the diameter of Earth. Like the other gas giant planets, Uranus consists mostly of gas. Its pale blue-green, cloudy atmosphere is made of 83 percent hydrogen, 15 percent helium, and small amounts of methane and other gases. Uranus gets its color because the methane in the atmosphere absorbs reddish light and reflects bluish-greenish light. Deep down below its atmosphere, a slushy mixture of ice, ammonia, and methane is thought to surround a rocky core.

Although it orbits the Sun in a perfectly ordinary, near-circular ellipse every eighty-four Earth years, Uranus has an extremely odd rotation compared to the other major planets. It rotates on its side, almost like a bowling ball rolling down its lane, and its polar axis is parallel rather than perpendicular to its orbital plane. This means that one end of Uranus faces the Sun for an entire half of its orbit, while the other end faces away during that time. So one "day" on Uranus is equal to forty-two Earth years! Most astronomers think that at some point in its history, Uranus was struck by a large (at least planet-sized) object that knocked it onto its "side," causing this unusual motion.

Uranus has multiple rings encircling it. Interestingly, the planet is tilted on its side compared to the other planets in our solar system. No one knows why this is, but a possible explanation is that during the formation of the solar system Uranus was struck by a protoplanet.

Uranus is orbited by at least twenty-seven moons and thirteen thin rings. During its flyby of Uranus, the *Voyager 2* space probe discovered a large and unusually shaped magnetic field around Uranus (probably unique because of the planet's odd rotational motion) and a chilly cloud-top temperature of –350 degrees Fahrenheit (–210 degrees Celsius).

What are the rings of Uranus like?

The first nine rings of Uranus were discovered in 1977. When *Voyager 2* flew by Uranus in 1986, it found two new rings, plus a number of ring fragments. About twenty years later, astronomers using the Hubble Space Telescope found two more faint rings far out past these eleven, bringing the total to thirteen. All are composed of small pieces of dust, rocky particles, and ice.

The eleven interior rings occupy the region between twenty-four thousand and thirty-two thousand miles (thirty-eight thousand and fifty-one thousand kilometers) from the planet's center. Each ring is between 1 to 1,500 miles (1 and 2,500 kilometers) wide. The additional presence of partial rings suggests that the rings of Uranus may be much younger than the planet they encircle; it is possible that the rings are made of fragments of a broken moon. The eleventh-farthest ring, called the epsilon ring, is particularly interesting; it is very narrow and comprised of ice boulders. Two of the small moons of Uranus, Cordelia and Ophelia, act as shepherd satellites to the epsilon ring. They orbit the planet within that ring, and are probably responsible for creating the gravitational field that confines the boulders into the pattern of a ring.

What are the physical properties of Neptune?

Neptune is the eighth major planet in our solar system, seventeen times more massive than Earth and about four times its diameter. The most remote of the four gas giant planets in our solar system, Neptune takes 165 Earth years to orbit the Sun once. A "day" on Neptune, however, is only sixteen Earth hours. Similar to Uranus, Neptune's cloud-top temperature is a frosty –350 degrees Fahrenheit (–210 degrees Celsius).

Neptune is bluish-green in color, which might seem fitting for a planet named after the Roman god of the sea. However, the color does not come from water; it is due to the gases in Neptune's atmosphere reflecting sunlight back into space. Neptune's atmosphere consists mostly of hydrogen, helium, and methane. Below the atmosphere, scientists think there is a thick layer of ionized water, ammonia, and methane ice, and deeper yet is a rocky core many times the mass of Earth.

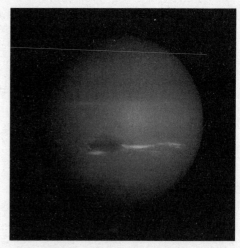

Neptune's distinctive blue color is due to a combination of helium, hydrogen, and methane in its atmosphere.

Neptune is so distant that very little was known about it until 1989, when the *Voyager 2* spacecraft flew by Neptune and obtained spectacular data about this mysterious gas giant. Today, we know of at least five rings—one of which is comprised of numerous partial arcs— and thirteen moons that orbit Neptune.

What is unique about how Neptune was discovered?

Neptune is the first planet whose existence was first predicted mathematically and then observed afterward. Soon after William Herschel discovered Uranus in 1781, astronomers measured a strange anomaly in its orbit, almost as if a massive object even more distant that Uranus itself were occasionally pulling on the planet. The German mathematician Karl Friedrich Gauss (1777–1855) made calculations based on these planetary movements that laid the groundwork for the discovery of another, more distant planet. In 1843, a self-taught astronomer named John Couch Adams (1819–1892) began a series of complicated calculations that pinpointed the location of such a planet; he finished the calculation in 1845. In 1846, a French astronomer named Urbain Jean Joseph Leverrier (1811–1877) also made a determination of this planet's location. The calculations of Adams matched those of Leverrier, though neither knew of the other's work at the time. On September 23, 1846, Johann Galle (1812–1910) and Heinrich d'Arrest (1822–1875) at the Urania Observatory in Berlin, Germany, found this planet based on the calculations of Leverrier, confirming the findings of both men.

MOONS

What is a moon?

A moon is a natural satellite that orbits a planet. As with planets, it is sometimes hard to know exactly what status a moon has. For example, whereas many moons (such as Earth's

Moon) formed at about the same time as the planets they orbit, many other moons probably formed as independent objects that were then captured in a planet's gravitational field.

How many moons does Mars have?

Mars has two moons, Phobos and Deimos. They were discovered by the American astronomer Asaph Hall (1829–1907) in 1877.

What are some of the characteristics of Jupiter's moons?

Most of Jupiter's dozens of moons (to date, more than sixty are known) are just a few miles across, and are probably captured asteroids. Four of Jupiter's moons stand out, however. They are called the Galilean moons because Galileo first discovered them in 1609. The aptly named *Galileo* spacecraft gave humans our closest look yet at these four remarkable planetary bodies, which are richly complex worlds unto themselves.

What is Jupiter's moon Io like?

Io, the closest of the Galilean moons to Jupiter, is affected so strongly by the gravitational tides exerted on it by Jupiter and the other moons that it is the most geologically active body in our solar system. The *Voyager* spacecraft first detected huge volcanoes spewing lava and ash into space, and the surface is completely recoated with fresh lava every few decades.

What is Jupiter's moon Europa like?

Europa is the second closest to Jupiter of the four Galilean moons. Its surface is covered with frozen water ice. Studies by the *Galileo* spacecraft show that the ice has been moving and shifting much the same way that densely packed ice behaves on Earth's polar oceans.

What is Jupiter's moon Ganymede like?

Ganymede is the largest moon in the solar system, about one-and-a-half times the diameter of Earth's Moon. It has a very thin atmosphere and its own magnetic field. Measurements taken by the *Galileo* spacecraft showed atomic hydrogen gas escaping from Ganymede's surface; and other measurements made using the Hubble Space Telescope showed excess oxygen on the surface of Ganymede's thick icy crust. Scientists think that the hydrogen and oxygen may come from molecules of frozen water ice on Ganymede's surface, which are then broken up into their component atoms by radiation from the Sun. These and other observations suggest that, like Europa, Ganymede may also have a vast underground sea of water.

What is Jupiter's moon Callisto like?

Callisto, the furthest away from Jupiter of the four Galilean moons, is scarred and pitted by ancient craters. Its surface may be the oldest of all the solid bodies in the solar system. There is evidence here, too (albeit weaker than that on Europa and Ganymede), that a magnetic field may exist around Callisto, which could be caused by a salty, liquid ocean far below its surface.

What are some of the characteristics of Saturn's moons?

Like Jupiter, Saturn has dozens of moons. Also like Jupiter, many of these are small moons that are likely to be asteroids captured in Saturn's gravitational field. The larger ones, however, have fascinating characteristics. Mimas, the victim of a huge cratering collision long ago, looks almost exactly like the fictional "Death Star" space station from the *Star Wars* movies. Enceladus has geysers of frosty water shooting out from its surface, suggesting the presence of liquid water deep in its core. The most complex moon of Saturn, however—perhaps the most complex moon in the entire solar system—is Saturn's largest moon, Titan.

What is Saturn's moon Titan like?

Titan was discovered by Christiaan Huygens (1629–1695) around 1655. Over the centuries, astronomers discovered that this largest of Saturn's moons is the only moon in the solar system with a substantial atmosphere—it is even denser than the atmosphere of planet Earth. Titan's atmosphere appears to be composed mainly of nitrogen and methane, with many other ingredients as well. Observations with the space probe *Voyager 1,* and with other telescopes, suggested that Titan might harbor liquid nitrogen or methane at its surface, perhaps in lakes and seas, and that its clouds may produce chemical rains and other weather patterns. Any detailed view is blocked by Titan's thick, opaque atmosphere, however.

The *Cassini* spacecraft launched the *Huygens* probe into the atmosphere of Titan in January 2005. That spacecraft slowly descended by parachute to that moon's surface, taking pictures all the way down. *Huygens* saw that, despite the numbing cold (–300 degrees Fahrenheit), there are topological features on Titan that look like tall mountains, rocky beaches, rivers, lakes, and even seas and shorelines. Liquid appears in abundance on the surface of Titan, but it is not liquid water. At those temperatures, water is frozen solid and as hard as granite. Rather, the liquid is probably methane—liquid natural gas.

What are some of Neptune's major moons?

Triton is Neptune's largest moon; it was discovered soon after Neptune itself was found. The second Neptunian moon to be discovered was Nereid, and that did not happen until 1949. It was discovered by the Dutch American astronomer Gerard Kuiper. During its 1989 flyby of Neptune, the *Voyager 2* found six other moons, ranging in size from 3 miles (50 kilometers) to 250 miles (400 kilometers) across. Several more have been discovered since then, all of them very small.

THE KUIPER BELT AND BEYOND

What is the Kuiper Belt?

The Kuiper Belt (also called the Kuiper-Edgeworth Belt) is a doughnut-shaped region that extends between about three to eight billion miles (five to twelve billion kilometers) out from the Sun. Its inner edge is about at the orbit of Neptune, while its outer edge is about twice that diameter.

What are Kuiper Belt Objects?

Kuiper Belt Objects (KBOs) are, as their name implies, objects that originate from or orbit in the Kuiper Belt. Only one KBO was known for more than sixty years: Pluto. Many KBOs have been discovered since 1992, however, and the current estimate is that there are millions, if not billions, of KBOs.

KBOs are basically comets without tails: icy dirtballs that have collected together over billions of years. If they get large enough—such as Pluto did—they evolve as other massive planetlike bodies do, forming dense cores that have a different physical composition than the mantle or crust above it. Most short-period comets—those with relatively short orbital times of a few years to a few centuries—are thought to originate from the Kuiper Belt.

A comparison of some of the largest Kuiper Belt Objects, including Pluto, Sedna, and Quaoar, compared with Earth and the Moon.

What are the largest Kuiper Belt Objects and how big are they?

The following table lists a few of the largest KBOs in our solar system that are currently known

Largest Kuiper Belt Objects

Name	Geometric Mean Diameter(km)
Eris	2,300
Pluto	2,300
Sedna	1,500
Quaoar	1,200
Charon	1,200
Orcus	940
Varuna	890
Ixion	820
Chaos	560
Huya	500

ASTEROIDS

What is an asteroid?

Asteroids are relatively small, primarily rocky or metallic chunks of matter that orbit the Sun. They are like planets, but much smaller; the largest asteroid, Ceres, is only about 580 miles (930 kilometers) across, and only ten asteroids larger than 155 miles (250 kilometers)

across are known to exist in the solar system. While most asteroids are primarily composed of carbon-rich rock, some are made at least partially of iron and nickel. Aside from the largest ones, asteroids tend to be irregular in shape, rotating and tumbling as they move through the solar system.

What is the asteroid belt?

The asteroid belt (or the "main belt") is the region between the orbit of Mars and the orbit of Jupiter—about 150 to 500 million miles (240 to 800 million kilometers) away from the Sun. The vast majority of known asteroids orbit in this belt. The main belt itself is divided into thinner belts, separated by object-free zones called Kirkwood Gaps. The gaps are named after the American astronomer Daniel Kirkwood (1814–1895), who first discovered them.

What are the largest asteroids in the asteroid belt?

The four largest asteroids are the dwarf planet Ceres, Pallas, Vesta, and Hygiea. Other well-known asteroids include Eros, Gaspra, Ida, and Dactyl. The following table lists other asteroids, as well.

Largest Asteroids in the Solar System

Name	Geometric Mean Diameter(km)
Ceres	950
Vesta	530
Pallas	530
Hygiea	410
Davida	330
Interamnia	320
52 Europa	300
Sylvia	290
Hektor	270
Euphrosyne	260
Eunomia	260
Cybele	240
Juno	240
Psyche	230

How far apart are the asteroids in the main asteroid belt?

Even though there are at least a million or more asteroids in the main belt, the typical distance between asteroids is huge—thousands or even millions of miles. That means that space chases through the belt dodging a hail of asteroids are dramatic but, alas, completely fictional.

What are near-Earth objects and are they dangerous?

There are more than ten thousand known NEOs—near-Earth objects—which are asteroids with orbits that cross Earth's orbit. An NEO could strike our planet, possibly unleashing cosmic destruction; indeed, astronomers have already classified more than one thousand NEOs as potentially hazardous asteroids.

COMETS

What is a comet?

Comets are basically "snowy dirtballs" or "dirty snowballs"—clumpy collections of rocky material, dust, and frozen water, methane, and ammonia that move through the solar system in long, highly elliptical orbits around the Sun. When they are far away from the Sun, comets are simple, solid bodies; but when they get closer to the Sun, they warm up, causing the ice in the comets' outer surface to vaporize. This creates a cloudy "coma" that forms around the solid part of the comet, called the "nucleus." The loosened comet vapor forms long "tails" that can grow to millions of miles in length.

When were the first comets observed?

Comets can be seen with the naked eye, and sometimes they are spectacularly bright and beautiful, so humans have undoubtedly been observing comets since time immemorial. On the other hand, comets are usually visible only for short periods of time—a few days or weeks—so almost all comet sightings have gone unrecorded and were misunderstood for most of that human history. For these and other reasons, a great deal of mythology and superstition has been associated with comets throughout the ages.

When did astronomers calculate how comets orbit the Sun?

By the 1600s, astronomers had reasoned that comets occur in space, beyond Earth's atmosphere, and were trying to figure out where a comet's journey begins and ends. Johannes Kepler (1571–1630), who observed a comet in 1607, concluded that comets follow straight lines, coming from an infinite distance and leaving forever once they passed Earth. Somewhat later, the German astronomer Johannes Hevelius (1611–1687) suggested that comets followed slightly curved paths. In the late 1600s, George Samuel Doerffel (1643–1688) suggested that comets followed a parabolic course. In 1695, Edmund Halley (1656–1742) finally deduced correctly that comets follow highly elliptical orbits around the Sun.

What is the Oort Cloud?

The Oort Cloud is a spherical region enveloping the Sun where most comets with orbital periods exceeding several hundred years (i.e. "long-period comets") originate. The dimensions of the Oort Cloud have never been measured, but it is estimated to be up to a trillion or more miles across. Scientists think that billions, perhaps even trillions, of comets and comet-like bodies are located in the Oort Cloud. Sedna may be the first Oort Cloud object ever discovered.

What are some of the best-known comets of modern times?

Halley's comet is probably the best-known comet in human history. It last flew by Earth in 1986. Other well-known comets in recent times include Comet Shoemaker-Levy 9, which

Who is Jan Hendrick Oort?

The Oort Cloud is named for Jan Hendrick Oort (1900–1992), who is widely considered to have been the leading Dutch astronomer of his generation. His scientific research covered a great range of subjects, from the structure of galaxies to the way comets are formed. He was also a pioneer of radio astronomy.

In 1927 Oort investigated the then-revolutionary concept that the Milky Way galaxy is rotating about its center. By studying the motion of stars near the Sun, Oort concluded that our solar system was not at the center of the galaxy, as had been previously believed, but somewhere toward the outer edge. Oort then set out to decipher the structure of the Milky Way, using theoretical models and the tools of radio astronomy.

Oort's work on the origin of comets led him to propose, in 1950, that a huge, shell-shaped zone of space, well beyond the orbit of Pluto and stretching out trillions of miles beyond the Sun in all directions, contains trillions of slowly orbiting, inactive comets. Those comets remain there until a passing gas cloud or star disturbs the orbit of a comet, sending it toward the Sun and inner solar system in a highly elliptical orbit. Today, this zone of long-period comets bears Jan Oort's name.

broke apart and crashed into Jupiter in 1994; Comet Hyakutake, which flew by Earth in 1996; Comet Hale-Bopp, considered by many to be the "comet of the twentieth century," which flew by Earth in 1997; and Comet McNaught, which in early 2007 was visible even in the daytime.

What is a meteorite?

A meteorite is a large particle from outer space that lands on Earth. They range in size from a grain of sand and up. About thirty thousand meteorites have been recovered in recorded history; about six hundred of them are made primarily of metal, and the rest are made primarily of rock.

What is a meteor?

A meteor is a particle from outer space that enters Earth's atmosphere, but does not land on Earth. Instead, the particle burns up in the atmosphere, leaving a short-lived, glowing trail that traces part of its path through the sky. Like meteorites, meteors can be as small as a grain and often burn up before reaching the ground; a meteor larger than about the size of a baseball can reach Earth; in which case, we call it a meteorite.

Where do meteors and meteorites come from?

Most meteors, especially those that fall during meteor showers, are the tiny remnants of comets left in Earth's orbital path over many, many years. Most meteorites, which are generally larger than meteors, are pieces of asteroids and comets that somehow came apart from their parent bodies—perhaps from a collision with another body—and orbited in the solar system until they collided with Earth.

What is a meteor shower?

Meteors are often called "shooting stars" because they are bright for a moment and move quickly across the sky. Usually, a shooting star appears in the sky about once an hour or so. Sometimes, though, a large number of meteors appear in the sky over the course of a several nights. These meteors will appear to come from the same part of the sky, and dozens or hundreds (sometimes even thousands) of meteors can be seen every hour. We call such dazzling displays meteor showers. The strongest meteor showers are sometimes called meteor storms.

Where are meteorites found?

Meteorites have been found pretty much all over the world. With modern civilization likely to have disturbed most landing sites, meteorites are most likely found today in remote, barren areas like deserts. The majority of meteorites have been discovered in what remains the largest uninhabited, undisturbed part of the world —Antarctica.

What is the largest known meteorite to strike Earth in the past 100,000 years?

About fifty thousand years ago, a metallic meteorite about one hundred feet across crashed into the Mogollon Rim area in modern-day Arizona. It disintegrated on impact, creating a hole in the desert nearly a mile across and nearly sixty stories deep. Meteor Crater (or the Barringer Meteor Crater, as it is more commonly known today) is a remarkable and lasting example of the amount of kinetic energy carried by celestial objects. Just the lip of the crater rises fifteen stories up above the desert floor. For a long time, scientists puzzled over the origin of this crater. It might have been volcanic in origin, they thought. But geological evidence, such as shallow metallic remnants in a huge radius miles around the crater, confirmed it was a meteorite strike.

Can humans prevent meteorite strikes or the potential damage they might cause?

About one hundred tons of extraterrestrial matter strikes Earth every day, so very few meteorite strikes need to be prevented. Stopping a large comet or asteroid from striking Earth—one large enough to destroy a city, for example—may be possible with modern technology, but that would require years of research and preparation, vast sums of money, and most likely broad international cooperation. So far, such tremendous preventive efforts have not yet been made. Fortunately, such strikes are very rare, so there is probably still enough time to prepare for the next major strike.

What are the best-known meteor showers?

Each year, the Perseid meteor shower happens in August, as Earth travels through the remnant tail of Comet 109P/Swift-Tuttle. In November, when our planet moves through the remnants of Comet 55P/Tempel-Tuttle, we enjoy the Leonid meteor shower. These showers get their name from the location in the sky where all the meteors seem to originate, called the radiant. As their names suggest, the radiants of the Perseid and Leonid meteor showers are the constellations Perseus and Leo, respectively.

427

OBSERVATION AND MEASUREMENT

Who is considered the founder of systematic astronomy?

The Greek scientist Hipparchus (fl. 146-127 b.c.e.) is considered to be the father of systematic astronomy. He measured as accurately as possible the directions of objects in the sky. He compiled the first catalog of stars, containing about 850 entries, and designated each star's celestial coordinates, indicating its position in the sky. Hipparchus also divided the stars according to their apparent brightness or magnitudes.

What is a light year?

A light year is a measure of distance, not time. It is the distance that light, which travels in a vacuum at the rate of 186,282 miles (299,792 kilometers) per second, can travel in a year (365.25 days). This is equal to 5.87 trillion miles (9.46 trillion kilometers).

Besides the light year, what other units are used to measure distances in astronomy?

The astronomical unit (AU) is often used to measure distances within the solar system. One AU is equal to the average distance between the Earth and the sun, or 92,955,630 miles (149,597,870 kilometers). The parsec is equal to 3.26 light years, or about 19.18 trillion miles (30.82 trillion kilometers).

How are new celestial objects named?

Many stars and planets have names that date back to antiquity. The International Astronomical Union (IAU), the professional astronomers organization, has attempted, in this century, to standardize names given to newly discovered celestial objects and their surface features.

Stars are generally called by their traditional names, most of which are of Greek, Roman, or Arabic origin. They are also identified by the constellation in which they appear, designated in order of brightness by Greek letters. Thus Sirius is also called alpha Canis Majoris, which means it is the brightest star in the constellation Canis Major. Other stars are called by catalog numbers, which include the star's coordinates. To the horror of many astronomers, several commercial star registries exist, and for a fee you can submit a star name to them. These names are not officially recognized by the IAU.

The IAU has made some recommendations for naming the surface features of the planets and their satellites. For example, features on Mercury are named for composers, poets,

---

What is widely considered to be one of the earliest celestial observatories?

Built in England over a period of years between 2500 and 1700 b.c.e., Stonehenge is one of the earliest observatories or observatory-temples. It is widely believed that its primary function was to observe the mid-summer and mid-winter solstices.

and writers; features of Venus for women; and features on Saturn's moon Mimas for people and places in Arthurian legend.

Comets are named for their discoverers. Newly discovered asteroids are first given a temporary designation consisting of the year of discovery plus two letters. The first letter indicates the half-month of discovery (A=first half of January, B=second half of January, etc.) and the second the order of discovery in that half-month. Thus asteroid 2002EM was the 13th (M) asteroid discovered in the first half of March (E) in 2002. After an asteroid's orbit is determined, it is given a permanent number and its discoverer is given the honor of naming it. Asteroids have been named after such diverse things as mythological figures (Ceres, Vesta), an airline (Swissair), and the Beatles (Lennon, McCartney, Harrison, Starr).

What is an astrolabe?

Invented by the Greeks or Alexandrians around 100 B.C.E. or before, an astrolabe is a two-dimensional working model of the heavens, with sights for observations. It consists of two concentric, flat disks, one fixed, representing the observer on Earth, the other moving, which can be rotated to represent the appearance of the celestial sphere at a given moment. Given latitude, date, and time, the observer can read off the altitude and azimuth of the sun, the brightest stars, and the planets. By measuring the altitude of a particular body, one can find the time. The astrolabe can also be used to find times of sunrise, sunset, twilight, or the height of a tower or depth of a well. After 1600, it was replaced by the sextant and other more accurate instruments.

Who invented the telescope?

Hans Lippershey (ca. 1570-1619), a German-Dutch lens grinder and spectacle maker, is generally credited with inventing the telescope in 1608 because he was the first scientist to apply for a patent. Two other inventors, Zacharias Janssen and Jacob Metius, also developed telescopes. Modern historians consider Lippershey and Janssen as the two likely candidates for the title of inventor of the telescope, with Lippershey possessing the strongest claim. Lippershey used his telescope for observing grounded objects from a distance.

In 1609, Galileo also developed his own refractor telescope for astronomical studies. Although small by today's standards, the telescope enabled Galileo to observe the Milky Way and to identify blemishes on the moon's surface as craters.

What are the differences between reflecting and refracting telescopes?

Reflecting telescopes capture light using a mirror while refracting telescopes capture light with a lens. The advantages of reflecting telescopes are: 1) they collect light with a mirror so there is no color fringing, and 2) since a mirror can be supported at the back there is no size limit. In an effort to alleviate the problem of color fringing always associated with lenses, Newton built a reflecting telescope in 1668 that collected light with mirrors.

What is the Very Large Array (VLA) and what information have we learned from it?

The Very Large Array (VLA) is one of the world's premier astronomical radio observatories. The VLA consists of 27 antennas arranged in a huge Y pattern up to 36km (22 miles) across—roughly one-and-a-half times the size of Washington, D.C. Each antenna is 25 meters (81 feet) in diameter; they are combined electronically to give the resolution of an antenna 36km

A series of radio telescope dishes make up the Very Large Array in New Mexico.

(22 miles) across, with the sensitivity of a dish 130 meters (422 feet) in diameter. Each of the 27 radio telescopes in the VLA is the size of a house and can be moved on train tracks. In its twenty-second year of operation, the VLA has been one of the most productive observatories with more than 2,200 scientists using it for more than 10,000 separate observing projects. The VLA has been used to discover water on the planet Mercury, radio-bright coronae around ordinary stars, micro-quasars in our galaxy, gravitationally induced Einstein rings around distant galaxies, and radio counterparts to cosmologically distant gamma-ray bursts. The vast size of the VLA has allowed astronomers to study the details of super-fast cosmic jets, and even map the center of our galaxy.

Who is the Hubble for whom the space telescope is named?

Edwin Powell Hubble (1889-1953) was an American astronomer known for his studies of galaxies. His study of nebulae, or clouds—the faint, unresolved luminous patches in the sky—showed that some of them were large groups of many stars. Hubble classified galaxies by their shapes as being spiral, elliptical, or irregular.

Hubble's Law establishes a relationship between the velocity of recession of a galaxy and its distance. The speed at which a galaxy is moving away from our solar system (measured by its redshift, the shift of its light to longer wavelengths, presumed to be caused by the Doppler effect) is directly proportional to the galaxy's distance from it.

The Hubble Space Telescope was deployed by the space shuttle Discovery on April 25, 1990. The telescope, which would be free of distortions caused by the Earth's atmosphere, was designed to see deeper into space than any telescope on land. However, on June 27, 1990, the National Aeronautics and Space Administration announced that the telescope had a defect in one of its mirrors that prevented it from properly focusing. Although other instruments, including one designed to make observations in ultraviolet light, were still operating, nearly 40 percent of the telescope's experiments had to be postponed until repairs were made. On December 2, 1993, astronauts were able to make the necessary repairs. Four of Hubble's six gyroscopes were replaced as well as two solar panels. Hubble's primary camera, which had a flawed mirror, was also replaced. Since that mission four other servicing missions have been conducted, dramatically improving the HST's capabilities.

EXPLORATION

Who was the first person to propose space rockets?

In 1903, Konstantin E. Tsiolkovsky, a Russian high school teacher, completed the first scientific paper on the use of rockets for space travel. Several years later, Robert H. Goddard of the United States and Herman Oberth of Germany awakened wider scientific interest in space travel. These three men worked individually on many of the technical problems of rocketry and space travel. They are known, therefore, as the "fathers of space flight." In 1919, Goddard wrote the paper, "A Method of Reaching Extreme Altitudes," which explained how rockets could be used to explore the upper atmosphere and described a way to send a rocket to the moon. During the 1920s Tsiolkovsky wrote a series of new studies that included detailed descriptions of multi-stage rockets. In 1923, Oberth wrote "The Rocket into Interplanetary Space," which discussed the technical problems of space flight and also described what a spaceship would be like.

What is the difference between zero-gravity and microgravity?

Zero-gravity is the absence of gravity; a condition in which the effects of gravity are not felt; weightlessness. Microgravity is a condition of very low gravity, especially approaching weightlessness. On a spaceship, while in zero- or microgravity, objects would fall freely and float weightlessly. Both terms, however, are technically incorrect. The gravitation in orbit is only slightly less than the gravitation on the earth. A spacecraft and its contents continuously fall toward earth. It is the spacecraft's immense forward speed that appears to make the earth's surface curve away as the vehicle falls toward it. The continuous falling seems to eliminate the weight of everything inside the spacecraft. For this reason, the condition is sometimes referred to as weightlessness or zero-gravity.

What is meant by the phrase "greening of the galaxy"?

The expression means the spreading of human life, technology, and culture through interstellar space and eventually across the entire Milky Way galaxy, the Earth's home galaxy.

When was the Outer Space Treaty signed?

The United Nations Outer Space Treaty was signed on January 23, 1967. The treaty provides a framework for the exploration and sharing of outer space. It governs the outer space activities of nations that wish to exploit and make use of space, the moon, and other celestial bodies. It is based on a humanist and pacifist philosophy and on the principle of the nonappropriation of space and the freedom that all nations have to explore and use space. A very large number of countries have signed this agreement, including those from the Western alliance, the former Eastern bloc, and non-aligned countries.

Space law, or those rules governing the space activities of various countries, international organizations, and private industries, has been evolving since 1957, when the General Assembly of the United Nations created the Committee on the Peaceful Uses of Outer Space (COPUOS). One of its subcommittees was instrumental in drawing up the 1967 Outer Space Treaty.

Russian Air Force Major Yuri Gagarin became the first man in space on April 12, 1961.

Who was the first man in space?

Yuri Gagarin (1934-1968), a Soviet cosmonaut, became the first man in space when he made a full orbit of the Earth in *Vostok I* on April 12, 1961. Gagarin's flight lasted only one hour and 48 minutes, but as the first man in space, he became an international hero. Partly because of this Soviet success, U.S. President John F. Kennedy (1917-1963) announced on May 25, 1961, that the United States would land a man on the moon before the end of the decade. The United States took its first step toward that goal when it launched the first American into orbit on February 20, 1962. Astronaut John H. Glenn Jr. (b. 1921) completed three orbits in *Friendship 7* and traveled about 81,000 miles (130,329 kilometers). Prior to this, on May 5, 1961, Alan B. Shepard Jr. (1923-1998) became the first American to pilot a spaceflight, aboard *Freedom 7*. This suborbital flight reached an altitude of 116.5 miles (187.45 kilometers).

What did NASA mean when it said *Voyager 1* and *2* would take a "grand tour" of the planets?

Once every 176 years the giant outer planets—Jupiter, Saturn, Uranus, and Neptune—align themselves in such a pattern that a spacecraft launched from Earth to Jupiter at just the right time might be able to visit the other three planets on the same mission. A technique called "gravity assist" used each planet's gravity as a power boost to point *Voyager* toward the next planet. The first opportune year for the "grand tour" was 1977.

Which astronauts have walked on the moon?

Twelve astronauts have walked on the moon. Each Apollo flight had a crew of three. One crew member remained in orbit in the command service module (CSM) while the other two actually landed on the moon.

Apollo 11, July 16-24, 1969
    Neil A. Armstrong
    Edwin E. Aldrin, Jr.
    Michael Collins (CSM pilot, did not walk on the moon)

Apollo 12, November 14-24, 1969
>   Charles P. Conrad
>   Alan L. Bean
>   Richard F. Gordon, Jr. (CSM pilot, did not walk on the moon)

Apollo 14, January 31-February 9, 1971
>   Alan B. Shepard, Jr.
>   Edgar D. Mitchell
>   Stuart A. Roosa (CSM pilot, did not walk on the moon)

Apollo 15, July 26-August 7, 1971
>   David R. Scott
>   James B. Irwin
>   Alfred M. Worden (CSM pilot, did not walk on the moon)

Apollo 16, April 16-27, 1972
>   John W. Young
>   Charles M. Duke, Jr.
>   Thomas K. Mattingly, II (CSM pilot, did not walk on the moon)

Apollo 17, December 7-19, 1972
>   Eugene A. Cernan
>   Harrison H. Schmitt
>   Ronald E. Evans (CSM pilot, did not walk on the moon)

When and what was the first animal sent into orbit?

A small female dog named Laika, aboard the Soviet *Sputnik 2*, launched November 3, 1957, was the first animal sent into orbit. This event followed the successful Soviet launch on October 4, 1957, of *Sputnik 1*, the first man-made satellite ever placed in orbit. Laika was placed in a pressurized compartment within a capsule that weighed 1,103 pounds (500 kilograms). After a few

Laika made history as the first living creature to orbit the Earth aboard the Soviet Sputnik 2.

days in orbit, she died, and *Sputnik 2* reentered the Earth's atmosphere on April 14, 1958. Some sources list the dog as a Russian samoyed laika named "Kudyavka" or "Limonchik."

What were the first monkeys and chimpanzees in space?

On a United States *Jupiter* flight on December 12, 1958, a squirrel monkey named Old Reliable was sent into space, but not into orbit. The monkey drowned during recovery.

On another *Jupiter* flight, on May 28, 1959, two female monkeys were sent 300 miles (482.7 kilometers) high. Able was a six-pound (2.7-kilogram) rhesus monkey and Baker was an 11-ounce (0.3-kilogram) squirrel monkey. Both were recovered alive.

A chimpanzee named Ham was used on a *Mercury* flight on January 31, 1961. Ham was launched to a height of 157 miles (253 kilometers) into space but did not go into orbit. His capsule reached a maximum speed of 5,857 miles (9,426 kilometers) per hour and landed 422 miles (679 kilometers) downrange in the Atlantic Ocean, where he was recovered unharmed.

On November 29, 1961, the United States placed a chimpanzee named Enos into orbit and recovered him alive after two complete orbits around the Earth. Like the Soviets, who usually used dogs, the United States had to obtain information on the effects of space flight on living beings before they could actually launch a human into space.

Who were the first man and woman to walk in space?

On March 18, 1965, the Soviet cosmonaut Alexei Leonov (b. 1934) became the first person to walk in space when he spent 10 minutes outside his *Voskhod 2* spacecraft. The first woman to walk in space was Soviet cosmonaut Svetlana Savitskaya (b. 1947), who, during her second flight aboard the *Soyuz T-12* (July 17, 1984), performed 3.5 hours of extravehicular activity.

The first American to walk in space was Edward White II (1930-1967) from the spacecraft *Gemini 4* on June 3, 1965. White spent 22 minutes floating free attached to the *Gemini* by a lifeline. The photos of White floating in space are perhaps some of the most familiar of all space shots. Kathryn D. Sullivan (b. 1951) became the first American woman to walk in space when she spent 3.5 hours outside the *Challenger* orbiter during the space shuttle mission 41G on October 11, 1984.

American astronaut Bruce McCandless II (b. 1937) performed the first untethered space walk from the space shuttle *Challenger* on February 7, 1984, using an MMU (manual maneuvering unit) backpack.

Who was the first woman in space?

Valentina V. Tereshkova-Nikolaeva (b. 1937), a Soviet cosmonaut, was the first woman in space. She was aboard the *Vostok 6*, launched June 16, 1963. She spent three days circling the Earth, completing 48 orbits. Although she had little cosmonaut training, she was an accomplished parachutist and was especially fit for the rigors of space travel.

The United States space program did not put a woman in space until 20 years later when, on June 18, 1983, Sally K. Ride (1951-2012) flew aboard the space shuttle *Challenger* mission STS-7. In 1987, she moved to the administrative side of NASA and was instrumental in issuing the "Ride Report," which recommended future missions and direction for NASA.

She retired from NASA in August 1987 to become a research fellow at Stanford University after serving on the Presidential Commission that investigated the *Challenger* disaster. She passed away as a result of pancreatic cancer in July 2012.

What were the first words spoken by an astronaut after touchdown of the lunar module on the Apollo 11 flight, and by an astronaut standing on the moon?

On July 20, 1969, at 4:17:43 P.M. Eastern Daylight Time (20:17:43 Greenwich Mean Time), Neil A. Armstrong (1930-2012) and Edwin E. Aldrin Jr. (b. 1930) landed the lunar module *Eagle* on the moon's Sea of Tranquility, and Armstrong radioed: "Houston, Tranquility Base here. The *Eagle* has landed." Several hours later, when Armstrong descended the lunar module ladder and made the small jump between the *Eagle* and the lunar surface, he announced: "That's one small step for man, one giant leap for mankind." The article "a" was missing in the live voice transmission, and was later inserted in the record to amend the message to "one small step for a man."

Astronaut Sally K. Ride became the first U.S. woman in space on June 18, 1983.

What are some of the accomplishments of female astronauts?

First American woman in space: Sally K. Ride—June 18, 1983, aboard *Challenger* STS-7.

First American woman to walk in space: Kathryn D. Sullivan—October 11, 1984, aboard *Challenger* STS 41G.

First woman to make three spaceflights: Shannon W. Lucid—June 17, 1985; October 18, 1989; and August 2, 1991.

First African American woman in space: Mae Carol Jemison—September 12, 1992, aboard *Endeavour*.

First American woman space shuttle pilot: Eileen M. Collins—February 3, 1995, aboard *Discovery*.

Who was the first African American in space?

Guion S. Bluford, Jr. (b. 1942), became the first African American to fly in space during the space shuttle *Challenger* mission STS-8 (August 30-September 5, 1983). Astronaut Bluford, who holds a Ph.D. in aerospace engineering, made a second shuttle flight aboard *Challenger* mission STS-61-A/Spacelab D1 (October 30-November 6, 1985). The first black man to fly in space was Cuban cosmonaut Arnaldo Tamayo-Mendez, who was aboard *Soyuz 38* and spent eight days aboard the Soviet space station *Salyut 6* during September 1980. Dr. Mae C. Jemison became the first African American woman in space on September 12, 1992 aboard the space shuttle Endeavour mission *Spacelab-J.*

Who were the first married couple to go into space together?

Astronauts Jan Davis and Mark Lee were the first married couple in space. They flew aboard the space shuttle *Endeavor* on an eight-day mission that began on September 12, 1992. Ordinarily, NASA bars married couples from flying together. An exception was made for Davis and Lee because they had no children and had begun training for the mission long before they got married.

Who has spent the most time in space?

As of December 31, 2001, cosmonaut Sergei Vasilyevich Avdeyev has accumulated the most spaceflight time—747.6 days in three flights.

When was the first United States satellite launched?

Explorer 1, launched January 31, 1958, by the U.S. Army, was the first United States satellite launched into orbit. This 31-pound (14.06-kilogram) satellite carried instrumentation that led to the discovery of the Earth's radiation belts, which would be named after University of Iowa scientist James A. Van Allen. It followed four months after the launching of the world's first satellite, the Soviet Union's *Sputnik 1.* On October 3, 1957, the Soviet Union placed the large 184-pound (83.5-kilogram) satellite into low Earth orbit. It carried instrumentation to study the density and temperature of the upper atmosphere, and its launch was the event that opened the age of space.

What is the mission of the *Galileo* spacecraft?

Galileo, launched October 18, 1989, required almost six years to reach Jupiter after looping past Venus once and the Earth twice. The *Galileo* spacecraft was designed to make a detailed study of Jupiter and its rings and moons over a period of years. On December 7, 1995, it released a probe to analyze the different layers of Jupiter's atmosphere. *Galileo* recorded a multitude of measurements of the planet, its four largest moons, and its mammoth magnetic field. The mission was originally scheduled to continue until the end of 1997, but, since it has continued to operate successfully, missions exploring Jupiter's moons were added in 1997, 1999, and 2001. *Galileo* is scheduled to plunge into Jupiter's atmosphere in September 2003.

Who was the founder of the Soviet space program?

Sergei P. Korolev (1907-1966) made enormous contributions to the development of Soviet manned space flight, and his name is linked with their most significant space achievements. Trained as an aeronautical engineer, he directed the Moscow group studying the principles of rocket propulsion, and in 1946 took over the Soviet program to develop long-range ballistic rockets. Under Korolev, the Soviets used these rockets for space projects and launched the world's first satellite on October 4, 1957. Besides a vigorous, unmanned, interplanetary research program, Korolev's goal was to place men in space, and following tests with animals his manned space flight program was initiated when Yuri Gagarin (1934-1968) was successfully launched into Earth's orbit.

What were some of the accomplishments of the first nine Challenger spaceflights?

First American woman in space—Sally Ride

First African American man in space—Guion S. Bluford Jr.

First American woman to spacewalk—Kathryn Sullivan

First shuttle spacewalk—Donald Peterson and Story Musgrave

First untethered spacewalk—Robert Stewart and Bruce McCandless

First satellite repair in orbit—Pinky Nelson and Ox Van Hoften

First Coke and Pepsi in orbit—1985

What is the composition of the tiles on the underside of the space shuttle and how hot do they get?

The 20,000 tiles are composed of a low-density, high purity silica fiber insulator hardened by ceramic bonding. Bonded to a Nomex fiber felt pad, each tile is directly bonded to the

Is anyone looking for extraterrestrial life?

A program called SETI (the Search for Extraterrestrial Intelligence) began in 1960, when American astronomer Frank Drake (b. 1930) spent three months at the National Radio Astronomy Observatory in Green Bank, West Virginia, searching for radio signals coming from the nearby stars Tau Ceti and Epsilon Eridani. Although no signals were detected and scientists interested in SETI have often been ridiculed, support for the idea of seeking out intelligent life in the universe has grown.

Project Sentinel, which used a radio dish at Harvard University's Oak Ridge Observatory in Massachusetts, could monitor 128,000 channels at a time. This project was upgraded in 1985 to META (Megachannel Extraterrestrial Assay), thanks in part to a donation by filmmaker Steven Spielberg. Project META is capable of receiving 8.4 million channels. NASA began a 10-year search in 1992 using radio telescopes in Arecibo, Puerto Rico, and Barstow, California.

Scientists are searching for radio signals that stand out from the random noises caused by natural objects. Such signals might repeat at regular intervals or contain mathematical sequences. There are millions of radio channels and a lot of sky to be examined. As of October 1995, Project BETA (Billion-channel Extraterrestrial Assay) has been scanning a quarter of a billion channels. This new design improves upon Project META 300-fold, making the challenge of scanning millions of radio channels seem less daunting. SETI has since developed other projects, some "piggybacking" on radio telescopes while engaged in regular uses. A program launched in 1999, SETI@HOME, uses the power of home computers while they are at rest.

Where are the space shuttles today?

C hallenger was destroyed during launch on January 28, 1986, with all seven crew members lost. *Columbia* disintegrated after reentering the atmosphere on February 1, 2003; again, all seven crew members perished. In 2011, the Space Shuttle program was ended and the shuttle fleet was retired. *Enterprise* resides today at the Intrepid Sea-Air-Space Museum in New York, NY; *Discovery* at the Udvar-Hazy Center of the National Air and Space Museum near Washington, DC; *Atlantis* at the Kennedy Space Center near Cape Canaveral, FL; and *Endeavour* at the California Science Center in Los Angeles, CA.

shuttle exterior. The maximum surface temperature can reach up to 922K to 978K (649°C to 704°C or 1,200°F to 1,300°F).

What are the liquid fuels used by the space shuttles?

Liquid hydrogen is used as a fuel, with liquid oxygen used to burn it. These two fuels are stored in chambers separately and then mixed to combust the two. Because oxygen must be kept below -183°C to remain a liquid, and hydrogen must be at -253°C to remain a liquid, they are both difficult to handle, but make useful rocket fuel.

Who constructed the International Space Station and why?

Construction on the International Space Station (ISS) began in 1998 and has been ongoing since then. Currently, the station orbits Earth and can accommodate six astronauts comfortably and is about the size of a five-bedroom house. It represents the cooperative efforts of several nations, including the United States, Russia, Japan, Canada, France, Germany, Italy, Belgium, Denmark, Spain, Sweden, Norway, Switzerland, the United Kingdom, and the Netherlands. The ISS is continually manned, and scientists aboard it primarily use it to conduct experiments that must be performed in a weightless environment.

What will be the next step for U.S. space travel?

Currently, U.S. astronauts have been flying aboard Russian spacecraft to reach the International Space Station because there are no American vehicles for the task. Some proposed projects, such as the X-33 that was to be a joint NASA/Lockheed Martin effort, failed because of lack of funding and political support.

Instead of a shuttle or space plane concept, NASA is now developing the Space Launch System (SLS) rocket, which is scheduled to have its first launch in 2018, carrying a cargo of satellites. One of these will be the SkyFire, a satellite that will orbit the Moon and look for water there.

In the meantime, private companies have been taking over duties formerly fulfilled by NASA. SpaceX, United Launch Alliance, and Space Exploration Technologies are just a few of these, and they have been successfully building craft that have, for example, taken supplies to the ISS.

EARTH

AIR

What is the composition of the Earth's atmosphere?

The Earth's atmosphere, apart from water vapor and pollutants, is composed of 78 percent nitrogen, 21 percent oxygen, and less than 1 percent each of argon and carbon dioxide. There are also traces of hydrogen, neon, helium, krypton, xenon, methane, and ozone. The Earth's original atmosphere was probably composed of ammonia and methane; 20 million years ago the air started to contain a broader variety of elements.

How many layers does the Earth's atmosphere contain?

The atmosphere, the "skin" of gas that surrounds the Earth, consists of five layers that are differentiated by temperature:

The troposphere is the lowest level; it averages about seven miles (11 kilometers) in thickness, varying from five miles (eight kilometers) at the poles to 10 miles (16 kilometers) at the equator. Most clouds and weather form in this layer. Temperature decreases with altitude in the troposphere.

The stratosphere ranges between seven and 30 miles (11 to 48 kilometers) above the Earth's surface. The ozone layer, important because it absorbs most of the sun's harmful ultraviolet radiation, is located in this band. Temperatures rise slightly with altitude to a maximum of about 32°F (0°C).

The mesosphere (above the stratosphere) extends from 30 to 55 miles (48 to 85 kilometers) above the Earth. Temperatures decrease with altitude to -130°F (-90°C).

The thermosphere (also known as the hetereosphere) is between 55 to 435 miles (85 to 700 kilometers). Temperatures in this layer range to 2696°F (1475°C).

The exosphere, beyond the thermosphere, applies to anything above 435 miles (700 kilometers). In this layer, temperature no longer has any meaning.

The ionosphere is a region of the atmosphere that overlaps the others, reaching from 30 to 250 miles (48 to 402 kilometers). In this region, the air becomes ionized (electrified) from the sun's ultraviolet rays, etc. This area affects the transmission and reflection of radio waves. It is divided into three regions: the D region (at 35 to 55 miles [56 to 88 kilometers]), the E Region (Heaviside-Kennelly Layer, 55 to 95 miles [88 to 153 kilometers]), and the F Region (Appleton Layer, 95 to 250 miles [153 to 402 kilometers]).

What are the Van Allen belts?

The Van Allen belts (or zones) are two regions of highly charged particles above the Earth's equator trapped by the magnetic field that surrounds the Earth. Also called the magnetosphere, the first belt extends from a few hundred to about 2,000 miles (3,200 kilometers) above the Earth's surface and the second is between 9,000 and 12,000 miles (14,500 to 19,000 kilometers). The particles, mainly protons and electrons, come from the solar wind and cosmic rays. The belts are named in honor of James Van Allen (b. 1914), the American physicist who discovered them in 1958 and 1959 with the aid of radiation counters carried aboard the artificial satellites, *Explorer I* (1958) and *Pioneer 3* (1959).

In May 1998 there were a series of large, solar disturbances that caused a new Van Allen belt to form in the so-called "slot region" between the inner and outer Van Allen belts. The new belt eventually disappeared once the solar activity subsided. There were also a number of satellite upsets around the same time involving the *Galaxy IV* satellite, Iridium satellites, and others. This is not the first time that a temporary new belt has been observed to form in the same region, but it takes a prolonged period of solar storm activity to populate this region with particles.

James Van Allen discovered two regions of highly charged particles above the Earth's equator. Van Allen appears here (center) with William Pickering and Wernher von Braun, holding a model of the first successfully launched U.S. satellite, *Explorer.*

Why is the sky blue?

The sunlight interacting with the Earth's atmosphere makes the sky blue. In outer space the astronauts see blackness because outer space has no atmosphere. Sunlight consists of light waves of varying wavelengths, each of which is seen as a different color. The minute particles of matter and molecules of air in the atmosphere intercept and scatter the white light of the sun. A larger portion of the blue color in white light is scattered, more so than any other color because the blue wavelengths are the shortest. When the size of atmospheric particles are smaller than the wavelengths of the colors, selective scattering occurs—the particles only scatter one color and the atmosphere will appear to be that color. Blue wavelengths especially are affected, bouncing off the air particles to become visible. This is why the sun looks yellow (yellow equals white minus blue). At sunset, the sky changes color because as the sun drops to the horizon, sunlight has more atmosphere to pass through and loses more of its blue wavelengths. The orange and red, having the longer wavelengths and making up more of sunlight at this distance, are most likely to be scattered by the air particles.

PHYSICAL CHARACTERISTICS, ETC.

What is the mass of the Earth?

The mass of the Earth is estimated to be 6 sextillion, 588 quintillion short tons (6.6 sextillion short tons) or 5.97×1024 kilograms, with the Earth's mean density being 5.515 times that of water (the standard). This is calculated from using the parameters of an ellipsoid adopted by the International Astronomical Union in 1964 and recognized by the International Union of Geodesy and Geophysics in 1967.

What is the interior of the Earth like?

The Earth is divided into a number of layers. The topmost layer is the crust, which contains about 0.6 percent of the Earth's volume. The depth of the crust varies from 3.5 to five miles (five to nine kilometers) beneath the oceans to 50 miles (80 kilometers) beneath some mountain ranges. The crust is formed primarily of rocks such as granite and basalt.

Between the crust and the mantle is a boundary known as the Mohorovičić discontinuity (or Moho for short), named for the Croatian seismologist, Andrija Mohorovičić (1857-1936), who discovered it in 1909. Below the Moho is the mantle, extending down about 1,800 miles (2,900 kilometers). The mantle is composed mostly of oxygen, iron, silicon, and magnesium, and accounts for about 82 percent of the Earth's volume. Although mostly solid, the upper part of the mantle, called the asthenosphere, is partially liquid.

The core-mantle boundary, also called the Gutenberg discontinuity for the German-American seismologist, Beno Gutenberg (1889-1960), separates the mantle from the core. Made up primarily of nickel and iron, the core contains about 17 percent of the Earth's volume. The outer core is liquid and extends from the base of the mantle to a depth of about 3,200 miles (5,155 kilometers). The solid inner core reaches from the bottom of the outer core to the center of the Earth, about 3,956 miles (6,371 kilometers) deep. The temperature of the inner core is estimated to be about 7,000°F (3,850°C).

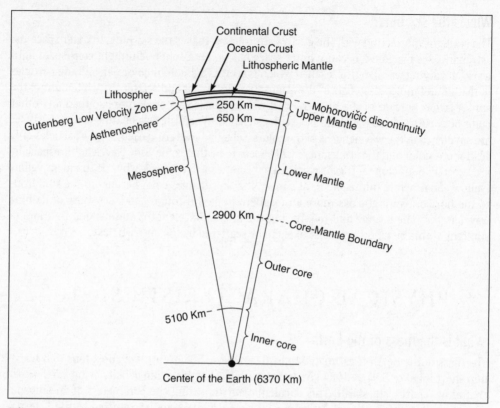

A diagram of the interior of the Earth.

What is at the center of the Earth?

Geophysicists have held since the 1940s that the Earth's interior core is a partly crystallized sphere of iron and nickel that is gradually cooling and expanding. As it cools, this inner core releases energy to an outer core called the fluid core, which is composed of iron, nickel, and lighter elements, including sulfur and oxygen. Another model called the "nuclear earth model" holds that there is a small core, perhaps five miles wide, of uranium and plutonium surrounded by a nickel-silicon compound. The uranium and plutonium work as a natural nuclear reactor, generating radiating energy in the form of heat, which in turn drives charged particles to create the Earth's magnetic field. The traditional model of the Earth's core is still dominant; however, scientists have yet to disprove the nuclear earth model.

How does the temperature of the Earth change as one goes deeper underground?

The Earth's temperature increases with depth. Measurements made in deep mines and drill-holes indicate that the rate of temperature increase varies from place to place in the world, ranging from 59° to 167°F (15 to 75°C) per kilometer in depth. Actual temperature measurements cannot be made beyond the deepest drill-holes, which are a little more than 6.2 miles (10 kilometers) deep. Estimates suggest that the temperatures at the Earth's center can reach values of 5,000°F (2,760°C) or higher.

What are the highest and lowest points on Earth?

The highest point on land is the top of Mt. Everest (in the Himalayas on the Nepal-Tibet border) at 29,028 feet (8,848 meters) above sea level, plus or minus 10 feet (three meters) because of snow. This height was established by the Surveyor General of India in 1954 and accepted by the National Geographic Society. Prior to that the height was taken to be 29,002 feet (8,840 meters). Satellite measurements taken in 1987 indicate that Mt. Everest is 29,864 feet (9,102 meters) high, but this measurement has not been adopted by the National Geographic Society.

The lowest point on land is the Dead Sea between Israel and Jordan, which is 1,312 feet (399 meters) below sea level. The lowest point on the Earth's surface is thought to be in the Marianas Trench in the western Pacific Ocean, extending from southeast of Guam to northwest of the Marianas Islands. It has been measured as 36,198 feet (11,034 meters) below sea level.

Which elements are contained in the Earth's crust?

The most abundant elements in the Earth's crust are listed in the table below. In addition, nickel, copper, lead, zinc, tin, and silver account for less than 0.02 percent with all other elements comprising 0.48 percent.

Element	Percentage
Oxygen	47.0
Silicon	28.0
Aluminum	8.0
Iron	4.5
Calcium	3.5
Magnesium	2.5
Sodium	2.5
Potassium	2.5
Titanium	0.4
Hydrogen	0.2
Carbon	0.2
Phosphorus	0.1
Sulfur	0.1

What are the highest and lowest elevations in the United States?

Named in honor of U.S. president William McKinley (1843-1901), Mt. McKinley, Alaska, at 20,320 feet (6,194 meters), is the highest point in the United States and North America. Located in central Alaska, it is part of the Alaska Range. Its south peak measures 20,320 feet (6,194 meters) high and the north peak is 19,470 feet (5,931 meters) high. It boasts one of the world's largest unbroken precipices and is the main scenic attraction at Denali National Park. Denali means the "high one" or the "great one" and is a native American name sometimes used for Mt. McKinley. Mt. Whitney, California, at 14,494 feet (4,421 meters), is the highest point in the continental United States. Death Valley, California, at 282 feet (86 meters) below sea level, is the lowest point in the United States and in the western hemisphere.

WATER

Does ocean water circulate?

Ocean water is in a constant state of movement. Horizontal movements are called currents while vertical movements are called upwelling and downwelling. Wind, tidal motion, and differences in density due to temperature or salinity are the main causes of ocean circulation. Temperature differentials arise from the equatorial water being warmer than water in the polar regions. In the Northern Hemisphere the currents circulate in a clockwise direction while in the Southern Hemisphere the currents circulate in a counter-clockwise direction. In the equatorial regions the currents move in opposite directions—from left to right in the north and from right to left in the south. Currents moving north and south from equatorial regions carry warm water while those in polar regions carry cold water.

Major Cold Currents	Major Warm Currents
California	North Atlantic (Gulf Stream)
Humboldt	South Atlantic
Labrador	South Indian Ocean
Canaries	South Pacific
Benguela	North Pacific
Falkland	Monsoons
West Australian	Okhotsk

If you melted all the ice in the world, how high would the oceans rise?

If you melted all the ice in the world, some 5.5 million cubic miles (23 million cubic kilometers) in all, the oceans would rise 1.7 percent or about 180 feet (60 meters), which is enough, for example, for 20 stories of the Empire State Building to be underwater.

What fraction of an iceberg shows above water?

Only one seventh to one-tenth of an iceberg's mass shows above water.

What is an aquifer?

Some rocks of the upper part of the Earth's crust contain many small holes, or pores. When these holes are large or are joined together so that water can flow through them easily, the rock is considered to be permeable. A large body of permeable rock in which water is stored and flows through is called an aquifer (from the Latin for "water" and "to bear"). Sandstones and gravels are excellent examples of permeable rock.

As water reservoirs, aquifers provide about 60 percent of American drinking water. The huge Ogallala Aquifer, underlying about two million acres of the Great Plains, is a major source of water for the central United States. It has been estimated that after oceans (containing 850 million cubic miles [1,370 million cubic kilometers] of water), aquifers, with an estimated 31 million cubic miles (50 million cubic kilometers), are the second largest store of water. Water is purified as it is filtered through the rock, but it can be polluted by spills,

How much of the Earth's surface is land and how much is water?

Approximately 30 percent of the Earth's surface is land. This is about 57,259,000 square miles (148,300,000 square kilometers). The area of the Earth's water surface is approximately 139,692,000 square miles (361,800,000 square kilometers), or 70 percent of the total surface area.

dumps, acid rain, and other causes. In addition, recharging of water by rainfall often cannot keep up with the volume removed by heavy pumping. The Ogallala Aquifer's supply of water could be depleted by 25 percent in the year 2020.

What is the chemical composition of the ocean?

The ocean contains every known naturally occurring element plus various gases, chemical compounds, and minerals. Below is a sampling of the most abundant chemicals.

Constituent	Concentration (parts per million)
Chloride	18,980
Sodium	10,560
Sulfate	2,560
Magnesium	1,272
Calcium	400
Potassium	380
Bicarbonate	142
Bromide	65
Strontium	13
Boron	4.6
Fluoride	1.4

What causes waves in the ocean?

The most common cause of surface waves is air movement (the wind). Waves within the ocean can be caused by tides, interactions among waves, submarine earthquakes or volcanic activity, and atmospheric disturbances. Wave size depends on wind speed, wind duration, and the distance of water over which the wind blows. The longer the distance the wind travels over water, or the harder it blows, the higher the waves. As the wind blows over water it tries to drag the surface of the water with it. The surface cannot move as fast as air, so it rises. When it rises, gravity pulls the water back, carrying the falling water's momentum below the surface. Water pressure from below pushes this swell back up again. The tug of war between gravity and water pressure constitutes wave motion. Capillary waves are caused by breezes of less than two knots. At 13 knots the waves grow taller and faster than they grow longer, and their steepness cause them to break, forming whitecaps. For a whitecap to form, the wave height must be one-seventh the distance between wave crests.

How deep is the ocean?

The average depth of the ocean floor is 13,124 feet (4,000 meters). The average depth of the four major oceans is given below:

| Ocean | Average depth | |
	Feet	Meters
Pacific	13,740	4,188
Atlantic	12,254	3,735
Indian	12,740	3,872
Arctic	3,407	1,038

There are great variations in depth because the ocean floor is often very rugged. The greatest depth variations occur in deep, narrow depressions known as trenches along the margins of the continental plates. The deepest measurements made—36,198 feet (11,034 meters), deeper than the height of the world's tallest mountains—was taken in Mariana Trench east of the Mariana Islands. In January 1960, the French oceanographer Jacques Piccard, together with the United States Navy Lieutenant David Walsh, took the bathyscaphe *Trieste* to the bottom of the Mariana Trench.

Ocean	Deepest point	Depth Feet	Meters
Pacific	Mariana Trench	36,200	11,033
Atlantic	Puerto Rico Trench	28,374	8,648
Indian	Java Trench	25,344	7,725
Arctic	Eurasia Basin	17,881	5,450

What is a tidal bore?

A tidal bore is a large, turbulent, wall-like wave of water that moves inland or upriver as an incoming tidal current surges against the flow of a more narrow and shallow river, bay, or estuary. It can be 10 to 16 feet (three to five meters) high and move rapidly (10 to 15 knots) upstream with and faster than the rising tide.

Where are the world's highest tides?

The Bay of Fundy (New Brunswick, Canada) has the world's highest tides. They average about 45 feet (14 meters) high in the northern part of the bay, far surpassing the world average of 2.5 feet (0.8 meter).

What is the difference between an ocean and a sea?

There is no neatly defined distinction between ocean and sea. One definition says the ocean is a great body of interconnecting salt water that covers 71 percent of the Earth's surface. There are four major oceans—the Arctic, Atlantic, Indian, and Pacific—but some sources do not include the Arctic Ocean, calling it a marginal sea. The terms "ocean" and "sea" are often used interchangeably but a sea is generally considered to be smaller than an ocean. The name is often given to saltwater areas on the margins of an ocean, such as the Mediterranean Sea.

How much salt is in brackish water?

Brackish water has a saline (salt) content between that of fresh water and sea water. It is neither fresh nor salty, but somewhere in between. Brackish waters are usually regarded as those containing 0.5 to 30 parts per thousand salt, while the average saltiness of seawater is 35 parts per thousand.

How salty is seawater?

Seawater is, on average, 3.3 to 3.7 percent salt. The amount of salt varies from place to place. In areas where large quantities of fresh water are supplied by melting ice, rivers, or rainfall, such as the Arctic or Antarctic, the level of salinity is lower. Areas such as the Persian Gulf and the Red Sea have salt contents over 4.2 percent. If all the salt in the ocean were dried, it would form a mass of solid salt the size of Africa. Most of the ocean salt comes from processes of dissolving and leaking from the solid Earth over hundreds of millions of years. Some is the result of salty volcanic rock that flows up from a giant rift that runs through all the ocean's basins.

Is the Dead Sea really dead?

Because the Dead Sea, on the boundary between Israel and Jordan, is the lowest body of water on the Earth's surface, any water that flows into it has no outflow. It is called "dead" because its extreme salinity makes impossible any animal or vegetable life except bacteria. Fish introduced into the sea by the Jordan River or by smaller streams die instantly. The only plant life consists primarily of halophytes (plants that grow in salty or alkaline soil). The concentration of salt increases toward the bottom of the lake. The water also has such a high density that bathers float on the surface easily.

Where is the world's deepest lake?

Lake Baikal, located in southeast Siberia, Russia, is approximately 5,371 feet (1,638 meters) deep at its maximum depth, Olkhon Crevice, making it the deepest lake in the world. Lake Tanganyika in Tanzania and Zaire is the second deepest lake, with a depth of 4,708 feet (1,435 meters).

Where are the five largest lakes in the world located?

Location	Area		Length		Depth	
	Square miles	Square Km[a]	Miles	Km[a]	Feet	Meters
Caspian Sea,[b] Asia-Europe	143,244	370,922	760	1,225	3,363	1,025
Superior, North America	31,700	82,103	350	560	1,330	406
Victoria, Africa	26,828	69,464	250	360	270	85
Huron, North America	23,010	59,600	206	330	750	229
Michigan, North America	22,300	57,800	307	494	925	282

[a] = Kilometers — [b] = Salt water lake

What is a yazoo?

A yazoo is a tributary of a river that runs parallel to the river, being prevented from joining the river because the river has built up high banks. The name is derived from the Yazoo River, a tributary of the Mississippi River, which demonstrates this effect.

Which of the Great Lakes is the largest?

Lake	Surface area Square miles	Square kilometers	Maximum depth Feet	Meters
Superior	31,700	82,103	1,333	406
Huron	23,010	59,600	750	229
Michigan	22,300	57,757	923	281
Erie	9,910	25,667	210	64
Ontario	7,540	9,529	802	244

Lake Superior is the largest of the Great Lakes. The North American Great Lakes form a single watershed with one common outlet to the sea—the St. Lawrence Seaway. The total volume of all five basins is 6,000 trillion gallons (22.7 trillion liters) equivalent to about 20 percent of the world's freshwater. Only Lake Michigan lies wholly within the United States' borders; the others share their boundaries with Canada. Some believe that Lake Huron and Lake Michigan are two lobes of one lake, since they are the same elevation and are connected by the 120-foot (36.5-meter) deep Strait of Mackinac, which is 3.6 to five miles (six to eight kilometers) wide. Gage records indicate that they both have similar water level regimes and mean long-term behavior, so that hydrologically they act as one lake. Historically they were considered two by the explorers who named them, but this is considered a misnomer by some.

What are the longest rivers in the world?

The two longest rivers in the world are the Nile in Africa and the Amazon in South America. However, which is the longest is a matter of some debate. The Amazon has several mouths that widen toward the South Atlantic, so the exact point where the river ends is uncertain. If the Pará estuary (the most distant mouth) is counted, its length is approximately 4,195 miles (6,750 kilometers). The length of the Nile as surveyed before the loss of a few

What are rip tides and why are they so dangerous?

At points along a coast where waves are high, a substantial buildup of water is created near the shore. This mass of water moves along the shore until it reaches an area of lower waves. At this point, it may burst through the low waves and move out from shore as a strong surface current moving at an abnormally rapid speed known as a rip current. Swimmers who become exhausted in a rip current may drown unless they swim parallel to the shore. Rip currents are sometimes incorrectly called rip tides.

miles of meanders due to the formation of Lake Nasser behind the Aswan Dam was 4,145 miles (6,670 kilometers). The table below lists the five longest river systems in the world.

River	Length Miles	Kilometers
Nile (Africa)	4,145	6,670
Amazon (South America)*	4,000	6,404
Chang jiang-Yangtze (Asia)	3,964	6,378
Mississippi-Missouri river system (North America)	3,740	6,021
Yenisei-Angara river system (Asia)	3,442	5,540

*excluding Pará estuary

What is the world's highest waterfall?

Angel Falls, named after the explorer and bush pilot Jimmy Angel, on the Carrao tributary in Venezuela is the highest waterfall in the world. It has a total height of 3,212 feet (979 meters) with its longest unbroken drop being 2,648 feet (807 meters).

It is difficult to determine the height of a waterfall because many are composed of several sections rather than one straight drop. The highest waterfall in the United States is Yosemite Falls on a tributary of the Merced River in Yosemite National Park, California, with a total drop of 2,425 feet (739 meters). There are three sections to the Yosemite Falls: Upper Yosemite is 1,430 feet (435 meters), Cascades (middle portion) is 675 feet (205 meters), and Lower Yosemite is 320 feet (97 meters).

LAND

Are there tides in the solid part of the Earth as well as in its waters?

The solid Earth is distorted about 4.5 to 14 inches (11.4 to 35.6 centimeters) by the gravitational pull of the sun and moon. It is the same gravitational pull that creates the tides of the waters. When the moon's gravity pulls water on the side of the Earth near to it, it pulls the solid body of the Earth on the opposite side away from the water to create bulges on both sides, and causing high tides. These occur every 12.5 hours. Low tides occur in those places from which the water is drained to flow into the two high-tide bulges. The sun causes tides on the Earth that are about 33 to 46 percent as high as those due to the moon. During a new moon or a full moon when the sun and moon are in a straight line, the tides of the moon and the sun reinforce each other to make high tides higher; these are called spring tides. At the quarter moons, the sun and moon are out of step (at right angles), the tides are less extreme than usual; these are called neap tides. Smaller bodies of water, such as lakes, have no tides because the whole body of water is raised all at once, along with the land beneath it.

Do the continents move?

In 1912, a German geologist, Alfred Lothar Wegener (1880-1930), theorized that the continents had drifted or floated apart to their present locations and that once all the continents had been a single land mass near Antarctica, which is called Pangaea (from the Greek word meaning *all-earth*). Pangaea then broke apart some 200 million years ago into two major continents called Laurasia and Gondwanaland. These two continents continued drifting and separating until the continents evolved their present shapes and positions. Wegener's theory was discounted, but it has since been found that the continents do move sideways (not drift) at an estimated 0.75 inch (19 millimeters) annually because of the action of plate tectonics. American geologist William Maurice Ewing (1906-1974) and Harry Hammond Hess (1906-1969) proposed that the Earth's crust is not a solid mass, but composed of eight major and seven minor plates that can move apart, slide by each other, collide, or override each other. Where these plates meet are major areas of mountain-building, earthquakes, and volcanoes.

How much of the Earth's surface is permanently frozen?

About one-fifth of the Earth's land is permafrost, or ground that is permanently frozen. This classification is based entirely on temperature and disregards the composition of the land. It can include bedrock, sod, ice, sand, gravel, or any other type of material in which the temperature has been below freezing for over two years. Nearly all permafrost is thousands of years old.

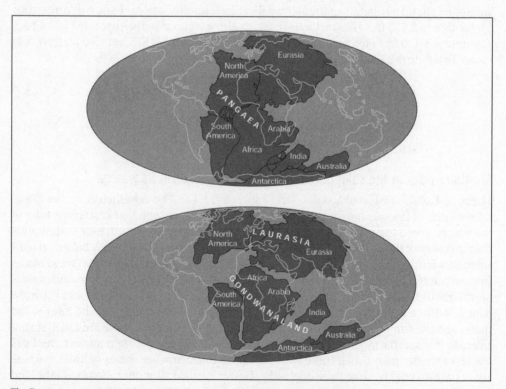

The Pangaea supercontinent (top) and its breakup into Laurasia and Gondwanaland.

When will Niagara Falls disappear?

The water dropping over Niagara Falls digs great plunge pools at the base, undermining the shale cliff and causing the hard limestone cap to cave in. Niagara has eaten itself seven miles (11 kilometers) upstream since it was formed 10,000 years ago. At this rate, it will disappear into Lake Erie in 22,800 years. The Niagara River connects Lake Erie with Lake Ontario, and marks the U.S.-Canada boundary (New York-Ontario).

Where are the northernmost and southernmost points of land?

The most northern point of land is Cape Morris K. Jesup on the northeastern extremity of Greenland. It is at 83 degrees, 39 minutes north latitude and is 440 miles (708 kilometers) from the North Pole. However, the *Guinness Book of Records* reports that an islet of 100 feet (30 meters) across, called Oodaq, is more northerly at 83 degrees, 40 minutes north latitude and 438.9 miles (706 kilometers) from the North Pole. The southernmost point of land is the South Pole (since the South Pole, unlike the North Pole, is on land).

In the United States, the northernmost point of land is Point Barrow, Alaska (71 degrees, 23 minutes north latitude), and the southernmost point of land is Ka Lae or South Cape (18 degrees, 55 minutes north latitude) on the island of Hawaii. In the 48 contiguous states, the northernmost point is Northwest Angle, Minnesota (49 degrees, 23 minutes north latitude); the southernmost point is Key West, Florida (24 degrees, 33 minutes north latitude).

How thick is the ice that covers Antarctica?

The ice that covers Antarctica is 15,700 feet (4,785 meters) in depth at its thickest point. This is about ten times taller than the Willis Tower (formerly the Sears Tower) in Chicago. However, the average thickness is 7,100 feet (2,164 meters).

Who was the first person on Antarctica?

Historians are unsure who first set foot on Antarctica, the fifth largest continent covering 10 percent of the Earth's surface with its area of 5.4 million square miles (14 million square kilometers). In 1773-1775 British Captain James Cook (1728-1779) circumnavigated the continent. American explorer Nathaniel Palmer (1799-1877) discovered Palmer Peninsula in 1820, without realizing that this was a continent. That same year, Fabian Gottlieb von Bellingshausen (1779-1852) sighted the Antarctic continent. American sealer John Davis went ashore at Hughes Bay on February 7, 1821. In 1823, sealer James Weddell (1787-1834) traveled the farthest south (74 degrees south) that anyone had until that time and entered what is now called the Weddell Sea. In 1840, American Charles Wilkes (1798-1877), who followed the coast for 1,500 miles, announced the existence of Antarctica as a continent. In 1841, Sir James Clark Ross (1800-1862) discovered Victoria Land, Ross Island, Mount Erebus, and the Ross Ice Shelf. In 1895, the whaler Henryk Bull landed on the Antarctic continent. Norwegian explorer Roald Amundsen (1872-1928) was the first to reach the South Pole on December 14, 1911. Thirty-four days later, Amundsen's rival Robert Falcon Scott (1868-1912) stood at the South Pole, the second to do so, but he and his companions died upon their return trip.

The 200-foot oceanic face of Antarctica's Ross Ice Shelf stretches straight across the horizon, dwarfed in the midst of Mount Erebus.

When was the Ice Age?

Ice ages, or glacial periods, have occurred at irregular intervals for over 2.3 billion years. During an ice age, sheets of ice cover large portions of the continents. The exact reasons for the changes in the Earth's climate are not known, although some think they are caused by changes in the Earth's orbit around the sun.

The Great Ice Age occurred during the Pleistocene Epoch, which began about two million years ago and lasted until 11,000 years ago. At its height, about 27 percent of the world's present land area was covered by ice. In North America, the ice covered Canada and moved southward to New Jersey; in the Midwest, it reached as far south as St. Louis. Small glaciers and ice caps also covered the western mountains. Greenland was covered in ice as it is today. In Europe, ice moved down from Scandinavia into Germany and Poland; the British Isles and the Alps also had ice caps. Glaciers also covered the northern plains of Russia, the plateaus of Central Asia, Siberia, and the Kamchetka Peninsula.

The glaciers' effect on the United States can still be seen. The drainage of the Ohio River and the position of the Great Lakes were influenced by the glaciers. The rich soil of the Midwest is mostly glacial in origin. Rainfall in areas south of the glaciers formed large lakes in Utah, Nevada, and California. The Great Salt Lake in Utah is a remnant of one of these lakes. The large ice sheets locked up a lot of water; sea level fell about 450 feet (137 meters) below what it is today. As a result, some states, such as Florida, were much larger during the ice age.

The glaciers of the last ice age retreated about 11,000 years ago. Some believe that the ice age is not over yet; the glaciers follow a cycle of advance and retreat many times. There are still areas of the Earth covered by ice, and this may be a time in between glacial advances.

What is a moraine?

A moraine is a mound, ridge, or any other distinct accumulation of unsorted, unstratified material or drift, deposited chiefly by direct action of glacier ice.

What is a hoodoo?

A hoodoo is a fanciful name for a grotesque rock pinnacle or pedestal, usually of sandstone, that is the result of weathering in a semi-arid region. An outstanding example of hoodoos occurs in the Wasatch Formation at Bryce Canyon, Utah.

What are sand dunes and how are they formed?

Mounds of wind-blown sand in deserts and coastal areas are called dunes. Winds transport grains of sand until it accumulates around obstacles to form ridges and mounds. Wind direction, the type of sand, and the amount of vegetation determine the type of dune. Dunes are named either for their shape (e.g. star dunes and parabolic dunes) or according to their alignment with the wind (e.g. longitudinal dunes and transverse dunes).

Which are the world's largest deserts?

A desert is an area that receives little precipitation and has little plant cover. Many deserts form a band north and south of the equator at about 20 degrees latitude because moisture-bearing winds do not release their rain over these areas. As the moisture-bearing winds from the higher latitudes approach the equator, their temperatures increase and they rise higher and higher in the atmosphere. When the winds arrive over the equatorial areas and come in contact with the colder parts of the Earth's atmosphere, they cool down and release all their water to create the tropical rain forests near the equator.

These sand dunes in California present a landscape of varying shapes, sizes and textures.

The Sahara Desert, the world's largest, is three times the size of the Mediterranean Sea. In the United States, the largest desert is the Mojave Desert in southern California with an area of 15,000 square miles (38,900 square kilometers).

Desert	Location	Area	
		Square miles	Square kilometers
Sahara	North Africa	3,500,000	9,065,000
Arabian	Arabian Peninsula	900,000	2,330,000
Australian	Australia	600,000	1,554,000
Gobi	Mongolia & China	500,000	1,295,000
Libyan	Libya, SW Egypt, Sudan	450,000	1,165,500

What is quicksand?

Quicksand is a mass of sand and mud that contains a large amount of water. A thin film separates individual grains of sand so the mixture has the characteristics of a liquid. Quicksand is found at the mouths of large rivers or other areas that have a constant source of water. Heavy objects, including humans, can sink when encountering quicksand and the mixture collapses. However, since the density of the sand/water mix is slightly greater than the density of the human body, most humans can actually float on quicksand.

Are all craters part of a volcano?

No, not all craters are of volcanic origin. A crater is a nearly circular area of deformed sedimentary rocks, with a central, ventlike depression. Some craters are caused by the collapse of the surface when underground salt or limestone dissolves. The withdrawal of groundwater and the melting of glacial ice can also cause the surface to collapse, forming a crater.

Craters are also caused by large meteorites, comets, and asteroids that hit the Earth. A notable impact crater is Meteor Crater near Winslow, Arizona. It is 4,000 feet (1,219 meters) in diameter, 600 feet (183 meters) deep and is estimated to have been formed 30,000 to 50,000 years ago.

How are caves formed?

Water erosion creates most caves found along coastal areas. Waves crashing against the rock over years wears away part of the rock forming a cave. Inland caves are also formed by water

What is the difference between spelunking and speleology?

Spelunking, or sport caving, is exploring caves as a hobby or for recreation. Speleology is the scientific study of caves and related phenomena, such as the world's deepest cave, Réseau Jean Bernard, in Haute Savoie, France, with a depth of 5,256 feet (1,602 meters), or the world's longest cave system, Mammoth Cave in Kentucky, with a length of 348 miles (560 kilometers).

erosion—in particular, groundwater eroding limestone. As the limestone dissolves, underground passageways and caverns are formed.

How is speleothem defined?

Speleothem is a term given to those cave features that form after a cave itself has formed. They are secondary mineral deposits that are created by the solidification of fluids or from chemical solutions. These mineral deposits usually contain calcium carbonate (CaCO3) or limestone, but gypsum or silica may also be found. Stalactites, stalagmites, soda straws, cave coral, boxwork and cave pearls are all types of speleothems.

What is a tufa?

It is a general name for calcium carbonate ($CaCO_3$) deposits or spongy porous limestone found at springs in limestone areas, or in caves as massive stalactite or stalagmite deposits. Tufa, derived from the Italian word for "soft rock," is formed by the precipitation of calcite from the water of streams and springs.

Which is the deepest cave in the United States?

Lechuguilla Cave, in Carlsbad Caverns National Park, New Mexico is the deepest cave in the United States. Its depth is 1,565 feet (477 meters). Unlike most caves in which carbon dioxide mixes with rainwater to produce carbonic acid, Carlsbad Caverns was shaped by sulfuric acid. The sulfuric acid was a result of a reaction between oxygen that was dissolved in groundwater and hydrogen sulfide that emanated from far below the cave's surface.

What and where is the continental divide of North America?

The Continental Divide, also known as the Great Divide, is a continuous ridge of peaks in the Rocky Mountains that marks the watershed separating easterly flowing waters from westerly flowing waters in North America. To the east of the Continental Divide, water drains into Hudson Bay or the Mississippi River before reaching the Atlantic Ocean. To the west, water generally flows through the Columbia River or the Colorado River on its way to the Pacific Ocean.

How long is the Grand Canyon?

The Grand Canyon, cut out by the Colorado River over a period of 15 million years in the northwest corner of Arizona, is the largest land gorge in the world. It is four to 13 miles (6.4 to 21 kilometers) wide at its brim, 4,000 to 5,500 feet (1,219 to 1,676 meters) deep, and 217 miles (349 kilometers) long, extending from the mouth of the Little Colorado River to Grand Wash Cliffs (and 277 miles, 600 feet [445.88 kilometers] if Marble Canyon is included).

However, it is not the deepest canyon in the United States; that distinction belongs to Kings Canyon, which runs through the Sierra and Sequoia National Forests near East Fresno, California, with its deepest point being 8,200 feet (2,500 meters). Hell's Canyon of the Snake River between Idaho and Oregon is the deepest United States canyon in low-relief territory. Also called the Grand Canyon of the Snake, it plunges 7,900 feet (2,408 meters) down from Devil Mountain to the Snake River.

A massive stalactite and stalagmite column takes center stage in South Africa's Cango Caves.

How does a stalactite differ from a stalagmite?

A stalactite is a conical or cylindrical calcite ($CaCO_3$) formation hanging from a cave roof. It forms from the centuries-long buildup of mineral deposits resulting from the seepage of water from the limestone rock above the cave. This water containing calcium bicarbonate evaporates, losing some carbon dioxide, to deposit small quantities of calcium carbonate (carbonate of lime), which eventually forms a stalactite.

A stalagmite is a stone formation that develops upward from the cave floor and resembles an icicle upside down. Formed from water containing calcite that drips from the limestone walls and roof of the cave, it sometimes joins a stalactite to form a column.

What are the LaBrea Tar Pits?

The tar pits are located in an area of Los Angeles, California, formerly known as Rancho LaBrea. Heavy, sticky tar oozed out of the Earth there, the scum from great petroleum reservoirs far underground. The pools were cruel traps for uncounted numbers of animals. Today, the tar pits are a part of Hancock Park, where many fossil remains are displayed along with life-sized reconstructions of these prehistoric species.

The tar pits were first recognized as a fossil site in 1875. However, scientists did not systematically excavate the area until 1901. By comparing Rancho La Brea's fossil specimens with their nearest living relatives, paleontologists have a greater understanding of the climate, vegetation, and animal life in the area during the Ice Age. Perhaps the most impressive fossil bones recovered belong to such large extinct mammals as the imperial mammoth and the saber-toothed cat. Paleontologists have even found the remains of the western horse and the camel, which originated in North America, migrated to other parts of the world, and became extinct in North America at the end of the Ice Age.

VOLCANOES

How are volcanoes formed?

Volcanoes are the result of magma rising or being pushed to the surface of the Earth. Hot liquid magma, which is located under the surface of the Earth, rises through cracks and weak sections of rock. The mountain surrounding a volcano is formed by lava (called magma until it arrives at the Earth's surface) that cools and hardens, making the volcano taller, wider, or both.

What is the difference between magma and lava?

Magma is hot, liquefied rock that lies underneath the surface of the Earth. When magma erupts or flows from a volcano onto the Earth's surface, it becomes lava. There is no difference in substance; only the name changes.

What is the Ring of Fire?

If you were to look at a map of the world's major earthquakes and volcanoes, you would notice a pattern circling the Pacific Ocean. This dense accumulation of earthquakes and volcanoes is known as the Ring of Fire. The ring is due to plate tectonics and the merger of the Pacific Plate with other surrounding plates, which creates faults and seismic activity (especially Alaska, Japan, Oceania, and coastal North and South America), along with volcanic mountain ranges, such as the Cascades of the U.S. Pacific Northwest and the Andes of South America.

How many active volcanoes are there in the world?

There are about 1,500 potentially active volcanoes around the world, but the number often depends on how we define active. Experts at the National Geographic Society consider ap-

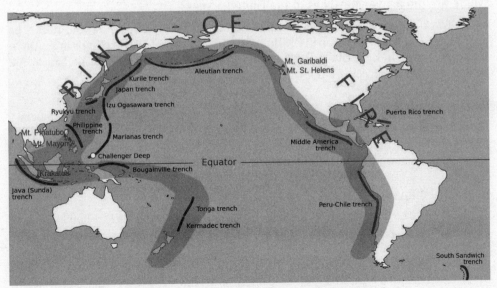

The Ring of Fire encircles the Pacific Ocean with volcanic and earthquake activity.

proximately 1,900 volcanoes on Earth to be active, with evidence of activity and a strong likelihood to explode again. Most are located in the Ring of Fire surrounding the Pacific Ocean. About one-tenth of the world's active volcanoes are located in the United States. A volcano is considered active if it has erupted in the last 10,000 years. If you were to consider how many volcanoes may be at the bottom of the sea floor, there could be many thousands more.

What are some of the world's most active volcanoes, in terms of numbers of years of eruptions?

The volcanoes that have been active the most number of years include Mt. Etna in Italy (3,500 years), Mt. Stromboli in Italy (2,000 years), and Mt. Yasur in Vanuatu (800 years).

How many active volcanoes are located in Europe?

There are more than sixty active volcanoes in Europe and more than forty dormant ones, many of which are located in Italy, Sicily, and Greece.

Which volcano poses the most risk to people in Europe?

Mt. Vesuvius, on the southwestern coast of Italy, lies very near a city of more than one million people: Naples. Although it last erupted in 79 C.E., it is still active, and geologists predict there is a very good chance it will erupt again, potentially putting the city of Naples and the surrounding area at risk.

How many active volcanoes does Iceland have?

Iceland, formed by volcanoes, lies between two tectonic plates along the Mid-Atlantic Ridge and is home to approximately 130 volcanoes. Of these, 30 are considered to be active.

Where are the active volcanoes in the United States?

Alaska, Washington, Oregon, and California have many potentially active volcanoes. The most recent large-scale eruption in the United States was that of Mt. St. Helens in southern Washington State in 1980. Other volcanoes in the region, such as Mt. Shasta, Mt. Lassen, Mt. Rainier, and Mt. Hood, could erupt with little warning.

What is so interesting about volcanoes in Alaska?

Alaska contains approximately 130 volcanoes, with 90 that have been active in the last 10,000 years. Volcanoes in the state of Alaska account for over 75% of all volcanoes that have erupted in the United States in the last two hundred years.

How was Pompeii destroyed?

In the year 79 C.E., the volcano Mt. Vesuvius erupted and buried the ancient Roman town of Pompeii under 20 feet (6 meters) of lava and ash. Pompeii is famous because excavations of the city, which began in 1748 and continue to this day, provide an excellent look at Roman life at the beginning of the millennium. The covering of the city by debris preserved not only the places where people last stood but also paintings, art, and many other artifacts. The nearby city of Herculaneum was also buried and perfectly preserved. Although a much smaller ver-

The ruins of Pompeii attract tourists today, but it is difficult to imagine the horror of an entire city wiped out by a volcano.

sion of Pompeii, it contains some of the best art, architecture, and examples of daily life in Roman times and is only twenty minutes away from Pompeii. Even loaves of bread that were baking on the day of the eruption are preserved in a nearly 2,000-year-old bakery.

EARTHQUAKES

What creates earthquakes?

The tectonic plates of the Earth are always in motion. Plates that lie side by side may not move very easily with respect to one another; they "stick" together, and occasionally they slip. These slips (from a few inches to many feet) create earthquakes and can often be very destructive to human lives and structures.

What is an epicenter?

An epicenter is the point on the Earth's surface that is directly above the hypocenter, or the point where earthquakes actually occur. Earthquakes do not usually occur at the surface of the Earth but at some depth below the surface.

What is a fault?

A fault is a fracture or a collection of fractures in the Earth's surface where movement has occurred. Most faults are inactive, but some, like California's San Andreas Fault, are quite active. Geologists have not discovered all of the Earth's faults, and sometimes earthquakes occur that take the world by surprise, like the one that occurred in 1994 in Northridge, California. When earthquakes occur on faults that were previously unknown, they are called blind faults.

What is the significance of the infamous San Andreas Fault?

The infamous San Andreas Fault lies at the border between the North American and the Pacific tectonic plates. This fault is situated in California and is responsible for some of the major earthquakes that occur there. Los Angeles is on the Pacific Plate, but San Francisco is on the North American Plate. The Pacific Plate is sliding northward with respect to the North American Plate, and, as a result, Los Angeles gets about half an inch closer to San Francisco every year. In a few million years, the two cities will be neighbors.

Was San Francisco destroyed by earthquake or by fire in 1906?

In 1906, a very powerful earthquake struck San Francisco, California, which sparked a fire that destroyed much of the city. In an effort to preserve San Francisco's image with residents and would-be visitors, official policy regarding the disaster stated that it was not the earthquake but mostly the fire that destroyed the city. Official books and publications produced after the earthquake referred to both the fire and the earthquake as having caused the damage. In fact, the earthquake did considerable damage to the city and killed hundreds.

What is the Richter scale?

The Richter scale measures the energy released by an earthquake. It was developed in 1935 by California seismologist Charles F. Richter. With each increase in Richter magnitude, there is an increase of thirty times the energy released by an earthquake. For example, a 7.0 earth-

A view of San Francisco taken from the Union Ferry Building and looking toward Market street shortly after the 1906 earthquake and fire.

Will California eventually fall into the ocean?

No, it will not. The famous San Andreas Fault, which runs along the western edge of California from the San Francisco Bay area to southern California, is known as a transverse fault. This means that the western side of the fault, which includes places like Monterey, Santa Barbara, and Los Angeles, is sliding northward with respect to the rest of the state. In a few million years, the state's two largest urban areas, San Francisco and Los Angeles, will be right next to each other. The fault is moving at about two centimeters (just under an inch) a year.

quake has thirty times the power of a 6.0 earthquake. Each earthquake only has one Richter magnitude. The strongest earthquakes are in the 8.0–9.0 range—8.6 for Alaska's 1964 earthquake and 8.0 for China's 1976 earthquake in Tangshan.

What is the Mercalli scale?

The Mercalli scale measures the power of an earthquake as felt by humans and structures. Italian geologist Giuseppe Mercalli developed it in 1902. The Mercalli scale is written in Roman numerals, and it ranges from I (barely felt) to XII (catastrophic). The Mercalli scale can be mapped surrounding an epicenter and will vary based on the geology of an area.

The Mercalli Scale of Earthquake Intensity

Scale	Effects
I	Barely felt
II	Felt by a few people, some suspended objects may swing
III	Slightly felt indoors as though a large truck were passing
IV	Felt indoors by many people, most suspended objects swing, windows and dishes rattle, standing autos rock
V	Felt by almost everyone, sleeping people are awakened, dishes and windows break
VI	Felt by everyone, some are frightened and run outside, some chimneys break, some furniture moves, causes slight damage
VII	Considerable damage in poorly built structures, felt by people driving, most are frightened and run outside
VIII	Slight damage to well-built structures, poorly built structures are heavily damaged, walls, chimneys, monuments fall
IX	Underground pipes break, foundations of buildings are damaged and buildings shift off foundations, considerable damage to well-built structures
X	Few structures survive, most foundations destroyed, water moved out of banks of rivers and lakes, avalanches and rockslides, railroads are bent
XI	Few structures remain standing, total panic, large cracks in the ground
XII	Total destruction, objects thrown into the air, the land appears to be liquid and is visibly rolling like waves

What does an earthquake feel like?

Smaller earthquakes or tremors feel disorienting at first. You feel a sense that the room is spinning, as if you are becoming dizzy. Usually preceding an earthquake, when the initial tremors hit, you can hear the sounds of things rattling that you have never heard before, like glasses rubbing against each other and windows vibrating. With larger earthquakes, as the earth nearby tears or opens, you can hear a very loud rumbling sound that is similar to a passing train.

How many mini-earthquakes happen each year on our planet?

Experts at the U.S. Geological Survey believe that if we consider earthquakes of low magnitudes of between 2 and 2.9, there are an estimated 1.3 million mini-earthquakes each year, somewhere on Earth.

How many really big earthquakes occur each year?

On average, there are about 134 earthquakes of a magnitude 6.0–6.9, about fifteen of a magnitude 7.0–7.9, and one huge magnitude 8.0–8.9 earthquake each year. Many of these really big earthquakes occur in the ocean, so we don't hear much about them.

Is a magnitude ten the top of the Richter scale?

While the media often refers to the Richter scale as being on a scale of one to ten, there is no upper limit, even though the strongest quakes are not as high as ten.

ROCKS AND MINERALS

How do rocks differ?

Rocks can be conveniently placed into one of three groups—igneous, sedimentary, and metamorphic.

Igneous rocks, such as granite, pegmatite, rhyolite, obsidian, gabbro, and basalt, are formed by the solidification of molten magma that emerges through the Earth's crust via volcanic activity. The nature and properties of the crystals vary greatly, depending in part on the composition of the original magma and partly on the conditions under which the magma solidified. There are thousands of different igneous rock types. For example, granite is formed by slow cooling of molten material (within the Earth). It has large crystals of quartz, feldspars, and mica.

Sedimentary rocks, such as brecchia, sandstone, shale, limestone, chert, and coals, are produced by the accumulation of sediments. These are fine rock particles or fragments, skeletons of microscopic organisms, or minerals leached from rocks that have accumulated from weathering. These sediments are then redeposited under water and later compressed in layers over time. The most common sedimentary rock is sandstone, which is predominantly quartz crystals.

Metamorphic rocks, such as marble, slate, schist, gneiss, quartzite, and hornsfel, are formed by the alteration of igneous and sedimentary rocks through heat and/or pressure. One example of these physical and chemical changes is the formation of marble from thermal changes in limestone.

What is petrology and what does a petrologist do?

Petrology is the science of rocks. A petrologist is a person who studies the mineralogy of rocks and the record of the geological past contained within rocks. From rocks, a petrologist can learn about past climates and geography, past and present composition of the Earth, and the conditions that prevail within the interior of the Earth.

How are fossils formed?

Fossils are the remains of animals or plants that were preserved in rock before the beginning of recorded history. It is unusual for complete organisms to be preserved; fossils usually represent the hard parts such as bones or shells of animals and leaves, seeds, or woody parts of plants.

Some fossils are simply the bones, teeth, or shells themselves, which can be preserved for a relatively short period of time. Another type of fossil is the imprint of a buried plant or animal that decomposes, leaving a film of carbon that retains the form of the organism.

Some buried material is replaced by silica and other materials that permeate the organism and replace the original material in a process called petrification. Some woods are replaced by agate or opal so completely that even the cellular structure is duplicated. The best examples of this can be found in the Petrified Forest National Park in Arizona.

Molds and casts are other very common fossils. A mold is made from an imprint, such as a dinosaur footprint, in soft mud or silt. This impression may harden, then be covered with other materials. The original footprint will have formed a mold and the sediments filling it will be a cast of the footprint.

How old are fossils?

The oldest known fossils are of bacteria that left their impressions approximately 3.5 billion years ago. The oldest animal fossils are of invertebrates that lived approximately 700 million years ago. The largest number of fossils come from the Cambrian period of 590-505 million years ago, when living organisms began to develop skeletons and hard parts. Since these parts tended to last longer than ordinary tissue, they were more likely to be preserved in clay and become fossilized.

What is a tektite?

Tektites are silica-rich glass objects (rocks) found scattered in selected regions of the Earth's surface. They are generally black, oblong, teardrop or dumbbell-shaped, and several centimeters in length. They are formed from molten rock resulting when a meteorite, asteroid, or comet fragment impacts the Earth's surface. The molten rock is hurled high into atmosphere, where it rapidly cools into its unique shape and physical characteristics. Their mode of formation is considered indisputable evidence of such impacts. Tektites range from 0.7 to 35 million years in age.

463

What are Indian Dollars?

They are six-sided, disk-shaped, twin crystals of aragonite ($CaCO_3$), which have altered to calcite but retained their outer form. They occur in large numbers in northern Colorado, where they are known as "Indian Dollars." In New Mexico they are called "Aztec Money" and in western Kansas they are called "Pioneer Dollars."

What is cinnabar?

Cinnabar is the main ore of the mineral mercury. Its cinnamon to scarlet-red color makes it a colorful mineral. It is produced primarily in the United States (California, Oregon, Texas and Arkansas), Spain, Italy, and Mexico. It is often used as a pigment.

How does a rock differ from a mineral?

Mineralogists use the term "mineral" for a substance that has all four of the following features: it must be found in nature; it must be made up of substances that were never alive (organic); it has the same chemical makeup wherever it is found; and its atoms are arranged in a regular pattern to form solid crystals.

While "rocks" are sometimes described as an aggregate or combination of one or more minerals, geologists extend the definition to include clay, loose sand, and certain limestones.

What is the Mohs scale?

The Mohs scale is a standard of 10 minerals by which the hardness of a mineral is rated. It was introduced in 1812 by the German mineralogist Friedrich Mohs (1773-1839). The minerals are arranged from softest to hardest. Harder minerals, with higher numbers, can scratch those with a lower number.

Hardness	Mineral	Comment
1	Talc	Hardness 1-2 can be scratched by a fingernail
2	Gypsum	Hardness 2-3 can be scratched by a copper coin
3	Calcite	Hardness 3-6 can be scratched by a steel pocket knife
4	Fluorite	
5	Apatite	
6	Orthoclase	Hardness 6-7 will not scratch glass
7	Quartz	
8	Topaz	Hardness 8-10 will scratch glass
9	Corundum	
10	Diamond	

Who was the first person to attempt a color standardization scheme for minerals?

The German mineralogist Abraham Gottlob Werner (c.1750-1817) devised a method of describing minerals by their external characteristics, including color. He worked out an arrangement of colors and color names, illustrated by an actual set of minerals.

What is pitchblende?

Pitchblende is a massive variety of uraninite, or uranium oxide, found in metallic veins. It is a radioactive material and the most important ore of uranium. In 1898, Marie and Pierre Curie discovered that pitchblende contained radium, a rare element that has since been used in medicine and the sciences.

What is galena?

Galena is a lead sulphide (PbS) and the most common ore of lead, containing 86.6 percent lead. Lead-gray in color, with a brilliant metallic luster, galena has a specific gravity of 7.5 and a hardness of 2.5 on the Mohs scale, and usually occurs as cubes or a modification of an octahedral form. Mined in Australia, it is also found in Canada, China, Mexico, Peru, and the United States (Missouri, Kansas, Oklahoma, Colorado, Montana, and Idaho).

What is stibnite?

Stibnite is a lead-gray mineral (Sb2S3) with a metallic luster. It is the most important ore of antimony, and is also known as antimony glance. One of the few minerals that fuse easily in a match flame (977°F or 525°C), stibnite has a hardness of two on the Mohs scale and a specific gravity of 4.5 to 4.6. It is commonly found in hydrothermal veins or hot springs deposits. Stibnite is mined in Germany, Romania, France, Bolivia, Peru, and Mexico. The Yellow Pine mine at Stibnite, Idaho, is the largest producer in the United States, but California and Nevada also have deposits.

What are Cape May diamonds?

They are pure quartz crystals of many sizes and colors, found in the vicinity of the Coast Guard station in Cape May, New Jersey. When polished and faceted, these crystals have the appearance of real diamonds. Prior to the development of modern gem examination equipment, many people were fooled by these quartz crystals. The possibility of finding a Cape May diamond on one's own, and the availability of already-polished faceted stones, has been a long-standing tourist attractions in the Cape May area.

How can a genuine diamond be identified?

There are several tests that can be performed without the aid of tools. A knowledgeable person can recognize the surface lustre, straightness and flatness of facets, and high light reflectivity. Diamonds become warm in a warm room and cool if the surroundings are cool. A simple test that can be done is exposing the stones to warmth and cold and then touching them to one's lips to determine their appropriate temperature. This is especially effective when the results of this test are compared to the results of the test done on a diamond known to be genuine. Another test is to pick up the stone with a moistened fingertip. If this can be done, then the stone is likely to be a diamond. The majority of other stones cannot be picked up in this way.

The water test is another simple test. A drop of water is placed on a table. A perfectly clean diamond has the ability to almost "magnetize" water and will keep the water from spreading. An instrument called a diamond probe can detect even the most sophisticated fakes. Gemologists always use this as part of their inspection.

What are the four "C"s of diamonds?

The four "C"s are cut, color, clarity, and carat. Cut refers to the proportions, finish, symmetry, and polish of the diamond. These factors determine the brilliance of a diamond. Color describes the amount of color the diamond contains. Color ranges from colorless to yellow with tints of yellow, gray, or brown. Colors can also range from intense yellow to the more rare blue, green, pink, and red. Clarity describes the cleanness or purity of a diamond as determined by the number and size of imperfections. Carat is the weight of the diamond.

How are diamonds weighed?

The basic unit is a carat, which is set at 200 milligrams (0.00704 ounces or 1/142 of an avoirdupois ounce). A well-cut, round diamond of one carat measures almost exactly 0.25 inch (6.3 millimeters) in diameter. Another unit commonly used is the point, which is one hundredth of a carat. A stone of one carat weighs 100 points. "Carat" as a unit of weight should not be confused with the term "karat" used to indicate purity of the gold into which gems are mounted.

Which diamond is the world's largest?

The Cullinan Diamond, weighing 3,106 carats, is the world's largest. It was discovered on January 25, 1905, at the Premier Diamond Mine, Transvaal, South Africa. Named for Sir Thomas M. Cullinan, chairman of the Premier Diamond Company, it was cut into nine major stones and 96 smaller brilliants. The total weight of the cut stones was 1,063 carats, only 35 percent of the original weight.

Cullinan I, also known as the "Greater Star of Africa" or the "First Star of Africa," is a pear-shaped diamond weighing 530.2 carats. It is 2.12 inches (5.4 centimeters) long, 1.75 inches (4.4 centimeters) wide, and one inch (2.5 centimeters) thick at its deepest point. It was presented to Britain's King Edward VII in 1907, and was set in the British monarch's sceptre with the cross. It is still the largest cut diamond in the world.

Cullinan II, also know as the "Second Star of Africa," is an oblong stone that weighs 317.4 carats. It is set in the British Imperial State Crown.

What are the common cuts of gemstones?

Modern gem cutting uses faceted cutting for most transparent gems. In faceted cutting, numerous facets—geometrically disposed to bring out the beauty of light and color to the best advantage—are cut. The four most common cuts are the brilliant, the rose, the baguette, and the step or trap cut. The step or trap cut is also known as the emerald cut and is used for emeralds. The brilliant and rose cuts are often used for diamonds.

What is cubic zirconium?

Cubic zirconium was discovered in 1937 by two German mineralogists. It became popular with jewelry designers in the 1970s after Soviet scientists learned how to "grow" the mineral in a laboratory. Most of the cubic zirconium on the market is chemically comprised of zirconium oxide and yttrium oxide. The two compounds are melted together at a very high temperature (almost 5,000°F) (2,760°C) using the skull melt method. This method uses a radio-frequency generator to heat the zirconium oxide. A careful cooling of the mixture produces the flawless crystals that become cubic zirconia gemstones.

How does the emerald get its color?

Emerald is a variety of green beryl ($Be_3Al_2Si_6O_{18}$) that is colored by a trace of chromium (Cr), which replaces the aluminum (Al) in the beryl structure. Other green beryls exist; but if no chromium is present, they are, technically speaking, not emeralds.

What is the difference between cubic zirconium and diamonds?

Cubic zirconium is a gemstone material that is an imitation of diamonds. The word "imitation" is key. The U.S. Federal Trade Commission defines imitation materials as resembling the natural material in appearance only. Cubic zirconia may be cut the same way as diamonds. It is very dense and solid, weighing 1.7 times more than a diamond of the same millimeter size.

Besides the Cullinan diamonds, what are the largest precious stones?

The largest ruby is a 8,500 carat stone that is 5.5 inches (14 centimeters) tall, carved to resemble the Liberty Bell. The largest star ruby is the 6,465 carat "Eminent Star" from India that has a six-line star. The largest cut emerald was found in Carnaiba, Brazil, in August 1974. It is 86,136 carats. A 2,302 carat sapphire from Anakie, Queensland, Australia, was carved into a 1,318 carat head of Abraham Lincoln, making it the largest carved sapphire. "The Lone Star," at 9,719.5 carats, is the largest star sapphire. The largest natural pearl is the "Pearl of Lao-tze," also called the "Pearl of Allah." Found in May 1934 in the shell of a giant clam at Palawan, Philippines, the pearl weighs 14 pounds, 1 ounce (6.4 kilograms).

How is the star in star sapphires produced?

Sapphires are composed of gem-quality corundum (Al_2O_3). Color appears in sapphires when small amounts of iron and titanium are present. Star stapphires contain needles of the mineral rutile that will display as a six-ray star figure when cut in the unfaceted cabochon (dome or convex) form. The most highly prized star sapphires are blue. Black or white star sapphires are less valuble. Since a ruby is simply the red variety of corundum, star rubies also exist.

What is a tiger's eye?

Tiger's eye is a semiprecious quartz gem that has a vertical luminescent band like that of a cat's eye. To achieve the effect of a cat's eye, veins of parallel blue asbestos fibers are first altered to iron oxides and then replaced by silica. The gem has a rich yellow to yellow-brown or brown color.

METALS

Which metallic element is the most abundant?

Aluminum is the most abundant metallic element on the surface of the Earth and moon; it comprises more than 8 percent of the Earth's crust. It is never free in nature, combining with oxygen, sand, iron, titanium, etc.; its ores are mainly bauxites (aluminum hydroxide). Nearly all rocks, particularly igneous rocks, contain aluminum as aluminosilicate minerals. Napoleon III (1808-1883) recognized that the physical characteristic of its lightness could revolutionize the arms industry, so he granted a large subsidy to French chemist Sainte-Claire Deville (1818-1881) to develop a method to make its commercial use feasible. In 1854, Deville obtained the first pure aluminum metal through the process of reduction of aluminum chloride. In 1886, the American Charles Martin Hall (1863-1914) and the Frenchman Paul Heroult (1863-1914) independently discovered an electrolytic process to produce aluminum from bauxite. Because of aluminum's resistance to corrosion, low density, and excellent heat-conducting property, the packaging industry uses a large percentage of the aluminum alloy that is produced for drink and food containers and covers, and foil pouches and wraps. It is a good conductor of electricity and is widely used in power and telephone cables, light bulbs, and electrical equipment. Large amounts of aluminum are used in the production of all types of vehicles; alloys have high tensile strengths and are of considerable industrial importance to the aerospace industry. The building construction industry uses aluminum alloys in such items as gutters, panels, siding, window frames, and roofing. Examples of the numerous other products containing aluminum and aluminum alloys are cookware, golf clubs, air conditioners, lawn furniture, license plates, paints, refrigerators, rocket fuel, and zippers.

What are the noble metals?

The noble metals are gold, silver, mercury, and the platinum group (including palladium, iridium, rhodium, ruthenium, and osmium). The term refers to those metals highly resistant to chemical reaction or corrosion and is contrasted with "base" metals, which are not so resistant. The term has its origins in ancient alchemy whose goals of transformation and perfection were pursued through the different properties of metals and chemicals. The term is not synonymous with "precious metals," although a metal, like platinium, may be both.

What are the precious metals?

This is a general term for expensive metals that are used for making coins, jewelry, and ornaments. The name is limited to gold, silver, and platinum. Expense or rarity does not make a metal precious, but rather it is a value set by law that states that the object made of these metals has a certain intrinsic value. The term is not synonymous with "noble metals," although a metal (such as platinum) may be both noble and precious.

How far can a troy ounce of gold, if formed into a thin wire, be stretched before it breaks?

Ductility is the characteristic of a substance to lend itself to shaping and stretching. A troy ounce of gold (31.1035 grams) can be drawn into a fine wire that is 50 miles (80 kilometers) long.

How thick is gold leaf?

Gold leaf is pure gold that is hammered or rolled into sheets or leaves so extremely thin that it can take 300,000 units to make a stack one inch high. The thickness of a single gold leaf is typically 0.0000035 inch (3.5 millionths of an inch), although this may vary widely according to which manufacturer makes it. Also called gold foil, it is used for architectural coverings and for hot-embossed printing on leather.

What is 24 karat gold?

The term "karat" refers to the percentage of gold versus the percentage of an alloy in a piece of jewelry or a decorative object. Gold is too soft to be usable in its purest form and has to be mixed with other metals. One karat is equal to one-24th part fine gold. Thus, 24 karat gold is 100 percent pure and 18 karat gold is 18/24 or 75 percent pure.

Karatage	Percentage of fine gold
24	100
22	91.75
18	75
14	58.5
12	50.25
10	42
9	37.8
8	33.75

What is sterling silver?

Sterling silver is a high-grade alloy that contains a minimum of 925 parts in 1,000 of silver (92.5 percent silver and 7.5 percent of another metal—usually copper).

What is German silver?

Nickel silver, sometimes known as German silver or nickel brass, is a silver-white alloy composed of 52 percent to 80 percent copper, 10 percent to 35 percent zinc, and 5 percent to 35 percent nickel. It may also contain a small percent of lead and tin. There are other forms of nickel silver, but the term "German silver" is the name used in the silverware trade.

Which metal is the main component of pewter?

Tin—at least 90 percent. Antimony, copper, and zinc may be added in place of lead to harden and strengthen pewter. Pewter may still contain lead, but high lead content will both tarnish the piece and dissolve into food and drink to become toxic. The alloy used today in fine quality pieces contain 91-95 percent minimum tin, 8 percent maximum antimony, 2.5 percent maximum copper, and 0-5 percent maximum bismuth, as determined by the European Standard for pewter.

Where were the first successful ironworks in America?

Although iron ore in this country was first discovered in North Carolina in 1585, and the manufacture of iron was first undertaken (but never accomplished) in Virginia in 1619, the first successful ironworks in America was established by Thomas Dexter and Robert Bridges near the Saugus River in Lynn, Massachusetts. As the original promoters of the enterprise,

What is high speed steel?

High speed steel is a general name for high alloy steels that retain their hardness at very high temperatures and are used for metal-cutting tools. All high speed steels are based on either tungsten or molybdenum (or both) as the primary heat-resisting alloying element. These steels require a special heat so that their unique properties can be fully realized. The manufacturing process consists of heating the steel to a temperature of 2,150°F to 2,400°F (1,175°C to 1,315°C) to obtain solution of a substantial percentage of the alloy carbides, quenching to room temperature, tempering at 1,000°F to 1,150°F (535°C to 620°C), and again cooling to room temperature.

they hired John Winthrop, Jr. from England to begin production. By 1645, a blast furnace had begun operations, and by 1648 a forge was working there.

Who invented stainless steel?

Metallurgists in several countries developed stainless steel, a group of iron-based alloys combined with chromium in order to be resistant to rusting and corrosion. Chromium was used in small amounts in 1872 to strengthen the steel of the Eads Bridge over the Mississippi River, but it wasn't until the 1900's that a truly rust-resistant alloy was developed. Metallurgists in several countries developed stainless steel between 1903 and 1912. An American, Elwood Haynes, developed several alloy steels and in 1911 produced stainless steel. Harry Brearly of Great Britain receives most of the credit for its development. Frederick Beckett, a Canadian-American metallurgist, and German scientists P. Monnartz and W. Borchers were among the early developers.

What material is used to make a tuning fork?

A tuning fork, an instrument that when struck emits a fixed pitch, is generally made of steel. Some tuning forks are made of aluminum, magnesium-alloy, fused quartz, or other elastic material.

Which countries have uranium deposits?

Uranium, a radioactive metallic element, is the only natural material capable of sustaining nuclear fission. But only one isotope, uranium-235, which occurs in one molecule out of 40 of natural uranium, can undergo fission under neutron bombardment. Mined in various parts of the world, it must then be converted during purification to uranium dioxide (UO_2). Uranium deposits occur throughout the world; the largest are in the United States (the Colorado Plateau and low-grade reserves in Florida, Tennessee, North Dakota, and South Dakota), Canada (Ontario, Northwest Territories, and west-central), South Africa (the Witwatersrand), and Gabon (Oklo). Other countries and areas having significant low-grade deposits are Brazil, Russia, North Africa, and Sweden. Previously significant reserves in Zaire are almost exhausted.

What is technetium?

Technetium (Tc, element 43) is a radioactive metallic element that does not occur naturally either in its pure form or as compounds; it is produced during nuclear fission. A fission product of molybdenum (Mo, element 42), Tc can also occur as a fission product of uranium (U, element 92). It was the first element to be made artificially in 1937 when it was isolated and extracted by C. Perrier and Emilio Segrè (1905-1989).

Tc has found significant application in diagnostic imaging and nuclear medicine. Ingested soluble technetium compounds tend to concentrate in the liver and are valuable in labeling and in radiological examination of that organ. Also, by technetium labeling of blood serum components, diseases involving the circulatory system can be explored.

NATURAL SUBSTANCES

What is obsidian?

Obsidian is a volcanic glass that usually forms in the upper parts of lava flows. Embryonic crystal growths, known as crystallites, make the glass an opaque, jet-black color. Red or brown obsidian could result if iron oxide dust is present. There are some well-known formations in existence, including the Obsidian Cliffs in Yellowstone Park and Mount Hekla in Iceland.

Is lodestone a magnet?

Lodestone is a naturally occurring variety of magnetic iron oxide or magnetite. Lodestone is frequently called a natural magnet because it attracts iron objects and possesses polarity. It was used by early mariners to find magnetic north. Other names for lodestone are loadstone, leading stone, and Hercules stone.

What is red dog?

Red dog is the residue from burned coal dumps. The dumps are composed of waste products incidental to coal mining. Under pressure in these waste dumps, the waste frequently ignites from spontaneous combustion, producing a red-colored ash, which is used for driveways, parking lots, and roads.

What are some uses for coal other than as an energy resource?

In the past, many of the aromatic compounds, such as benzene, toluene, and xylene were made from coal. These compounds are now chiefly byproducts of petroleum. Naphthalene and phenanthrene are still obtained from coal tar. Coal tar, a byproduct of coal, is used in roofing.

What is diatomite?

Diatomite (also called diatomaceous earth) is a white- or cream-colored, friable, porous rock composed of the fossil remains of diatoms (small water plants with silica cell walls). These fossils build up on the ocean bottoms to form diatomite, and in some places these areas have become dry land or diatomacceous earth. Chemically inert and having a rough texture and other unusual physical properties, it is suitable for many scientific and industrial purposes, including use as a filtering agent; building material; heat, cold, and sound insulator; catalyst carrier; filler absorbent; abrasive; and ingredient in pharmaceutical preparations. Dynamite is made from it by soaking it in the liquid explosive nitroglycerin.

What is fly ash?

Fly ash is the very fine portion or ash residue that results from the combustion of coal. The fly ash portion is usually removed electrostatically from the coal combustion gasses before they are released to the atmosphere. About 31 percent of the 57 million metric tons produced annually in the United States are beneficially used; the remainder must be disposed of in ponds or landfills.

In coal mining what is meant by damp?

Damp is a poisonous or explosive gas in a mine. The most common type of damp is firedamp, also known as methane. White damp is carbon monoxide. Blackdamp (or chokedamp) is a mixture of nitrogen and carbon dioxide formed by mine fires and explosion of firedamp in mines. Blackdamp extinguishes fire and suffocates its victims.

What is fuller's earth?

It is a naturally occurring white or brown clay containing aluminum magnesium silicate. Fuller's earth acts as a catalyst and was named for a process known as fulling—a process used to clean grease from wool and cloth. It is currently used for lightening the color of oils and fats, as a pigment extender, as a filter, as an absorbent (for example, in litter boxes to absorb animal waste), and in floor sweeping compounds.

How is charcoal made?

Commercial production of charcoal uses wood processing residues, such as sawdust, shavings, milled wood and bark as a raw material. Depending on the material, the residues are placed in kilns or furnaces and heated at low oxygen concentrations. A Herreshoff furnace can produce at least a ton of charcoal per hour.

How much wood is used to make a ton of paper?

In the United States, the wood used for the manufacture of paper is mainly from small diameter bolts and pulpwood. It is usually measured by the cord or by weight. Although the fiber used in making paper is overwhelmingly wood fiber, a large percentage of other ingredients is needed. One ton of a typical paper requires two cords of wood, but also requires 55,000 gallons (208,000 liters) of water, 102 pounds (46 kilograms) of sulfur, 350 pounds (159 kilograms) of lime, 289 pounds (131 kilograms) of clay, 1.2 tons of coal, 112 kilowatt hours of power, 20 pounds (9 kilograms) of dye and pigments, and 108 pounds (49 kilograms) of starch, as well as other ingredients.

What does one acre of trees yield when cut and processed?

There are about 660 trees on one acre in a forest. When cut, one acre of trees may yield approximately 105,000 board feet of lumber or more than 30 tons of paper or 16 cords of firewood.

What products come from tropical forests?

Products from Tropical Forests

Woods	Houseplants	Spices	Foods
Balsa	*Anthurium*	Allspice	Avocado
Mahogany	Croton	Black pepper	Banana
Rosewood	*Dieffenbachia*	Cardamom	Coconut
Sandalwood	*Dracaena*	Cayenne	Grapefruit
Teak	Fiddle-leaf fig	Chili	Lemon
	Mother-in-law's tongue	Cinnamon	Lime
Fibers	Parlor ivy	Cloves	Mango
Bamboo	Philodendron	Ginger	Orange
Jute/Kenaf	Rubber tree plant	Mace	Papaya
Kapok	*Schefflera*	Nutmeg	Passion fruit
Raffia	Silver vase bromeliad	Paprika	Pineapple
Ramie	*Spathiphyllum*	Sesame seeds	Plantain
Rattan	Swiss cheese plant	Turmeric	Tangerine
	Zebra plant	Vanilla bean	Brazil nuts
Gums, resins	Cane sugar	Chicle latex	
Oils, etc.		Cashew nuts	
Copaiba	Camphor oil		Chocolate
Copal	Cascarilla oil		Coffee
Gutta percha	Coconut oil		Cucumber
Rubber latex	Eucalyptus oil		Hearts of palm
Tung oil	Oil of star anise		Macadamia nuts
	Palm oil		Manioc/tapioca
	Patchouli oil		Okra
	Rosewood oil		Peanuts
	Tolu balsam oil		Peppers
	Annatto		Cola beans
	Curare		Tea
	Diosgenin		
	Quinine		
	Reserpine		
	Strophanthus		
	Strychnine		
	Yang-Yang		

Does any type of wood sink in water?

Ironwood is a name applied to many hard, heavy woods. Some ironwoods are so dense that their specific gravity exceeds 1.0 and they are therefore unable to float in water. North American ironwoods include the American hornbeam, the mesquite, the desert ironwood, and leadwood (*Krugiodendron ferreum*), which has a specific gravity of 1.34-1.42, making it the heaviest in the United States.

The heaviest wood is black ironwood (*Olea laurifolia*), also called South African ironwood. Found in the West Indies, it has a specific gravity of 1.49 and weighs up to 93 pounds (42.18 kilograms) per foot. The lightest wood is *Aeschynomene hispida*, found in Cuba, with a specific gravity of 0.044 and a weight of 2.5 pounds (1.13 kilograms) per foot. Balsa wood (*Ochroma pyramidale*) varies between 2.5 and 24 pounds (one to 10 kilograms) per foot.

What is amber?

Amber is the fossil resin of trees. The two major deposits of amber are in the Dominican Republic and Baltic. Amber came from a coniferous tree that is now extinct. Amber is usually yellow or orange in color, semitransparent or opaque with a glossy surface. It is used by both artisans and scientists.

What is rosin?

Rosin is the resin produced after the distillation of turpentine, obtained from several varieties of pine trees, especially the longleaf pine (*Pinus palustris*) and the slash pine (*Pinus caribaea*). Rosin has many industrial uses, including the preparation of inks, adhesives, paints, sealants, and chemicals. Rosin is also used by athletes and musicians to make smooth surfaces less slippery.

What are naval stores?

Naval stores are products of such coniferous trees as pine and spruce. These products include pitch, tar, resin, turpentine, pine oil, and terpenes. The term "naval stores" originated in the seventeenth century when these materials were used for building and maintaining wooden sailing ships.

Why are essential oils called "essential"?

Called essential oils because of their ease of solubility in alcohol to form essences, essential oils are used in flavorings, perfumes, disinfectants, medicine, and other products. They are naturally occurring volatile aromatic oils found in uncombined forms within various parts of plants (leaves, pods, etc.). These oils contain as one of their main ingredients a substance belonging to the terpene group. Examples of essential oils include bergamot, eucalyptus, ginger, pine, spearmint, and wintergreen oils. Extracted by distillation or enfleurage (extraction using fat) and mechanical pressing, these oils can now be made synthetically.

What is gutta percha?

Gutta percha is a rubberlike gum obtained from the milky sap of trees of the Sapotaceae family, found in Indonesia and Malaysia. Once of great economic value, gutta percha is now being replaced by plastics in many items, although it is still used in some electrical insulation and dental work. The English natural historian John Tradescant (c. 1570-1638) introduced gutta percha to Europe in the 1620s, and its inherent qualities gave it a slow but growing place in world trade. By the end of World War II, however, many manufacturers switched from gutta percha to plastics, which are more versatile and cheaper to produce.

What is excelsior?

Excelsior is a trade name dating from the mid-nineteenth century for the curly, fine wood shavings used as packing material when shipping breakable items. It is also used as a cushioning and stuffing material. Poplar, aspen, basswood or cottonwood are woods that are often made into excelsior.

What is ambergris?

Ambergris, a highly odorous, waxy substance found floating in tropical seas, is a secretion from the sperm whale (*Physeter catodon*). The whale secretes ambergris to protect its stomach from the sharp bone of the cuttlefish, a squid-like sea mollusk, which it ingests. Ambergris is used in perfumery as a fixature to extend the life of a perfume and as a flavoring for food and beverages. Today ambergris is synthesized and used by the perfume trade, which has voluntarily refused to purchase natural ambergris to protect sperm whales from exploitation.

From where do frankincense and myrrh originate?

Frankincense is an aromatic gum resin obtained by tapping the trunks of trees belonging to the genus *Boswellia*. The milky resin hardens when exposed to the air and forms irregular lumps—the form in which it is usually marketed. Also called olibanum, frankincense is used in pharmaceuticals, as a perfume, as a fixative, and in fumigants and incense. Myrrh comes from a tree of the genus *Commiphora*, a native of Arabia and Northeast Africa. It too is a resin obtained from the tree trunk and is used in pharmaceuticals, perfumes, and toothpaste.

Where does isinglass come from?

Isinglass is the purest form of animal gelatin. It is manufactured from the swimming bladder of sturgeon and other fishes. It is used in the clarification of wine and beer as well as in the making of some cements, jams, jellies, and soups.

OBSERVATION AND MEASUREMENT

What is magnetic declination?

It is the angle between magnetic north and true north at a given point on the Earth's surface. It varies at different points on the Earth's surface and at different times of the year.

Which direction does a compass needle point at the north pole?

At the north magnetic pole, the compass needle would be attracted by the ground and point straight down.

What is a Foucault pendulum?

An instrument devised by Jean Foucault (1819-1868) in 1851 to prove that the Earth rotates on an axis, the pendulum consisted of a heavy ball suspended by a very long fine wire. Sand beneath the pendulum recorded the plane of rotation of the pendulum over time.

A reconstruction of Foucault's experiment is located in Portland, Oregon, at its Convention Center. It swings from a cable 90 feet (27.4 meters) long, making it the longest pendulum in the world.

What are the major eras, periods, and epochs in geologic time?

Modern dating techniques have given a range of dates as to when the various geologic time periods have started, as they are listed below:

Era	Period	Epoch	Beginning date (Est. millions of years)
Cenozoic	Quaternary	Holocene	10,000 years ago
		Pleistocene	1.9
	Tertiary	Pliocene	6
		Miocene	25
		Oligocene	38
		Eocene	55
		Paleocene	65
Mesozoic	Cretaceous		135
	Jurassic		200
	Triassic		250
Paleozoic	Permian		285
	Carboniferous (divided into Mississippian and Pennsylvanian periods by some in the U.S.)		350
	Devonian		410
	Silurian		425
	Ordovician		500
	Cambrian		570
Precambrian	Proterozoic		2500
	Archeozoic		3800
	Azoic		4600

What is the prime meridian?

The north-south lines on a map run from the North Pole to the South Pole and are called "meridians." The word "meridian" means "noon": When it is noon on one place on the line, it is noon at any other point as well. The lines are used to measure longitudes, or how far east or west a particular place might be, and they are 69 miles (111 kilometers) apart at the equator. The east-west lines are called parallels, and, unlike meridians, are all parallel to each other. They measure latitude, or how far north or south a particular place might be.

There are 180 lines circling the Earth, one for each degree of latitude. The degrees of both latitude and longitude are divided into 60 minutes, which are then further divided into 60 seconds each.

The prime meridian is the meridian of 0 degrees longitude, used as the origin for measurement of longitude. The meridian of Greenwich, England, is used almost universally for this purpose.

What is Mercator's projection for maps?

The Mercator projection is a modification of a standard cylindrical projection, a technique used by cartographers to transfer the spherical proportions of the Earth to the flat surface of a map. For correct proportions, the parallels, or lines of latitude, are spaced at increasing distances toward the poles, resulting in severe exaggeration of size in the polar regions. Greenland, for example, appears five times larger than it actually is. Created by Flemish cartographer Gerardus Mercator in 1569, this projection is useful primarily because compass directions appear as straight lines, making it ideal for navigation.

Who is regarded as the founder of American geology?

Born in Scotland, the American William Maclure (1763-1840) was a member of a commission set up to settle claims between the United States and France from 1803 through 1807. In 1809 he made a geographical chart of the United States in which the land areas were divided by rock types. In 1817 he revised and enlarged this map. Maclure wrote the first English language articles and books on United States geology.

When were relief maps first used?

The Chinese were the first to use relief maps, in which the contours of the terrain were represented in models. Relief maps in China go back at least to the third century B.C.E. Some early maps were modeled in rice or carved in wood. It is likely that the idea of making relief maps was transmitted from the Chinese to the Arabs and then to Europe. The earliest known relief map in Europe was a map showing part of Austria, made in 1510 by Paul Dox.

From what distance are satellite photographs taken?

U.S. Department of Defense satellites orbit at various distances above the Earth. Some satellites are in low orbit, 100 to 300 miles (160 to 483 kilometers) above the surface, while others are positioned at intermediate altitudes from 500 to 1,000 miles (804 to 1,609 kilometers) high. Some have an altitude of 22,300 miles (35,880 kilometers).

What are Landsat maps?

They are images of the Earth taken at an altitude of 567 miles (912 kilometers) by an orbiting Landsat satellite, or ERTS (Earth Resources Technology Satellite). The Landsats were originally launched in the 1970s. Rather than cameras, the Landsats use multispectral scanners, which detect visible green and blue wavelengths, and four infrared and near-infrared wavelengths. These scanners can detect differences between soil, rock, water, and vegetation; types of vegetation; states of vegetation (e.g., healthy/unhealthy or underwatered/well-watered); and mineral content. The differences are especially accurate when multiple wavelengths are compared using multispectral scanners. Even visible light images have proved useful—some of the earliest Landsat images showed that some small Pacific islands were up to 10 miles (16 kilometers) away from their charted positions.

The results are displayed in "false-color" maps, where the scanner data is represented in shades of easily distinguishable colors—usually, infrared is shown as red, red as green, and green as blue. The maps are used by farmers, oil companies, geologists, foresters, foreign governments, and others interested in land management. Each image covers an area approximately 115 square miles (185 square kilometers). Maps are offered for sale by the United States Geological Survey.

Other systems that produce similar images include the French SPOT satellites, Russian Salyut and Mir manned space stations, and NASA's Airborne Imaging Spectrometer, which senses 128 infrared bands. NASA's Jet Propulsion Laboratories are developing instruments that will sense 224 bands in infrared, which will be able to detect specific minerals absorbed by plants.

What is Global Positioning System (GPS) and how does it work?

The Global Positioning System (GPS) has three parts: the space part, the user part, and the control part. The space part consists of 24 satellites in orbit 11,000 nautical miles (20,300 kilometers) above the Earth. The user part consists of a GPS receiver, which may be hand-held or mounted in a vehicle. The control part consists of five ground stations worldwide to assure the satellites are working properly. Using a GPS receiver an individual can determine his or her location on or above the Earth to within about 300 feet (90 meters).

CLIMATE

DEFINITIONS

What is the difference between climate and weather?

Climate is the long-term (usually 30-year) average weather for a particular place. The weather is the current condition of the atmosphere. So, on a particular day, the weather in Barrow, Alaska, might be a hot 70° Fahrenheit, but its tundra climate is generally polar-like and cold.

How are different types of climates classified?

In 1884, the German climatologist Wladimir Köppen developed a climate classification system that is still used today, albeit with some modifications. He classified climates into five categories: tropical/megathermal, dry, temperate/mesothermal, continental/microthermal, polar, and alpine. He also created subcategories for these classifications. His climate map is often found in geography texts and atlases. In the 1960s, the climate classifications were updated to take into account vegetation that is native to certain climatic zones, providing more accuracy to the classification system.

What is a Mediterranean climate?

A Mediterranean climate is a climate similar to the one found along the Mediterranean Sea: warm, hot, and dry in the summer and mild, cool, and wet in the winter. Areas that are renowned for having a Mediterranean climate but are not near the Mediterranean Sea are California, southwestern Oregon, southwestern South Africa, and Chile.

What is global warming?

Global warming is the gradual increase of the Earth's average temperature—which has been rising since the Industrial Revolution (late eighteenth century–early nineteenth century C.E.). If temperatures continue to increase, some scientists predict major climatic changes, including the rise of ocean levels due to ice melting at the poles. According to many scientists, global warming is primarily due to the greenhouse effect.

What is the greenhouse effect?

The greenhouse effect is a natural process of the atmosphere that traps some of the sun's heat near the Earth. The problem with the greenhouse effect, however, is that it has been unnaturally increased, causing more heat to be trapped and the temperature on the planet to rise. The gasses that have caused the greenhouse effect were added to the atmosphere as a byproduct of human activities, especially combustion from automobiles, output from factories, and the burning of forests.

What is the effect of global warming and climate change on Earth?

By the year 2100, relative to 1990, world temperatures could rise from 2 to 11.5° Fahrenheit (1.1 to 6.4° Celsius), and sea levels may rise 7.2 to 23.6 inches (18 to 59 centimeters). According to scientists at NASA, for 650,000 years, atmospheric carbon dioxide, a main contributor to warming, has never been above 300 parts per million. Since 1950, this number has steadily increased to nearly 400 parts per million in 2014.

What is air pollution?

Air pollution is caused by many sources. There are natural pollutants that have been around as long as the Earth, such as dust, smoke, volcanic ash, and pollens. Humans have added to air pollution with chemicals and particulates due to combustion and industrial activity.

What are the most polluted cities in the world in terms of air quality?

Scientists measure pollutants that are present in the air that we breathe by measuring the size of the particulate, including cancer-causing ammonia, carbon, nitrates, and sulfate. These pollutants easily pass into our bloodstream when we breathe. The places in the world where we may find severe concentrations of these chemicals in the air include New Delhi, India; Patna, India; Gwalior, India; Raipur, India; and Karachi, Pakistan. Of the top twenty most polluted cities in the world, according to the World Bank, thirteen are in India. The rest include Doha, Qatar; Igdir, Turkey; and Khorramabad, Iran.

What are the sources of air pollution?

Air pollution has two main sources: anthropogenic (man-made) and natural. Man-made sources of pollution include factories, cars, motorcycles, ships, incinerators, wood burning, oil refining, chemicals, consumer product emissions like aerosol sprays and fumes from paint, methane from garbage in landfills, and pollution from nuclear and biological weapons production and testing. Natural sources of pollution may include dust, methane from human and animal waste, radon gas, smoke from wildfires, and volcanic activity.

> ## How did the Inca civilization experiment with climate?
>
> In the Urubamba Valley in Peru, in a city called Moray, are the remains of a great amphitheater-like terraced system. Archaeologists and scientists now believe that this was a great agricultural laboratory, where each area of the terrace exhibited completely different climates, allowing the Incas to experiment on cultivated vegetation with different climates and growing techniques.

THE ATMOSPHERE

How much pressure does the atmosphere exert upon us?

Average air pressure is 14.7 pounds per square inch (1.0335 kilograms per square centimeter) at sea level.

Why is the sky blue?

This is one of the world's most frequently pondered questions, and, contrary to what some people believe, the sky's blue color is not due to the reflection of water. Light from the sun is composed of the spectrum of colors. When sunlight strikes the Earth's atmosphere, ultraviolet and blue waves of light are the most easily scattered by particles in the atmosphere. So, other colors of light continue to the Earth while blue and ultraviolet waves remain in the sky. Our eyes can't see ultraviolet light, so the sky appears the only color remaining that we can see: blue.

How many layers are in the atmosphere?

There are five layers that make up the Earth's atmosphere. They extend from just above the surface of the Earth to outer space. The layer of the atmosphere that we breathe and exist in is called the troposphere and extends from the ground to about 10 miles (16 km) above the surface. From about 10 miles to 30 miles (16 to 48 km) up lies the stratosphere. The mesosphere lies from 30 to 50 miles (48 to 80 km) above the surface. A very thick layer, the thermosphere, lies from 50 miles all the way to 125 miles up (80 to 200 km). Above the 125-mile (200-km) mark lies the exosphere and space.

What is the air made of?

The air near the Earth's surface is primarily nitrogen and oxygen—nitrogen comprises 78.09% and oxygen 20.95%. The remaining 1% is mostly argon (0.93%), a little carbon dioxide (0.039%), and other gasses (0.06%).

Why can I hear an AM radio station from hundreds of miles away at night but not during the day?

At night, AM radio waves bounce off of a layer of the ionosphere, the "F" layer, and can travel hundreds, if not thousands, of miles from their source. During the day, the same reflection of radio waves cannot occur because the "D" layer of the ionosphere is present and it absorbs radio waves.

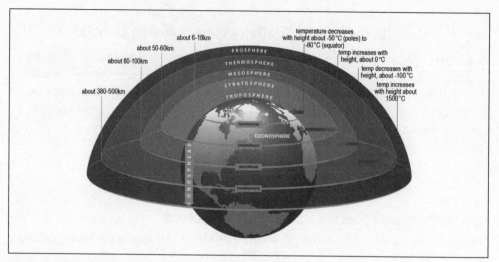

Earth's atmosphere is much thicker than most people think. Many just consider it the part that is the troposphere, but it actually extends about 6,200 miles (10,000 kilometers) into space.

Why don't FM radio waves travel very far?

FM radio waves are "line of site," which means they can only travel as far as their power and the height of their radio antenna will allow. The taller the antenna, the farther the waves can travel along the horizon (as long as they have enough power).

Does air pressure change with elevation?

Yes, it does. The higher you go, the less air (or atmospheric) pressure there is. Air pressure is also involved in weather systems. A low-pressure system is more likely to bring rain and bad weather versus a high-pressure system, which is usually drier and brings clear skies. At about 15,000 feet (4,572 meters), air pressure is half of what it is at sea level.

What are the different kinds of clouds?

There are dozens of types of clouds, but they can all be classified into three main categories: cirriform, stratiform, and cumuliform. Cirriform clouds are feathery and wispy; they are made of ice crystals and occur at high elevations. Stratiform clouds are sheet-like and spread out across the sky. Cumuliform clouds are the ubiquitous cloud that we often see—puffy and individual. These clouds can be harmless, or they can be the source of torrential storms and tornadoes.

How much of the Earth is usually covered by clouds?

At any given time, about one-half of the planet is covered by clouds.

How do airplanes create clouds?

When the air conditions are right and it's sufficiently moist, the exhaust from jet airplane engines often creates condensation trails, known as contrails. Contrails are narrow lines of clouds that evaporate rather quickly. Contrails can turn into cirrus clouds if the air is close to being saturated with water vapor.

OZONE

What is the ozone layer?

The ozone layer is part of the stratosphere, a layer of the Earth's atmosphere that lies about 10 to 30 miles (16 to 48 km) above the surface of the Earth. Ozone is very important to life on the planet because it shields us from most of the damaging ultraviolet radiation from the sun.

Is the ozone layer being depleted?

Scientists have recognized that a hole has developed in the ozone layer that has been growing since 1979. The hole is located over Antarctica and has been responsible for increased ultraviolet radiation levels in Antarctica, Australia, and New Zealand. As the ozone hole grows, it will increase the amount of harmful ultraviolet light reaching the Earth, causing cancer and eye damage and killing crops and microorganisms in the ocean.

How much of the ozone layer is being depleted?

Since 1975, scientists believe that more than 33% of the ozone layer has disappeared. There is a seasonal factor to the reduction in ozone at any given time during the year, too. At different times, the ozone layer naturally declines or rises. But scientists also know that chlorofluorocarbons (CFCs), which are used for air conditioning, aerosol sprays, halon in fire extinguishers, and the interaction of man-made chemicals with nitrogen in our atmosphere directly cause ozone depletion. It is a man-made problem that requires a man-made solution. By 1989, 193 countries signed an agreement, called the Montreal Protocol, limiting the use of CFCs. And by 2011, all countries in the world signed this agreement, which ultimately has had a mitigating effect on the ozone hole, which was being observed as growing over Antarctica. Scientists at NASA who monitor the ozone in our atmosphere believe that the ozone depletion issue for the inhabitants on Earth is no longer a great problem today because concentrations of man-made ozone-depleting chemicals in use have stopped increasing and are actually declining.

How do CFCs destroy ozone?

When CFCs rise up in the atmosphere to the ozone layer, ultraviolet rays break them down into bromine and chlorine, which destroy ozone molecules.

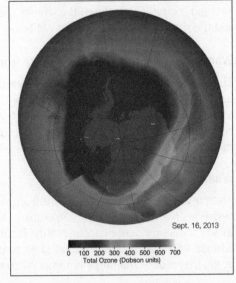

Sept. 16, 2013

0 100 200 300 400 500 600 700
Total Ozone (Dobson units)

This 2013 graphic shows the extent of ozone depletion over Antarctica.

483

CLIMATIC TRENDS

What is El Niño?

El Niño (also known as the El Niño Southern Oscillation [ENSO]), is a large patch of warm water that moves between the eastern and western Pacific Ocean near the equator. When the warm water of El Niño, about 1.8 degrees Fahrenheit (1 degree Celsius) warmer than normal, is near South America, the warm water affects the weather in the southwestern United States by increasing rainfall and is responsible for changes in the weather throughout the world. El Niño lasts for about four years in the eastern Pacific Ocean and then returns to the western Pacific near Indonesia for another four years. When the warm water is in the western Pacific, it is known as La Niña, the opposite of El Niño. When La Niña is in action, we have "normal" climatic conditions. Scientists at the National Oceanic and Atmospheric Administration (NOAA) monitor the effects of these types of changes to determine how they may influence our weather each year.

Can people live in a torrid zone?

The ancient Greeks divided the world into climatic zones that were not accurate. The three zones included frigid, temperate, and torrid. They believed that civilized people could only live in the temperate zone (which, of course, was centered around Greece). From Europe northward was part of the inhospitable frigid zone, while most of Africa was torrid. Unfortunately, this three-zone classification system stuck and was later expanded to five zones once the Southern Hemisphere was explored. People identify everything north of the Arctic Circle (near northern Russia) and south of the Antarctic Circle (near the coast of Antarctica) as frigid, everything between the tropics and the Arctic and Antarctic circles as temperate, and the zone between the Tropics of Cancer and Capricorn as torrid.

Where does the name El Niño come from?

The phenomenon of El Niño was discovered by Peruvian fishermen who noticed an abundance of exotic species that arrived with the warmer water. Since this usually occurred around the Christmas season, they called the phenomenon El Niño, which means "the baby boy" in Spanish, in honor of the birth of Jesus Christ. La Niña, the opposite cycle of El Niño, means "the baby girl."

What is continentality?

Areas of a continent that are distant from an ocean (such as the central United States) experience greater extremes in temperature than do places that are closer to an ocean. These inland areas experience continentality. It might be very hot during the summer, but it can also get very cold in winter. Areas close to oceans experience moderating effects from the ocean that reduce the range in temperatures.

What are ice core samples and why are they important?

An ice core sample is a thick column of ice, sometimes hundreds of feet long, that is produced by drilling a circular, pipelike device into thick ice and then pulling out the cylindrical piece. Ice core samples from places like Greenland and Antarctica provide scientists with important clues about past climates. Air trapped in the ice remains there for thousands of years, so when scientists collect ice cores, they can analyze the air to determine the chemical composition of the atmosphere at the time the ice was formed. Sediments and tiny bugs are also found in the ice and provide additional clues to the state of the natural world at the time the ice was first deposited.

What are the horse latitudes?

Horse latitudes are high-pressure regions, more formally known as subtropic highs, which are warm and don't have much wind. Legend has it that the lack of wind sometimes caused sailors of the sixteenth and seventeenth centuries to throw their horses overboard in an effort to conserve water on board. That's how the region, centered around 30° latitude, got its name.

WEATHER

How does land turn into desert?

The process known as desertification is complicated and results from such activities as overgrazing, inefficient irrigation systems, and deforestation. It is most widespread in the Sahel region of Africa, a strip of land along the southern margin of the Sahara Desert. The Sahara grows larger because of desertification. Desertification can be reversed by changing agricultural practices and by replanting forests.

As water use rises due to agriculture and increasing populations, lakes and even small seas are disappearing. The Aral Sea in Uzbekistan, for example, has almost disappeared over the last fifteen years.

485

What are Fahrenheit and Celsius?

Fahrenheit and Celsius are two common temperature scales used throughout the world. Temperature in Fahrenheit can be converted to Celsius by subtracting 32 and multiplying by five; divide that number by nine, and you have Celsius. Conversely, you can convert Celsius to Fahrenheit by adding 32, multiplying by nine, and finally dividing by five. Kelvin, a system used by scientists, is based on the same scale as Celsius. All you have to do is add 273 to your Celsius temperature to obtain Kelvin. Zero degrees Kelvin is negative 273° Celsius.

What is a low high temperature and a high low temperature?

When meteorologists look at daily temperature, there is always a low and a high temperature for each day. If the high temperature is the coldest high temperature for that day or for the month, you have a new record—a new low high. Conversely, if the low temperature for a day is quite warm and breaks records, that's a new high low!

Why is it hotter in the city than in the countryside?

Cities have higher temperatures due to an effect known as the urban heat island. The extensive pavement, buildings, machinery, pollution from automobiles, and other things urban cause an increase in warmth in the city. Cities such as Los Angeles can be up to five degrees hotter than surrounding areas due to the urban heat island effect. The term comes from temperature maps of cities where the hotter, urban areas look like islands when isotherms (lines of equal temperature) are drawn.

What are some world weather records?

The following are some amazing weather records. The wettest: Cherrapunji, and the town of Mawsynram nearby in India, near the border of Bangladesh, have the highest average rainfall per year in the world, averaging 467 inches (11,872 mm); the coldest: the East Antarctic Plateau, Antarctica, with a measurement of –136° Fahrenheit (–93.2° Celsius); the driest: Dry Valleys of Antarctica which receives 0 inches (0 centimeters) of rainfall per year; and the hottest: Lut Desert, Iran, which has sizzled at 159.3° Fahrenheit (70.7° Celsius) in five of the seven years from 2004 to 2009.

Why is it more likely to rain in a city during the week than on the weekend?

Urban areas have an increased likelihood of precipitation during the workweek because intense activity from factories and vehicles produce particles that allow moisture in the at-

Why are there so many discrepancies in the world records of weather?

The discrepancies in the data reflect the length of time that we use to measure weather phenomena. Some records were set by observing the weather over decades; others only occurred during the span of a few years, months, or even hours or minutes.

mosphere to form raindrops. These same culprits also produce warm air that rises to create precipitation. A study of the city of Paris found that precipitation increased throughout the week and dropped sharply on Saturday and Sunday.

What does a 40% chance of rain really mean?

When the morning weather report speaks of a 40% chance of rain, it means that throughout the area (usually the metropolitan area), there is a four in ten chance that at least 0.001 of an inch of rain (0.0025 centimeters) will fall on any given point in the area.

Why is it more wet on one side of a mountain than the other?

It's much more wet on one side of a mountain than the other because of a process known as orographic precipitation. Orographic precipitation causes air to rise up the side of a mountain range and cool off, creating storms. The storms deposit a great deal of precipitation on that side of the mountain and create a rain shadow effect on the opposite side of the range. The Sierra Nevada Mountains are an excellent example of orographic precipitation because the mountains of the western Sierras receive considerable rainfall (far more than California's Central Valley), while the eastern Sierras are quite dry.

What is a rain shadow?

When the moisture in the air is squeezed out by orographic precipitation, there's not much left for the other side of the mountains. The dry side of the mountain experiences a rain shadow effect because they are in the shadow of the rain.

What is a thunderstorm?

Thunderstorms are localized atmospheric phenomena that produce heavy rain, thunder and lightning, and sometimes hail. They are formed in cumulonimbus clouds (clouds that are big and bulbous) that rise many miles into the sky. Most of the southeastern United States has over forty days of thunderstorm activity each year, and there are about 100,000 thunderstorms across the country annually. Thunderstorms are different from typical rainstorms because of their lightning, thunder, and occasional hail.

What are monsoons?

Occurring in southern Asia, monsoons are winds that flow from the ocean to the continent during the summer and from the continent to the ocean in the winter. The winds come from the southwest from April to October and from the northeast (the opposite direction) from October to April. The summer monsoons bring a great deal of moisture to the land. They cause deadly floods in low-lying river valleys, but they also provide the water southern Asia relies upon for agriculture.

What is the origin of the word "monsoon"?

The word "monsoon" comes from several source languages, including from the Portuguese word *moncau*, the Arabic word *mawsim*, and the early Dutch word *monsun*.

487

WIND

What are dust devils?

These columns of brown, dust-filled air, which can rise dozens of feet, are not as evil as the name suggests. They are caused by warm air rising on dry, clear days. Winds associated with dust devils can reach up to 60 miles (96.5 km) per hour and cause some damage, but they are not as destructive as tornadoes and usually die out pretty quickly.

Dust devils are like very weak tornadoes that never cause any damage.

What causes the wind to blow?

The Earth's atmospheric pressure varies at different places and times. Wind is simply caused by the movement of air from areas of higher pressure to areas of lower pressure. The greater the difference in pressure, the faster the wind blows. Some detailed weather maps show wind speed along with isobars (areas of equal air pressure) indicating the level of air pressure.

In which direction does the west wind blow?

It blows from the west to the east. Wind direction is always named after the direction from where it originates.

What is the jet stream?

The jet stream is a band of swiftly moving air located high in the atmosphere, meandering across the troposphere and stratosphere, up to 30 miles high (48 km). The jet stream affects the movement of storms and air masses closer to the ground.

What are the westerlies?

These westerly winds flow at mid-latitudes (30 to 60 degrees north and south of the equator) from west to east around the Earth. The high-altitude winds known as the jet stream are also westerlies.

What is katabatic wind?

Katabatic wind is high-density air that moves from a higher elevation down a slope because of the force of gravity. These winds are sometimes known as "fall winds."

What is the windiest place on Earth?

Because of katabatic winds, Antarctica frequently wins the top honors for being the windiest place on Earth. Winds near Commonwealth Bay, which was discovered in 1912, are frequently recorded to be 150 miles per hour (240 km per hour), with an average wind speed over the course of a year of 50 miles per hour (80 km per hour).

Is Chicago really the "Windy City"?

Chicago is not the windiest big city in the lower 48 states of the United States. Chicago's average wind speed of 10.3 miles (16.58 km) per hour is beat by Boston (12.3 mph/19.79 kph), Dallas (10.7 mph/17.22 kph), Oklahoma City (12.2 mph/19.63 kph), Buffalo (11.8 mph/18.99 kph), and Milwaukee (11.5 mph/18.51 kph).

What is the origin of the name "Windy City"?

Although Chicago is not really that windy compared with other American cities, the name has been used since the nineteenth century. It refers not necessarily to the weather but to the observations by many when describing Chicago politicians, metaphorically, as "talkative," "boastful," and "self-promoting."

What world weather record does the United States hold?

The United States claims the world's highest surface wind, 318 miles per hour (511.77 km per hour), during a tornado in Oklahoma in 2009.

THE ENVIRONMENT

ECOLOGY, RESOURCES, ETC.

What is biodiversity?

Biodiversity refers to genetic variability within a species, diversity of populations of a species, diversity of species within a natural community, or the wide array of natural communities and ecosystems throughout the world. Some scientists estimate that there may be between 15 and 100 million species throughout the world. Biodiversity is threatened at the present time more than at any other time in history. In the time since the North American continent was settled, as many as 500 plant and animal species have disappeared. Some recent examples of threats to biodiversity in the United States include: 50 percent of the United States no longer supports its original vegetation; in the Great Plains, 99 percent of the original prairies are gone; and across the United States, we destroy 100,000 acres of wetlands each year.

What is a biome?

It is a plant and animal community that covers a large geographical area. Complex interactions of climate, geology, soil types, water resources, and latitude all determine the kinds of plants and animals that thrive in different places. Fourteen major ecological zones, called "biomes," exist over five major climatic regions and eight zoogeographical regions. Important land biomes include tundra, coniferous forests, deciduous forests, grasslands, savannas, deserts, chaparral, and tropical rainforests.

How does the process work in a food chain?

A food chain is the transfer of food energy from the source in plants through a series of organisms with repeated eating and being eaten. The number of steps or "links" in a sequence is usually four to five. The first trophic level (group of organisms that get their energy the same way) is plants; the animals that eat plants (called herbivores) form the second trophic level. The third level consists of primary carnivores (animal-eating animals like wolves) who

491

eat herbivores, and the fourth level are animals (like killer whales) that eat primary carnivores. Food chains overlap because many organisms eat more than one type of food, so that these chains can look more like food webs. In 1891 German zoologist Karl Semper introduced the food chain concept.

What is a food web?

A food web consists of interconnecting food chains. Many animals feed on different foods rather than exclusively on one single species of prey or one type of plant. Animals that use a variety of food sources have a greater chance of survival than those with a single food source. Complex food webs provide greater stability to a living community.

What is eutrophication?

Eutrophication is a process in which the supply of plant nutrients in a lake or pond is increased. In time, the result of natural eutrophication may be dry land where water once flowed, caused by plant overgrowth.

Natural fertilizers, washed from the soil, result in an accelerated growth of plants, producing overcrowding. As the plants die off, the dead and decaying vegetation depletes the lake's oxygen supply, causing fish to die. The accumulated dead plant and animal material eventually changes a deep lake to a shallow one, then to a swamp, and finally it becomes dry land.

A saguaro cactus forest thrives within this Sonoran Desert biome near Tucson, Arizona.

While the process of eutrophication is a natural one, it has been accelerated enormously by human activities. Fertilizers from farms, sewage, industrial wastes, and some detergents all contribute to the problem.

How many acres of wetlands have been lost in the United States?

Wetlands are the lands between aquatic and terrestrial areas, such as bogs, marshes, swamps, and coastal waters. At one time considered wastelands, scientists now recognize the importance of wetlands to improve water quality, stabilize water levels, prevent flooding, regulate erosion, and sustain a variety of organisms. The United States has lost approximately 100 million acres of wetland areas between colonial times and the 1970s. The 1993 Wetlands Plan established a goal of reversing the trend of 100,000 acres of wetland loss to 100,000 acres of wetland recovery.

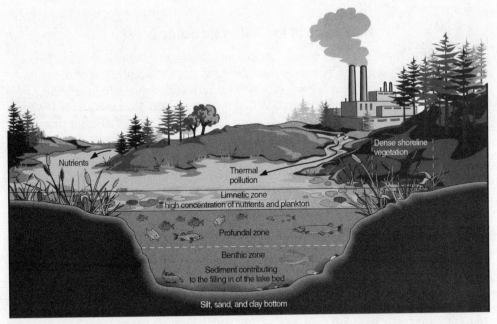

The structure of a eutrophic lake.

How does ozone benefit life on Earth?

Ozone, a form of oxygen with three atoms instead of the normal two, is highly toxic; less than one part per million of this blue-tinged gas is poisonous to humans. In the Earth's upper atmosphere (stratosphere), it is a major factor in making life on Earth possible. About 90 percent of the planet's ozone is in the ozone layer. The ozone belt shields and filters the Earth from excessive ultraviolet (UV) radiation generated by the sun. Scientists predict that a diminished or depleted ozone layer could lead to increased health problems for humans, such as skin cancer, cataracts, and weakened immune systems. Increased UV can also lead to reduced crop yields and disruption of aquatic ecosystems, including the marine food chain. While beneficial in the stratosphere, near ground level it is a pollutant that helps form photochemical smog and acid rain.

What is the greenhouse effect?

The greenhouse effect is a warming near the Earth's surface that results when the Earth's atmosphere traps the sun's heat. The atmosphere acts much like the glass walls and roof of a greenhouse. The effect was described by John Tyndall (1820-1893) in 1861. It was given the greenhouse analogy much later in 1896 by the Swedish chemist Svante Arrhenius (1859-1927). The greenhouse effect is what makes the Earth habitable. Without the presence of water vapor, carbon dioxide, and other gases in the atmosphere, too much heat would escape and the Earth would be too cold to sustain life. Carbon dioxide, methane, nitrous oxide, and other greenhouse gases absorb the infrared radiation rising from the Earth and hold this heat in the atmosphere instead of reflecting it back into space.

In the 20th century, the increased build-up of carbon dioxide, caused by the burning of fossil fuels, has been a matter of concern. There is some controversy concerning whether the

493

How large is the Antarctic ozone hole?

How large is the Antarctic ozone hole?

The term "hole" is widely used in popular media when reporting on ozone. However, the concept is more correctly described as a low concentration of ozone. In September 2000, scientists at the National Aeronautics and Space Administration announced that the "hole" over Antarctica, first discovered in 1985, was measured to be 9.3 million square miles (24 million square kilometers) in size in 2007. But this was a smaller hole than the record, set in September 2006, when the ozone hole was a gaping 10.6 million square miles in area.

increase noted in the Earth's average temperature is due to the increased amount of carbon dioxide and other gases, or is due to other causes. Volcanic activity, destruction of the rainforests, use of aerosols, and increased agricultural activity may also be contributing factors.

What compounds cause ozone depletion in the stratosphere?

Research in the 1970s linked chlorofluorocarbons (CFCs), such as freon, to the depletion of the ozone layer. In 1978, the use of CFC propellants in spray cans was banned in the United States. In 1987, the Montreal Protocol was signed and the signatory nations committed themselves to a reduction in the use of CFCs and other ozone-depleting substances.

What are the greenhouse gases?

Scientists recognize carbon dioxide (CO_2), methane (CH4), chlorofluorocarbons (CFCs), nitrous oxide (N_2O), and water vapor as significant greenhouse gases. Greenhouse gases account for less that one percent of the Earth's atmosphere. These gases trap heat in the Earth's atmosphere, preventing the heat from escaping back into space. Human activities, such as using gasoline for automobiles for fuel, account for the release of carbon dioxide and nitrogen oxides.

Emissions of Greenhouse Gases in the United States, 1990-2000
(Million Metric Tons of Gas)

Gas	1990	1995	1996	1997	1998	1999	P2000
Carbon Dioxide	4,969.4	5,273.5	5,454.8	5,533.0	5,540.0	5,630.7	5,805.5
Methane	31.7	31.1	29.9	29.6	28.9	28.7	28.2
Nitrous Oxide	1.2	1.3	1.2	1.2	1.2	1.2	1.2
HFCs, PFCs, and SF6	*	*	*	*	*	*	*

P = Preliminary data, *Less than 0.05 million metric tons of gas, HFCs = hydrofluorocarbons, PFCs = perfluorocarbons, SF6 = sulfur hexafluoride

Why is El Niño harmful?

Along the west coast of South America, near the end of each calendar year, a warm current of nutrient-poor tropical water moves southward, replacing the cold, nutrient-rich surface water. Because this condition frequently occurs around Christmas, local residents call it El

Niño (Spanish for child), referring to the Christ child. In most years the warming lasts for only a few weeks. However, when El Niño conditions last for many months, the economic results can be catastrophic. It is this extended episode of extremely warm water that scientists now refer to as El Niño. During a severe El Niño, large numbers of fish and marine plants may die. Decomposition of the dead material depletes the water's oxygen supply, which leads to the bacterial production of huge amounts of smelly hydrogen sulfide. A greatly reduced fish (especially anchovy) harvest affects the world's fishmeal supply, leading to higher prices for poultry and other animals that normally are fed fishmeal. Anchovies and sardines are also major food sources for marine mammals, such as sea lions and seals. When the food source is in short supply, these animals travel further from their homes in search of food. Not only do many sea lions and seals starve, but also a large proportion of the infant animals die. The major El Niño event of 1997-1998 indirectly caused 2,100 deaths and $33 billion in damage globally.

What percentage of the Earth's surface is tropical rain forest?

Rain forests account for approximately 7 percent of the Earth's surface, or about three million square miles (7.7 million square kilometers).

What is the rate of species extinction in the tropical rain forests?

Biologists estimate that tropical rain forests contain approximately one-half of the Earth's animal and plant species. These forests contain 155,000 of the 250,000 known plant species and innumerable insect and animal species. Nearly 100 species become extinct each day. This is equivalent to four species per hour. At the current rates, 5-10 percent of the tropical rain forest will become extinct every decade.

What is the largest rain forest?

The Amazon Basin is the world's largest continuous tropical rain forest. It covers about 2.7 million square miles (6.9 million square kilometers).

 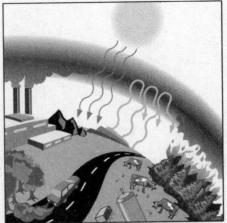

An atmosphere with natural levels of greenhouse gases (left) compared with an atmosphere of increased greenhouse effect (right).

How rapidly is deforestation occurring?

Worldwide, we are losing enough forestland annually to cover an area the size of the state of Panama. To put that figure into numbers, that is a net loss of 7.3 million hectares (18 million acres) every year. Actually, about 13 million hectares (32 million acres) are being chopped down yearly, but there are restoration projects going on that help replant forests. This rate of loss (which is an average taken from the years 2000 through 2005) is somewhat better than the 8.9 million hectare (22 million acre) loss that was experienced during the previous decade. Although replanting is great, new forest growth does not make for as healthy a habitat for wildlife as old forest growth.

How rapidly is the tropical rain forest being destroyed?

Tropical rain forests once covered more than four billion acres (1.6 billion hectares) of the Earth. Today, nearly half of the tropical rain forests are gone. Approximately 33.8 million acres of tropical forest are lost per year. This translates to 2.8 million acres lost per month, which can be broken down to 93,000 acres/day, 3,800 acres/hour, or 64 acres/minute. It equals more than the total area of New Hampshire, Vermont, Massachusetts, Rhode Island, Connecticut, New Jersey, and Delaware combined. At the current rate, scientists predict that no rain forests will remain by the middle of the twenty-first century.

Which countries have the largest amount of protected areas?

Protected areas include national parks, nature reserves, national monuments, and other sites. There are at least 44,3000 protected areas around the world, covering more than 10 percent of the total land area.

Country	Protected Area (miles^2)	Protected Area (km^2)	Total %
Venezuela	217,397	563,056	61.7
Greenland	379,345	1,025,405	45.2
Saudi Arabia	318,811	825,717	34.4
United States	902,091	2,336,406	24.9
Indonesia	138,002	357,425	18.6
Australia	395,911	1,025,405	13.4
Canada	357,231	925,226	9.3
China	263,480	682,410	7.1
Brazil	215,312	557,656	6.6
Russia	204,273	529,067	3.1

What causes the most forest fires in the western United States?

Lightning is the single largest cause of forest fires in the western states.

What is the importance of the rain forest?

Half of all medicines prescribed worldwide are originally derived from wild products, and the United States National Cancer Institute has identified more than two thousand tropical rainforest plants with the potential to fight cancer. Rubber, timber, gums, resins and waxes, pesticides, lubricants, nuts and fruits, flavorings and dyestuffs, steroids, latexes, essential and edible oils, and bamboo are among the forest's products that would be drastically affected by the depletion of the tropical forests.

What was the United States' first national park?

On March 1,1872, an Act of Congress signed by Ulysses S. Grant established Yellowstone National Park as the first national park, inspiring a worldwide national park movement.

When was the U.S. National Park Service established?

The National Park Service was created by an Act signed by President Woodrow Wilson on August 25, 1916.

What are some of the largest National Parks?

The largest National Parks are in Alaska:

Park	Area (acres)
Wrangell-St. Elias	8,323,148
Gates of the Arctic	7,523,898
Denali	4,740,912
Katmai	3,674,530
Glacier Bay	3,224,840
Lake Clark	2,619,733
Kobuk Valley	1,750,737

The five largest parks in the 48 contiguous states are:

Park	Location	Area (acres)
Death Valley	California	3,291,779
Yellowstone	Idaho, Montana, Wyoming	2,219,791
Everglades	Florida	1,398,903
Grand Canyon	Arizona	1,217,403
Glacier	Montana	1,013,572

Who is considered the founder of modern conservation?

American naturalist John Muir (1838-1914) was the father of conservation and the founder of the Sierra Club. He fought for the preservation of the Sierra Nevada Mountains in California, and the creation of Yosemite National Park. He directed most of the Sierra Club's conservation efforts and was a lobbyist for the Antiquities Act.

Another prominent influence was George Perkins Marsh (1801-1882), a Vermont lawyer and scholar. His outstanding book *Man and Nature* emphasizes the mistakes of past civilizations that resulted in destruction of natural resources. As the conservation movement

John Muir (left), founder of the Sierra Club and modern conservation movement, pictured here with fellow advocate John Burroughs.

swept through the country in the last three decades of the 19th century, a number of prominent citizens joined the efforts to conserve natural resources and to preserve wilderness areas. Writer John Burroughs, forester Gifford Pinchot, botanist Charles Sprague Sargent, and editor Robert Underwood Johnson were early advocates of conservation.

Who coined the term "Spaceship Earth"?

American inventor and environmentalist Buckminster Fuller (1895-1983) coined the term "Spaceship Earth" as an analogy of the need for technology to be self-contained and to avoid waste.

Who started Earth Day?

The first Earth Day, April 22, 1970, was coordinated by Denis Hayes at the request of Gaylord Nelson, a U.S. senator from Wisconsin. Nelson is sometimes called the father of Earth Day. His main objective was to organize a nationwide public demonstration so large it would get the attention of politicians and force the environmental issue into the political dialogue of the nation. Important official actions that began soon after the celebration of the first Earth Day were: the establishment of the Environmental Protection Agency (EPA); the creation of the President's Council on Environmental Quality; and the passage of the Clean Air Act, establishing national air quality standards. In 1995 Gaylord Nelson received the Presidential Medal of Freedom for his contributions to the environmental protection movement.

When was the Environmental Protection Agency created?

In 1970, President Richard M. Nixon created the Environmental Protection Agency (EPA) as an independent agency of the U.S. government by executive order. The creation of a federal

What is red tide and what causes it?

Red tide is a term used for a brownish or reddish discoloration occurring in ocean, river, or lake water. It is caused by the rapid reproduction of a variety of toxic organisms, especially the toxic red dinoflagellates that are members of the genera *Gymnodidium* and *Gonyaulax*. Some red tides are harmless, but millions of fish may be killed during a "bloom," as the build-up is called. Other red tides can poison shellfish and the birds or humans who eat the contaminated food. Scientists do not fully understand why the "bloom" occurs.

agency by executive order rather than by an act of the legislative branch is somewhat of an exception to the rule. The EPA was established in response to public concern about unhealthy air, polluted rivers and groundwater, unsafe drinking water, endangered species, and hazardous waste disposal. Responsibilities of the EPA include environmental research, monitoring, and enforcement of legislation regulating environmental activities.

What is a "green product"?

Green products are environmentally safe products that contain no chlorofluorocarbons, are degradable (can decompose), and are made from recycled materials. "Deep-green" products are those from small suppliers who build their identities around their claimed environmental virtues. "Greened-up" products come from the industry giants and are environmentally improved versions of established brands.

EXTINCT AND ENDANGERED PLANTS AND ANIMALS

When was the term "dinosaur" first used?

The term *dinosaur* was first used by Richard Owen in 1841 in his report on British fossil reptiles. The term, meaning "fearful lizard" was used to describe the group of large extinct reptiles whose fossil remains had been found by many collectors.

What is the name of the early Jurassic mammal that is now extinct?

The fossil site of the mammal *hadrocodium wui* was in Yunnan Province, China. This newly described mammal is at least 195 million years old. The estimated weight of the whole mammal is about 0.07 ounces (2 grams). Its tiny skull was smaller than a human thumbnail.

Did dinosaurs and humans ever coexist?

No. Dinosaurs first appeared in the Triassic Period (about 220 million years ago) and disappeared at the end of the Cretaceous Period (about 65 million years ago). Modern humans

(*Homo sapiens*) appeared only about 25,000 years ago. Movies that show humans and dinosaurs existing together are only Hollywood fantasies.

How long did dinosaurs live?

The life span has been estimated at 75 to 300 years. Such estimates are educated guesses. From examination of the microstructure of dinosaur bones, scientists have inferred that they matured slowly and probably had proportionately long life spans.

How does a mastodon differ from a mammoth?

Although the words are sometimes used interchangeably, the mammoth and the mastodon were two different animals. The mastodon seems to have appeared first, while a side branch may have led to the mammoth.

The *mastodon* lived in Africa, Europe, Asia, and North and South America. It appeared in the Oligocene epoch (25 to 38 million years ago) and survived until less than one million years ago. It stood a maximum of 10 feet (three meters) tall and was covered with dense woolly hair. Its tusks were aligned straight forward and were nearly parallel to each other.

The *mammoth* evolved less than two million years ago and died out about 10 thousand years ago. It lived in North America, Europe, and Asia. Like the mastodon, the mammoth was covered with dense, woolly hair, with a long, coarse layer of outer hair to protect it from the cold. It was somewhat larger than the mastodon, standing 9 to 15 feet (2.7 to 4.5 meters). The mammoth's tusks tended to spiral outward, then up.

The gradual warming of the Earth's climate and the change in environment were probably primary factors in the animals' extinction. Early man killed many of them as well, perhaps hastening the process.

Why did dinosaurs become extinct?

There are many theories as to why dinosaurs disappeared from the Earth about 65 million years ago. Scientists debate whether dinosaurs became extinct gradually or all at once. The gradualists believe that the dinosaur population steadily declined at the end of Cretaceous Period. Numerous reasons have been proposed for this. Some claim the dinosaurs' extinction was caused by biological changes that made them less competitive with other organisms, especially the mammals that were just beginning to appear. Overpopulation has been argued, as has the theory that mammals ate too many dinosaur eggs for the animals to reproduce themselves. Others believe that disease—everything from rickets to constipation—wiped them out. Changes in climate, continental drift, volcanic eruptions, and shifts in the Earth's axis, orbit, and/or magnetic field have also been held responsible.

The catastrophists argue that a single disastrous event caused the extinction not only of the dinosaurs but also of a large number of other species that coexisted with them. In 1980, American physicist Luis Alvarez (1911-1988) and his geologist son, Walter Alvarez (b. 1940), proposed that a large comet or meteoroid struck the Earth 65 million years ago. They pointed out that there is a high concentration of the element iridium in the sediments at the boundary between the Cretaceous and Tertiary Periods. Iridium is rare on Earth, so the only source of such a large amount of it had to be outer space. This iridium anomaly has since been discovered at over 50 sites around the world. In 1990, tiny glass fragments, which could have been caused by the extreme heat of an impact, were identified in Haiti. A 110-mile (177-kilometer) wide crater in the Yucatan Peninsula, long covered by sediments, has been dated to 64.98 million years ago, making it a leading candidate for the site of this impact.

A hit by a large extraterrestrial object, perhaps as much as six miles (9.3 kilometers) wide, would have had a catastrophic effect upon the world's climate. Huge amounts of dust and debris would have been thrown into the atmosphere, reducing the amount of sunlight reaching the surface. Heat from the blast may also have caused large forest fires, which would have added smoke and ash to the air. Lack of sunlight would kill off plants and have a domino-like effect on other organisms in the food chain, including the dinosaurs.

It is possible that the reason for the dinosaurs' extinction may have been a combination of both theories. The dinosaurs may have been gradually declining, for whatever reason. The impact of a large object from space merely delivered the coup de grâce.

The fact that dinosaurs became extinct has been cited as proof of their inferiority and that they were evolutionary failures. However, these animals flourished for 150 million years. By comparison, the earliest ancestors of humanity appeared only about three million years ago. Humans have a long way to go before they can claim the same sort of success as the dinosaurs.

How did the dodo become extinct?

The dodo became extinct around 1800. Thousands were slaughtered for meat, but pigs and monkeys, which destroyed dodo eggs, were probably most responsible for the dodo's extinction. Dodos were native to the Mascarene Islands in the Central Indian Ocean. They became extinct on Mauritius soon after 1680 and on Réunion about 1750. They remained on Rodriguez until 1800.

What is the difference between an "endangered" species and a "threatened" species?

An "endangered" species is one that is in danger of extinction throughout all or a significant portion of its range. A "threatened" species is one that is likely to become endangered in the foreseeable future.

Under what conditions is a species considered "endangered"?

This determination is a complex process that has no set of fixed criteria that can be applied consistently to all species. The known number of living members in a species is not the sole factor. A species with a million members known to be alive but living in only one small area could be considered endangered, whereas another species having a smaller number of members, but spread out in a broad area, would not be considered so threatened. Reproduction data—the frequency of reproduction, the average number of offspring born, the survival rate, etc.—enter into such determinations. In the United States, the director of the U.S. Fish and Wildlife Service (within the Department of the Interior) determines which species are to be considered endangered, based on research and field data from specialists, biologists, botanists, and naturalists.

According to the Endangered Species Act of 1973, a species can be listed if it is threatened by any of the following:

When did the last passenger pigeon die?

At one time, 200 years ago, the passenger pigeon (*Ectopistes migratorius*) was the world's most abundant bird. Although the species was found only in eastern North America, it had a population of three to five billion birds (25 percent of the North American land bird population). Overhunting caused a chain of events that reduced their numbers below minimum threshold for viability. In the 1890s several states passed laws to protect the pigeon, but it was too late. The last known wild bird was shot in 1900. The last passenger pigeon, named Martha, died on September 1, 1914, in the Cincinnati Zoo.

1. The present or threatened destruction, modification, or curtailment of its habitat or range.

2. Utilization for commercial, sporting, scientific, or educational purposes at levels that detrimentally affect it.

3. Disease or predation.

4. Absence of regulatory mechanisms adequate to prevent the decline of a species or degradation of its habitat.

5. Other natural or man-made factors affecting its continued existence.

If the species is so threatened, the director then determines the "critical habitat," that is the species' inhabitation areas that contain the essential physical or biological features necessary for the species' preservation. The critical habitat can include non-habitation areas, which are deemed necessary for the protection of the species.

What is the status of the elephant in Africa?

From 1979 to 1989, Africa lost half of its elephants from poaching and illegal ivory trade, with the population decreasing from an estimated 1.3 million to 600,000. This led to the transfer of the African elephant from threatened to endangered status in October 1989 by CITES (the Convention on International Trade in Endangered Species). An ivory ban took effect on January 18, 1990. Botswana, Namibia, and Zimbabwe have agreed to restrict the sale of ivory to a single, government-controlled center in each country. All countries have further pledged to allow independent monitoring of the sale, packing, and shipping processes to ensure compliance with all conditions. Finally, all three countries have promised that all net revenues from the sale of ivory will be directed back into elephant conservation for use in monitoring, research, law enforcement, other management expenses or community-based conservation programs within elephant range.

Are turtles endangered?

Worldwide turtle populations have declined due to several reasons, including habitat destruction; exploitation of species by humans for their eggs, leather, and meat; and their becoming accidentally caught in the nets of fishermen. In particular danger are sea turtles, such as Kemp's ridley sea turtle (*Lepidochelys kempii*), which is believed to have a population of only a few hundred. Other species include the Central American river turtle (*Dermatemys mawii*), the green sea turtle (*Chelonia mydas*), and the leatherback sea turtle (*Dermochelys coriacea*). Endangered tortoises include the angulated tortoise (*Geochelone yniphora*), the desert tortoise (*Gopherus agassizii*), and the Galapagos tortoise (*Geochelone elephantopus*).

What is a dolphin-safe tuna?

The order *Cetacea,* composed of whales, dolphins, and porpoises, were spared from the extinction of large mammals at the end of the Pleistocene about 10,000 years ago. But from 1000 B.C.E. on they, especially the whale, have been relentlessly hunted by man for their valuable products. The twentieth century, with its many technological improvements, has become the most destructive period for the *Cetacea*. In 1972, the United States Congress passed the Marine Mammal Protection Act; one of its goals was to reduce the number of small cetaceans (notably Stenalla and Delphinus) killed and injured during commercial fishing operations, such as the incidental catch of dolphins in tuna purse-seines (nets that

In a span of just 200 years the passenger pigeon passed from the world's most abundant bird species into extinction.

close up to form a huge ball to be hoisted aboard ship). Dolphins are often found swimming with schools of yellowfin tuna and are caught along with the tuna by fisherman who use purse-seine nets. The dolphins are drowned by this fishing method because they must be able to breathe air to survive. The number of incidental deaths and injuries in 1972 was estimated at 368,000 for United States fishing vessels and 55,078 for non-United States vessels. In 1979 the figures were reduced to 17,938 and 6,837 respectively. But in the 1980s, the dolphins killed by foreign vessels rose dramatically to over 100,000 a year. Most of the slaughter occurs in the eastern Pacific Ocean from Chile to Southern California. In 1999, the United States attempted to weaken the definition of dolphin-safe tuna by allowing tuna fleets to chase and net dolphins. The ruling was not upheld by the United States District Court.

To further reduce the numbers of dolphins killed during tuna catches, the three largest sellers of canned tuna in the United States, spearheaded by the Starkist company, decided that they would not sell tuna that has been caught by these methods harmful to dolphins.

POLLUTION

How are hazardous waste materials classified?

There are four types of hazardous waste materials—corrosive, ignitable, reactive, and toxic.

Corrosive materials can wear away or destroy a substance. Most acids are corrosive and can destroy metal, burn skin, and give off vapors that burn the eyes.

Ignitable materials can burst into flames easily. These materials pose a fire hazard and can irritate the skin, eyes, and lungs. Gasoline, paint, and furniture polish are ignitable.

Reactive materials can explode or create poisonous gas when combined with other chemicals. Combining chlorine bleach and ammonia, for example, creates a poisonous gas.

Toxic materials or substances can poison humans and other life. They can cause illness or death if swallowed or absorbed through the skin. Pesticides and household cleaning agents are toxic.

What is bioremediation?

Bioremediation is the degradation, decomposition, or stabilization of pollutants by microorganisms such as bacteria, fungi, and cyanobacteria. Oxygen and organisms are injected into contaminated soil and/or water (e.g. oil spills). The microorganisms feed on and eliminate the pollutants. When the pollutants are gone, the organisms die.

What is the Pollutant Standard Index?

The U.S. Environmental Protection Agency and the South Coast Air Quality Management District of El Monte, California, devised the Pollutant Standard Index to monitor concentrations of pollutants in the air and inform the public concerning related health effects. The scale measures the amount of pollution in parts per million, and has been in use nationwide since 1978.

PSI Index	Health Effects	Cautionary Status
0	Good	
50	Moderate	
100	Unhealthful	
200	Very unhealthful	Alert: elderly or ill should stay indoors and reduce physical activity.
300	Hazardous	Warning: General population should stay indoors and reduce physical activity.
400	Extremely hazardous	Emergency: all people remain indoors windows shut, no physical exertion.
500	Toxic	Significant harm; same as above.

What is the Toxic Release Inventory (TRI)?

TRI is a government mandated, publicly available compilation of information on the release of over 650 individual toxic chemicals and toxic chemical categories by manufacturing facilities in the United States. The law requires manufacturers to state the amounts of chemicals they release directly to air, land, or water, or that they transfer to off-site facilities that treat or dispose of wastes. The U.S. Environmental Protection Agency compiles these reports into an annual inventory and makes the information available in a computerized database. In 2000, 23,484 facilities released 7.1 billion pounds (3.2 billion kilograms) of toxic chemicals into the environment. Over 260 million pounds (118 million kilograms) of this total were released into surface water; 1.9 billion pounds (0.86 million kilograms) were emitted into the air; over 4.13 billion pounds (1.87 billion kilograms) were released to land; and over 278 million pounds (126 million kilograms) were injected into underground wells. The total amount of toxic chemicals released in 2000 was 6.7 percent lower than the amount released in 1999.

What chemicals, which were once hailed as wonder chemicals that would benefit society, are now banned or strictly controlled ?

Dichlorodiphenyl-trichloro-ethene (DDT), polychlorinated biphenyls (PCBs) and chlorofluorocarbons (CFCs) were once widely used. Increased awareness of the detrimental effects on the environment from these chemicals led to all of them being banned or strictly controlled.

Which industries release the most toxic chemicals?

The metal mining industry released the most toxic chemicals for the year 2000, accounting for 47.3 percent of total chemical releases.

Industry	Total Releases (pounds)	Percent of Total
Metal mining	3,357,765,313	47.3
Manufacturing industries	2,284,399,698	32.2
Electric utilities	1,152,242,786	16.2
Hazardous waste/Solvent recovery	284,950,589	4.0
Coal mining	15,968,001	0.2
Petroleum terminals/bulk storage	3,878,087	0.1
Chemical wholesale distributors	1,611,790	0.02

How did DDT affect the environment?

Although DDT was synthesized as early as 1874 by Othmar Zeidler, it was the Swiss chemist Paul Müller (1899-1965) who recognized its insecticidal properties in 1939. He was awarded the 1948 Nobel Prize in medicine for his development of dichloro-diphenyl-trichloro-ethene, or DDT. Unlike the arsenic-based compounds then in use, DDT was effective in killing insects and seemed not to harm plants and animals. In the following 20 years it proved to be effective in controlling disease-carrying insects (mosquitoes that carry malaria and yellow fever, and lice that carry typhus) and in killing many plant crop destroyers. Publication of Rachel Carson's *Silent Spring* in 1962 alerted scientists to the detrimental effects of DDT. Increasingly, DDT-resistant insect species and the accumulative hazardous effects of DDT on plant and animal life cycles led to its disuse in many countries during the 1970s.

What are PCBs?

Polychlorinated biphenyls (PCBs) are a group of chemicals that were widely used before 1970 in the electrical industry as coolants for transformers and in capacitors and other electrical devices. They caused environmental problems because they do not break down and can spread through the water, soil, and air. They have been linked by some scientists to cancer and reproductive disorders and have been shown to cause liver function abnormalities. Government action has resulted in the control of the use, disposal, and production of PCBs in nearly all areas of the world, including the United States.

How do chlorofluorocarbons affect the Earth's ozone layer?

Chlorofluorocarbons (CFCs) are hydrocarbons, such as freon, in which part or all of the hydrogen atoms have been replaced by fluorine atoms. These can be liquids or gases, are non-flammable and heat-stable, and are used as refrigerants, aerosol propellants, and solvents. When released into the air, they slowly rise into the Earth's upper atmosphere, where they are broken apart by ultraviolet rays from the sun. Some of the resultant molecular fragments react with the ozone in the atmosphere, reducing the amount of ozone. The CFC molecules' chlorine atoms act as catalysts in a complex set of reactions that convert two molecules of ozone into three molecules of ordinary oxygen. This is depleting the beneficial ozone layer faster than it can be recharged by natural processes. The resultant "hole" lets through more ultraviolet light to the Earth's surface and creates health problems for humans, such as cataracts and skin cancer, and disturbs delicate ecosystems (for example, making plants produce fewer seeds). In 1978 the United States government banned the use of fluorocarbon aerosols, and currently aerosol propellants have been changed from fluorocarbons to hydrocarbons, such as butane. The Montreal Protocol of 1987 initiated worldwide cooperation to reduce the use of CFCs.

Since the late 1980s a substantial slowdown has taken place in the atmospheric buildup of two prime ozone-destroying compounds, CFC 11 and CFC 12. Based upon these measurements, experts suggest that concentrations of these CFCs will peak before the turn of the century, allowing the ozone layer to begin the slow process of repairing itself. It is believed that it will take 50 to 100 years for reactions in the atmosphere to reduce the concentrations of ozone-destroying chlorine and bromine back to natural levels. Until then, these chemicals will continue to erode the global ozone layer.

What are the components of smog?

Smog, the most widespread pollutant in the United States, is a photochemical reaction resulting in ground-level ozone. Ozone, an odorless, tasteless gas in the presence of light can initiate a chain of chemical reactions. Ozone is a desirable gas in the stratospheric layer of the atmosphere, but it can be hazardous to health when found near the Earth's surface in the troposphere. The hydrocarbons, hydrocarbon derivations, and nitric oxides emitted from such sources as automobiles are the raw materials for photochemical reactions. In the presence of oxygen and sunlight, the nitric oxides combine with organic compounds, such as the hydrocarbons from unburned gasoline, to produce a whitish haze, sometimes tinged with a yellow-brown color. In this process, a large number of new hydrocarbons and oxyhydrocarbons are produced. These secondary hydrocarbon products may comprise as much as 95 percent of the total organics in a severe smog episode.

What is an example of how we can alleviate air pollution?

The scrubbing of flue gases refers to the removal of sulfur dioxide (SO_2) and nitric oxide (NO), which are major components of air pollution. Wet scrubbers use a chemical solvent of lime, limestone, sodium alkali, or diluted sulfuric acid to remove the SO_2 formed during combustion. Dry scrubbing uses either a lime/limestone slurry or ammonia sprayed into the flue gases.

What was the distribution of radioactive fallout after the 1986 Chernobyl accident?

Radioactive fallout, containing the isotope cesium 137, and nuclear contamination covered an enormous area, including Byelorussia, Latvia, Lithuania, the central portion of the then Soviet Union, the Scandinavian countries, the Ukraine, Poland, Austria, Czechoslovakia, Germany, Switzerland, northern Italy, eastern France, Romania, Bulgaria, Greece, Yugoslavia, the Netherlands, and the United Kingdom. The fallout, extremely uneven because of the shifting wind patterns, extended 1,200 to 1,300 miles (1,930 to 2,090 kilometers) from the point of the accident. Roughly 5 percent of the reactor fuel—or seven tons of fuel containing 50 to 100 million curies—was released. Estimates of the effects of this fallout range from 28,000 to 100,000 deaths from cancer and genetic defects within the next 50 years. In particular, livestock in high rainfall areas received unacceptable dosages of radiation.

What has the damage been after the 2011 Fukushima disaster?

Following a powerful earthquake on March 11, 2011, in Japan, a tsunami smashed into the coast by the city of Fukushima, where there was a nuclear power plant. The generators that were used to cool the nuclear reactors were damaged, causing them to overheat and leading to a nuclear meltdown (the company running the plant, the Tokyo Electric Power Company, did not adequately maintain the reactors and they did not meet safety requirements). There were several explosions and radiation was released into the air. The city was evacuated (about 368,000 people), as well as everyone within about a twelve-mile (twenty kilometer) radius. Fortunately, the radiation released was only about ten percent of the Chernobyl disaster and prevailing winds blew much of that out into the ocean. The area, which is north of Tokyo, remains off limits to people today.

What is acid rain?

The term "acid rain" was coined by British chemist Robert Angus Smith (1817-1884) who, in 1872, published *Air & Rain: The Beginnings of a Chemical Climatology*. Since then, acid rain has unfortunately become an increasingly used term for rain, snow, sleet, or other precipitation that has been polluted by acids such as sulfuric and nitric acids.

When gasoline, coal, or oil are burned, their waste products of sulfur dioxide and nitrogen dioxide combine in complex chemical reactions with water vapor in clouds to form acids. The United States alone discharges 40 million metric tons of sulfur and nitrogen oxides into the atmosphere. This, combined with natural emissions of sulfur and nitrogen compounds, has resulted in severe ecological damage. Hundreds of lakes in North America (especially northeastern Canada and United States) and in Scandinavia are so acidic that they cannot support fish life. Crops, forests, and building materials, such as marble, limestone, sandstone, and bronze, have been affected as well, but the extent is not as well documented. However, in Europe, where so many living trees are stunted or killed, the new word "Waldsterben" (forest death) has been coined to describe this new phenomenon.

In 1990, amendments to the U.S. Clean Air Act contained provisions to control emissions that cause acid rain. It included the reductions of sulfur dioxide emissions from 19 million tons to 9.1 million tons annually and the reduction of industrial nitrogen oxide emissions from six to four million tons annually.

Year	Sulfur Dioxide Emissions (million tons)	Nitrogen Oxide Emissions (million tons)
1990	15.73	6.66
1995	11.87	6.09
1996	12.51	5.91
1997	12.96	6.04
1998	13.13	5.97
1999	12.45	5.49
2000	11.28	5.11

How acidic is acid rain?

Acidity or alkalinity is measured by a scale known as the pH (potential for Hydrogen) scale. It runs from zero to 14. Since it is logarithmic, a change in one unit equals a tenfold increase or decrease. So a solution at pH 2 is 10 times more acidic than one at pH 3 and 100 times as acidic as a solution at pH 4. Zero is extremely acid, 7 is neutral, and 14 is very alkaline. Any rain below 5.0 is considered acid rain; some scientists use the value of 5.6 or less. Normal rain and snow containing dissolved carbon dioxide (a weak acid) measure about pH 5.6. Actual values vary according to geographical area. Eastern Europe and parts of Scandinavia have 4.3 to 4.5; the rest of Europe is 4.5 to 5.1; eastern United States and Canada ranges from 4.2 to 4.6, and Mississippi Valley has a range of 4.6 to 4.8. The worst North American area, having 4.2, is centered around Lake Erie and Lake Ontario. For comparison, some common items and their pH values are listed below:

Concentrated sulfuric acid	1.0
Lemon juice	2.3
Vinegar	3.3
Acid rain	4.3
Normal rain	5.0 to 5.6
Normal lakes and rivers	5.6 to 8.0
Distilled water	7.0
Human blood	7.35 to 7.45
Seawater	7.6 to 8.4

What are the sources of oil pollution in the oceans?

Most oil pollution results from accidental discharges of oil when oil tankers are loaded and unloaded and minor spillage from tankers. Other sources of oil pollution include improper disposal of used motor oil, oil leaks from motor vehicles, routine ship maintenance, leaks in pipelines that transport oil, and accidents at storage facilities and refineries.

Source	Percent of total oil spillage
Runoff from rivers and surface water	31%
Tanker activity (loading, unloading, etc.)	20%
Sewage plants and refineries	13%
Natural seepage from ocean floor	9%
Smaller craft (fishing vessels, ferries, etc.)	9%
Oil tanker accidents	3-5%

What are the most commonly collected debris items found along ocean coasts?

Debris Item	Total number reported (2000)	Percentage of total collected (2000)
Cigarette butts	1,027,303	20.25%
Plastic pieces	337,384	6.65%
Food bags/wrappers (plastic)	284,287	5.6%
Foamed plastic pieces	268,945	5.3%
Caps, lids (plastic)	255,253	5.03%
Paper pieces	219,256	4.32%
Beverage cans	184,294	3.63%
Beverage bottles (glass)	177,039	3.49%
Straws	161,639	3.19%

What causes formaldehyde contamination in homes?

Formaldehyde contamination is related to the widespread construction use of wood products bonded with urea-formaldehyde resins and products containing formaldehyde. Major formaldehyde sources include subflooring of particle board; wall paneling made from hardwood plywood or particle board; and cabinets and furniture made from particle board, medium density fiberboard, hardwood plywood, or solid wood. Urea-formaldehyde foam insulation (UFFI) has received the most media notoriety and regulatory attention. Formaldehyde is also used in drapes, upholstery, carpeting, wallpaper adhesives, milk cartons, car bodies, household disinfectants, permanent-press clothing, and paper towels. In particular, mobile homes seem to have higher formaldehyde levels than houses do. Six billion pounds (2.7 billion kilograms) of formaldehyde are used in the United States each year.

The release of formaldehyde into the air by these products (called outgassing) can develop poisoning symptoms in humans. The EPA classifies formaldehyde as a potential human carcinogen (cancer-causing agent).

Which pollutants lead to indoor air pollution?

Indoor air pollution, also known as "tight building syndrome," results from conditions in modern, high energy efficiency buildings, which have reduced outside air exchange, or have inadequate ventilation, chemical contamination, and microbial contamination. Indoor air pollution can produce various symptoms, such as headache, nausea, and eye, nose, and throat irritation. In addition, houses are affected by indoor air pollution emanating from consumer and building products and from tobacco smoke. Some of the most common indoor pollutants are carbon monoxide, nitrogen dioxide, formaldehyde, asbestos, lead, mercury, radon, pesticides, organic gases (e.g., from paint, paint strippers, aerosol sprays, cleaning and disinfectant supplies), and biological pollutants (mold, mildew, bacteria, viruses).

What is the Resource Conservation and Recovery Act?

In 1976, the United States Congress passed the Resource Conservation and Recovery Act (RCRA), which was amended in 1984 and 1986. This law requires the EPA to identify hazardous wastes and set standards for their management including generation, transportation, treatment, storage, and disposal of hazardous waste. The law requires all firms that store, treat, or dispose of more than 220 pounds (100 kilograms) of hazardous wastes per month to have a permit stating how such wastes are managed.

What is the Toxic Substances Control Act (TOSCA)?

In 1976, the United States Congress passed the Toxic Substances Control Act (TOSCA). This act requires the premarket testing of toxic substances. When a chemical substance is planned to be manufactured, the producer must notify the Environmental Protection Agency (EPA), and, if the data presented is determined to be inadequate to approve its use, the EPA will require the manufacturer to conduct further tests. Or, if it is later determined that a chemical is present at a level that presents an unreasonable public or environmental risk, or if there is insufficient data to know the chemical's effects, manufacturers have the burden of evaluating the chemical's characteristics and risks. If testing does not convince the EPA of the chemical's safety, the chemical's manufacturing, sale, or use can be limited or prohibited.

What is the Superfund Act?

In 1980, the United States Congress passed the Comprehensive Environmental Response, Compensation, and Liability Act, commonly known as the Superfund program. This law (along with amendments in 1986 and 1990) established a $16.3-billion Superfund financed jointly by federal and state governments and by special taxes on chemical and petrochemical industries (which provide 86 percent of the funding). The purpose of the Superfund is to identify and clean up abandoned hazardous-waste dump sites and leaking underground tanks that threaten human health and the environment. To keep taxpayers from footing most of the bill, cleanups are based on the polluter-pays principle. The EPA is charged with locating dangerous dump sites, finding the potentially liable culprits, ordering them to pay for the entire cleanup and suing them if they don't. When the EPA can find no responsible party, it draws money out of the Superfund for cleanup.

How many hazardous waste sites are there?

As of 2009, there were 1,650 sites.

What is the NIMBY syndrome?

NIMBY is the acronym for "Not In My Back Yard," referring to major community resistance to new incinerator sitings, landfills, prisons, roads, etc. NIMFY is "Not In My Front Yard."

What are Brownfields?

The Environmental Protection Agency defines Brownfields as abandoned, idled, or underused industrial or commercial sites where expansion or redevelopment is complicated by real or perceived environmental contamination. Real estate developers perceive Brownfields as inappropriate sites for redevelopment. There are approximately 450,000 Brownfields in the United States, with the heaviest concentrations being in the Northeast and Midwest.

Which government agencies regulate the storage of nuclear waste?

The Department of Energy, Environmental Protection Agency, and Nuclear Regulatory Commission are responsible for the disposal of spent nuclear fuel and other radioactive waste. The Department of Energy (DOE) has the responsibility for developing permanent disposal capacity for spent fuel and other high-level radioactive waste. The Environmental Protection Agency (EPA) has responsibility for developing environmental standards to evaluate the safety of a geologic repository. The Nuclear Regulatory Commission (NRC) has responsibility for developing regulations to implement the EPA safety standards and for licensing the repository.

How is nuclear waste stored?

Nuclear wastes consist either of fission products formed from the splitting of uranium, cesium, strontium, or krypton, or from transuranic elements formed when uranium atoms absorb free neutrons. Wastes from transuranic elements are less radioactive than fission products; however, these elements remain radioactive far longer— hundreds of thousands of years. The types of waste are irradiated fuel (spent fuel) in the form of 12-foot (4-meter) long rods, high-level radioactive waste in the form of liquid or sludge, and low-level waste (non-transuranic or legally high-level) in the form of reactor hardware, piping, toxic resins, water from fuel pool and other items that have become contaminated with radioactivity.

Currently, most spent nuclear fuel in the United States is safely stored in specially designed pools at individual reactor sites around the country. If pool capacity is reached, licensees may move toward use of above-ground dry storage casks. The three low-level radioactive waste disposal sites are Barnwell located in South Carolina, Hanford located in Washington, and Envirocare located in Utah. Each site accepts low-level radioactive waste from specific regions of the country.

Most high-level nuclear waste has been stored in double-walled, stainless-steel tanks surrounded by three feet (one meter) of concrete. The current best storage method, devel-

The United States is currently home to more than 9,000 landfill sites.

oped by the French in 1978, is to incorporate the waste into a special molten glass mixture, then enclose it in a steel container and bury it in a special pit. The Nuclear Waste Policy Act of 1982 specified that high-level radioactive waste would be disposed of underground in a deep geologic repository. Yucca Mountain, Nevada, was chosen as the single site to be developed for disposal of high-level radioactive waste. However, as of the late 1990s, selection of the Yucca Mountain site was controversial due to dormant volcanoes in the vicinity and known earthquake fault lines.

When was the first garbage incinerator built?

The first garbage incinerator in the United States was built in 1885 on Governor's Island in New York Harbor.

Why did the ship *Mobro* gain international fame?

The *Mobro* was the Long Island, New York, garbage barge that was loaded with garbage and could not dispose of it. It was rejected by six states and three countries, drawing attention to the landfill capacity shortage in the Northeast. The garbage was finally burned in Brooklyn and the ash brought to a landfill near Islip.

How critical is the problem of landfilling in the United States?

Landfilling has been an essential component of waste management for several decades. In 1960, 62 percent of all garbage was sent to landfills, and by 1980 the figure had risen to 81 percent. By 1990, 84 percent of the 269 million tons of municipal solid waste that was generated was sent to landfills. An increased awareness of the benefits of recycling has brought a decline in the actual number of landfills from 4,482 in 1995 to 2,142 in 2000 as well as a decrease in

When was metal recycling started?

The first metal recycling in the United States occurred in 1776 when patriots in New York City toppled a statue of King George III, which was melted down and made into 42,088 bullets.

the amount of municipal solid waste that is sent to landfills. Figures for 2000 indicate that only 60 percent of the municipal solid waste generated was sent to landfills. The total amount of recycled waste increased from 8 percent to 33 percent between 1990 and 2000.

How much methane fuel does a ton of garbage make?

Over a period of 10 to 15 years, a ton of garbage will make 14,126 cubic feet (400 cubic meters) of fuel, although a landfill site will generate smaller amounts for 50 to 100 years. One ton of garbage can produce more than 100 times its volume in methane over a decade. Landfill operators tend not to maximize methane production.

How much space does a recycled ton of paper save in a landfill?

Each ton (907 kilograms) saves more than three cubic yards of landfill space.

What natural resources are saved by recycling paper?

One ton (907 kilograms) of recycled waste paper would save an average of 7,000 gallons (26,460 liters) of water, 3.3 cubic yards (2.5 cubic meters) of landfill space, three barrels of oil, 17 trees, and 4,000 kilowatt-hours of electricity—enough energy to power the average home for six months. It would also reduce air pollution by 74 percent.

How much newspaper must be recycled to save one tree?

One 35 to 40 foot (10.6 to 12 meter) tree produces a stack of newspapers four feet (1.2 meters) thick; this much newspaper must be recycled to save a tree.

How much waste paper does a newspaper generate?

An average yearly newspaper subscription (for example, the *San Francisco Chronicle*) received every day produces 550 pounds (250 kilograms) of waste paper per subscription per year. The average *New York Times* Sunday edition produces eight million pounds (3.6 million kilograms) of waste paper.

What problems may be encountered when polyvinyl chloride (PVC) plastics are burned?

Chlorinated plastics, such as PVC, contribute to the formation of hydrochloric acid gases. They also may be a part of a mix of substances containing chlorine that form a precursor to dioxin in the burning process. Polystyrene, polyethylene, and polyethylene terephthalate (PET) do not produce these pollutants.

When was paper recycling started?

Paper recycling was actually born in 1690 in the United States when the first paper mill was established by the Rittenhouse family on the banks of Wissahickon Creek, near Philadelphia. The paper at this mill was made from recycled rags.

How can plastics be made biodegradable?

Plastic does not rust or rot. This is an advantage in its usage, but when it comes to disposal of plastic the advantage turns into a liability. Degradable plastic has starch in it so that it can be attacked by starch-eating bacteria to eventually disintegrate the plastic into bits. Chemically degradable plastic can be broken up with a chemical solution that dissolves it. Used in surgery, biodegradable plastic stitches slowly dissolve in the body fluids. Photodegradable plastic contains chemicals that disintegrate over a period of one to three years when exposed to light. One-quarter of the plastic yokes used to package beverages are made from a plastic called Ecolyte, which is photodegradable.

What do the numbers inside the recycling symbol on plastic containers mean?

The Society of the Plastics Industry developed a voluntary coding system for plastic containers to assist recyclers in sorting plastic containers. The symbol is designed to be imprinted on the bottom of the plastic containers. The numerical code appears inside three arrows that form a triangle. A guide to what the numbers mean is listed below. The most commonly recycled plastics are polyethylene terephthalate (PET) and high-density polyethylene (HDPE).

Code	Material	Examples
1	Polyethylene terephthalate (PET/PETE)	2-liter soft drink bottle
2	High-density polyethylene (HDPE)	Milk and water jugs
3	Vinyl (PVC)	Plastic pipes, shampoo bottles
4	Low-density polyethylene (LDPE)	Produce bags, food storage containers
5	Polypropylene (PP)	Squeeze bottles, drinking straws
6	Polystyrene (PS)	Fast-food packaging, packaging
7	Other	Food containers

How many curbside recycling programs are there in the United States?

The first municipal-wide curbside recycling program was started in 1974 in University City, Missouri, where city officials designed and distributed a container for collecting newspapers. Curbside recycling programs continue to increase in the United States. In 1997, there were 7,375 curbside recycling programs. By 1999 the number of curbside recycling programs had increased to 9,349.

What products are made from recycled plastic?

Resin	Common Uses	Products Made from Recycled Resin
HDPE	Beverage bottles, milk jugs, milk and soft drink crates, pipe, cable, film	Motor oil bottles, detergent bottles, pipes and pails
LDPE	Film bags such as trash bags, coatings, and plastic bottles	New trash bags, pallets, carpets, fiberfill, non-food
PET	Soft drink, detergent, and juice bottles	Bottles/containers
PP	Auto battery cases, screw-on caps and lids; some yogurt and	Auto parts, batteries, carpets margarine tubs, plastic film
PS	Housewares, electronics, fast food carry-out packaging, plastic utensils	Insulation board, office equipment, reusable cafeteria trays
PVC	Sporting goods, luggage, pipes, auto parts. In packaging for shampoo bottles, blister packaging, and films	Drainage pipes, fencing, house siding

A new clothing fiber called Fortrel EcoSpun is made from recycled plastic soda bottles. The fiber is knit or woven into garments such as fleece for outerwear or long underwear. The processor estimates that every pound of Fortrel EcoSpun fiber results in 10 plastic bottles being kept out of landfills.

When offered a choice between plastic or paper bags for your groceries, wich should you choose?

The answer is neither. Both are environmentally harmful and the question of which is the more damaging has no clear-cut answer. On one hand, plastic bags degrade slowly in landfills and can harm wildlife if swallowed, and producing them pollutes the environment. On the other hand, producing the brown paper bags used in most supermarket uses trees and pollutes the air and water. Overall, white or clear polyethylene bags require less energy for manufacture and cause less damage to the environment than do paper bags not made from recycled paper. Instead of having to choose between paper and plastic bags, you can bring your own reusable canvas or string containers to the store, and save and reuse any paper or plastic bags you get.

Is washing dishes by hand better for the environment than using an automatic dishwasher?

Dishwashers often save energy and water compared to hand washing. Depending on the brand, dishwashers typically consume 7.5 to 12 gallons (28 to 45 liters) of water per normal wash. Hand-washing a day's worth of dishes may use up to 15 gallons (57 liters) of water. One university study found that dishwashers consume about 37 percent less water than washing by hand.

Several steps can be taken for additional energy savings when using a dishwasher. The setting on a home's water heater can be turned down to 120°F (49°C) if the dishwasher has a booster heater. While some machines feature a no-heat, air-dry setting, simply opening the door after the final rinse to let the dishes air dry will save energy. Prewashing the dishes before loading generally wastes water since most machines can handle even heavily soiled plates.

What is a WOBO?

A WOBO (world bottle) is the first mass-produced container designed for secondary use as a building product. It was conceived by Albert Heineken of the Heineken beer family. The beer bottles were designed in a special shape to be used, when empty, as glass bricks for building houses. The actual building carried out with WOBOs was only a small shed and a double garage built on the Heineken estate at Noordwijk, near Amsterdam. Although not implemented, WOBO was a sophisticated and intelligent design solution to what has emerged as a major environmental issue in recent years.

BIOLOGY

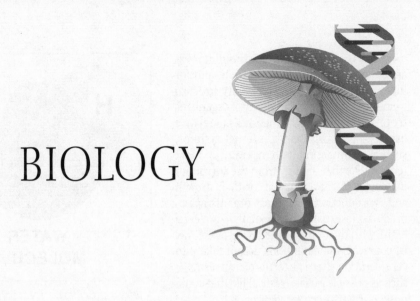

What is biology?

Biology is often called the science of life in studies that include everything from an organism's conception to its death. It is mainly concerned with the study of living systems—from animal to plant and everything in between—and includes the study of various organisms' cells, metabolism, reproduction, growth, activity of systems, and response to the stimuli in their environment.

Who coined the term "biology"?

French biologist Jean-Baptiste Pierre Antoine de Monet de Lamarck (1744–1829) is credited with coining the term "biology" (from the Greek terms *bios*, meaning "life," and *logy*, meaning "study of") in 1802 to describe the science of life. He was also the first to publish a version of an evolutionary tree that described the ancestral relationships among species (an early classification system), first to distinguish between vertebrates and invertebrates—and is often considered one of the first evolutionists.

What is life?

The definition of "life" is the most controversial subject—just mention the word to scientists would undoubtedly be a heated debate. It affects every branch of biology—from life on Earth to the possibility of life in outer space. But some general, often agreed-upon criteria exist for the definition of life (although some creatures exist that are contrary to the rules): Living organisms are usually complex and highly organized (with exceptions); most

Jean-Baptiste Lamarck's theories on evolution preceded and influenced those of Charles Darwin.

creatures respond to external stimuli (for example, plants that recoil on touch, and for higher level organisms, the ability to learn from the stimulus); the majority of organisms try to sustain internal homeostasis (a relative balance of an organism's internal systems, such as maintaining its temperature); most tend to take their energy from the surrounding environment and use it for their growth and reproduction; and most organisms reproduce (asexually or sexually—or even both), with their offspring evolving over time. Of course, these definitions do not take into consideration alternate forms of organisms— such as possible extraterrestrial life that could upset our Earth-centric view of life!

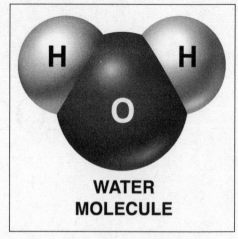

A water molecule is essential to life on Earth. Its slightly positive and negative poles encourages other molecules to organize themselves in aqueous solutions.

Could life on Earth have been based on silicon instead of carbon?

Yes, technically, life on Earth could have been based on silicon instead of carbon because the element has the same bonding properties as carbon. But silicon is second only to carbon in its presence on Earth, thus carbon-based life evolved. (Note: Silicon is never found alone in nature, but always exists as silica [silicon dioxide] or silicates [made up of a compound made of silicon, oxygen, and at least one metal].) But that does not mean no organisms exist that contain silica. For example, a plant called horsetail has one of the highest contents of silica in the plant kingdom. Called a "living fossil," it is the descendant of plants that lived over a hundred million years ago.

Why is water so important to life?

We are all aqueous creatures, whether because of living in a watery environment or because of the significant amount of water contained within living organisms. Therefore, all chemical reactions in living organisms take place in an aqueous environment. Water is important to all living organisms due to its unique molecular structure (H_2O), which is V-shaped, with hydrogen atoms at the points of the V and an oxygen atom at the apex of the V. In the covalent bond between oxygen and hydrogen, the electrons spend more time closer to the oxygen nucleus than to the hydrogen nucleus. This uneven or unequal sharing of electrons results in a water molecule with a slightly negative pole and a slightly positive pole.

Water is the universal solvent in biological systems, so what does this mean for living organisms?

A solvent is a substance that can dissolve other matter; because all chemical reactions that support life occur in water, water is known as the universal solvent. In fact, it is the polar nature of the water molecule (it contains both positive and negative poles) that causes it to act as a solvent—and any substance with an electric charge will be attracted to one end of the molecule. (If a molecule is attracted to water, it is termed hydrophilic; if it is repelled by water, it is termed hydrophobic.)

How many organisms have lived on Earth since life began?

How many organisms have lived on the Earth since life began continues to be a very controversial subject. Some scientists believe more than two billion species have lived on our Earth over time, including those living today. In fact, some scientists estimate that about 90 to 99.9 percent of all animal and plant species that have ever lived on our world are now extinct. There are reasons why this number is difficult to pin down, including the fact that much of early life—especially those with soft bodies—left no trace. In addition, many of the fossils that exist are buried deep into the ground or have been weathered away by natural physical processes (for example, glacial or water erosion).

CELLS

What is a cell?

In general, a cell is the basic unit of all forms of life. Cells are considered to be specialized depending on their function, such as tissue cells, cells of the various animal organs, or even the cells that create a tomato plant. They can range in size from microscopic to the size of a chicken egg. In addition, an organism can be only one cell (single-celled) or multicelled, such as a human—an organism with more than 100,000,000,000,000 cells.

What is the cell theory?

The cell theory is the concept that all living things are made up of essential units called cells and that they are the fundamental components of all life. The cell is the simplest collection of matter that can live. They represent diverse forms of life, existing as single-celled organisms or more complex organisms, such as multicellular plants and animals. They also include diverse specialized cells that cannot survive for long on their own. In addition, everything an organism does occurs fundamentally at the cellular level. Finally, all cells come from preexisting cells, and they are related by division to earlier cells—all of which have been modified in various ways during the long evolutionary history of life on Earth.

What is cytology?

Cytology is the study of cellular structure based on microscopic techniques. Cytology became a separate branch of biology in 1892, when the German embryologist Oscar Hertwig (1849–1922) proposed that organic processes are reflections of cellular processes.

What are the differences between prokaryotic and eukaryotic cells?

In 1937, the French marine biologist Edouard Chatton (1883–1947) first proposed the terms *procariotique* and *eucariotique* (French for prokaryotic and eukaryotic, respectively). Prokaryotic, meaning "before nucleus," was used to describe bacteria, while eukaryotic, meaning "true nucleus," was used to describe all other cells. Today, the terms are more well defined: eukaryotic cells are much more complex than prokaryotic cells, having compartmentalized interiors and membrane-contained organelles (small structures within cells that perform dedicated functions) within their cytoplasm. The major feature of a eukaryotic cell is its membrane-bound nucleus—the active part of the cell that contains genetic information; prokaryotic cells do not have a nuclear membrane (the membrane that surrounds the nucleus of the cell).

The cells also differ in size: Eukaryotic cells are generally much larger and more complex than prokaryotic cells. In fact, most eukaryotic cells are one hundred to 1,000 times the volume of typical prokaryotic cells. The following lists the general differences between these cells.

Comparison of Prokaryotic and Eukaryotic Cells

Characteristic	Prokaryotic Cells	Eukaryotic Cells
Organisms	Eubacteria and Archaebacteria	Protista, Fungi, Plantae, Animalia
Cell size	Usually 1–10 MGRm across	Usually 10–100 MGRm across
Membrane-bound organelles	No	Yes
Ribosomes	Yes, very small	Yes, larger
Type of cell division	Cell fission	Mitosis and meiosis
DNA location	Nucleoid	Nucleus
Membranes	No internal	Many
Cytoskeleton	No	Yes
Metabolism	Anaerobic or aerobic	Aerobic

How do the cells of bacteria, plants, and animals compare to each other?

Numerous differences exist between the cells of bacteria, plants, and animals—all of which make these organisms unique. The following table lists some of those major differences and even a few similarities:

	Bacterium (Prokaryote)	Plant (Eukaryote)	Animal (Eukaryote)
Exterior structures			
Cell wall	Present (protein polysaccharide)	Present (cellulose)	Absent
Plasma membrane	Present	Present	Present
Interior structures			
Endoplasmic reticulum	Absent	Usually present	Usually present
Ribosome	Present	Present	Present
Microtubule	Absent	Present	Present
Centriole	Absent	Absent	Present
Golgi apparatus	Absent	Present	Present
Cytoskeleton	Absent	Present	Present
Other organelles			
Nucleus	Absent	Present	Present
Mitochondrion	Absent	Present	Present
Chloroplast	Absent	Present	Absent

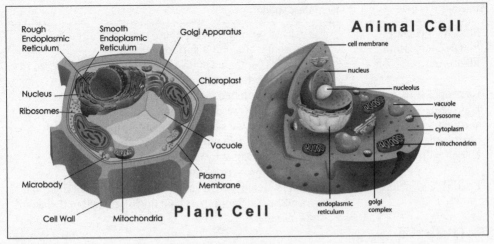

Plant and animal cells share some attributes, such as cell walls, nuclei, and mitochondria, but they also have differences, such as the chloroplasts that only exist in plant cells.

	Bacterium (Prokaryote)	Plant (Eukaryote)	Animal (Eukaryote)
Nucleolus	Absent	Present	Present
Chromosome Multiple;	A single circle of naked DNA		Multiple;
		DNA-protein complex	DNA-protein complex
Lysosome	Absent	Absent	Present
Vacuole	Absent	Usually a large single vacuole	Absent

What are the major components of the eukaryotic cell?

Many major components in eukaryotic cells exist, all of various sizes and functions. The following table lists the major structures in the cell nucleus, the cytoplasmic organelles, and the cytoskeleton (for both animals and plants):

Structure	Description
Cell Nucleus	
Nucleus	Large structure surrounded by double membrane
Nucleolus	Special body within nucleus; consists of RNA and protein
Chromosomes	Composed of a complex of DNA and protein known as chromatin; resemble rodlike structures after cell division
Cytoplasmic Organelles	
Plasma membrane	Membrane boundary of living cell
Endoplasmic	Network of internal membranes extending through reticulum (E.R.) cytoplasm

Structure	Description
Smooth endoplasmic	Lacks ribosomes on the outer surface reticulum
Rough endoplasmic	Ribosomes stud outer surface reticulum
Ribosomes	Granules composed of RNA and protein; some attached to E.R. and some are free in cytosol
Golgi apparatus	Stacks of flattened membrane sacs
Lysosomes	Membranous sacs (in animals)
Vacuoles	Membranous sacs (mostly in plants, fungi, and algae)
Microbodies (e.g., peroxisomes)	Membranous sacs containing a variety of enzymes
Mitochondria	Sacs consisting of two membranes; inner membrane is folded to form cristae and encloses matrix
Plastids (e.g., chloroplasts)	Double membrane structure enclosing internal thylakoid membranes; chloroplasts contain chlorophyll in thylakoid membranes
The Cytoskeleton	
Microtubules	Hollow tubes made of subunits of tubulin protein
Microfilaments	Solid, rodlike structures consisting of actin protein
Centrioles	Pair of hollow cylinders located near center of cell; each centriole consists of nine microtubule triplets
Cilia	Relatively short projections extending from surface of cell; covered by plasma membrane; made of two central and nine peripheral microtubules
Flagella	Long projections made of two central and nine peripheral microtubules; extend from surface of cell; covered by plasma membrane

What are the main components of the nucleus?

A nucleus contains numerous parts. The following lists some of the main components:

- *Nuclear envelope*—The boundary surrounding the nucleus consists of two membranes—an inner one and an outer one—that form the nuclear envelope (or nuclear membrane). It separates the nucleoplasm from the cytoplasm.

- *Nuclear pores*—Nuclear pores are small openings in the nuclear envelope that permit molecules to move between the nucleus and the cytoplasm in a controlled way—for example, molecules like messenger RNA (mRNA) that are too large to diffuse through the nuclear envelope. The pores are not merely perforations, but channels composed of more than one hundred different proteins. Their numbers vary, too; for example, a typical nucleus in a mammalian cell has 3,000 to 4,000 pores, which translates to around ten to twenty pores per square micrometer (mm).

- *Nucleolus*—The nucleolus is a prominent structure within the nucleus. It is a large, spherical structure present in the nucleus of a eukaryotic cell. It is the site where ribosome subunits are assembled and where both ribosomal RNA synthesis and processing occur. It was first accurately described by Rudolph Wagner (1806–1864) in 1835. In addition, the size of the nucleolus varies between cells. For example, cells with a high rate of pro-

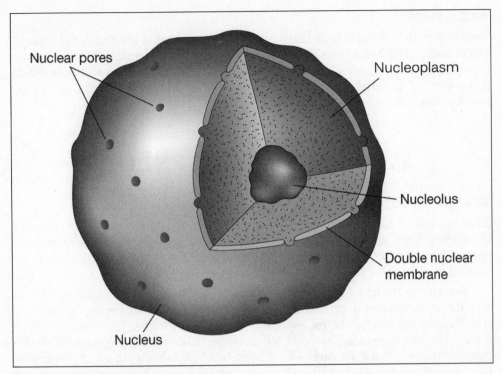

The basic parts of a cell nucleus.

tein synthesis have a large number of ribosomes. In these active cells, nucleoli tend to be large and can account for 20 to 25 percent of the nuclear volume.

- *Nucleoplasm*—The nucleoplasm is the interior space of the nucleus.

- *Chromosomes*—In addition, the DNA-bearing chromosomes of the cell are found in the nucleus. Thus, the nucleus is the repository for the cell's genetic information and the "control center" for the expression of that information.

What are the stages of mitosis?

Mitosis involves the replication of DNA and its separation into two new daughter cells. While only four phases of mitosis are often listed, the entire process is actually comprised of six phases:

- *Interphase*—Involves extensive preparation for the division process.

- *Prophase*—The condensation of chromosomes; the nuclear membrane disappears; formation of the spindle apparatus; chromosomes attach to spindle fibers.

- *Metaphase*—Chromosomes, attached by spindle fibers, align along the midline of a cell.

- *Anaphase*—The centromere splits, and chromatids move apart.

- *Telophase*—The nuclear membrane reforms around newly divided chromosomes.

- *Cytokinesis*—The division of cytoplasm, cell membranes, and organelles occur. In plants, a new cell wall forms.

What is meiosis?

Meiosis is often referred to as reduction division, meaning that the number of chromosomes present is reduced from 2N (diploid) to N (haploid). The meiotic process consists of two separate cell divisions and occurs in the gonads (female ovaries and male testes). It is important to sexual reproduction because of the genetic variation that occurs as a result of this process.

EVOLUTION AND GENETICS

Who was Mendel?

Austrian monk Gregor Mendel (1822–1884) was the founding father of modern genetics. His work with the garden pea, *Pisum sativuum*, was not consistent with the nineteenth-century ideas of inheritance. In his world, scientists believed that inheritance was essentially a mix of fluid that blended and passed from parents to children.

Mendel was the first to demonstrate that distinct physical characteristics could be passed from generation to generation. In particular, Mendel studied peas of distinct and recognizable plant varieties; his experiments included the characteristics of height, flower color, pea color, pea shape, pod color, and the position of flowers on the stem. His theory was one called particulate inheritance, in which certain inherited characteristics were carried by what he called elementes, which eventually became the now well-known name "genes."

Why was Mendel successful in his work while others were not?

Using a simple organism like the garden pea, Mendel was able to control pollination among his experimental plants, and most importantly, he used true breeding plants with easily observable characteristics, such as flower color and height. He also kept meticulous records and discovered consistent data that involved thousands of plant-breeding experiments over eleven years. Interestingly, he studied physics and math under Christian Doppler (1803–1853; the eventual discoverer of the Doppler Effect) at the University of Vienna, which helped Mendel understand statistics and experimentation and eventually led him to determine the laws for his famous heredity works.

What was the principle of dominance?

Gregor Mendel discovered this principle (also often called the law of dominance) in his classic studies of inheritance patterns. When genes of certain allelic pairs have contrasting

Austrian monk Gregor Mendel is considered the father of modern genetics.

524

effects on the same trait, only one can be expressed, while the other one will remain "masked." The gene that is expressed is called the dominant allele; the one that is masked is the recessive allele. In order to understand this, geneticists use symbols to represent the genes—usually the dominant genes are represented by capital (italicized or not) letters, while the recessive genes are represented by lowercase (italicized or not) letters.

For example, in the garden pea, the allele for "tall" plants is T (tall plants are dominant) and for "short" plants t (short plants are recessive). If a plant is pure tall (TT) and is crossed with a pure small plant (tt), the offspring will be a hybrid, but will only exhibit the dominant trait (the recessive trait remains "hidden"). The following shows this example:

$$TT \times tt = \text{offspring.}$$

	T	T
t	Tt	Tt
t	Tt	Tt

All tall offspring result in the above example.

What are phenotypes and genotypes?

The phenotype is the physical manifestation of the genotype and the polypeptides it codes for—for example, the rose. The color and shape of the petals (the phenotype) are the result of chemical reactions within the cells of each petal. Polypeptides synthesized from the directions encoded within the cell's genes (the genotype) are part of those reactions. Different versions of a gene will produce different polypeptides, which in turn will cause different molecular interactions and ultimately a different phenotype.

What is a hybrid?

A hybrid is produced as the offspring of two true breeding organisms of different strains (AA × aa). If the hybrids (Aa) are then mated, the result is a hybrid cross.

Who was Charles Robert Darwin?

English naturalist Charles Robert Darwin (1809–1882) was the first to propose the theory of natural selection—an idea that revolutionized all aspects of natural science. Darwin was born into a family of physicians and planned to follow his father and grandfather in that profession. Unable to stand the sight of blood, he studied divinity at Cambridge and received a degree from the university in 1830.

What were the *Beagle* voyages?

The HMS *Beagle* was a naval survey ship that left England in December 1831 to chart the

A 1874 photo of Charles Darwin, long after he had become famous for his theory of natural selection.

coastal waters of Patagonia, Peru, and Chile—it carried onboard the not yet famous naturalist Charles Darwin. On the five-year voyage, Darwin's job as unpaid companion to the captain on board the *Beagle* allowed him time to satisfy his interests in natural history. On its way to Asia, the ship spent time in the Galapagos Islands off the coast of Ecuador; Darwin's observations of flora and fauna on those islands helped him to generate several ideas, especially his theory of natural selection.

Who was Alfred Russel Wallace?

Alfred Russel Wallace (1823–1913) was an English naturalist whose work was presented with Charles Robert Darwin's (1809–1882) at the Linnaean Society of London in 1858. After extensive travels in the Amazon basin, Wallace independently came to the same conclusions as Darwin on the significance of natural selection in driving the diversification of species. Wallace also worked as a natural history specimen collector in Indonesia, and, like Darwin, also read the works of British cleric and scholar Thomas Malthus (1766–1834). During an attack of malaria in Indonesia, Wallace made the connection between the Malthusian concept of the struggle for existence and a mechanism for change within populations. From this, Wallace wrote the essay that was eventually presented with Darwin's work in 1858.

What is the Darwin-Wallace theory?

The Darwin-Wallace theory can be summarized as follows: Species as a whole demonstrate descent with modification from common ancestors, and natural selection is the sum of the environmental forces that drive those modifications. The modifications or adaptations make the individuals in the population better suited to survival in their environment, more "fit" as it were.

What is the significance of Charles Darwin's *On the Origin of Species*?

Charles Darwin (1809–1882) first proposed a theory of evolution based on natural selection in his treatise *On the Origin of Species*—a publication that ushered in a new era in our thinking about the nature of man. In fact, it is said that the intellectual revolution this work caused, and the impact it had on man's concept of himself and the world, were greater than those by the works of English physicist Isaac Newton (1642–1727) and other individuals. The effect of the publication was immediate—the first edition sold out on the day of publication (November 24, 1859). *Origin* has been referred to as "the book that shook the world." Every modern discussion of man's future, the population explosion, the struggle for existence, the purpose of man and the universe, and man's place in nature rests on Darwin.

The work was a product of his analyses and interpretations of his findings from his voyages on the HMS *Beagle*. In Darwin's day, the prevailing explanation for organic diversity was the story of creation as told in the Bible's book of Genesis. Darwin's book was the first to present scientifically sound, well-organized evidence for the theory of evolution. The theory was based on natural selection, in which the best, or fittest, individuals survive more often than those who are less fit. If a difference exists in the genetic endowment among these individuals that correlates with fitness, the species will change over time and will eventually resemble more closely (as a group) the fittest individuals. It is a two-step process: the first

What is the significance of Charles Darwin's study of finches?

In his studies on the Galapagos Islands, Charles Robert Darwin observed patterns in animals and plants that suggested to him that species changed over time to produce new species. Darwin collected several species of finches; they were all similar, but each had developed beaks and bills specialized to catch food in a different way. Some species had heavy bills for cracking open tough seeds, while others had slender bills for catching insects; still another species used twigs to probe for insects in tree cavities. All the species resembled one species of South American finch. In fact, all the plants and animals of the Galapagos Islands were similar to those of the nearby coast of South America. Darwin felt that the simplest explanation for this similarity was that a few species of plants and animals from South America must have migrated to the Galapagos Islands, then changed as they adapted to the environment on their new home, eventually giving rise to many new species. These observations led to part of his theory on evolution—that species change over time in response to environmental challenges.

consists of the production of variation and the second of the sorting of this variability by natural selection in which the favorable variations tend to be preserved.

Who coined the phrase "survival of the fittest"?

Although frequently associated with Darwinism, this phrase was coined by Herbert Spencer (1820–1903), an English sociologist. It is the process by which organisms that are less well adapted to their environment tend to perish and better-adapted organisms tend to survive.

What is evolution?

Although it was originally defined in the nineteenth century as "descent with modification," evolution is currently described as the change in frequency of genetic traits (also known as the allelic frequency) within populations over time.

What were early ideas on evolution?

In the 1700s, "natural theology" (the explanation of life as the manifestation of the creator's plan) was a popular belief in Europe. This idea was the motive force behind the work of Swedish naturalist Carolus Linnaeus (Carl von Linné, 1707–1778), who was the first to classify all known living things by kingdom. Also popular prior to the work of Charles Darwin (1809–1882) were the theories of "special creation" (creationism), "blending inheritance" (that offspring were always the mixture of the traits of their two parents), and "acquired characteristics."

What is Lamarckian evolution?

The French biologist Jean-Baptiste de Lamarck (1744–1829) is credited as the first person to propose a theory that attempts to explain how and why evolutionary change occurs in living organisms. The mechanism Lamarck proposed is known as "the inheritance of acquired characteristics," meaning that what individuals experience during their lifetime will be passed along to their offspring as genetic traits. This is sometimes referred to as the theory of "use and disuse." A classic example of this would be the giraffe's neck: Lamarckian evolution would predict that as giraffes stretch their necks to reach higher branches on trees, their necks grow longer. As a result, this increase in neck length will be transmitted to egg and sperm such that the offspring of giraffes whose necks have grown will also have long necks. While Lamarck's idea was analytically based on available data (giraffes have long necks and give birth to offspring with long necks as well), he did not know that, in general, environmental factors do not change genetic sequences in such a direct fashion.

A bronze statue of French biologist Jean-Baptiste de Lamarck can be seen at the Jardin des Plantes botanical garden in Paris, France.

Who disproved Lamarck's theory?

In the 1880s, the German biologist August Weismann (1834–1914) formulated the germ-plasm theory of inheritance. Weismann reasoned that reproductive cells (germ cells) were separate from the functional body cells (soma or somatic cells). Therefore, changes to the soma would not affect the germ-plasm and would not be passed on to the offspring. In order to prove that the disuse or loss of somatic structures would not affect the subsequent offspring, Weismann removed the tails of mice and then allowed them to breed. After twenty generations of this experimental protocol, he found that mice still grew tails of the same length as those who had never been manipulated. This not only disproved Lamarck's theory of use and disuse, it also increased understanding of the new field of genetics.

What was the Scopes (monkey) trial?

John T. Scopes (1900–1970), a high-school biology teacher, was brought to trial by the State of Tennessee in 1925 for teaching the theory of evolution. He challenged a law passed by the Tennessee legislature that made it unlawful to teach in any public school any theory that denied the divine creation of man. He was convicted and sentenced, but the decision was reversed later and the law repealed in 1967.

In the early twenty-first century, pressure against school boards still affects the teaching of evolution. Recent drives by anti-evolutionists either have tried to ban the teaching of evolution or have demanded "equal time" for "special creation" as described in the biblical book of Genesis. This has raised many questions about the separation of church and state, the teaching of controversial subjects in public schools, and the ability of scientists to communicate with the public. The gradual improvement of the fossil record, the result of comparative anatomy, and many other developments in biological science has contributed toward making evolutionary thinking more palatable.

What is the value of fossils to the study of evolution?

Fossils are the preserved remains of once living organisms. The value of fossils comes not only from the information they give us about the structures of those animals, but the placement of common fossils in the geologic layers also gives researchers a method for dating other, lesser-known samples.

How do fossils form?

Fossils form rarely, since an organism is usually consumed totally or scattered by scavengers after death. If the structures remain intact, fossils can be preserved in amber (hardened tree sap), Siberian permafrost, dry caves, or rock. Rock fossils are the most common. In order to form a rock fossil, three things must happen: 1) the organism must be buried in sediment; 2) the hard structures must mineralize; and 3) the sediment surrounding the fossil must harden and become rock. Many rock fossils either erode before they can be discovered, or they remain in places inaccessible to scientists.

How are fossils dated?

Fossils are dated using two methods: Relative dating determines the age of the surrounding rock, giving an approximate age to the fossils therein based on their distance from the surface (older rocks are generally deeper from the surface). Other fossils within the rock can also be used to give an approximate date. The second method is absolute dating, based on the known rates of radioactive decay within rocks. By measuring the ratio between the radioactive forms of an element like uranium-238 to its nonradioactive, "decayed" form, scientists can determine when the rock formed.

SPECIES AND POPULATION

What is a species?

A species can be defined in several ways, and scientists will use different definitions depending on whether they are referring to a fossil (extinct) species or a living (extant) one. For example, an extant species can be defined as all the individuals of all the populations capable of interbreeding. A group of populations that are evolutionarily distinct from all other populations may also be defined as a species, even if they are incapable of interbreeding due to extinction.

What are a subspecies and a strain?

A subspecies is another way of describing a distinct population or variety. This term is used to describe the generation of hybrids that can occur when two different populations meet and interbreed. A strain or variety is a subcategory of a species. For example, Gregor Mendel's (1822–1884) work with garden peas involved various strains; one strain had purple flowers while another had white.

529

What is speciation?

Speciation is the process by which new species are formed. This occurs when populations become separated from the rest of the species. At this point, the isolated group will respond independently to natural selection until the population becomes reproductively isolated. The group is then considered a new species. If a population becomes reproductively isolated, then individuals within the population will no longer exchange genetic material with the rest of the species. At that point environmental factors (for example, natural selection) will work on the genetic variation within that population until it has become a new species.

What are convergent and divergent evolution?

Convergent evolution occurs when diverse species develop similar adaptations in response to the same environmental pressure. For example, dolphins and sharks are descended from different ancestors, but as a result of sharing an aquatic environment, they have similar adaptations in body shape. When two species move away from the traits that they share with a common ancestor as they adapt to their own environments, the result is called divergent evolution. As an example, imagine the diversity among bird species. Ducks, hummingbirds, ostriches, and penguins are all descended from an ancestral bird species, yet they have all diverged as they adapted to their particular environments.

What are microevolution and macroevolution?

Microevolution is the change in allelic frequencies that occurs at the level of the population or species. When individuals with certain traits are more successful at reproduction, the ensuing generation will have more copies of that trait. Should the trend continue, eventually the traits will become so common in the population that the population profile will change. This is microevolution. Macroevolution is large-scale change that can generate entire new groups of related species, also known as a clade. One example would be the movement of plants onto land; all terrestrial plants are descended from that event, which occurred during the Devonian period about 400 million years ago.

What is cloning?

A clone is a group of cells derived from the original cell by fission (one cell dividing into two cells) or by mitosis (cell nucleus division with each chromosome splitting into two). Cloning perpetuates an existing organism's genetic makeup—in simpler terms, cloning produces genetically identical copies of a biological entity. Gardeners have been making clones of plants for centuries by taking cuttings of plants to make genetically identical copies. Such simple cloning starts with taking a cutting of a plant that best satisfies such criteria as reproductive success, beauty, or some other standard. Since all of the plant's cells contain the genetic information that will allow the entire plant to be reconstructed, in most cases, the cutting can be taken from any part of the plant (although some plants do better with cuttings from a stem, others from leaves, and some even the time of the year the cutting is made). The cutting is then added to a culture medium having nutritious chemicals (such as a fertilized soil) and sometimes a growth hormone (not all plants need a root-growing hormone). The cells in the cutting eventually divide, doubling in size every six weeks until the mass of cells produces small white globular points called embryoids. These embryoids develop roots, or shoots, and begin to look like tiny plants. Transplanted into rich soils and compost, these plants grow into exact copies of the parent plant, with the process taking only a few months to over a year for the cloned plant to mature. This process is called tissue culture and has been used to make clones of asparagus, pineapples, strawberries, bananas, carnations, ferns, and others. Besides making highly productive copies of the best plant available, this method often controls viral diseases that are passed through normal seed generations.

Can human beings be cloned?

In theory, yes—but in reality, human cloning has many technical obstacles, as well as moral, ethical, philosophical, religious, and economic issues to be resolved before a human being can be cloned. At the present time, most scientists would agree that cloning a human being is unsafe—too many variables are involved in such an endeavor—and many continue to say it is ethically wrong. But that doesn't mean some researchers will not stop trying to push the issue: For example, in 2004, South Korean researchers claimed to have cloned a human embryo in a test tube, but no proof was found, and the researchers retracted their claim in 2006.

What was the first animal to be successfully cloned?

In 1970, the British developmental biologist John B. Gurdon (1933–) cloned a frog. He transplanted the nucleus of an intestinal cell from a tadpole into a frog's egg that had had its nucleus removed. The egg developed into an adult frog that had the tadpole's genome in all of its cells and was therefore a clone of the tadpole.

What was the first mammal to be successfully cloned?

The first mammal cloned from mature (somatic) cells was Dolly, a ewe born in July 1996 in Scotland—it only took 276 attempts! English embryologist Ian Wilmut (1944–) led the team of biologists that removed a nucleus from a mammary (udder) cell of a six-year-old adult ewe and transplanted it into an enucleated egg extracted from a second ewe. Electrical pulses were administered to fuse the nucleus with its new host. When the egg began to divide and develop into an embryo, it was transplanted into a surrogate mother ewe. Dolly was the genetic twin of the ewe that donated the mammary cell nucleus. On April 13, 1998, Dolly gave birth to Bonnie—the product of a normal mating between Dolly and a Welsh mountain ram. This event demonstrated that Dolly was a healthy, fertile sheep, able to produce healthy offspring.

What is genetic engineering?

In general, genetic engineering—also popularly known as molecular cloning or gene cloning—is the artificial recombination of nucleic acid molecules in a test tube; their insertion into a virus, bacteria, or other system; and the subsequent incorporation of the molecules into a host organism where they are able to propagate. The construction of such molecules has also been termed gene manipulation because it usually involves unique genetic combinations using biochemical means.

Genetic engineering techniques include cell fusion and the use of recombinant DNA or gene splicing; the following describes these two techniques:

Cell fusion—In cell fusion the tough outer membranes of sperm and egg cells are removed by enzymes, then the fragile cells are mixed and combined with the aid of chemicals or viruses. The result may be the creation of a new life form from two species (called a chimera; see below).

Recombinant DNA techniques—These techniques (also called gene-splicing) transfer a specific genetic activity from one organism to the next through special DNA and enzymes. Simply put, the recombinant DNA process begins with the isolation and fragmentation of suitable DNA strands. After these fragments are combined with vectors, they are carried into bacterial cells, where the DNA fragments are "spliced" on to plasmid DNA that has been opened up. These hybrid plasmids are then mixed with host cells to form transformed cells. Since only some of the transformed cells will exhibit the desired characteristic or gene activity, the transformed cells are separated and grown individually in cultures. This methodology has been successful in producing large quantities of hormones (such as insulin) for the biotechnology industry. And although it is more difficult to transform animal and plant cells in this way, this technique is often used to generate plants that are more resistant to diseases and to make animals grow larger.

LIFE PROCESSES, STRUCTURES, ETC.

What is a biological clock?

First recognized by the Chinese in the third century b.c.e., the biological clock is an intrinsic mechanism that controls the rhythm of various metabolic activities of plants and animals. Some, such as mating, hibernation, and migration, have a yearly cycle; others, such as ovulation and menstrual cycles of women, follow a lunar month. The majority, however, have a 24-hour, day-night cycle called the circadian rhythm. This day-night cycle, first recognized in plants over 250 years ago and existing in virtually all species of plants and animals, regulates these organisms' metabolic functions: plants opening and closing their petals or leaves, germination and flowering functions, changes in human body temperature, hormone secretion, blood sugar and blood pressure levels, and sleep cycles.

Research in chronobiology, the study of these daily rhythms, reveals that many accidents occur between 1 and 6 a.m., that most babies are born in the morning hours, that heart attacks tend to occur between 6 and 9 a.m., and that most Olympic records are broken in the late afternoon. The clock regulator may be the pineal gland located in the heads of animals (including humans).

Is there any scientific basis for biorhythms?

There is little, if any, scientific support for this theory, which claims there are three precise cycles that control human behavior. These are: a physical cycle of 23 days; an emotional cycle of 28 days; and an intellectual cycle of 33 days. Hazardous critical days are proposed to occur when two or more cycles intersect.

In contrast, biological rhythms such as activity cycles, feeding cycles, and sleeping cycles are well known. They vary from individual to individual and most are tied to the 24-hour rotation period of the Earth. Biological rhythms are real; biorhythms are a hoax.

What is the "Spiegelman monster"?

Sol Spiegelman, an American microbiologist, conducted an experiment to identify the smallest molecule capable of replicating itself. He began with a virus called QB, which consisted of a single molecule of ribonucleic acid (RNA) composed of 4,500 nucleotides (units of nucleic acid).

Usually this virus is able to make copies of itself only by invading a living cell because it requires a cellular enzyme called replicase. When Spiegelman added the replicase along with a supply of free nucleotides in a test tube to the virus, the virus replicated itself for several generations when a mutant appeared having fewer than 4,500 nucleotides. Being smaller, this mutant replicated faster than the original virus. Then another mutant appeared and displaced the first, and so it went. Finally, the virus degenerated into a little piece of ribonucleic acid with only 220 nucleotides, the smallest bit necessary for recognizing the replicase. This little test tube monster could continue to replicate at high speed, provided it had a source of building blocks.

Who was regarded as the founder of biochemistry?

Jan Baptista van Helmont (1577-1644) is called the father of biochemistry because he studied and expressed vital phenomena in chemical terms. The term "biochemistry," coined by F. Hoppe-Seyler in 1877, is the science dealing with the dynamics of living chemical processes or metabolism. It was formed from both the chemists' animal and vegetable chemistry, and the biologists' and doctors' physiological, zoological, or biological chemistry.

Helmont devoted his life to the study of chemistry as the true key to medicine and is considered to be one of the founders of modern pathology because he studied the external agents of diseases as well as the anatomical changes caused by diseases.

What was the first amino acid to be discovered?

Asparagine, isolated from the asparagus plant, was discovered in 1806 by the French chemist Nicolas-Louis Vauquelin.

CLASSIFICATION, MEASUREMENTS, AND TERMS

What is bioinformatics?

Bioinformatics is the field of science in which biology, computer science, and information technology merge into a single discipline. The ultimate goal of the field is to enable the discovery of new biological insights as well as to create a global perspective from which unifying principles in biology can be discerned. There are three important sub-disciplines within bioinformatics: 1) the development of new algorithms and statistics with which to assess relationships among members of the large data sets; 2) the analysis and interpretation of various types of data including nucleotide and amino acid sequences, protein domains, and protein structures; and 3) the development and implementation of tools that enable efficient access and management of different types of information.

What is radiocarbon dating?

Radiocarbon dating is a process for determining the age of a prehistoric object by measuring its radiocarbon content. The technique was developed by an American chemist, Dr. Willard F. Libby (1908-1980), in the late 1940s. All living things contain radiocarbon (carbon 14), an isotope that occurs in a small percentage of atmospheric carbon dioxide as a result of cosmic ray bombardment. After an animal or plant dies, it no longer absorbs radiocarbon and the radiocarbon present begins to decay (break down by releasing particles) at an exact and uniform rate. Its half-life of 5,730 years made it useful for measuring prehistory and events occurring within the past 35,000 to 50,000 years. A recent development, called the Accelerated Mass Spectrometer, which separates and detects atomic particles of different mass, can establish more accurate dates with a smaller sample. The remaining radiocarbon can be measured and compared to that of a living sample. In this way, the age of the 50,000-year-old or less animal or plant (or more precisely the elapsed time since its death) can be determined.

Since Libby's work, other isotopes having longer half-lives have been used as "geologic clocks" to date very old rocks. The isotope uranium-238 (decaying to lead-206) has a half-life of 4.5 billion years, uranium-235 (decaying to lead-207) has a value of 704 million years, thorium-232 (decaying to lead-278) has a half-life of 14 billion years, rubidium-87 (decaying to strontium-87) has a half-life value of 48.8 billion years, potassium-40 (decaying to argon-40) has a value of 1.25 billion years, and samarium-147 (decaying to neodymium-143) has a value of 106 billion years. These isotopes are used in dating techniques of gas formation light emission (called thermoluminescence). Other ways to date the past include dating by tree rings (counting its annual growth rings), and dating by thermoremanent magnetism (the magnetic field of the rock is compared to a date chart of changes in the Earth's magnetic field).

What are the origins of the science of biology?

Biology was first used by Karl Burdach (1776-1847) to denote the study of man. Jean Baptiste Pierre Antoine de Monet Lamarck (1744-1829) gave the term a broader meaning in 1812. He believed in the integral character of science. For the special sciences, chemistry, meteorology, geology, and botany-zoology, he coined the term "biology." Lamarckism epitomizes the belief that changes acquired during an individual's lifetime as the result of active, quasi-purposive, functional adaptations can somehow be imprinted upon the genes, thereby becoming part of the heritage of succeeding generations. Today, very few professional biologists believe that anything of the kind occurs—or can occur.

Biology is the science that deals with living things (Greek *bios*, "life"). Once broadly divided into two areas—zoology (Greek *zoon*, "animal"), the study of animals, and botany (Greek *botanes*, "plant"), the study of plants—biology is now divided and sub-divided into hundreds of special fields involving the structure, function, and classification of forms of life. These include anatomy, ecology, embryology, evolution, genetics, paleontology, and physiology.

Where did the term molecular biology originate?

Warren Weaver (1898-1978), the director of the Rockefeller Foundation's Division of Natural Sciences, originated the term molecular biology. Weaver used X-ray diffraction to investigate the molecular basis of inheritance and the structure of biological macromolecules. He called this relatively new field molecular biology in a 1938 report.

What is gnotobiotics?

Gnotobiotics is the scientific study of animals or other organisms that are raised in germ-free environments or ones that contain only specifically known germs. These animals are first removed from the womb and then are placed in sterilized cages called isolators. Scientists are able to use these animals to determine how specific agents, such as viruses, bacteria, and fungi, affect the body.

What are the five kingdoms presently used to categorize living things?

Carolus Linnaeus (1707-1778) in 1735 divided all living things into two kingdoms in his classification system that was based on similarities and differences of organisms. However, since then, fungi seemed not to fit nicely into either kingdom. Although fungi were generally considered plants, they had no chlorophyll, roots, stems, or leaves, and hardly resemble any true plant. They also have several features found in the animal kingdom, as well as unique features characteristic of themselves alone. So fungi were placed into a third kingdom. In 1959, R. H. Whittaker proposed the current five kingdom system, based on new evidence from biochemical techniques and electron microscope observations that revealed fundamental differences among organisms. Each kingdom is listed below.

Monera—One-celled organisms lacking a membrane around the cell's genetic matter. Prokaryote (or procaryote) is the term used for this condition where the genetic material lies free in the cytoplasm of the cell without a membrane to form the nucleus of the cell. The kingdom consists of bacteria and blue-green algae (also called blue-green bacteria or cyanobacteria). Bacteria do not produce their own food but blue-green algae do. Blue-green algae, the primary form of life 3.5 to 1.5 billion years ago, produce most of the world's oxygen through photosynthesis.

Protista—Mostly single-celled organisms with a membrane around the cell's genetic material called eukaryotes (or eucaryotes) because of the nuclear membrane and other organelles found in the cytoplasm of the cell. Protista consists of true algae, diatoms, slime molds, protozoa, and euglena. Protistans are diverse in their modes of nutrition, etc. They may be living examples of the kinds of ancient single cells that gave rise to the kingdoms of multicelled eukaryotes (fungi, plants, and animals).

Fungi—One-celled or multicelled eukaryotes (having a nuclear membrane or a membrane around the genetic material). The nuclei stream between cells, giving the appearance that cells have multiple nuclei. This unique cellular structure, along with the unique sexual reproduction pattern, distinguishes the fungi from all other organisms. Consisting of mushrooms, yeasts, molds, etc., the fungi do not produce their own food.

Plantae—Multicellular organisms having cell nuclei and cell walls, which directly or indirectly nourish all other forms of life. Most use photosynthesis (a process by which green plants containing chlorophyll utilize sunlight as an energy source to synthesize complex organic material, especially carbohydrates from carbon dioxide, water, and inorganic salts) and most are autotrophs (produce their own food from inorganic matter).

Animalia—Multicellular organisms whose eukaryotic cells (without cell walls) form tissues (and from tissues form organs). Most get their food by ingestion of other organisms; they are heterotrophs (cannot produce their food from inorganic elements). Most are able to move from place to place (mobile) at least during part of the life cycle.

Who devised the current animal and plant classification system?

The naming and organizing of the millions of species of plants and animals is frequently called taxonomy; such classifications provide a basis for comparisons and generalizations. A common classification format is a hierarchical arrangement in which a group is classified within a group, and the level of the group is denoted in a ranking.

Carolus Linnaeus (1707-1778) composed a hierarchical classification system for plants (1753) and animals (1758) using a system of nomenclature (naming) that continues to be used today. Every plant and animal was given two scientific names (binomial method) in Latin, one for the species and the other for the group or genus within the species. He categorized the organisms by perceived physical differences and similarities. Although Linnaeus started with only two kingdoms, contemporary classifiers have expanded them into five kingdoms. Each kingdom is divided into two or more phyla (major groupings; phylum is the singular form). Members within one phylum are more closely related to one another than they are to members of another phylum. These phyla are subdivided into parts again and again; members of each descending level have a closer relationship to each other than those of the level above. Generally, the ranking of the system, going from general to specific, are Kingdom, Phylum (plant world uses the term division), Class, Order, Family, Genus, and Species. In addition, intermediate taxonomic levels can be created by adding the prefixes "sub" or "super" to the name of the level, for example, "subphylum" or "superfamily." Zoologists working on parts of the animal classification many times are not uniform in their groupings. The system is still evolving and changing as new information emerges and new interpretations develop. Below is listed a comparison of hierarchy for four of the five kingdoms.

Taxonomist Carolus Linnaeus devised a classification system for animal and plant species still used to this day.

Taxonomic level	Human	Grasshopper	White Pine	Typhoid Bacterium
Kingdom	Animalia	Animalia	Plantae	Protista
Phylum	Chordata	Anthropoda	Tracheophyta	Schizomycophyta
Class	Mammalia	Insecta	Gymnospermae	Schizomycetes
Order	Primates	Orthoptera	Coniferales	Eubacteriales
Family	Hominidae	Arcridiidae	Pinaceae	Bacteriaceae
Genus	Homo	Schistocerca	Pinus	Eberthella
Species	sapiens	americana	strobus	typhosa

FUNGI, BACTERIA, ALGAE, ETC.

Are any bacteria visible to the naked eye?

Epulopiscium fishelsoni, which lives in the gut of surgeonfish, was first identified in 1985 and mistakenly classified as a protozoan. Later studies analyzed the organism's genetic material and proved it to be a bacterium of unprecedented size—0.015 inches (0.38 millimeters) in diameter, or about the size of a period in a small-print book.

How fast do bacteria reproduce?

Bacteria can reproduce very rapidly in a favorable environment, whether in a laboratory culture or a natural habitat. For example, *Escherichia coli* growing under optimal conditions can divide every 20 minutes. A laboratory culture started with a single cell can produce a colony of 10^7 to 10^8 bacteria in about 12 hours.

What is anthrax?

Bacillus anthracis, the etiologic agent of anthrax, is a large, gram-positive, non-motile, spore-forming bacterial rod. The three virulence factor of *B. anthracis* are edema toxin, lethal toxin, and a capsular antigen. Human anthrax has three major clinical forms: cutaneous, inhalation and gastrointestinal. If left untreated, anthrax in all forms can lead to septicemia (blood poisoning) and death.

What are diatoms?

Diatoms are microscopic algae in the phylum bacillarrophyte of the protista kingdom. Yellow or brown in color, almost all diatoms are single-celled algae, dwelling in fresh and salt water, especially in the cold waters of the North Pacific Ocean and the Antarctic. Diatoms are an important food source for marine plankton (floating animal and plant life) and many small animals.

Diatoms have hard cell walls; these "shells" are made from silica that they extract from the water. It is unclear how they accomplish this. When they die, their glassy shells, called frustules, sink to the bottom of the sea, which hardens into rock called diatomite. One of the most famous and accessible diatomites is the Monterrey Formation along the coast of central and southern California.

What is the scientific study of fungi called?

Mycology is the science concerning fungi. In the past, fungi have been classified in other kingdoms, but currently they are recognized as a separate kingdom based on their unique cellular structure and their unique pattern of sexual reproduction.

Fungi are heterotrophs (cannot produce their own food from inorganic matter). They secrete enzymes that digest food outside their bodies and their fungal cells absorb the products. Their activities are essential in the decomposition of organic material and cycling of nutrients in nature.

Some fungi, called saprobes, obtain nutrients from non-living organic matter. Other fungi are parasites; they obtain nutrients from the tissues of living host organisms. The great majority of fungi are multicelled and filamentous. A mushroom is a modified reproductive structure in or upon which spores develop. Each spore dispersed from it may grow into a new mushroom.

How is a fairy ring formed?

A fairy ring, or fungus ring, is found frequently in a grassy area. There are three types: those that do not affect the surrounding vegetation, those that cause increased growth, and those that damage the surrounding environment. The ring is started from a mycelium (the underground, food-absorbing part of a fungus). The fungus growth is on the outer edge of the grassy area because the inner band of decaying mycelium "use-up" the resources in the soil at the center. This creates a ring effect. Each succeeding generation is farther out from the center.

What is a lichen?

Lichens are organisms that grow on rocks, tree branches, or bare ground. They are composed of a green algae and a colorless fungus living together symbiotically. They do not have roots, stems, flowers, or leaves. The fungus, having no chlorophyll, cannot manufacture its own food, but can absorb food from the algae that it enwraps completely, providing protection from the sun and moisture.

This relationship between the fungus and algae is called symbiosis (a close association of two organisms not necessarily to both their benefits). Lichens were the first recognized and are still the best examples of this phenomenon. A unique feature of lichen symbiosis is that it is so perfectly developed and balanced as to behave as a single organism.

Who was first to coin the word virus?

The English physician Edward Jenner (1749-1823), founder of virology and a pioneer in vaccination, first coined the word "virus." Using one virus to immunize against another one was precisely the strategy Jenner used when he inoculated someone with cowpox (a disease

How many different organisms have been identified by biologists?

Approximately 1.5 million different species of plants, animals and microorganisms have been described and formally named. Some biologists believe another 10 million species are still to be discovered, classified, and named.

that attacks cows) to make them immune to smallpox. This procedure is called vaccination, from the word vaccine (the Latin name for cowpox). Vaccines are usually a very mild dose of the disease-causing bacteria or virus (weakened or dead). These vaccines stimulate the creation of antibodies in the body that recognize and attack a particular infection. A virus is a minute parasitic organism that reproduces only inside the cell of its host. Viruses replicate by invading host cells and taking over the cell's "machinery" for DNA replication. Viral particles then can break out of the cells, causing disease.

French chemist Louis Pasteur is considered one of the founders of modern bacteriology.

Who were the founders of modern bacteriology?

The German bacteriologist Robert Koch (1843-1910) and the French chemist Louis Pasteur (1822-1895) are considered the founders. Pasteur devised a way to heat food or beverages at a temperature low enough not to ruin them, but high enough to kill most of the microorganisms that would cause spoilage and disease. This process is called pasteurization in his honor. By demonstrating that tuberculosis was an infectious disease caused by a specific bacillus and not by bad heredity, Koch laid the groundwork for public health measures that would significantly reduce such diseases. His working methodologies for isolating microorganisms, his laboratory procedures, and his four postulates for determination of disease agents gave medical investigators valuable insights into the control of bacterial infections.

Why are Koch's postulates significant?

The German bacteriologist Robert Koch (1843-1910) developed four rules in his study of disease-producing organisms, which later investigators found useful. The following conditions must be met to prove that a bacterium causes a particular disease:

1. The microorganism must be found in large numbers in all diseased animals but not in healthy ones.

2. The organism must be isolated from a diseased animal and grown outside the body in a pure culture.

3. When the isolated microorganism is injected into other healthy animals, it must produce the same disease.

4. The suspected microorganism must be recovered from the experimental hosts, isolated, compared to the first microorganism, and found to be identical.

PLANT WORLD

What is botany?

Botany is the study of plants, and although this is a simplistic explanation, today's plants are descendants of some of the oldest known organisms on Earth.

How many species of plants live on Earth?

The exact number of plant species on Earth is hard to determine—mainly because so many plants have yet to be found and identified, such as in the deep forests of the Amazon River Basin. But overall, many scientists believe about 300,000 to 315,000 species exist, with the great majority (estimated at about 260,000–290,000) being seed plants.

What are the phyla of plants?

The phyla—the major species of an organism—of plants include a multitude of species, all varying in characteristics, function, and number. The following lists the many phyla of plants (note: this is only one plant classification system—many others exist):

Phyla	Number of Species	Characteristics	Example
Bryophyta	12,000	Nonvascular	Mosses
Hepaticophyta	6,500	Nonvascular	Liverworts
Anthocerotophyta	100	Nonvascular	Hornworts
Psilophyta	6	Vascular, homosporous, no differentiation between root and shoot	Whisk ferns
Lycophyta	1,000	Vascular, homosporous or heterosporous	Club mosses
Arthrophyta	15	Vascular, homosporous	Horsetails
Pterophyta	12,000	Vascular, homosporous	Ferns

Cycadophyta	100	Vascular, heterosporous, seed-forming	Cycads (commonly known as "sago palms")
Ginkgophyta	1	Vascular, heterosporous, seed-forming, deciduous tree	Ginkgo
Gnetophyta	70	Vascular, heterosporous, seed-forming	Ephedra, shrubs, vines
Coniferophyta	550	Vascular, heterosporous, seed-forming	Conifers (pines, spruces, firs, yews, and redwoods)
Anthophyta	240,000	Vascular, heterosporous, seed-forming	Flowering plants

What are the major groups of plants?

Dividing plants is an interesting study, as so many types and varieties exist. But scientists have managed to divide plants into groups based on whether the plants have transport vessels or not. The following is the way most scientists organize the two groups.

Bryophytes—These are the nonvascular plants. Because bryophytes lack a system for conducting water and nutrients, they are restricted in size and live in moist areas close to the ground. Examples of bryophytes are mosses, liverworts, and hornworts and are most often found in moist environments—mainly because they require water to reproduce sexually. (However, species inhabit almost every environment, from hot, dry deserts to the coldest regions of the Antarctica continent.) Overall, they are the second largest group of land plants after flowering plants. They are generally small, compact plants that rarely grow to more than 8 inches (20 centimeters) tall. They have parts that appear leaflike, stemlike, and rootlike and lack vascular tissue (xylem and phloem). Most species have certain structures that help them to retain moisture around their sperm-producing and egg-producing structures and large gametophytes that hold on to sporophytes.

Tracheophytes—These are the vascular plants, which are further divided into seedless plants and those that contain seeds. Plants with seeds are divided into flowering and non-flowering groups. Examples of seedless, vascular plants are ferns, horsetails, and club mosses. The cone-bearing conifers are seed-bearing, nonflowering vascular plants. It's interesting to note that the majority of plants on Earth are seed-bearing, flowering, vascular plants—known as angiosperms.

PLANT STRUCTURES

How are plants defined?

Plants are defined in many ways due to their great number. In general, a plant is a multicellular, eukaryotic organism with cellulose-rich cell walls and chloroplasts that has starch as its primary carbohydrate food reserve. Most are photosynthetic and are primarily terrestrial, autotrophic (capable of making their own food) organisms.

What are the major characteristics of vascular (tracheophyte) plants?

The majority of vascular plants consist of roots, shoots, and leaves. The root system penetrates the soil below ground and anchors the plant; there, the roots absorb water and various materials necessary for plant nutrition. The shoot system consists of the stem and the leaves and is the part of the plant above ground level. The stem provides the framework for the positioning of the leaves; the leaves are the sites of photosynthesis. Growing plants maintain a balance between the size of the root system and the shoot system. The total water- and mineral-absorbing surface area in young seedlings usually far exceeds the photosynthesizing surface area. As a plant ages, the root-to-shoot ratio decreases. Additionally, if the root system is damaged, shoot growth is reduced by lack of water, minerals, and root-produced hormones.

What are the types of plant tissue?

Plants have three types of tissue, each with its own function. They include the dermal tissue, which includes the epidermis, and the vascular tissue, which includes the xylem and phloem. The following gives more detail about these tissues:

Epidermis—Several types of specialized cells occur in the epidermis (outside), including guard cells and root hairs. Flattened epidermal cells—one layer thick and coated by a thick layer of cuticle—cover all parts of the primary plant body.

Xylem—Xylem (from the Greek term *xylos*, meaning "wood") is the main water- and mineral-conducting tissue of plants and consists of dead, hollow, tubular cells arranged end to end. The water transported in xylem replaces water that is lost through evaporation (through the leaf's stomata). Water-conducting cells come in two types. Water flows from a plant's roots up through the shoot via pits in the secondary walls of cells called tracheids; vessel element cells have perforations in their end walls that allow the water to flow between cells.

Phloem—The phloem conducts foods for the plant—including carbohydrates (mainly sucrose), hormones, amino acids, and other substances for the plant's growth and nutrition. The two kinds of cells in the phloem (from the Greek term *phloios*, meaning "bark") are sieve cells (in the seedless vascular plants and gymnosperms) and sieve-tube members (in angiosperms). Both are elongated, slender, tubelike cells arranged end to end with clusters of pores at each cell junction. Sugars (especially sucrose), other compounds, and some mineral ions move between adjacent food-conducting cells.

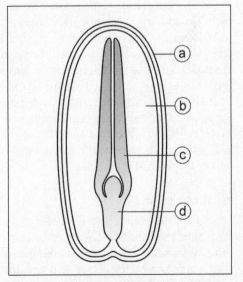

What is a seed?

A seed is a mature, fertilized ovule. The seed (of a dicot plant) is made up of a seed coat

This simple seed diagram shows the a) seedcoat, b) endosperm, c) cotyledons, and d) embryo.

(for protection), an embryo, and the nutrient-rich tissue called the endosperm (or cotyledon). The seed embryo is actually a miniature root and shoot. Once the seed is protected and enclosed in a seed coat, it ceases further development and becomes dormant. It is interesting to note here that although the seed is not growing, it still "breathes," needing oxygen in order to stay viable enough to eventually grow. When it does begin to grow, the embryonic root (or radicle) is the first organ to emerge from the germinating seed.

What are the functions of the root system?

The major functions of roots are: 1) to anchor the plant in the soil; 2) the storage of energy resources, such as the carrot and sugar beet; 3) absorption of water and minerals from the soil; and 4) to conduct water and minerals to and from the shoot. The roots store the food (energy resources) of the plant, which is either used by the roots themselves or digested; the products of digestion are transported back up through the phloem to the above-ground portions of the plant. Plant hormones are synthesized in certain regions of the roots and transported upward in the xylem to the upper parts of the plant, thus stimulating growth and development.

What are aerial roots?

Aerial roots form on above-the-ground structures, such as a leaf or stem, instead of the roots in soil. They serve different functions in different species; for example, the banyan tree (*Ficus benghalensis*) and red mangrove (*Rhizophora mangle*) have aerial roots called prop roots since they support the plant. The aerial roots of ivy (*Hedera helix*) and Spanish moss (*Tillandsia usneoides*) cling to the surface of an object, providing support for the stem.

What are the parts and functions of a stem?

All stems vary in shape and size; in addition, some plants have modified stems. For example, strawberry plants have runners (stolons) that are horizontal stems growing along the surface of the ground. Iris plants also have horizontal stems (rhizomes). Most stems have nodes and internodes: The nodes are the points where the leaves are attached to the stem, while the internodes are the parts of the stem between the nodes. The four main functions of stems are: 1) to support leaves; 2) produce carbohydrates; 3) store materials such as water and starch; and 4) transport water and solutes between roots and leaves and also provide the link between the water and dissolved nutrients of the soil and the leaves.

What are leaves?

Leaves are the main photosynthetic organ for plants; they are also organized to maximize sugar production while making sure little water loss occurs. Thus, they are also important in gas exchange and water movement throughout the whole plant. Leaves—

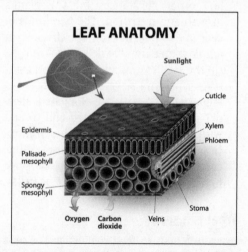

A cutaway of a typical leaf shows its interior structure.

Why are banyan trees in Southeast Asia so amazing?

The banyan tree, *Ficus benghalensis*, native to tropical regions of Southeast Asia, is a member of the genus Ficus. It is a magnificent evergreen that can reach 100 feet (30.48 meters) in height. As the massive limbs spread horizontally, the tree sends down roots that develop into secondary, pillarlike supporting trunks. Over a period of years, a single tree may spread to occupy as much as 2,000 feet (610 meters) around its periphery.

outgrowths of the shoot tips—are found in a variety of shapes, sizes, and arrangements. Most leaves have a blade (the flattened portion of the leaf), a petiole (the slender stalk of the leaf), and leaflike stipules (found on some leaves and located at the base of the petiole where it joins the stem). Cross-sections of a leaf also show a variety of features, including the cuticle (the outer covering to minimize water loss), veins (also called vascular bundles, which carry water and nutrients from the soil to the leaf and also carry sugar), stoma (plural stomata; water escapes through the stoma; they open and close), guard cells (modified epidermal cells that contain chloroplasts and control the opening of the stoma), and palisade and spongy mesophyll cells (for photosynthesis).

What are some examples of modified leaves?

Some plants have leaves that perform functions other than photosynthesis. While the tendrils of some plants are modifications to the stems and provide support for the plant, in other species, such as pea plants (*Pisum sativum*), the tendrils are modified leaves. In carnivorous plants, such as the Venus flytrap (*Dionaea muscipula*) and the pitcher plant (*Sarracenia purpurea*), the leaves attract, capture, and digest the insects with enzymes. Other examples of modified leaves include certain desert plants: Many grow mainly underground, with only a small transparent "window" tip protruding above the soil surface—allowing light to penetrate and reach the site of photosynthesis. The soil covering the leaf protects it from dehydration by the harsh desert winds.

How does water move up a tree?

Water is carried up a tree through the xylem tissue in a process called transpiration. At the bottom of the tree, the roots absorb the vast majority of water that a tree needs. Above ground, the constant evaporation from the leaves creates a flow of water from roots to shoots. The properties of cohesion and adhesion allow the water to move up a tree regardless of its height: Cohesion allows the individual water molecules to stick together in one continuous stream, while adhesion permits the water molecules to adhere to the cellulose molecules in the walls of xylem cells. When the water reaches a leaf, it evaporates—thus allowing additional water molecules to be drawn up through the tree.

What are the main parts of a flower?

Flowers have four main parts—all of which help to identify the flower and to allow the flower to be easily pollinated, often by specific pollinators. If a flower has all of these parts, it is called complete; if it lacks any of them, it is called incomplete. For example, some flowers may not have any petals or sepals. In terms of sexual reproduction in flowers, only stamens and pistils are necessary; some flowers contain only the male structures, while others only the female reproductive structures. Flowers with both structures are called perfect, but if they lack either one or the other they are called imperfect.

The following is a list of the plant parts and some of their components.

Sepals—The sepals are found on the outside of the bud or on the underside of the open flower. They serve to protect the flower bud from drying out. Some sepals ward off predators by displaying spines or secreting chemicals. Collectively, the sepals form the calyx.

Petals—The petals attract pollinators and are usually dropped shortly after pollination occurs. Collectively, the petals form a corolla.

Stamen—The stamen is the male part of a flower. It consists of a filament and anther, where pollen is produced.

Pistil—The pistil is the female part of a flower. It consists of the stigma, style, pollination tube, and ovary, which contains ovules. After fertilization, the ovules mature into seeds.

What are the types of plant pollination?

Effective pollination occurs when viable pollen is transferred to a plant's stigmas, ovule-bearing organs, or ovules (seed precursors). Without pollination, no fertilization would occur. Since plants are immobile organisms, they usually need external agents to transport their pollen from where it is produced in the plant to where fertilization can occur. This situation produces cross-pollination, wherein one plant's pollen is moved by an agent to another plant's stigma. Some plants are able to self-pollinate—transfer their own pollen to their own stigmas. But of the two methods, cross-pollination seems more advantageous, for it allows new genetic material to be introduced.

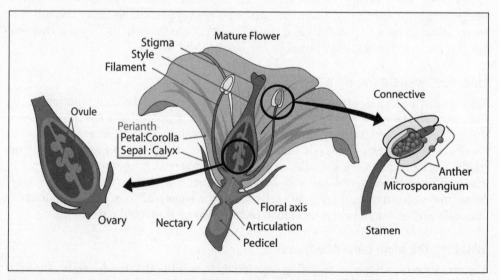

The parts of a flower. Many flowers can be identified based upon the number of their parts.

How does cross-pollination occur?

Cross-pollination agents include insects, wind, birds, mammals, and water. Many times flowers offer one or more "rewards" to attract these agents—sugary nectar, oil, solid food bodies, perfume, a place to sleep, or sometimes the pollen itself. Other times the plant can "trap" the agent into transporting the pollen. Plant structure can accommodate the type of agent used. For example, plants such as grasses and conifers, whose pollen is carried by the wind, tend to have a simple structure lacking petals, with freely exposed and branched stigmas to catch airborne pollen and dangling anthers (pollen-producing parts) on long filaments. This type of anther allows the light round pollen to be easily caught by the wind. These plants are found in areas such as prairies and mountains, where insect agents are rare. In contrast, semi-enclosed, nonsymmetrical, long-living flowers such as irises, roses, and snapdragons have a "landing platform" and nectar in the flower base to accommodate insect agents such as the bee. The sticky, abundant pollen can easily become attached to the insect to be borne away to another flower.

PLANT RESPONSES TO STIMULI

What is symbiosis?

Symbiosis is the close association of two or more different organisms. One type of symbiosis is known as mutualism, defined as an association that is advantageous to both parties. The most common (and possibly the most important) mutualistic, symbiotic relationship in the plant kingdom is known as mycorrhiza—a specialized association between the roots of plants and fungi that occurs in the vast majority of both wild and cultivated plants.

What is tropism?

Tropism is the movement of a plant in response to a stimulus. The following lists the categories of tropism in plants:

Chemotropism—This is a response to chemicals by plants in which in-curling of leaves may occur.

Gravitropism—Formerly called geotropism, this is a plant's response to gravity, in which the plant moves in relation to gravity. Shoots of a plant are negatively geotropic (growing upward), while roots are positively geotropic (growing downward).

Hydrotropism—This is a plant's response to water or moisture, in which roots grow toward the water source.

Paraheliotropism—This is a response by the plant leaves to avoid exposure to the Sun.

Phototropism—This is a plant's response to light, in which the plant may be positively phototropic (moving toward the light source) or negatively phototropic (moving away from the light source). For example, the main axes of shoots are usually positively phototropic, whereas roots are generally insensitive to light.

Thermotropism—This is a response to temperature by plants and is greatly variable between plant species.

Thigmotropism or *haptotropism*—This is a plant's response to touch by the climbing organs of a plant. For example, the plant's tendrils—such as in a pea plant—may touch and then curl around a wire or string support.

TRACHEOPHYTES–FERNS

What are tracheophytes—vascular plants?

Scientists classify plants as bryophytes—nonvascular plants—or tracheophytes, which are vascular plants. They are represented by the seedless plants (such as ferns that reproduce by spores) and seed plants (separated into gymnosperms, or conifers, and angiosperms, or flowering plants). The word "vascular" comes from the Latin word *vasculum*, meaning "vessel" or "duct." Members of the extinct genus *Cooksonia*—named for the paleobotanist Isabel Cookson (1893–1973)—were the first ancient vascular plants to be identified.

What is the oldest group of vascular plants?

The oldest group of vascular plants is still a hotly debated topic among botanists—especially as new plant fossils are found. It is believed that the first vascular plants were members of the division *Rhyniophyta*, which flourished around 400 million years ago but are now extinct. Still other scientists think the fossil record points to the club mosses (lycopods) as the most ancient—and in particular a genus of early lycopsid plants called Baragwanathia, found in Australian rocks from about 420 million years ago.

Tree ferns like these in Southland, New Zealand, evoke a sense of a primitive forest from the Cretaceous Period.

What are some types of ferns?

Ferns are seedless, vascular plants that reproduce by spores instead of seeds; they produce only one type of spore that develops into a bisexual gametophyte—giving these seedless plants the name homosporous. Their sporophytes are large, dominant, and nutritionally independent. They include the ferns of the genus *Pterophyta*, the largest group; the whisk ferns of the genus *Psilophyta*; the club mosses of the genus *Lycophyta*; and the horsetails of the genus *Arthrophyta*. These plants have leaves, roots, cuticles, stomata, specialized stems, conducting tissues, and, in most cases, seeds.

TRACHEOPHYTES–GYMNOSPERMS

What are gymnosperms?

Gymnosperms (from the Greek terms *gymnos*, meaning "naked," and *sperma*, meaning "seed") produce seeds that are totally exposed (thus "naked," or not enclosed inside a fruit like angiosperms) or borne on the scales of cones. These "naked-seed" plants—truly a misnomer because the seeds are really highly protected under the scales of developing cones—first included the cycad and ginkgo; later, the sequoia, cypress, and pines evolved.

Why are gymnosperms important to the wood and paper industry?

Gymnosperms account for approximately 75 percent of the world's timber and a large amount of the wood pulp used to make paper. In North America the white spruce, *Picea glauca*, is the main source of pulp wood used for newsprint and other paper. Other spruce wood is used to manufacture violins and similar string instruments because the wood produces a desired resonance. The Douglas fir, *Pseudotsuga menziesii*, provides more timber than any other North American tree species and produces some of the most desirable lumber in the world. The wood is strong and relatively free of knots. Uses for the wood include house framing, plywood production, structural beams, pulp wood, railroad ties, boxes, and crates. Since most naturally occurring areas of growth have been harvested, the Douglas fir is being grown in managed forests. The wood from the redwood *Sequoia sempervirens* is used for furniture, fences, posts, some construction, and has various garden uses.

How else are gymnosperms important to other industries?

In addition to the wood and paper industry, gymnosperms are important in making resin and turpentine. Resin, the sticky substance in the resin canals of conifers, is a combination of turpentine, a solvent, and a waxy substance called rosin. Turpentine is an excellent paint and varnish solvent but is also used to make deodorants, shaving lotions, medications, and limonene—a lemon flavoring used in the food industry. Resin has many uses; it is used by baseball pitchers to improve their grip on the ball and by batters to improve their grip on the bat; violinists apply resin to their bows to increase friction with the strings; dancers apply resin to their shoes to improve their grip on the stage.

How do you tell fir, pine, and spruce trees apart?

The best way to tell the difference between these trees is by their cones and needles:

Species	Needles	Cones
Balsam fir	Needles are 1–1.5 in (2.54–3.81 cm) long, flat, and arranged in pairs opposite each other	Upright, cylindrical, and 2–4 in (5–10 cm) long
Blue spruce	Needles are roughly 1 in (2.54 cm) long, grow from all sides of the branch, are silvery blue in color, and are very stiff and prickly	3.5 in (8.89 cm) long
Douglas fir	Needles are 1–1.5 in (2.54–3.81 cm) long, occur singularly, and are very soft	Cone scales have bristles that stick out
Fraser fir	Similar to Balsam fir, but needles are smaller and more rounded	Upright, 1.6—2.4 inches (4–6 cm) long
Scotch pine	Two needles in each bundle; needles are stiff, yellow green, and 1.5–3 in (3.81–7.62 cm) long	2–5 in (5–12.7 cm) long
White pine	Five needles in each bundle; needles are soft and 3–5 in (7.62–12.7 cm) long	4–8 in (10–20.3 cm) long
White spruce	Dark-green needles are rigid but not prickly; needles grow from all sides of the twig and are less than an inch (2.54 cm) long	1–2.5 in (2.54–6.35 cm) long and hang downward

Are giant redwood trees found only in California?

No, but although redwoods extend somewhat into southern Oregon, the vast majority of giant redwoods are found in California. The closest relative to this form of redwood is the Japanese cedar found in regions of Asia. This tree grows to a height of 150 feet (45.7 meters) with a circumference of 25 feet (7.6 meters). The genus *Sequoia* has two species, which are commonly known as the redwood and big tree. Both can be seen in either Redwood National Park or Sequoia National Park. At the latter park, the most impressive tree is known as the General Sherman Tree at 272 feet (83 meters) tall; other trees found in Sequoia National Park exceed 300 feet (91.4 meters) in height, but are more slender.

How do hardwoods differ from softwoods?

"Hardwood" and "softwood" are terms used commercially to distinguish woods. Hardwoods are the woods of dicots, regardless of how hard or soft they are, while softwoods are the woods of conifers. Many hardwoods come from the tropics, while almost all softwoods come from the forests of the northern temperate zone.

Why do tree leaves turn color in the fall?

The carotenoids (pigments in the photosynthesizing cells)—responsible for the fall colors—are present in the leaves during the entire growing season. However, the colors are eclipsed by the green chlorophyll. Toward the end of summer, when chlorophyll production ceases, the other colors of the carotenoids (such as yellow, orange, red, or purple) become visible. Two factors are necessary in the production of red autumn leaves: Warm, bright, sunny days, during which the leaves manufacture sugar, which must be followed by cool nights with temperatures below 45°F (7°C). This weather combination traps the sugar and other materials in the leaves, thus resulting in the manufacture of red (anthocyanin). But a warm cloudy day restricts the formation of bright colors. With decreased sunlight, sugar production is decreased, and this small amount of sugar is transported back to the trunk and roots, where it has no color effect.

What is, to date, the oldest living tree(s) in the world?

The potential age of the bristlecone pine is very young when compared to the world's oldest recorded tree—a spruce tree in the Dalarna province of Sweden that is thought to be 9,550 years old. This discovery, made around 2008, included several more old spruce trees, including another that was 9,000 years old (the ages were determined using carbon-14 dating methods), and others that were over 8,000 years old.

The "General Sherman" redwood tree in California's Sequoia National Park is one of the largest in the world, standing at height of 272 feet (83 meters).

What is the oldest surviving species of tree in the world?

The oldest surviving species in the world is thought to be the maidenhair tree (*Ginkgo biloba*) of China. This species of tree first appeared during the Jurassic period, some 160 million years ago. Also called *icho*, or the *ginkyo* (meaning "silver apricot"), this species has been cultivated in Japan since 1100 B.C.E. Ginkgos are also grown in the United States and are known, of course, for their hardiness.

TRACHEOPHYTES–FLOWERING PLANTS (ANGIOSPERMS)

What are the major characteristics of angiosperms?

Angiosperms are seed plants whose reproductive structures are fruits and flowers. They are the most diverse plant species in the world and include about 90 percent of all plants—more

551

than 240,000 species. When angiosperms reproduce, their sperm does not have to "swim" with flagella in order for fertilization to occur, but can use numerous other ways to get the sperm to fertilize the plant, such as by wind, insects, and wildlife.

What define the two major groups of angiosperms—monocots and dicots?

Angiosperms are classified into two major groups, monocots and dicots. The description of monocots and dicots is based on the first leaves that appear on the plant embryo: monocots have one seed leaf, while dicots have two seed leaves. Approximately 65,000 species of monocots and 175,000 species of dicots exist. Orchids, bamboo, palms, lilies, grains, and many grasses are examples of monocots. Dicots include most trees that are nonconiferous, shrubs, ornamental plants, and many food crops.

Several more differences exist between the two groups. The seed leaves, also called cotyledons, differ: monocots have one cotyledon, while dicots have two cotyledons. Other differences include the floral parts—monocots have them usually in threes, dicots usually in fours or fives; roots—monocots have fibrous roots, dicots have taproots; and vacular bundles in the plant's stem—monocots are parallel, dicots are in a ring.

What is the most important angiosperm family and why?

Flowering plants (angiosperms) include the grass family, considered more important than any other family of flowering plants. The reason has to do with what humans around the world have eaten for centuries: the edible grains of these cultivated grasses, known as cereals, are (and have been) a basic food of most civilizations. Wheat, rice, and corn are the most extensively grown of all food crops, with other important cereals being barley, sorghum, oats, millet, and rye.

What are carnivorous plants, and how are they categorized?

Carnivorous plants are plants that attract, catch, and digest animal prey, absorbing the bodily juices of prey for the nutrient content. Carnivorous plants can be divided into more than 400 species, with each one classified according to the nature of their trapping mechanism. All carnivorous plants have traps made of modified leaves with various incentives or attractants—such as nectar or an enticing color—that can lure prey.

The three major types of traps are as follows: The Venus flytrap, *Dionaea muscipula*, and the bladderwort, *Utricularia vulgaris*, have active traps that rapidly imprison victims. Each leaf is a two-sided trap with trigger hairs on each side. When the trigger hairs are touched, the trap shuts tightly around the prey. Semi-active traps—such as

The Venus Flytrap, which is native to the U.S. east coast, adapted to nutrient-poor soil by becoming carnivorous.

those of the sundew (*Drosera capensis*) and butterwort (*Pinguicula vulgaris*)—employ a two-stage trap in which the prey is caught in adhesive fluid. As prey struggles, the plant is triggered to slowly tighten its grip. Finally, passive traps—with shapes resembling a vase or pitcher, such as the pitcher plant (*Sarracenia purpurea*)—entice insects using nectar. Once lured to the leaf, the prey falls into a reservoir of accumulated rainwater and drowns.

What is the difference between poison ivy, oak, and sumac?

These North American woody plants grow in almost any habitat and are quite similar in appearance. Each variety of plant has three-leaf compounds that alternate berrylike fruits and rusty brown stems. Poison ivy (*Rhus radicans*) grows like a vine rather than a shrub and can grow very high, covering tall, stationary items such as trees. The fruit of *R. radicans* is gray in color and is without "hair," and the leaves of the plant are slightly lobed. *Rhus toxicodendron*, commonly known as poison oak, usually grows as a shrub, but it can also climb. Its leaflets are lobed and resemble the leaves of oak trees, and its fruit is hairy. Poison sumac (*Rhus vernix*) grows only in acidic, wet swamps of North America. This shrub can grow as high as 12 feet (3.6 meters). The fruit it produces hangs in a cluster and ranges from gray to brown in color. Poison sumac has dark-green leaves that are sharply pointed, compound, and alternating; it also has inconspicuous flowers that are yellowish green. All parts of poison ivy, poison oak, and poison sumac can cause serious dermatitis.

What are succulents?

A group of more than thirty plant families, including the amaryllis, lily, and cactus families form what is known as the succulents (from the Latin term *succulentis*, meaning "fleshy" or "juicy"). Most members of the group are resistant to droughts, as they are dry-weather plants. Even when they live in moist, rainy environments, these plants need very little water.

PLANT USES

What are some specific examples of how plants are economically important?

Materials of plant origin are found in a wide variety of industries, including paper, food, textile, and construction—a list too long to mention here. But familiar examples are available in abundance: Chocolate is made from cocoa seeds, specifically seeds of the species *Theobroma cacao*. Foxglove (*Digitalis purpurea*) contains cardiac glycosides used to treat congestive heart failure. The berries obtained from the plant *Piper nigrum* produce black pepper; the berries are dried, resulting in black peppercorns, which can then be cracked or ground. Tea can be made from the leaves of *Camellia sinensis*. Fibers taken from the stem of flax plants (*Linum usitatissimum*) have been used to make linen, while the seeds are commonly consumed and are a source of linseed oil. Paper money is even made from flax fibers!

How much wood is needed to make one ton of paper?

In the United States, wood pulp is usually used in paper manufacturing. Pulp is measured by cord or weight. Although the fiber used in making paper is derived overwhelmingly from wood, many other ingredients are needed as well. One ton of paper typically requires two cords of wood, 55,000 gallons (208,000 liters) of water, 102 pounds (46 kilograms) of sulfur, 350 pounds (159 kilograms) of lime, 289 pounds (131 kilograms) of clay, 1.2 tons of coal, 112 kilowatt hours of power, 20 pounds (9 grams) of dye and pigment, and 108 pounds (49 kilograms) of starch. Other ingredients may also be necessary.

What is herbal medicine?

Herbal medicine treats disease and promotes health using plant materials. For centuries, herbal medicine was the primary method of administering medically active compounds. The following lists some herbs used for medicinal purposes:

Herb	Botanical Name	Common Use
Aloe	*Aloe vera*	Skin, gastritis
Black cohosh	*Cimicifuga racemosa*	Menstrual problems, menopause
Dong quai	*Angelica sinensis*	Menstrual problems, menopause
Echinacea	*Echinacea angustifolia*	Colds, immune health
Evening primrose oil	*Oenothera biennis*	Eczema, psoriasis, menopause
Feverfew	*Tanacetum parthenium*	Migraine headaches
Garlic	*Allium sativum*	Cholesterol, hypertension
Ginkgo biloba	*Ginkgo biloba*	Cerebrovascular insufficiency, memory problems
Ginseng	*Panax ginseng, Panax quinquifolius, Panax pseudoginseng, Eleutherococcus senticosus*	Energy, immunity, libido
Goldenseal	*Hydrastis candensis*	Immune health, colds
Hawthorne	*Crateaegus laeviagata*	Cardiac function
Kava kava	*Piper methysticum*	Anxiety
Milk thistle	*Silybum marianum*	Liver disease
Peppermint	*Mentha piperita*	Dyspepsia, irritable bowel syndrome
Saw palmetto	*Serona repens*	Prostate problems
St. John's Wort	*Hypericum perforatum*	Depression, anxiety, insomnia
Tea tree oil	*Malaleuca alternifolia*	Skin infections
Valerian	*Valeriana officinalis*	Anxiety, insomnia

What are some common culinary herbs?

Herbs are often used to enhance flavors in food. They usually come from the leaves of non-woody plants and sometimes the fruits or bulbs. The following lists some of the more familiar culinary herbs:

Common Name	Scientific Name	Part Used
Basil	*Ocimum basilicum*	Leaves
Bay leaves	*Laurus nobilis*	Leaves
Cumin	*Cuminum cyminum*	Fruit
Dill	*Anethum graveolens*	Fruit, leaves
Garlic	*Allium satiavum*	Bulbs

Common Name	Scientific Name	Part Used
Mustard	*Brassica alba; Brassica nigra*	Seed
Onion	*Allium cepa*	Bulb, some leaves
Oregano	*Origanum vulgare*	Leaves
Parsley	*Petroselinum crispum*	Leaves
Peppermint	*Mentha piperita*	Leaves
Sage	*Salvia officinalis*	Leaves
Tarragon	*Artemesia dracunculus*	Leaves
Thyme	*Thymus vulgaris*	Leaves

What plants are commonly used in the perfume industry?

Perfumes are made of a mixture of a large variety of scents. Although many perfumes are created synthetically, the expensive designer scents still use natural essential oils extracted from plants. The perfume industry uses all parts of the plant to create a unique blend of scents. Some commonly used plant materials for essential-oil extraction are:

Plant Part	Source
Bark	Indonesia and Ceylon cinnamons and cassia
Flowers	Rose, carnation, orange blossoms, ylang-ylang, violet, and lavender
Gums	Balsam and myrrh
Leaves and stems	Rosemary, geranium, citronella, lemongrass, and a variety of mints
Rhizomes	Ginger
Roots	Sassafras
Seeds and fruits	Orange, lemon, and nutmeg
Wood	Cedar, sandalwood, and pine

What parts of plants are sources for spices?

Spices are aromatic seasonings derived from many different parts of plants, including the bark, buds, fruit, roots, seeds, and stems. Some common spices and their sources are as follows:

Spice	Scientific Name of Plant	Part Used
Allspice	*Pimenta dioica*	Fruit
Black pepper	*Piper nigrum*	Fruit
Capsicum peppers	*Capsicum annum; Capsicum baccatum; Capsicum chinense; Capsicum frutescens*	Fruit
Cassia	*Cinnamomum cassia*	Bark
Cinnamon	*Cinnamomum zeylanicum*	Inner bark
Cloves	*Eugenia caryophyllata*	Flower
Ginger	*Zingiber officinale*	Rhizome
Mace	*Myristica fragrans*	Seed
Nutmeg	*Myristica fragrans*	Seed
Saffron	*Crocus sativus*	Stigma
Turmeric	*Curcuma longa*	Rhizome
Vanilla	*Vanilla planifolia*	Fruit

GARDENING, FARMING, ETC.

What is considered the most fertile, productive type of soil?

There are three broad categories of garden soils: clay, sandy, and loam. Clay soils are heavy with the particles sticking close together. Working clay soil with your fingers you should get a shiny ball in your hand. Most plants have a hard time getting at the nutrients in clay soil, and the soil tends to get waterlogged. Clay soils can be good for a few deep rooted plants, such as mint, peas, and broad beans.

Sandy soils are light and have particles that do not stick together. Rolling sandy soil in your hand produces crumbs that split apart. A sandy soil is good for many alpine and arid plants, some herbs such as tarragon and thyme, and vegetables such as onions, carrots and tomatoes.

Loam soils are considered the best garden soils, because they are a well balanced mix of smaller and larger materials. They give up nutrients to plant roots easily and they drain well, but loam also retains water very well. Loam soil forms a ball in your fingers, but it feels gritty and shouldn't shine like clay soil.

What do the numbers on a bag of fertilizer indicate?

The three numbers, such as 15-20-15, refer to the percentages by weight of macronutrients found in the fertilizer. The first number stands for nitrogen, the second for phosphorus, and the third for potassium. In order to determine the actual amount of each element in the fertilizer, multiply the percentage by the fertilizer's total weight in pounds. For example, in a 50-pound bag of 15-20-15, there are 7.5 pounds of nitrogen, 10 pounds of phosphorus, and 7.5 pounds of potassium. The remaining pounds are filler.

What does "pH" mean when applied to garden soil?

Literally, pH stands for "potential of hydrogen" and is the term used by soil scientists to represent the hydrogen ion concentration in a soil sample. The relative alkalinity and acidity is commonly expressed in terms of the symbol pH. The neutral point in the scale is seven. Soil testing below seven is said to be acid; soil testing above pH seven is alkaline. The pH values are based on logarithms with a base of ten. Thus, a soil testing pH 5 is ten times as acidic as soil testing pH 6, while a soil testing pH 4 is one hundred times as acidic as soil testing pH 6.

What is the best soil pH for growing plants?

Nutrients such as phosphorous, calcium, potassium, and magnesium are most available to plants when the soil pH is between 6.0 and 7.5. Under highly acid (low pH) conditions, these nutrients become insoluble and relatively unavailable for uptake by plants. High soil pH can also decrease the availability of nutrients. If the soil is more alkaline than pH 8, phosphorous, iron, and many trace elements become insoluble and unavailable for plant uptake.

Is there a quick and easy way to test for soil acidity or alkalinity?

Some gardeners make a simple taste and smell test to check the soil. Acid soil smells and tastes sour. Some put a soil sample in a jar of vinegar. If the vinegar starts to bubble, your

> ## What is meant by the term double-digging?
>
> Double-digging produces an excellent deep planting bed for perennials, especially if the area is composed of heavy clay. It involves removing the top 10 inches (25 centimeters) of soil and moving it to a holding area, then spading the next 10 inches (25 centimeters) and amending this layer with organic matter and/or fertilizer. Then the soil from the "first" digging is amended as well, then replaced.

soil has plenty of lime. If there are no bubbles, lime the soil with four ounces (113 grams) of lime for every square yard (0.84 square meter).

When is the best time to work the soil?

Although it is possible to prepare the soil at any time of year, fall digging is the best time. Dig in the fall and leave the ground rough. Freezing and thawing during winter breaks up clods and aerates the soil. Insects that otherwise survive the winter are mostly turned out. The soil settling during winter will lessen the likelihood of air pockets in the soil when planting the following spring. Fall preparation provides time for soil additives such as manure and compost to break down before planting time.

How can garden soil be used as potting soil?

The garden soil must be pasteurized and then mixed with coarse sand and peat moss. Soil may be pasteurized by putting the soil in a covered baking dish in the oven. When a meat thermometer stuck in the soil has registered 180°F (82°C) for 30 minutes, the soil is done.

What is the composition of synthetic soil?

Synthetic soil is composed of a variety of organic and inorganic materials. Inorganic substances used include pumice, calcinated clay, cinders, vermiculite, perlite, and sand. Vermiculite and perlite are used for water retention and drainage. Organic materials used include wood residues, manure, sphagnum moss, plant residues, and peat. Sphagnum peat moss is also helpful for moisture retention and lowers the pH of the mixture. Lime may be added to offset the acidity of peat. Synthetic soil may also be referred to as growing medium, soil mixes, potting mixture, plant substrate, greenhouse soil, potting soil, and amended soil. Most synthetic soils are deficient in important mineral nutrients, which can be added during the mixing process or with water.

What is meant by the phrase rain shadow in gardening?

The ground in the lee of a wall or solid fence receives less rainfall than the ground on the windward side. The wall or fence creates an area of rain shadow.

What is meant by xeriscaping?

A xeriscape, a landscape of low water-use plants, is the modern approach to gardening in areas that experience water shortages. Taken from the Greek word xeros, meaning dry, this

What does the term hydroponics mean?

This term refers to growing plants in some medium other than soil; the inorganic plant nutrients (such as potassium, sulphur, magnesium, and nitrogen) are continuously supplied to the plants in solution. Hydroponics is mostly used in areas where there is little soil or unsuitable soil. Since it allows precise control of nutrient levels and oxygenation of the roots, it is often used to grow plants used for research purposes. Julius von Sachs (1832-1897), a researcher in plant nutrition, pioneered modern hydroponics. Research plants have been grown in solution culture since the mid-1800s. William Gericke, a scientist at the University of California, defined the word hydroponics in 1937. In the 50 years that hydroponics has been used on a commercial basis, it has been adapted to many situations. NASA will be using hydroponics in the space station for crop production and to recycle carbon dioxide into oxygen. Although successful for research, hydroponics has many limitations and may prove frustrating for the amateur gardener.

type of gardening uses drought-resistant plants and low maintenance grasses, which require water only every two to three weeks. Drip irrigation, heavy mulching of plant beds, and organic soil improvements are other xeriscape techniques that allow better water absorption and retention, which in turn decrease garden watering time.

When a plant is said to be "double dormant," what does that mean?

Plants that are double dormant require a unique sort of layering or stratification in order for the seeds to germinate. The seeds of these plants must have a period of warmth and moisture followed by a cold spell. Both the seed coat and the seed embryo require this double dormancy if they are to germinate. In nature this process usually takes two years. Some well-known plants that live the life of double dormancy include some lilies, dogwood, junipers, lilac, tree peony, and viburnum.

How are seedlings hardened off before planting?

Hardening off is a gardening term for gradually acclimatizing seedlings raised indoors to the outdoor environment. Place the tray of seedlings outdoors for a few hours each day in a semi-protected spot. Lengthen the amount of time they stay out by an hour or so each day; at the end of the week, they will be ready for planting outdoors.

What is the difference between container-grown, balled-and-burlapped, and bare-rooted plants?

Container-grown plants have been grown in some kind of pot—usually peat, plastic, or clay—for most or all of their lives. Balled-and-burlapped plants have been dug up with the soil carefully maintained around their roots in burlap. Bare-rooted plants have also been dug from their growing place but without retaining the root ball. Typically, plants from a mail-order nursery come bare-rooted with their roots protected with damp sphagnum moss. Bare-rooted plants are the most susceptible to damage.

What is meant by companion planting?

There is not a lot of scientific documentation on this subject, but gardeners and farmers have noticed for years certain affinities that some plants have when planted near other plants. Nasturtiums, for example, lure aphids away from apple trees and attract blackfly away from vegetables. Onions and garlic act as both a fungicide and an insecticide, possibly because they accumulate sulfur very efficiently, and many pests avoid the odor. Some plants do not make good neighbors. Below is a sample list of good and bad companion plants:

	Close Neighbors	Distant Neighbors
Bush Beans	Potatoes, lettuce, tomatoes	Onions
Carrots	Leaf lettuce, onions, tomatoes	—
Corn	Potatoes, beans, cucumbers	—
Cucumbers	Beans, corn	Potatoes
Lettuce	Carrots, cucumbers	—
Onions	Tomatoes, lettuce	Beans
Potatoes	Beans, corn	Cucumbers
Tomatoes	Onions, carrots	Potatoes

Which plants are best for container gardening?

Most vegetables can be grown in a container—even large ones like pumpkins. Miniature varieties of vegetables are better because they require less space and develop earlier. Fluorescent lights help leaf crops to grow indoors even in winter. Most root crops are best grown outdoors. Fruit crops such as tomatoes can be grown indoors, but need warm temperatures and at least six hours of summer sunshine. Some of the plants that may be grown are: bush beans, pole beans, beets, broccoli, cabbage, carrots, cucumbers, kale, lettuce, onions, peppers, summer squash, and tomatoes.

What is the difference between an arboretum and a botanical garden?

An arboretum is technically a garden or collection of trees, often rare ones grown for study, research, or ornamentation. In practice, most arboretums also display shrubs and other plants. A botanical garden is primarily an institution for research in the field of botany and horticulture. The modern botanic garden has large collections of growing plants in a greenhouse and outdoors usually in elaborate gardens, in addition to research laboratories, a library and herbarium.

Who established the first botanical garden in the United States?

John Bartram planned and laid out a botanic garden of five to six acres (two to 2.5 hectare) in 1728. It is located in Philadelphia, Pennsylvania.

What is Ikebana?

Ikebana is the Japanese expression for "the arrangement of living material in water." It is the ancient Japanese art of flower arrangement. Ikebana follows certain ancient rules that aim

---

Is there a "best" time to weed in the vegetable garden?

Weeding is usually the most unpopular and the most time-consuming garden chore. Some studies (using weeding with peas and beans as examples) have shown that weeding done during the first three to four weeks of vegetable growth produced the best crops and that unabated weed growth after that time did not significantly reduce the vegetable yields.

---

at achieving perfect harmony, beauty, and balance. Some describe Ikebana as sculpture with flowers. In Japan it has been practiced for fourteen hundred years. Buddhist monks in the sixth century practiced the art using pebbles, rock, and wood with plants and flowers. In Japan Ikebana was evolved and practiced exclusively by men—priests first, then warriors and noblemen. Today, of course, Ikebana is practiced by millions of women as well as men, although the great flower schools in Japan are mostly headed by men.

What was a victory garden?

During World War I, patriots grew "liberty gardens." In World War II, U.S. Secretary of Agriculture Claude R. Wickard encouraged householders to plant vegetable gardens wherever they could find space. By 1945 there were said to be 20 million victory gardens producing about 40 percent of all American vegetables in many unused scraps of land. Such sites as the strip between a sidewalk and the street, town squares, and the land around Chicago's Cook County jail were used. The term "victory garden" derives from an English book by that title written by Richard Gardner in 1603.

Should tomato plants be staked?

There are only a few advocates who continue to recommend non-staking. They argue for the natural sprawling growing method because it tends to give a greater yield. Staking keeps the plants off the ground, where they are susceptible to disease and attacks by snails. Staked tomatoes are much easier to harvest and make better use of garden space. They ripen faster and more evenly when staked. The method of staking has different advocates as well. Some say a sturdy five-foot stick is best, while others argue for a wire cage, and still others claim a wooden teepee arrangement is best.

What are the best annual and perennial plants to grow to attract butterflies?

Ageratum, cosmos, globe candytuft, heliotrope, lantana, marigold, mexican sunflower, torch flower, nasturtium, sweet alyssum, buddleias (known as butterfly bush), dianthus, violas, and zinnia attract butterflies.

Which flowers should be planted in the garden to attract hummingbirds?

Scarlet trumpet honeysuckle, weigela, butterfly bush, beardtongue, coralbells, red-hot-poker, foxglove, beebalm, nicotiana, petunia, summer phlox, and scarlet sage provide brightly colored (in shades of reds and orange), nectar-bearing attractants for hummingbirds.

Why should lawn clippings be left on the grass after mowing?

The clippings are a valuable source of nutrients for the lawn. They provide nitrogen, potassium, and phosphorous to feed the new grass and reduce the need for fertilizer. Young, tender, short clippings decompose fast. Furthermore, when clippings are left on the lawn instead of being added to the trash collection, the amount of waste added to landfills is decreased.

What is snowmold and how do you treat it?

Snowmold is a lawn disease common in the northern United States, characterized by a white, cottony growth. The fungus *Fusarium nivale* often grows beneath the snow as it melts in early spring. Avoiding late fall fertilizing in wet areas can prevent the spread of this disease. The lawn may be treated at the first sign of the disease with a fungicide and again in 10 to 14 days.

How can daffodils be encouraged to bloom the year after they are planted?

Try fertilizing daffodils (*Narcissus pseudonarcissus*) as soon as the new shoots appear. This helps the roots renew themselves and will also aid in leaf and flower development. If they don't bloom, the problem could be overcrowding, which hinders flower production. Try digging the bulbs up every third or fifth year, separating them, and re-spacing them.

How can geraniums be kept alive during the winter?

While they must be kept from freezing, geraniums can survive the winter happily in a cool sunny spot, such as a cool greenhouse, a bay window, or a sunny unheated basement. They need only occasional watering while in this semi-dormant state. Cuttings from these plants can be rooted in late winter or early spring for a new crop of geraniums (some sources suggest rooting in the fall). In homes without a suitable cool and sunny spot, the plants can be forced into dormancy by allowing the soil to dry completely, then gently knocking the soil off of the roots. While the plants can simply be hung from the rafters in a cool (45° to 50°F, or 7° to 10°C), slightly humid room, they will do better if put into individual paper bags, with the openings tied shut. The plants should be checked regularly. The leaves will dry and shrivel, but if the stems shrivel, the plants should be lightly misted with water. If any show mold or rot, cut off the affected sections, move the plants to a drier area, and leave the bags open for a day or two. In the early spring, prune the stems back to healthy green tissue and pot in fresh soil.

What is meant by the chilling requirement for fruit trees?

When a fruit tree's fruiting period has ended, a dormant period must follow, during which the plant rests and regains strength for another fruit set the following year. The length of this set is measured in hours and occurs at temperatures between 32° and 45°F (0° to 7.2°C). A cherry tree requires about 700 hours of chilling time.

What is a five-in-one tree?

These very curious trees consist of a rootstock with five different varieties of the same fruit—usually apples—grafted to it. The blooming period is usually magnificent with various colors of blooms appearing on the same tree.

What is meant by espaliering a fruit tree and why is it done?

To espalier a fruit tree means to train it to grow flat against a surface. It can be grown in small places such as against a wall, and it will thrive even if its roots are underneath sidewalks or driveways. Since many fruit trees must be planted in pairs, espaliered fruit trees can be planted close together, providing pollen for each other, yet taking up little space.

How are seedless grapes grown?

Since seedless grapes cannot reproduce in the conventional way that grapes usually do (i.e., dropping seeds), growers have to take cuttings from other seedless grape plants and root them. Although the exact origin of seedless grapes is unknown, they might have been first cultivated in present-day Iran or Afghanistan thousands of years ago. Initially, the first seedless grape was a genetic mutation in which the hard seed casing failed to develop—the mutation is called stenospermoscarpy. One modern seedless grape commonly bought today is the green Thompson seedless grape, from which 90 percent of all raisins are made.

What is a dwarf conifer?

Conifers are evergreen shrubs and trees with needle-shaped leaves, cones, and resinous wood, such as the pines, spruces, firs, and junipers. After 20 years, dwarf or slow-growing forms of these otherwise tall trees are typically about three feet (91 centimeters) tall.

What is the secret of bonsai, the Japanese art of growing dwarf trees?

These miniature trees with tiny leaves and twisted trunks can be centuries old. To inhibit growth of the plants, they have been carefully deprived of nutrients, pruned of their fastest-growing shoots and buds, and kept in small pots to reduce the root systems. Selective pruning, pinching out terminal buds, and wiring techniques are devices used to control the shape of the trees. Bonsai possibly started during the Chou dynasty (900-250 b.c.e.) in China, when emperors made miniature gardens that were dwarf representations of the provincial lands that they ruled.

What is a natural way to get rid of poison ivy?

Poison ivy can be killed by spraying or treating the plants with a saltwater solution. Large plants can be killed by cutting the vines at or below ground level and soaking the base with brine. A second application after two weeks may be needed. Do not burn the plants; smoke and ash may cause the rash on exposed parts of the body, eyes, nasal passages, and lungs.

What is pleaching?

Pleaching is a method of shearing closely planted trees or shrubs into a high wall of foliage. Many kinds of trees have been used, including maples, sycamores, and lindens. Because of the time needed in caring for pleached allees, as the walls of foliage are called, they are infrequently seen in American gardens, but they are frequently observed in European ones.

What is the railroad worm?

The apple maggot (*Rhagoletis pomonella*), which becomes the apple fruit fly, is frequently called the railroad worm. Inhabiting orchards in the eastern United States and Canada, the larvae feed on the fruit pulp of apples, plums, cherries, etc., and cause damage to fruit crops.

How can fruit trees be protected from being eaten by field mice?

Valuable trees, especially newly planted fruit trees, can be protected by wrappings or guards of wire, wood veneer, or plastic. Other controls, such as pieces of lava rocks soaked in garlic, are effective as repellents, and garlic sprays will repel most rodents.

Which type of fence protects a garden from deer?

A post and wire-mesh fence with a sharp-angled, narrow gate, which people and small animals can navigate, but deer cannot, plus the installation of a motion-sensing security light with a beeper helps keep deer away. Electric fences are also a good deterrent, but for smaller gardens snow fencing works well.

How can squirrels be kept away from vegetable and flower gardens?

Squirrels like to take a bite out of tomatoes, cucumbers, and melons, dig up bulbs, and ruin anything colorful in the flower garden. The traditional recommendation of spreading mothballs around is apparently not too successful. A better method is laying down one to two inch (2.5 to five centimeter) mesh sheets of chicken wire. Squirrels will avoid the mesh, apparently because they fear getting their toes stuck in it. Another method to try is sprinkling hot pepper around the plants, renewing it after it rains.

Agricultural chemist George Washington Carver developed important methods of crop management and hundreds of new uses for crops.

Before chemical sprays came along to control plant disease and pests, what were some of the traditional spray formulas used on plants?

Gardeners have used kitchen cupboard and organic plant materials for a very long time. Baking soda spray is a good fungicide. Mix two tablespoons of baking soda in four pints of water. Garlic spray is made by crushing a large garlic bulb into two pints of water. Boil for five minutes and allow to cool. Garlic spray is a good insecticide and fungicide. The weed horsetail, the leaves of elder, and the leaves of the fern bracken have been made into sprays and used to fight mildew, black spot, many fungi and bacteria attacking garden plants.

What were some of the accomplishments of Dr. George Washington Carver?

Because of the work of Dr. George Washington Carver (1864-1943) in plant diseases, soil analysis, and crop management, many southern farmers who adopted his methods increased their crop yields and profits. Carver developed recipes using cowpeas, sweet potatoes, and peanuts. He eventually made 118 products from sweet potatoes, 325 from peanuts, and 75 from pecans. He promoted soil diversification and the adoption of peanuts, soybeans, and other soil-enriching crops. His other work included developing plastic material from soy beans, which Henry Ford later used in part of his automobile. He extracted dyes and paints from the Alabama red clay and worked with hybrid cotton. Carver was a widely talented man who became an almost mythical American folk hero.

ANIMAL WORLD

ANIMALS IN GENERAL

What are the main characteristics of animals?

Animals are an *extremely* diverse group of organisms, with all of them sharing a number of characteristics. In general biological terms, animals are multicellular eukaryotes that are heterotrophic, ingesting and digesting food inside the body. Their cells lack the cell walls that provide support in the bodies of plants and fungi. The majority of animals have muscle systems and nervous systems, responsible for movement and rapid response to stimuli in their environment.

Most animals reproduce sexually; one reason for this versus asexual reproduction is variation, with each offspring being the product of both parents, giving them a better chance of survival. In most animal species, a large, nonmotile (movable) egg is fertilized by a small, flagellated sperm; this forms what is called a diploid zygote (or the fertilized egg). The transformation of the zygote into an animal's specific form depends on special regulatory genes in the cells of the developing embryo.

Can animals be grouped according to body symmetry?

Yes, animals are often divided into two groups according to their symmetry—the arrangement of body structures in relation to the axis of the body. For example, the bodies of most primitive animals such as jellyfish, sea anemones, and starfish have radial symmetry—a body in the form of a wheel or cylinder, with similar structures arranged as spokes from a central axis. Animals with bilateral symmetry have right and left halves that are mirror images of each other; they also have top (dorsal) and bottom (ventral) portions and a front (anterior) end and back (posterior) end. More sophisticated animals fall into this category, such as flatworms. Some organisms even exhibit both—such as the echinoderms that have bilateral symmetry as larvae and revert to radial symmetry as adults.

How do the structures of most animals develop?

The structures of most animals develop from three embryonic tissue layers. The outer layer (ectoderm) gives rise to the outer covering of the body and the nervous system. The inner layer (endoderm) forms the lining of the digestive tube and other digestive organs. The middle layer (mesoderm) gives rise to most other body structures, including muscles, skeletal structures, and the circulatory system.

What are the major characteristics of chordates?

All chordates—which include fish, amphibians, reptiles, birds, and mammals—share several features, the major ones being a notochord, dorsal nerve cord, and pharyngeal gill pouches. The notochord, a supporting rod made of cartilage, runs along the dorsal part of the body. It is always found in embryos, but in most vertebrates it is replaced during late embryonic development by a backbone of bony or cartilagelike vertebrae. The tubular dorsal nerve cord, near the notochord, is also formed during development of the embryo. In most vertebrates, the nerve cord eventually becomes a hollow cord and is protected by the backbone. The pharyngeal gill pouches appear during embryonic development on both sides of the throat region (the pharynx), but in some species, it does not develop. In human embryos, these gill pouches show a series of folds (thus the word pouches) that look similar to those of early fish embryos. But while in fish they would develop into gills, in humans (and other mammals) they develop into the ear's Eustachian tube and middle ear, tonsils, parathyroid, and thymus.

What is the difference between an invertebrate and a vertebrate?

Invertebrates are animals that lack a backbone. In fact, almost all animals (99 percent) are invertebrates—biologists believe millions more may be yet undiscovered. Vertebrates are animals with backbones (vertebral column); with more than one million identified animals on the planet, vertebrates represent only 42,500—around 25 percent—of those animals.

What are the largest and heaviest invertebrates?

The largest invertebrate to date is the colossal squid, or the Antarctic or Giant Cranch squid—it even has its own genus: Mesonychoteuthis (*Mesonychoteuthis hamiltoni*). It is estimated that the squid measures about 50 feet (15 meters) in length and lives at depths of at least 7,218 feet (2,200 meters) in the Southern Ocean. It also has what is thought to be the largest eyes in the animal world, measuring 11 inches (27 centimeters) across.

The heaviest invertebrate is highly debated. Some scientists believe a bivalve called the giant clam, *Tridacna gigas*, found in the coral reefs of the South Pacific and Indian Oceans, holds the record. This invertebrate has an average weight of around 440 pounds (200 kilograms), although reports have been heard of a giant clamshell found in the twentieth century that weighed close to 750 pounds. It has a shell around 47 inches (120 centimeters) in length and is thought to have a life span of more than 100 years.

What are the major features shown by all vertebrates?

Animals in the subphylum Vertebrata are distinguished by several features. Most prominent is the endoskeleton of bone or cartilage, centering around the vertebral column (spine or backbone). Composed of separate vertebrae, a vertebral column combines flexibility with enough strength to support even a large body. Other vertebrate features include: 1) complex dorsal kidneys; 2) a tail (lost via evolution in some groups) extending between the anus; 3) a closed circulatory system with a single, well-developed heart; 4) a brain at the top end of the spinal cord, with ten or more pairs of cranial nerves; 5) a cranium (skull) protecting the brain; 6) paired sex organs in both males and females; and 7) two pairs of movable appendages (this would be fins in the fish that evolved into legs in land vertebrates).

What are the largest and smallest vertebrates?

Of the more than 60,000 vertebrates currently known to humans, finding the largest doesn't seem to be too much of a problem. To date, scientists believe the largest vertebrate known is the marine mammal called the blue whale (*Balaenoptera musculus*); it is also considered the largest known animal on Earth (and one of the loudest animals on Earth). Mature blue whales can reach around 75 to 100 feet (23–30.5 meters) in length; they can weigh up to 150 tons (136 metric tons), although because of whaling hunts, the largest of the whales are thought to have dwindled in number, with the average being about 75 to 80 feet (23–25 meters) long. Even baby blue whales are bigger than most animals, averaging, at birth, about 25 feet (7.6 meters) long.

For obvious reasons, determining the smallest vertebrates can be very difficult, and it is often debated how to measure different animals, such as a frog versus a fish. One of the latest contenders was found in 2012—a new species of frog from New Guinea called *Paedophryne amauensis* that measured around one-third of an inch (7.7 millimeters) in size. It was also found with a "bigger cousin"—the frog *Paedophryne swiftorum*—that averaged only about 0.33 inch (8.5 millimeters) in size. Still other scientists point to a creature called a *Paedocypris progenetica* found in 2006—a fish that measures about 0.31 inch (7.9 millimeters) long and lives in the acid swamps of Sumatra.

The following chart lists the largest and smallest vertebrates known to date:

Name	Average Length and Weight
Largest vertebrates	
Sea mammal Blue whale	75–100 ft (23–30.5 m) long; (*Balaenoptera musculus*) weighs around 150 tons (135 metric tons)
Land mammal African bush elephant	Bull is 10.5 ft (3.2 m) tall (*Loxodonta africana*) at shoulder; weighs 5.25–6.2 tons (4.8–5.6 metric tons)
Living bird North African ostrich	8–9 ft (2.4–2.7 m) tall; (*Struthio c. camelus*) weighs 345 lb (156.5 kg)
Fish Whale shark (*Rhincodon typus*)	41 ft (12.5 m) long; weighs 16.5 tons (15 metric tons)
Reptile Saltwater crocodile (*Crocodylus porosus*)	14–16 ft (4.3–4.9 m) long; weighs 900–1,500 lb (408–680 kg)

567

Name	Average Length and Weight
Rodent	
Capybara (*Hydrochoerus hydrochaeris*)	3.25–4.5 ft (1–1.4 m) long; weighs 250 lbs (113.4 kg)
Smallest vertebrates	
Sea mammal	
Commerson's dolphin (*Cephalorhynchus commersonii*)	Weighs 50–70 lbs (236.7–31.8 kg)
Land mammal	
Bumblebee bat or Kitti's hog-nosed bat (*Craseonycteris thong longyai*) or the pygmy shrew (*Suncus erruscus*)	Bat is 1 in (2.54 cm) long; weighs 0.062–0.07 oz (1.6–2 g); 1.5–2 in (3.8–5 cm) long, weighs 0.052–0.09 oz (1.5–2.6 g)
Bird	
Bee hummingbird (*Mellisuga helenea*)	2.25 in (5.7 cm) long; weighs 0.056 oz (1.6 gm)
Fish	
Dwarf pygmy goby (*Trimmatam nanus*)	0.35 in (8.9 mm) long
Reptile	
Gecko (*Spaerodactylus parthenopion*)	0.67 in (1.7 cm) long
Rodent	
Pygmy mouse (*Baiomys taylori*)	4.3 in (10.9 cm) long; weighs 0.24–0.28 oz (6.8–7.9 g)

What was the first group of vertebrates?

The first vertebrates were fish that appeared 500 million years ago around the beginning of the Cambrian period (on the geologic time scale). They are called agnathans (from the Greek *a*, meaning "without," and *gnath*, meaning "jaw")—small, jawless fish up to about 8 inches (20 centimeters) long. They have also been called ostracoderms ("shell skin") because their bodies were covered with bony plates, most notably a head shield protecting the brain.

What is the largest group of vertebrates?

The largest group of vertebrates is fish, a diverse group that includes almost 21,000 species, more than all other kinds of vertebrates combined. Most members of this group are oste-ichythes, or "bony fish," which includes fish well known to fishermen and fish-lovers alike, such as bass, trout, and salmon.

Do animals ever help each other?

Populations of organisms within an environment may engage in a variety of relationships with each other. For example, in a relationship known as mutualism, each species provides a benefit to the other; for instance, it can occur between two animal species like large coral reef fish and smaller species like the wrasses that swim into their mouths and eat the parasites that may have taken up residence there.

What is the difference between ectotherms and endotherms?

Ectotherms, also known as cold-blooded animals, warm their bodies by absorbing heat from their surroundings. These animals have large variations in normal body temperature due to their changing environment, with the most common ectotherms being invertebrates, fish, reptiles, and amphibians. The body temperature of endotherms, also known as warm-blooded animals, depends on the heat produced by the animal's metabolism. Mammals, birds, some fish, and some insects are endotherms. Their normal body temperature is fairly constant, even when vast temperature differences in their environment occur.

What is the meaning of the phrase "ontogeny recapitulates phylogeny"?

Ontogeny is how an organism develops from fertilized egg to adult; phylogeny is the evolutionary history of a group of organisms. The phrase "ontogeny recapitulates phylogeny" originated with German biologist and naturalist Ernst Haeckel (1834–1919), and it means that as an embryo of an advanced organism grows, it will pass through stages that look very much like the adult phase of less advanced organisms. Although further research demonstrated that early stage embryos are not representative of our evolutionary ancestors, Haeckel's general concept does reveal some clues about evolutionary history. In particular, animals with recent common ancestors tend to share more similarities during development than those that do not. For example, a dog embryo and a pig embryo will look more alike through most stages of development than a dog embryo and a salamander embryo.

AQUATIC ANIMALS

How many animals exist in the oceans?

Because the oceans are so vast—taking up around 70 percent of the Earth's "surface"—the number of marine animals is not truly known. What is known is that the numbers are immense; for example, of living species, to date, about 800 species of cephalopods (including squids and octopi), around 28,000 species of fish, and estimates of 50,000 to 120,000 species of mollusks exist.

What is a sponge?

A sponge is member of the phylum Porifera—one of the most primitive animals in the world. Overall, approximately 5,000 species of marine (saltwater) sponges and 150 species of freshwater sponges exist. These living invertebrates may be brightly colored—green, blue, yellow, orange, red, or purple—or they may be white or drab. The bright colors are due to the various bacteria or algae that live on or within the sponge.

A sponge's body contains holes that lead to an inner water chamber. The organisms pump water through those pores and expel it through a large opening at the top of the chamber. As water passes through the body, the sponge gathers nutrients, oxygen is absorbed, and waste is eliminated. Sponges are distinctive in possessing choanocytes (special flagellated

What types of sponges are used in households?

A sponge is supported by a skeleton made of hard crystals called spicules, which can be calcareous (made of calcium carbonates, the material found in limestone) or siliceous (made of silica—essentially, glass). Either type of sponge forms into a delicate network, giving the sponge its characteristic "holey-spongy" look.

A type of sponge called the demosponge has siliceous spicules and a network of fibrous proteins called sponging; they are the source of all natural household sponges. These utilitarian sponges are made by soaking the dead sponges in shallow water until all the once living cellular material has decayed, leaving the spongin network behind. Because this process is so labor intensive—and it also depletes the numbers of natural sponges—most sponges now sold for household use are plastic or fiber and have nothing to do with real sponges.

cells whose beating drives water through the body cavity) that characterizes them as suspension feeders (also known as filter feeders). A marine sponge that is 4 inches (10 centimeters) tall and 0.4 inch (1 centimeter) in diameter pumps about 23 quarts (22.5 liters) of water through its body in one day. To obtain enough food to grow by 3 ounces (100 grams), a sponge must filter about 275 gallons (1,000 kilograms) of seawater!

What animals are members of the phylum Cnidaria?

Cnidarians include the corals, jellyfish, sea anemones, and hydras. The name Cnidaria refers to the stinging structures that are characteristic of some of these animals. These organisms have a vase-shaped body plan and a digestive cavity with only one opening to the outside; this opening is surrounded by a ring of tentacles used to capture food and defend against predators. The tentacles—and sometimes the outer body surface—contain longer, harpoonlike structures called stingers or nematocysts; the stinging cells are called cnidocytes.

What are the two distinct body forms of cnidarians?

The two forms of cnidarians are called the polyp stage and the medusa (plural, medusae), or jellyfish, stage. Polyps generally live attached to a hard surface and bud to produce more polyps and, in some cnidarians, to produce the medusa stage of the life cycle. These medusae, or jellyfish, drift with the ocean currents or swim by pulsating their umbrella-shaped bodies. They also release sperm and eggs into the water; after external fertilization, the embryo develops into a larva that eventually settles to the ocean bottom, becoming another polyp and completing the life cycle. Not all cnidarians go through both polyp and medusa stages; some, such as corals and sea anemones, exist only as polyps.

What is the longest jellyfish?

The longest (and thus, probably the largest) jellyfish is the *Cyanea capillata*, a "jelly" that has no skeleton and lives in the cold, northern ocean regions, such as the North Atlantic, Arctic, and North Pacific Oceans. Called the lion's-mane jellyfish, it is one of the largest invertebrates and normally ranges in bell size (the jellyfish's bulbous body) from about 5 to 6 feet (1.5–1.8 meters) across, with some reports of bell diameter as wide as 9 feet (2.7 meters). The tentacles add to their size, and some have been known to be up to 100 feet (30 meters) long.

What are some interesting features of jellyfish?

Jellyfish live close to the ocean shorelines, spending most of their time floating near the water's surface. They have bell-shaped, see-through (called gelatinous) bodies that are between 95 percent and 96 percent water; they have a muscular ring around the margin of a bell-shaped body that contracts rhythmically to propel them through the water. Jellyfish are carnivores, subduing their prey with stinging tentacles and drawing the paralyzed animal into the digestive cavity. For humans, such a sting from most types of jellyfish is extremely painful.

How are coral reefs formed, and how fast are they built?

Coral reefs grow only in warm, shallow water. The calcium carbonate skeletons of dead corals serve as a framework upon which layers of successively younger animals attach themselves. Such accumulations, combined with rising water levels, slowly lead to the formation of reefs that can be hundreds of meters deep and long. For example, the major reef builder in Florida and Caribbean waters, *Montastrea annularis* (star coral), requires about one hundred years to form a reef just 3 feet (1 meter) high.

The coral animal, or polyp, has a columnar form; its lower end is attached to the hard floor of the reef, while the upper end is free to extend into the water, with the whole colony consisting of thousands of such individual polyps. Two kinds of corals exist, hard and soft, depending on the type of skeleton secreted. The polyps of hard corals deposit around themselves a solid skeleton of calcium carbonate (chalk), so most swimmers see only the skeleton of the coral; the animal is in a cuplike formation into which it withdraws during the daytime.

What is a hydra?

A hydra, a well-known member of phylum Cnidaria, is a tiny (0.4 inch or 1 centimeter in length) organism found in freshwater ponds. It exists as a single polyp that sits on a basal disk that it uses to glide around—it can also move by somersaulting. It usually has six to ten tentacles, which it uses to capture food, and they reproduce both sexually and asexually (bud-

---

What fish have a symbiotic relationship with the Portuguese man-of-war?

The Portuguese man-of-war (*Physalia physalis*) is a floating hydrozoan and is actually a colony of four types of polyps—each with a "duty," such as allowing the organism to float or gathering food. Certain fish, such as the yellowjack and the clownfish, all live within the tentacles. Some of these fish, in particular the clownfish, produce a slimy mucus that causes the man-of-war not to fire its stingers, while other types of fish rely on a specialized swimming pattern—swimming near the surface in various directions to avoid the man-of-war's stings.

ding). Hydras are named after the multiheaded monster of Greek mythology that was able to grow two new heads for each head cut off. When a hydra is cut into several pieces, each piece is able to regrow all the missing parts and become a whole animal.

What are the major groups of mollusks?

The four major groups of mollusks (phyla Mollusca) are: 1) chitons; 2) gastropods, including snails, slugs (mostly marine, but some freshwater), and nudibranches. This is the largest and most diverse group of mollusks (around 40,000 different species); 3) bivalves, including clams, oysters, and mussels; and 4) cephalopods, including squids and octopuses. Although mollusks vary widely in external appearance, some share the following body plan: a muscular foot, usually used for movement; a mass containing most of their internal organs; and a mantle, or a fold, of tissue that drapes over the mass and secretes a shell (that is, in organisms that have a shell).

How are pearls created?

Pearls are formed in saltwater oysters and freshwater clams. A curtainlike tissue called the mantle is within the body of these mollusks. Certain cells on the side of the mantle toward the shell secrete nacre, also known as mother-of-pearl, during a specific stage of the shell-building process.

A pearl is the result of an oyster's reaction to a foreign body, such as a piece of sand or a parasite, within the oyster's shell. The oyster neutralizes the invader by secreting thin layers of nacre around the foreign body, eventually building it into a pearl. The thin layers are alternately composed of calcium carbonate, argonite, and conchiolin. Humans can also have a hand in the formation of pearls—in particular, they intentionally place irritants within an oyster—resulting in what we often see in a jewelry display as "cultured pearls."

What are the major groups of echinoderms?

According to one common classification, six principle groups of echinoderms (phyla Echinodermata, from the Greek terms *echina*, meaning "spiny," and *derma*, meaning "skin") exist: 1) class Crinoidea (sea lilies and feather stars); 2) class Asteroidea (sea stars, also called starfish); 3) class Ophiuroidea (basket stars and brittle stars); 4) class Eichinoidea (sea urchins and sand dollars); 5) class Holothuroidea (sea cucumbers); and 6) class Concentricycloidea (sea daisies that live on waterlogged wood in the deep ocean and were first discovered in 1986).

Do all starfish (sea stars) have five arms?

No, this type of echinoderm has a variety of arms. They are members of the class Asteroidea, and their bodies consist of a central disk; from that disk, from five to more than twenty arms radiate.

FISH

What were some early studies about fish?

Fish have been a mainstay of food for thousands of years. Because of this, they were often studied along the way. For example, in 1656, Italian mathematician and physiologist Giovanni Alfonso Borelli (1608–1679) showed that a fish moved primarily by moving its tail, not its fins. In 1738, Swedish naturalist Petrus (Peter) Artedi (1705–1735) wrote the book *Petri Arted, seuci, medici, ichthyologia sive opera omnia de piscibus*—about fish and fish taxonomy—giving him the title of "the father of ichthyology" (which is the study of fish). And between 1788 and 1804, French scientist Bernard Lacepede (1756–1825) wrote forty-four volumes for his *Histoire Naturelle*—initially started by the French scientist Georges-Louis Leclerc, Comte de Buffon (1707–1788)—with eight of the volumes devoted to serpents and fish.

What fish is called a "living fossil"?

In a South African fish market in 1908, and in a small trawler fishing off the coast of west Africa in 1938, a certain type of fish was caught—a sea cave-dwelling, 5-foot (16.5-meter) ferocious predatory fish with limblike fins and a three-lobe tail called an African coelacanth. This was what is now called a "living fossil" (a term coined by naturalist Charles Robert Darwin), based on the fact that the fish closely resemble their more than three-hundred-million-year-old fossil ancestors—animals thought to have gone extinct around seventy million years ago. It took until the early 1950s for another live specimen to be caught, and since then, several more have been found.

In 2013, an international team of researchers delved even deeper into the fish's past—decoding the genome of a coelacanth—with its 2.8 billion units of DNA, about the same size as a human genome. They found that the genes in the fish are evolving more slowly than other organisms—possibly because of a lack of predators and/or that the fish do not *have* to change. This may be due to a characteristic of the fish's habitat: They live off the Eastern African coast (and another species off the coast of Indonesia) at dimly lit ocean depths of about 500 feet (496.7 meters)—regions that have not changed for thousands, if not millions, of years.

Does a connection between fish and humans exist?

Besides the obvious answer—yes, many people eat fish—researchers are also currently working on one puzzling possible connection: Did humans evolve from fish? In 2013, scientists decoded the genome of the coelacanth, a "living fossil" that resembles fossil fish that existed about 300 million years ago. Between the coelacanth and the lungfish (an air-breathing freshwater fish)—both with lobed fins that look like limbs—scientists are trying to see which animal may be closer to the first ancestral fish that used their fins to walk on land. Whatever the creatures were, they gave rise to the tetrapods—all the vertebrate animals from reptiles and birds—and to mammals, such as humans. Scientists label lobe-finned fish like the coelacanth and lungfish as sarcopterygians ("fleshy fins"); tetrapods, including humans, are descended from the sarcopterygians—and thus, the coelacanth is probably more closely related to people than to other fish!

How many fish species inhabit the Earth—from freshwater to oceans?

According to recent estimates, more than 28,000 fish species inhabit freshwater and ocean waters. They are divided into thirty-six orders and 400 families in one of the more common classification systems. The majority of fish species are bony fish (class Osteichthyes, often called true fish), with skeletons made mostly or only of bones; others have skeletons of cartilage (class Chondrichthyes).

573

How much electricity does an electric eel generate?

An electric eel (*Electrophorus electricus*) has current-producing organs made up of electric plates (modified muscle cells) on both sides of its vertebral column running almost its entire body length. The charge—350 volts on average, but as great as 550 volts—is released by the central nervous system. The shock consists of four to eight separate charges, each of which lasts only two- to three-thousandths of a second. These shocks, used as a defense mechanism, can be repeated up to 150 times per hour without any visible fatigue to the eel. The most powerful electric eel, found in the rivers of Brazil, Colombia, Venezuela, and Peru, produces a shock of 400 to 650 volts.

What general characteristics do all fish have in common?

All fish have the following characteristics: 1) gills that extract oxygen from water; 2) an internal skeleton with a skin that surrounds the dorsal nerve cord; 3) single-loop blood circulation in which the blood is pumped from the heart to the gills and then to the rest of the body before returning to the heart; and 4) nutritional deficiencies, particularly some amino acids that must be consumed and cannot be synthesized.

How do fish swimming in a school change their direction simultaneously?

About 80 percent of the approximately 28,000 fish species travel in schools. Fish travel in schools for both protection and for efficiency. Safety in numbers (in a school) is a form of predator avoidance, because trying to catch one fish in a large, moving school can be difficult for a predator. Secondly, fish that travel in schools have less drag (friction) and therefore use less energy for swimming. Also, when fish spawn, a school ensures that some eggs will evade predators and live to form another school.

The movements of a school of fish, which confuse predators, happen because the fish detect pressure changes in the water. The detection system, called the lateral line, is found along each side of the fish's body. Along the line are clusters of tiny hairs inside cups filled with a jellylike substance. If a fish becomes alarmed and turns sharply, it causes a pressure wave in the water around it. This wave pressure deforms the "jelly" in the lateral line of nearby fish. The deformation moves the hairs that trigger nerves, and a signal is sent to the brain telling the fish to turn.

What are sharks?

Chondrichthyes are fish that have a cartilaginous skeleton rather than a bony skeleton and include sharks, skates, and rays. Of those animals, one of the most well known, and often feared, is the shark. The 375 species of sharks currently known about range in length from 6 inches (15 centimeters) to 49 feet (15 meters)—only around a dozen are considered to be dangerous to humans. The relatively rare great white shark (*Carcharodan carcharias*) is the largest predatory fish, with some specimens reaching 20 feet, 4 inches (6.2 meters) long and weighing 5,000 pounds (2,270 kilograms). The largest shark is the whale shark (*Rhincodon typus*) that measures around 60 feet (20 meters) long; the smallest is the Caribbean Ocean's deepwater dogfish shark (*Etmopterus perryi*) that measures 8 inches (20 centimeters) long. The fastest shark is thought to be the shortfin mako (*Isurus oxyrinchus*), reported to swim 20 miles (32 kilometers) per hour.

Why do people fear sharks?

One of the major reasons why humans are afraid of sharks is obvious: We can't see underwater, and a shark can come seemingly out of nowhere. While around thirty species are known to have attacked humans, in the United States, shark attacks average about sixteen per year, with around one fatality every two years (around the world, shark attacks number around fifty to seventy per year). In one study, the researchers found that most shark attacks occur near shore, which is not surprising since most people who enter the water stay close to the shore. Some researchers believe that shark attacks on humans will only increase over time, as more people live—and play—along ocean coastlines.

What is unusual about shark's teeth?

Sharks were among the first vertebrates to develop teeth. The teeth are not set into the jaw, but rather sit on top of it—thus, they are not firmly anchored and are easily lost. The teeth are arranged in six to twenty rows, with the ones in front doing the biting and cutting. Behind these teeth, others grow. When a tooth breaks or is worn down, a replacement moves forward. In fact, one shark may eventually develop and use more than 20,000 teeth in its lifetime.

AQUATIC MAMMALS

What freshwater mammal is venomous?

The male duck-billed platypus (*Ornithorhynchus anatinus*) has venomous spurs located on its hind legs. When threatened, the animal will drive the spurs into the skin of a potential enemy, inflicting a painful sting. The venom released is relatively mild and generally not harmful to humans, but for most animals that try to bother the platypus, it makes them hesitate to attack the platypus again.

What is the difference between porpoises and dolphins?

Marine dolphins (family Delphinidae) and porpoises (family Phocoenidae) together comprise about forty species. The chief differences between dolphins and porpoises occur in the snout and teeth: True dolphins have a beaklike snout and cone-shaped teeth, while true porpoises have a rounded snout and flat or spade-shaped teeth.

What are the fastest and slowest whales?

The orca or killer whale (*Orcinus orca*) is the fastest-swimming whale. In fact, it is the fastest-swimming marine mammal, with speeds that reach 31 miles (50 kilometers) per hour. Right whales (*Eubalaena japonica*) are one of the slowest whale species, typically traveling at 1.2 to 2.5 miles (2–4 kilometers) per hour.

What are manatees?

In the winter, the marine mammal called the West Indian manatee (*Trichechus manatus*) moves to the more temperate parts of Florida, such as the warm headwaters of the Crystal and Homosassa rivers in central Florida or the tropical waters of southern Florida. When the air temperature rises to 50°F (10°C), it will wander back along the Gulf Coast and up the Atlantic Coast as far as Virginia. Long-range offshore migrations to the coast of Guyana and South America have been documented. In 1983, when the population of manatees in Florida was reduced to several thousand, the state gave it legal protection from being hunted or commercially exploited. However, many animals continue to be killed or injured by environmental problems (such as water pollution or "red tide," also known as algal blooms) and the encroachment of humans. Entrapment in locks and dams, collisions with barges and power boat propellers, and so on cause at least 30 percent of manatee deaths, which total 125 to 130 annually. According to researchers, it is difficult to tell how many manatees are in all of Florida's waters, but in 2013, estimates put the animal's population at about 5,000.

IN BETWEEN SEA AND LAND

AMPHIBIANS

What are amphibians?

The word "amphibian," from the Greek *amphi* ("both") and *bios* ("life"), refers to the animal's double life on land and in water. The usual life cycle of amphibians begins with eggs laid in water, which develop into aquatic larvae with external gills; in a development that shows its evolution, the fishlike larva develops lungs and limbs and becomes an adult—thus, amphibians have made a partial transition to terrestrial life. The living amphibians include newts, salamanders, frogs, and toads. Although lungfish made a partial transition to living out of the water, amphibians were the first to struggle onto land and become adapted to a life of breathing air while not constantly surrounded by water. They were the first vertebrates to have true legs, tongues, ears, and a voicebox—with branches of certain amphibians eventually giving rise to the reptiles.

What fossil amphibian was once mistaken for a human skeleton?

In 1731, Swiss geologist Johann Scheuchzer (1672–1733) found a fossil of what he thought was a human skeleton—what he called *Homon diluvii testis*, or "man, a witness of the flood," in reference to the Bible. What he had actually discovered was the fossil of a twenty million-year-old extinct giant salamander.

Why must amphibians stay near water or moist environments?

Although amphibians breathe air and walk on crude legs—for example, alligators—they cannot stray too far from water. This is because they need to lay their eggs in water, and their larval stage needs water. For example, frogs and toads start their early life as eggs deposited in water (or near water), then develop into tadpoles—they must live in water to survive. At the adult stage, amphibians can either be amphibious (live on land and in the water) or totally aquatic, with some exceptions: For example, some species of frogs live only on land (but in a moist area), and some are more common in arid regions. For example, some desert amphibians store water in their bladders; they wait for cyclic rains (such as the Arizona "monsoon" season), then use the resulting water puddles to reproduce.

Do amphibians hibernate?

Yes, some amphibians hibernate—those that live in the colder climates of the north hibernate during the winter. Those that live in the more arid, desert climates do not hibernate, but estivate—become inactive—during the hottest times of the year.

What are the major groups of amphibians?

More than 4,000 species of amphibians are known to live on Earth and are found on every continent except Antarctica, which are divided into three major groups. The following lists those groups, their order (in terms of classification), and the known number (to date) of living species:

Group	Order	No. of Species
Frogs and toads	Anura (Salientia)	3,800
Salamanders and newts	Caudata (Urodela)	360
Caecilians	Apoda (Gymnophiona)	160

What's the difference between a frog and a toad?

Frogs and toads are different animals, but distinguishable from each other. Frogs and toads are of the same order, either Anura or Salientia (depending on the classification system). They breed and have their young in similar ways, and they both hunt for food at twilight or at night (although some toads are active during the day).

What frog is carrying a deadly fungus?

In 2013, scientists discovered that the African clawed frog—a species found all over the world—is carrying a deadly amphibian disease and is thus threatening hundreds of species of frogs and salamanders. Initially, the frogs were shipped around the world for use in human pregnancy tests from the 1930s to 1950s; if a female frog began ovulating within about ten hours after being injected with a woman's urine, the woman was probably pregnant. Because other methods were developed to determine if a woman is pregnant, the frogs were released into the wild and are now spreading a fungus called *Batrachochytrium dendrobatidis* (Bd). Most of the surviving African clawed frogs have found a way to survive the fungus, but other amphibians are not as lucky. The disease infects the skin, causing it to thicken to around forty times more than normal—toppling the creature's electrolyte balance and literally causing a heart attack.

If you can get close enough before either creature dives into the pond as you approach, though, you can see the differences: Frogs have much smoother skin than toads; toads almost always have warts; frogs live near moist areas, but toads can live in drier places; frogs lay their eggs in clumps, whereas toads tend to lay them in long strands in a pond; toads are more fat-bodied, while frogs tend to be slimmer; toads have an oval, raised glandular area behind the eye, but frogs do not; and toads have an L-shaped ridge between and in back of their eyes, while frogs do not.

What are the caecilians?

The caecilians are mostly legless, wormlike amphibians found everywhere around the world, but mostly in tropical regions. Many are eyeless, have smooth skins, and burrow into the ground like earthworms. Not much is known about this group, and they are the least studied of the living amphibians. But it is thought their ancestors may have played an important part in the development of early amphibians.

WORMS

What are the three phyla of worms?

The many types of worms in the world are divided into three phyla: Flatworms belong to the phylum Platyhelminthes and are flat, elongated animals that have bilateral symmetry and primitive organs (they include the planarians, flukes, and tapeworms). The phylum Nematoda includes the roundworms, or unsegmented worms, also with bilateral symmetry, but have little in terms of sensory organs. Most of them are parasitic, including the parasite *Trichinella* that causes trichinosis from uncooked pork. The third phylum is Annellia, or segmented worms, including sandworms, tube worms, earthworms, and leeches. They also

Why are leeches important in the field of medicine?

Leeches have been used in the practice of medicine since ancient times. During the 1800s, leeches were widely used for bloodletting because of the mistaken idea that body disorders and fevers were caused by an excess of blood—thus, leech collecting and cultures were practiced on a commercial scale during this time.

The medical leech, *Hirudo medicinalis*, is used even today to remove blood that has accumulated within tissues as a result of injury or disease. Leeches have also been applied to fingers or toes that have been surgically reattached to the body. The sucking by the leech unclogs small blood vessels, permitting blood to flow normally again through the body part. The leech releases hirudin, secreted by the salivary glands, which is an anticoagulant that prevents blood from clotting and dissolves preexisting clots. Other salivary ingredients dilate blood vessels and act as an anesthetic. A medicinal leech can absorb as much as five to ten times its body weight in blood. Complete digestion of this blood takes a long time, and these leeches feed only once or twice a year in this manner.

have bilateral symmetry, a digestive tract that is a tube within a tube—complete with a crop, gizzard, and intestine—and a closed circulatory system.

What are the most common tapeworm infections in humans?

Earthworms serve an important function in the ecosystem by aerating and fertilizing soil, which is beneficial to all plants.

The long, flat bodies of tapeworms have long been associated with humans—especially in association with eating certain meals that contain the tapeworm. For example, the beef tapeworm (*Taenia saginata*) comes from eating rare beef and is the most common of tapeworms in humans; the pork tapeworm (*Taenia solium*) comes from eating rare pork, but is less common than the beef tapeworm; and the fish tapeworm (*Diphyllobothrium latum*) is found most often in the Great Lakes region of the United States when eating rare or poorly cooked fish. It is also the largest tapeworm and can grow to a length of 66 feet (20 meters); to compare, the beef tapeworm may only reach around 33 feet (10 meters).

How numerous are roundworms?

Roundworms, or nematodes, are members of the phylum Nematoda (from the Greek term *nematos*, meaning "thread") and are numerous in two respects: 1) number of known and potential species; and 2) the total number of these organisms in a habitat. Approximately 12,000 species of nematodes have been named, but it has been estimated that if all species were known, the number would be closer to 500,000. Nematodes live in a variety of habitats ranging from the sea to soil. Six cubic inches (100 cubic centimeters) of soil may contain several thousand nematodes, a square yard (.85 square meters) of woodland or agricultural soil may contain several million of them, and good topsoil may contain billions per acre.

In what ways are earthworms beneficial?

Earthworms are extremely beneficial to gardeners and growers by making the soil more fertile. An earthworm literally eats its way through soil and decaying vegetation. As it moves about, the soil is turned, aerated, and enriched by nitrogenous wastes. (In fact, English naturalist Charles Robert Darwin once calculated that a single earthworm could eat its own weight in soil every day.) Much of what is eaten is then excreted on the Earth's surface in the form of "casts." The worms then rebury these casts with their burrowing process.

What are giant tube worms?

Giant tube worms were discovered near the hydrothermal (hot water) ocean vents in 1977 as the submersible Alvin was exploring the ocean floor of the Galapagos Ridge (located 1.5 miles [2.4 kilometers] below the Pacific Ocean surface). Growing to lengths of 5 feet (1.5 meters), *Riftia pachyptila Jones*, named after worm expert Meredith Jones of the Smithsonian Museum of Natural History, lack both mouth and gut and are topped with feathery plumes composed of over 200,000 tiny tentacles. The phenomenal growth of these worms is due to their internal food source—symbiotic bacteria, over one hundred billion per ounce of tissue, that live within the worms' troposome tissues. To these tissues, the tube worms transport absorbed oxygen from the water, together with carbon dioxide and hydrogen sulfide. Using this supply, the bacteria in turn produce carbohydrates and proteins that the worms need to thrive.

What is the largest leech known?

Most leeches are between 0.75 inch and 2 inches (2–6 centimeters) in length, but some "medicinal" leeches reach 8 inches (20 centimeters). The giant of all leeches is the Amazonian *Haementeria ghilanii* (from the Greek term *haimateros*, meaning "bloody") that can reach up to 12 inches (30 centimeters) in length.

AQUATIC AND LAND ARTHROPODS

What are arthropods?

Members of the phylum Arthropoda are characterized by jointed appendages and an exoskeleton of chitin. More than one million species of arthropods are currently known to science, and many biologists believe that millions more will be identified. Arthropods are the most biologically successful group of animals on Earth today. This is because they are the most diverse organisms and live in a greater range of habitats than do the members of any other animal phylum, from land to the oceans. One major reason for their abundance is one of their classes—the Insecta class, the organisms we all fondly (or not too fondly) call insects; they are the most successful organisms on Earth in terms of diversity, geographic distribution, number of species, and number of individuals. In fact, to date, more than 900,000 different kinds of insects are known (and amazingly, it is estimated that ten quintillion (10,000,000,000,000,000,000) individual insects are alive at any given time!

What are the major groups of arthropods?

More than one million arthropod species have been described, with insects making up the vast majority of them. Zoologists estimate that the arthropod population of the world numbers about a billion million (10^{18}) individuals; in fact, two out of every three organisms known on Earth are arthropods, and the phylum is represented in nearly all habitats of the biosphere. About 90 percent of all arthropods are insects, and about half of the named species of insects are beetles. Several groups of arthropods contain a mix of animals that inhabit water environments and animals that live on land. They include the subphyla of Chelicerata (horseshoe crabs, spiders, scorpions, ticks, and mites); Crustacea (lobsters, crabs, shrimps, isopods, copepods, and barnacles); and Unirania (grasshoppers, roaches, ants, bees, butterflies, flies, beetles, centipedes, and millipedes).

Is there a difference between beetles and bugs?

Yes, there is a definite difference between beetles and bugs—a subject that is confusing to most of us, especially since we often use the term "bug" for almost any type of tiny, flying creature! The biggest difference is that they belong to two distinct insect groups—in most biological classifications, bugs are actually called "true bugs," and are listed under the Order Hemiptera, while beetles are under the Order Coleoptera. There are some similarities, as both true bugs and beetles have the overall characteristics of the insect world: six jointed legs, antennae, a relatively hard exoskeleton, and three main body parts: the head, thorax, and abdomen. But there are differences, too, which is the reason for the two orders:

True bugs—For example, assassin bugs, stink bugs, and bed bugs—have piercing-sucking mouthparts (many of them suck nectar and sap); membrane-thin wings, if they have any at all; and the juveniles look like miniature adult bugs, except they don't have wings quite yet (if at all).

Beetles—For example, Asian ladybugs, weevils, and dung beetles—eat a wide range of materials, from plants, leaves, and bark to animals; they have small, thick sheaths (called elytra) that fold out when they are ready to fly; and their life cycle runs from larva to adult. This order makes up around forty percent of all insects species around the world—and it is estimated that they represent between twenty-five to thirty percent of all animal species on Earth.

What marine and freshwater invertebrates are some of the most important of all animals?

Copepods, tiny crustaceans, are the link between the photosynthetic life in the ocean or pond and the rest of the aquatic food web. They are primary consumers grazing on algae in the waters of the oceans and ponds. These organisms, among the most abundant multicellular animals on Earth, are then consumed by a variety of small predators, which are eaten by larger predators, and so on. Virtually all animal life in the ocean depends on the copepods, either directly or indirectly. Although humans do not eat copepods directly, our sources of food from the ocean would disappear without the copepods.

What arthropods can affect humans (in the United States)?

Many arthropods can affect humans, especially in terms of unhealthy bites, itches, scratches, diseases, and allergies. The following lists only a few of these creatures that live in various spots in the United States:

Arthropod	Effect on Human Health
Black widow spider (*Latrodectus mactans*)	Venomous bite; most in South
Brown recluse or violin spider (*Loxosceles reclusa*)	Venomous bite
Scorpion (*Centruroides exilicauda*)	Venomous bite; most in South and Western states
Chiggers (*Trombiculid mites*)	Dermatitis; most in South
Itch mite (*Sarcoptes scabiei*)	Scabies
Deer tick (*Ixodes dammini*)	Bite can transmit lyme disease
Dog tick, wood tick (*Dermacentor species*)	Bite can transmit Rocky Mountain spotted fever in some places in the U.S.
Mosquitoes	Bite can transmit diseases (for example, West Nile virus, encephalitis, filarial worms)

Arthropod	Effect on Human Health
Horseflies, deerflies	Female has painful bite
Houseflies	Many transmit bacteria and viruses
Fleas	Dermatitis
Bees, wasps, ants	Venomous stings (single stings not dangerous unless person is allergic)

What are the only crustaceans that don't move around?

Barnacles are the only sessile (permanently attached to one location) crustaceans. They were described by the nineteenth-century naturalist Louis Agassiz (1807–1873) as "nothing more than a little shrimplike animal standing on its head in a limestone house and licking food into its mouth." Accumulations of barnacles may become so great that the speed of a ship may be reduced by up to 40 percent, necessitating dry-docking the ship to remove the barnacles.

What are "sea monkeys"?

"Sea monkeys" are often sold as sea creatures by a variety of companies. But in reality, they are crustaceans—a type of brine shrimp called *Artemia salina*. Other types of brine shrimp *not* sold as "sea monkeys" are a very important part of the marine food chain—and as food for fish and people. The sea monkeys you buy also have some strange characteristics. For example, they breathe through their feet; can survive for years without water by hibernating; and are born with one eye, but eventually develop two more.

What are the largest and smallest aerial spider webs?

The largest aerial webs are spun by the tropical orb weavers of the genus *Nephila*, which produce webs that measure up to 18.9 feet (6 meters) in circumference. The smallest webs are produced by the species *Glyphesis cottonae*; their webs cover an area of about 0.75 square inch (4.84 square centimeters).

Do male mosquitoes bite humans?

No, male mosquitoes live on plant juices, sugary saps, and liquids from decomposition. They do not have a biting mouth that can penetrate human skin, but female mosquitoes do. In some species, the females, who lay as many as 200 eggs, need blood to lay their eggs—which leads to those painful bites that make humans and other animals itch.

Black Widow spiders are easily distinguished by the bright-red hourglass marking on their abdomens. Their bite is venomous and very painful, although not usually lethal for healthy adults. Nevertheless, if you are bitten, obtain treatment as soon as possible.

Do bat-eating spiders exist?

Yes, bat-eating spiders live everywhere in the world except Antarctica. About 90 percent of these invertebrates live in the warmer regions of the globe and include some web-building spider species such as the *Argiope savignyl* and a tarantula species *Poecilotheria rufilata*; both are known to capture and kill small bats. Some tropical orb-weaving spiders—with a leg span of 4 to 6 inches (10–15 centimeters)—catch bats in webs that can reach 5 feet (16.5 meters) in diameter. Still other spiders have been seen capturing and killing a small bat, such as the huntsman spider (*Heteropoda ventoria*) in India. But they are not the only creatures the spiders eat—some larger species have also been known to capture and eat fish, frogs, and even snakes and mice.

Why are insects considered the most successful group of animals?

With more than one million described species (and perhaps millions more not yet identified), class Insecta is the most successful group of animals on Earth. In the United States alone, about 91,000 different species have been described, with an estimated 73,000 species not yet described. In fact, the largest numbers of species in the U.S. fall into the four insect Orders: Coleoptera (beetles) at about 23,700; Diptera (flies) at about 19,600; Hymenoptera (ants, bees, wasps) at about 17,500; and Lepidoptera (moths and butterflies) at about 11,500.

More species of insects have been identified than of all other groups of animals combined. What insects lack in size, they make up for in sheer numbers. If we could weigh all the insects in the world, their weight would exceed that of all the remaining terrestrial animals. About 200 million insects are alive at any one time for each human. And why are they successful? Flight is one key to the great success of insects. An animal that can fly can escape many predators, find food and mates, and disperse to new habitats much faster than an animal that must crawl about on the ground.

Does a connection exist between early flowering plants and insects?

Yes, a connection is possible. Early flowering plants—although a debate is still up as to when they first arose, from 140 to 190 million years ago to 215 million years ago—are thought to be connected to the rise of insects. Modern insects such as bees and wasps rely on flowers for pollen and nectar, and if the plants evolved 215 million years ago, it may be why both became very successful on land.

What is a "bug," biologically speaking?

The biological meaning of the word "bug" is significantly more restrictive than in common usage. People often refer to all insects as "bugs," even using the word to include such organisms as bacteria and viruses as well as glitches in computer programs. In the strictest biological sense, a "bug" is a member of the order Hemiptera, also called true bugs. Members of Hemiptera include bedbugs, squash bugs, clinch bugs, stink bugs, and water striders.

What is the largest group of insects that has been identified and classified?

The largest group of insects that has been identified and classified is the order Coleoptera (beetles, weevils, and fireflies), with some 350,000 to 400,000 species. Beetles are the dominant form of life on Earth, as one of every five living species is a beetle.

What are beneficial insects?

Beneficial insects include bees, wasps, flies, butterflies, moths, and others that pollinate plants. Many fruits and vegetables depend on insect pollinators for the production of seeds. Insects are an important source of food for birds, fish, and many animals. In some countries, such insects as termites, caterpillars, ants, and bees are eaten as food by people. Products derived from insects include honey and beeswax, shellac, and silk. Some predators such as mantises, ladybugs or lady beetles, and lacewings feed on other harmful insects. Other helpful insects are parasites that live on or in the body of harmful insects. For example, some wasps lay their eggs in caterpillars that damage tomato plants.

What animals fluoresce?

Fluorescence is luminescence caused by a natural pigment molecule; pigments are molecules that absorb some colors of light while reflecting others. For example, green pigments (like those in leaves) absorb red and blue wavelengths of light but reflect green wavelengths. After being energized by photons (units of light energy), the electrons of some pigment molecules actually give off light as they fall back to their normal state. Chlorophyll molecules that play a role in photosynthesis have this ability, as do molecules found in several organisms, such as certain jellyfish. The body of the insect *Photinus pyralis*, better known as a lightning bug, has the enzyme luciferase, which generates the chemical reaction that leads to a drop in the energy state of electrons—a reaction similar to that which occurs in a chlorophyll molecule—allowing the insect to "glow" on and off during its mating season.

What are some of the most destructive insects in the world?

The most destructive insect is the desert locust (*Schistocera gregaria*), the locust of the Bible; their habitat ranges from the dry and semi-arid regions of Africa and the Middle East through Pakistan and northern India. This short-horn grasshopper can eat its own weight in food a day, and during long migratory flights a large swarm can consume 20,000 tons (18,144,000 kilograms) of grain and vegetation a day.

What is the gypsy moth?

The gypsy moth (*Porthetria dispar*) lays its eggs on the leaves of oaks, birches, maples, and other hardwood trees. When the yellow hairy caterpillars hatch from the eggs, they devour the leaves in such quantities that the tree becomes temporarily defoliated. Some trees can withstand two years of such defoliation, but other trees often die in the infestation year. In 1869, Professor Leopold Trouvelot (1827–1895) originally brought gypsy moth egg masses from France to Medford, Massachusetts. His intention was to breed the gypsy moth with the silkworm to overcome a wilt disease of the silkworm. He placed the egg masses on a window ledge, and evidently the wind blew them away. Only a decade later, the caterpillars covered trees in that vicinity, and in twenty years trees in eastern Massachusetts were being defoliated. Since that time, it has spread (in cycles) to at least twenty-five states in the United States.

What are "killer bees"?

Africanized honeybees—the term entomologists prefer rather than killer bees—are a hybrid bee originating in Brazil, where African honeybees were imported in 1956. The breeders, hoping to produce a bee better suited to producing more honey in the tropics, instead found that African bees soon hybridized with and mostly displaced the familiar European honeybees. Although they produce more honey, Africanized honeybees (*Apis mellifera scutellata*) are more dangerous than European bees because they attack intruders in greater numbers. Since their introduction, they have been responsible for approximately 1,000 human deaths.

In addition to such safety issues, concern is growing regarding the effect of possible hybridization on the U.S. beekeeping industry. In October 1990, the bees crossed the Mexican border into the United States; in 1996, these bees were found in parts of Texas, Arizona, New Mexico, Nevada, and California; by 2009, they had crept up even further into those states and added southern Oklahoma, Louisiana, and Florida—even Puerto Rico and the U.S. Virgin Islands—to the list. Their migration northward has slowed—probably because they are a tropical insect and cannot live in colder climates.

How many flowers produce 1 pound of honey?

Bees must gather 4 pounds (1.8 kilograms) of nectar, which requires the bees to tap about two million flowers, in order to produce 1 pound (454 grams) of honey. The honey is gathered by worker bees, whose life span is three to six weeks, long enough to collect about a teaspoon of nectar.

What is a "daddy longlegs"?

The name applies to a harmless, nonbiting, long-legged arachnid. Also called a harvestman, it is often mistaken for a spider, but it lacks a spider's segmented body shape. Although it has the same number of legs (eight) as a spider, the harvestman's legs are far longer and thinner. These very long legs enable it to raise its body high enough to avoid ants or other small enemies. Harvestmen are largely carnivorous, feeding on a variety of small invertebrates such as insects, spiders, and mites. They never spin webs as spiders do. They also eat some juicy plants and in captivity can be fed almost anything edible, from bread and milk to meat, and also need to drink frequently. (The term "daddy longlegs" is also another name for a cranefly—a thin-bodied insect with long legs—and a snoutlike structure with which it sucks water and nectar.)

LAND ANIMALS

EARLY LAND ANIMALS

What were the earliest animals to walk on land?

The only way scientists know about the earliest land animals on Earth is through fossils found in ancient rock. And from these fossils, we know that almost all species of animals have changed dramatically since the first animals walked on land. The changes became necessary as the Earth has gone though such environmentally changing events as volcanic eruptions, the movement of the continents, changes in climate, and massive extinctions.

But what animals were responsible for first walking on land remains a highly debated topic. One possibility was suggested in 2013, in which researchers suggested that a toothy creature called the *Ichthyostega* represented one of the first transitions between fish and terrestrial animals. It lived about 374 to 359 million years ago and is thought to have lived in the shallow water of swampy areas—either along coastlines or waterways. The best guess is that the animal was looking for something to eat and was lured by the possible food on land. The four-legged creature probably dragged itself out of the water and on land by using its front legs and dragging its back legs, much like how modern seals move. The creature also had a string of bones in its chest that may have been the precursors to the sternum that holds the ribcage—necessary for supporting the weight of its chest as it moved on land.

How does a mastodon differ from a mammoth?

Although the words are sometimes used interchangeably, the mammoth and the mastodon were two different species. The mastodon seems to have appeared first, and a side branch may have led to the mammoth. The mastodon lived in Africa, Europe, Asia, and North and South America, appearing in the Oligocene era (38 to 25 million years ago) and surviving until less than one million years ago. It stood a maximum of 10 feet (3 meters) tall and was covered with dense, woolly hair; its tusks were straight forward and nearly parallel to each other. The mammoth evolved less than two million years ago and died out about 10,000 years ago; they lived in the cooler regions of North America, Europe, and Asia. Like the mastodon, the mammoth was covered with a long, coarse layer of outer hair to protect it from the cold. It was somewhat larger than the mastodon, standing 9 to 15 feet (2.7–4.5 meters); the mammoth's tusks tended to spiral outward, then up.

The reasons for both creatures' demise are still a matter of speculation. When it comes to the mammoths, the evidence is more "recent": After finding several mammoths frozen in such places as Siberia, scientists believe that the gradual warming of the Earth's climate—and thus a change in the animals' environments—was the primary factor in the mammoth's

Did dinosaurs and humans ever coexist?

One of the most famous of all the ancient animals were the dinosaurs—creatures that only lived on land (so far, no dinosaurs are known to have lived in the air or water)—first appearing in the early Triassic period (about 220 million years ago) and all but disappearing at the end of the Cretaceous period (about sixty-five million years ago). It is thought that modern humans (*Homo sapiens sapiens*) appeared only about 25,000 years ago. Although we know movies that show humans and dinosaurs existing together are only Hollywood fantasies, one caveat remains: Many scientists believe that modern birds are the ancestors of the dinosaurs—and thus, in some ways, we can say that the dinosaurs never truly became extinct!)

extinction. But they suggest that early humans may have killed many mammoths as well—perhaps hastening the extinction process.

Why are cockroaches so amazing?

The word "cockroach" can often send chills up a human's spine. They are considered pests by most, but in reality, they've been on Earth for much longer than humans. The earliest cockroach fossils are about 350 million years old; by about 220 million years ago, cockroaches were so prolific—and are thought to have been the first organism to master flight—that many paleontologists nickname that time the "Age of Cockroaches."

Modern cockroaches (order Blattaria or Blattodea) are nocturnal scavenging insects that eat not only human food, but book bindings, ink, paper, and seemingly everything in between. Of the about 4,500 species of cockroaches, only thirty species are associated with human habitats, and of those, only about four are considered definite pests. The most well-known one in the United States is the American cockroach (*Periplaneta americana*) that can measure about 1.2 inches (30 millimeters) long—although when you see them invade your kitchen at night, they seem to look much larger! The world's heaviest cockroach is the Australian giant burrowing cockroach—a creature that can measure 3.5 inches (9 centimeters) long. They are related to the termite; in fact, recent genetic evidence suggests that termites evolved directly from true cockroaches. And they are amazing creatures that have adapted well to life on Earth; they can even go for a month without food, for two weeks without water, and the female mates once and can stay pregnant for all of her life.

REPTILES AND BIRDS

What is the difference between a reptile and an amphibian?

Reptiles are clad in scales, shields, or plates, and their toes have claws; amphibians have moist, glandular skins, and their toes lack claws. Reptile eggs have a thick, hard, or parchmentlike shell that protects the developing embryo from moisture loss, even on dry land. The eggs of amphibians lack this protective outer covering and are always laid in water or in damp places. Young reptiles are miniature replicas of their parents in general appearance, if not always in coloration and pattern. Juvenile amphibians pass through a larval (usually aquatic) stage before they metamorphose (change in form and structure) into the adult form. Reptiles include alligators, crocodiles, terrapins, tortoises, turtles, lizards, and snakes; amphibians include salamanders, toads, and frogs.

Were reptiles the first group of vertebrates to become truly terrestrial?

Yes, reptiles were the first group of vertebrates to become true land animals. They had several adaptations: Legs were arranged to support the body's weight more effectively than in amphibians, allowing reptile bodies to be larger and to be able to run. Reptilian lungs were more developed, with a greatly increased surface area for gas exchange than the saclike lungs of amphibians. The three-chambered heart of reptiles was more efficient than the amphibian heart. In addition, the skin was covered with hard, dry scales to minimize water loss. However, the most important evolutionary adaptation was the amniotic egg, in which an

587

embryo could survive and develop on land. The eggs were surrounded by a protective shell that prevented the developing embryo from drying out.

What is the most successful and diverse group of terrestrial vertebrates?

Birds, members of the class Aves, are the most successful of all terrestrial vertebrates. Twenty-eight orders of living birds with almost 10,000 species are distributed over almost the entire Earth. The success of birds is mostly due to the development of the feather, providing insulation from the cold, allowing them to fly, and as protective coloration, not only as camouflage, but for territorial displays for mating.

Are birds related to dinosaurs?

According to many scientists, birds are essentially modified dinosaurs with feathers. American paleontologists Robert T. Bakker (1945–) and John H. Ostrom (1928–2005) did extensive research on the relationship between birds and dinosaurs in the 1970s. They suggested that the bony structure of small dinosaurs was very similar to *Archaeopteryx*, the first animal classified as a bird (it had true feathers)—thus dinosaurs and birds probably evolved from the same ancestors. Ostrom also suggested that dinosaurs may have been warm-blooded and thus more active and similar to birds. The evidence since that time has become stronger, as paleontologists continue to discover more dinosaur fossils—some that show even more evidence of birdlike feathers. In fact, in 2013, several researchers found yet another dinosaur fossil with evidence of feathers and suggested that dinosaurs were not "overgrown lizards," but that feathered dinosaurs were actually the norm.

What birds have some of the largest wingspans?

An African wading bird called the Marabou stork (*Leptoptilos crumeniferus*) has the largest wingspan of any bird (to date), measuring about 13.2 feet (4 meters). The albatross family has the next largest wingspans, including the wandering albatross (*Diomedea exculans*), the royal albatross (*Diomedea epomophora*), and the Amsterdam Island albatross (*Diomeda amsterdiamensis*), with a spread from 8 to 11 feet (2.5–3.3 meters). The next in line is the Trumpeter Swan (*Cygnus buccinator*), with a wingspan of about 11 feet (3.3 meters), which is the largest (and heaviest) bird in North America.

Will wild birds reject baby birds that have been touched by humans?

Contrary to popular belief, birds generally will not reject hatchlings touched by human hands. The best thing to do for newborn birds (probably with the exception of large birds such as raptors—call a wildlife rehabilitator for help in that instance) that have fallen or have been pushed out of the nest is to locate the nest as quickly as possible, put on some gloves, gently pick up the baby, and carefully put them back into the nest (especially if other nestlings are in the nest). If you cannot find the nest, leave the bird alone and watch from a distance—usually the mother will return and get the baby back to the nest in a relatively short time. If no mother returns within a few hours (or less if it is snowing or raining), contact your local wildlife rehabilitator for more information.

MAMMALS

What characterizes a mammal?

The class Mammalia includes more than 5,000 species in about twenty-six orders (depending on which classification system you use), which are found on all continents and in all oceans and seem to have a disproportionately large ecological role compared to their abundance—mainly because their metabolism is so high, they have to eat more. In general, most mammals have several characteristics—especially three not found in other animals: The females produce milk using modified sweat glands (called mammary glands, which can vary from two to a dozen or more); have hair (mostly made of a protein called keratin, similar to what makes up human fingernails and mostly developed to insulate the mammal against extreme environments); and have three middle ear bones (the malleus, incus, and stapes, allowing mammals to better hear sounds).

Do any mammals fly?

Bats (around 1,200 species) are the only truly flying mammals, although several gliding mammals are referred to as "flying" (such as the flying squirrel and flying lemur). The "wings" of bats consist of double membranes of skin stretching from the sides of the body to the hind legs and tail that are actually skin extensions of the back and belly. The wing membranes are supported by the elongated fingers of the forelimbs (or arms).

Do any cats live in the desert?

The sand cat (*Felis margarita*) is the only member of the cat family tied directly to desert regions. Found in the deserts of North Africa, the Arabian Peninsula, Turkmenistan, Uzbekistan, and western Pakistan, the sand cat has adapted to extremely arid desert areas. The padding on the soles of its feet is well suited to the loose sandy soil, and it can live without drinking freestanding water. Having sandy or grayish-ochre dense fur, its body length is 17.5 to 22 inches (45–57 centimeters). Mainly nocturnal (active at night), the cat feeds on ro-

This Gambian epauletted fruit bat is one of 1,200 species of bat, the only true flying mammal on our planet.

dents, hares, birds, and reptiles. The Chinese desert cat (*Felis bieti*) does not live in the desert as its name implies, but inhabits the steppe country and mountains. Likewise, the Asiatic desert cat (*Felis silvestris ornata*) inhabits the open plains of India, Pakistan, Iran, and Asiatic Russia.

What are the smallest and largest bear species?

The smallest bear in the world—and also considered the least studied—is the sun (or honey) bear that lives in the human lowland tropics of Southeast Asia. They have short, sleek, and dense black fur (for protection from dirt and insects), are good tree climbers, are omnivores (eating anything they can find in the rain forest, especially honey and bee larvae), and can weigh about 100 pounds (45 kilograms). The largest bear species is the Polar Bear (or "sea bears") that live around the Arctic Circle, including the North Pole, and northern parts of Europe, Asia, and North America (with about 60 percent of the population in Canada). Their fur looks white, but it can also be yellow or even greenish depending on the light. They are one of the largest land predators in the world, can reach about 10 feet (305 centimeters) in height and weight between 800 and 1,600 pounds (360–720 kilograms), although females weigh less. The largest recorded polar bear was a male that weighed over 2,200 pounds (990 kilograms) and was over 12 feet (365 centimeters) tall.

Do camels store water in their humps?

The hump or humps do not store water, since they are fat reservoirs. The ability to go long periods without drinking water, up to ten months if plenty of green vegetation and dew is available to feed on, results from a number of physiological adaptations of the animal. For example, camels can lose up to 40 percent of their body weight with no ill effects; they can also withstand a variation of their body temperature by as much as 14°F (8°C).

What is one of the most successful groups of mammals known?

Contrary to what you may think—that humans are the most successful—other animals beat us, in particular the bat. These creatures have more than 1,200 species that comprise about one-fifth of all mammal species, and other than owls, hawks, spiders, and snakes, they have few natural enemies.

How long do animals, in particular mammals, live?

Of the mammals, humans and fin whales live the longest. The following lists the maximum life span for various longer-lived animal species:

Animal (Latin name)	Maximum Life Span (in years)
Marion's tortoise (*Testudo sumeirii*)	152+
Quahog (*Venus mercenaria*)	c. 150
Common box tortoise (*Terrapene Carolina*)	138
European pond tortoise (*Emys orbicularis*)	120+
Spur-thighed tortoise (*Testudo graeca*)	116+
Fin whale (*Balaenoptera physalus*)	116
Human (*Homo sapiens sapiens*)	116 (although this is probably closer to 125)

Why are nine-banded armadillos so amazing?

Nine-banded armadillos—found in the U.S. and Central and South America—are not well known to most people, but they have fascinating features for a mammal. For example, they are always born as same-sex identical quadruplets, and hungry armadillos can eat up to 40,000 ants at a single "meal." They are also excellent in the water, holding their breath for up to ten minutes by inhaling air into their lungs, stomach, and intestines, all of which make them buoyant, too. They also can feel by walking along the bottom of a river or shallow lake—all by letting their breath out.

Animal (Latin name)	Maximum Life Span (in years)
Deep-sea clam (*Tindaria callistiformis*)	c. 100
Killer whale (*Orcinus orca*)	c. 90
European eel (*Anguilla anguilla*)	88
Lake sturgeon (*Acipenser fulvescens*)	82
Freshwater mussel (*Margaritana margaritifera*)	80 to 70
Asiatic elephant (*Elephas maximus*)	78
Andean condor (*Vultur gryphus*)	72+
Whale shark (*Rhiniodon typus*)	c. 70
African elephant (*Loxodonta africana*)	c. 70
Great eagle-owl (*Bubo bubo*)	68+
American alligator (*Alligator mississipiensis*)	66
Ostrich (*Struthio camelus*)	62.5
Horse (*Equus caballus*)	62
Orangutan (*Pongo pygmaeus*)	c. 59
Hippopotamus (*Hippopotamus amphibious*)	54.5
Chimpanzee (*Pan troglodytes*)	51
Gorilla (*Gorilla gorilla*)	50+
Domestic goose (*Anser a. domesticus*)	49.75
European brown bear (*Ursus arctos arctos*)	47
Blue whale (*Balaenoptera musculus*)	c. 45
Goldfish (*Carassius auratus*)	41
Common toad (*Bufo bufo*)	40
Roundworm (*Tylenchus polyhyprus*)	39
Giraffe (*Giraffa camelopardalis*)	36.25
Domestic cat (*Felis catus*)	34
Canary (*Serinus caneria*)	34
American bison (*Bison bison*)	33
Bobcat (*Felis rufus*)	32.3
Sperm whale (*Physeter macrocephalus*)	32+
American manatee (*Trichechus manatus*)	30
Domestic dog (*Canis familiaris*)	29.5
Lion (*Panthera leo*)	c. 29

Animal (Latin name)	Maximum Life Span (in years)
Theraphosid spider (*Mygalomorphae*)	c. 28
Tiger (*Panthera tigris*)	26.25
Giant panda (*Ailuropoda melanoleuca*)	26
American badger (*Taxidea taxus*)	26
Common wombat (*Vombatus ursinus*)	26
Bottle-nosed dolphin (*Tursiops truncates*)	25
Domestic chicken (*Gallus g. domesticus*)	25
Gray squirrel (*Sciurus carolinensis*)	23.5
Aardvark (*Orycteropus afer*)	23
Coyote (*Canis latrans*)	21+
Domestic goat (*Capra hircus domesticus*)	20.75
Queen ant (*Myrmecina graminicola*)	18+
Common rabbit (*Oryctolagus cuniculus*)	18+
Walrus (*Odobenus rosmarus*)	16.75
Domestic turkey (*Melagris gallapave domesticus*)	16
American beaver (*Castor Canadensis*)	15+
Land snail (*Helix spiriplana*)	15
Guinea pig (*Cavia porcellus*)	14.8
Hedgehog (*Erinaceus europaeus*)	14
Golden hamster (*Mesocricetus auratus*)	10
Millipede (*Cylindroiulus landinensis*)	7
House mouse (*Mus musculus*)	6
Common octopus (*Octopus vulgaris*)	2 to 3
Monarch butterfly (*Danaus plexippus*)	1.13
Bedbug (*Cimex lectularius*)	0.5 or 182 days
Black widow spider (*Latrodectus mactans*)	0.27 or 100 days
Common housefly (*Musca domesticus*)	0.04 or 17 days

PETS

What are the different classifications of dogs?

Dogs are divided into groups according to the purpose for which they have been bred.

Group	Purpose	Representative breeds
Sporting dogs	Retrieving game birds and water fowl	Cocker spaniel, English setter, English springer spaniel, golden retriever, Irish setter, Labrador retriever, pointer.
Hounds	Hunting	Basenji, beagle, dachshund, foxhound, greyhound, saluki, Rhodesian ridgeback.

Terriers	Hunting small animals such as rats and foxes	Airedale terrier, Bedlington terrier, bull terrier, fox terrier, miniature schnauzer, Scottish terrier, Skye terrier, West Highland white terrier.
Toy dogs	Small companions or lap dogs	Chihuahua, Maltese, Pekingese, Pomeranian, pug, Shih Tzu, Yorkshire terrier.
Herding dogs	Protect sheep and other livestock	Australian cattle dog, bouviers des Flandres, collie, German shepherd, Hungarian puli, Old English sheepdog, Welsh corgi.
Working dogs	Herding, rescue, and sled dogs	Alaskan malamute, boxer, Doberman pinscher, great Dane, mastiff, St. Bernard, Siberian husky.
Non-sporting dogs	No specific purpose, not toys	Boston terrier, bulldog, Dalmatian, Japanese akita, keeshond, Lhasa apso, poodle.

What is the oldest breed of dog?

Dogs are the oldest domestic animal, originating 12,000 to 14,000 years ago. They are believed to be descendants of wild canines, most likely wolves, which began to frequent human settlements where food was more readily available. The more aggressive canines were probably driven off or killed, while the less dangerous ones were kept to guard, hunt, and later herd other domesticated animals, such as sheep. Attempts at selectively breeding desirable traits likely began soon after.

The oldest purebred dog is believed to be the Saluki. Sumerian rock carvings in Mesopotamia that date to about 7000 b.c.e. depict dogs bearing a striking resemblance to the Saluki. The dogs are 23 to 28 inches (58 to 71 centimeters) tall with a long, narrow head. The coat is smooth and silky and can be white, cream, fawn, gold, red, grizzle (bluish-gray) and tan, black and tan, or tricolor (white, black, and tan). The tail is long and feathered. The Saluki has remarkable sight and tremendous speed, which makes it an excellent hunter.

The oldest American purebred dog is the American Foxhound. It descends from a pack of foxhounds belonging to an Englishman named Robert Brooke who settled in Maryland in 1650. These dogs were crossed with other strains imported from England, Ireland, and France to develop the American Foxhound. This dog stands 22 to 25 inches (56 to 63.5 centimeters) tall. It has a long, slightly domed head, with a straight, squared-out muzzle. The coat is of medium length and can be any color. They are used primarily for hunting.

Which breeds of dogs are best for families with young children?

Research has shown that golden retriever, Labrador retriever, beagle, collie, bichon frise, cairn terrier, pug, coonhound, boxer, basset hound or mixes of these breeds are best for families with young children.

Wolves, like this red wolf, are believed to be the ancestors of all domestic dog breeds.

Which dogs are the easiest to train?

In a study of 56 popular dog breeds the top breeds to train were Shetland sheepdogs, Shih Tzus, miniature toy and standard poodles, Bichons Frises, English Springer Spaniels and Welsh Corgis.

Why do dogs hear more than humans?

A dog's ears are highly mobile, allowing it to scan its environment for sounds. The ears capture the sounds and funnel them down to the eardrum. Dogs can hear sounds from four times farther away than humans.

Why do dogs howl at sirens?

The high pitch of a siren is very similar to the pitch of a dog's howl. A dog's howl is a way of communicating with other dogs—either to indicate location or to define territory. When a dog responds to an ambulance or fire engine siren, he is "returning the call of the wild."

What breeds of dogs do not shed?

Poodles, Kerry blue terriers, and schnauzers do not shed.

Which breed is known as the wrinkled dog?

The shar-pei, or Chinese fighting dog, is covered with folds of loose skin. It stands 18 to 20 inches (46 to 51 centimeters) tall and weighs up to 50 pounds (22.5 kilograms). Its solid-colored coat can be black, red, fawn, or cream. The dog originated in Tibet or the northern provinces of China some 2,000 years ago. The People's Republic of China put such a high tax on shar-peis, however, that few people could afford to keep them, and the dog was in danger of extinction. But a few specimens were smuggled out of China, and the breed has made a comeback in the United States, Canada, and the United Kingdom. Although bred as a fighting dog, the shar-pei is generally an amiable companion.

Which breed is known as the voiceless dog?

The basenji dog does not bark. When happy, it will make an appealing sound described as something between a chortle and a yodel. It also snarls and growls on occasion. One of the oldest breeds of dogs, and originating in central Africa, the basenji was often given as a present to the pharaohs of ancient Egypt. Following the decline of the Egyptian civilization, the basenji was still valued in central Africa for its hunting prowess and its silence. The dog was rediscovered by English explorers in the 19th century, although it was not widely bred until the 1940s.

The basenji is a small, lightly built dog with a flat skull and a long, rounded muzzle. It measures 16 to 17 inches (40 to 43 centimeters) in height at the shoulder and weighs 22 to 24 pounds (10 to 11 kilograms). The coat is short and silky in texture. The feet, chest, and tail tip are white; the rest of the coat is chestnut red, black, or black and tan.

What food odors do dogs like best?

In a study of different foods, researchers found that liver and chicken ranked higher than everything else, including hamburgers, fish, vegetables, and fresh fruit.

What is the rarest breed of dog?

The Tahltan bear dog, of which only a few remain, is thought to be the rarest dog. In danger of extinction, this breed was once used by the Tahltan Indians of western Canada to hunt bear, lynx, and porcupine.

What was the contribution to medical science of a dog named Marjorie?

Marjorie was a diabetic black-and-white mongrel that was the first creature to be kept alive by insulin, a substance that controls the level of sugar in the blood.

Do dogs and cats have good memories?

Dogs do have long-term memories, especially for those whom they love. Cats have a memory for things that are important to their lives. Some cats seem to have extraordinary "mem-

How is the age of a dog or cat computed in human years?

When a cat is one year old, it is about 20 years old in human years. Each additional year is multiplied by four. Another source counts the age of a cat slightly differently. At age one, a cat's age equals 16 human years. At age two, a cat's age is 24 human years. Each additional year is multiplied by four.

When a dog is one year old, it is about 15 years old in human years. At age two it is about 24; after age two, each additional year is multiplied by four.

ories" for finding places. Taken away from their homes, they seem able to remember where they live. The key to this "homing" ability could be a built-in celestial navigation, similar to that used by birds, or the cats' navigational ability could be attributed to the cats' sensitivity to Earth's magnetic fields. When magnets are attached to cats, their normal navigational skills are disrupted.

What is the original breed of domestic cat in the United States?

The American shorthair is believed by some naturalists to be the original domestic cat in America. It is descended from cats brought to the New World from Europe by the early settlers. The cats readily adapted to their new environment. Selective breeding to enhance the best traits began early in the 20th century.

The American shorthair is a very athletic cat with a lithe, powerful body, excellent for stalking and killing prey. Its legs are long, heavy, and muscular, ideal for leaping and for coping with all kinds of terrain. The fur, in a wide variety of color and coat patterns, is thick enough to protect the animal from moisture and cold, but short enough to resist matting and snagging.

Although this cat makes an excellent house pet and companion, it remains very self-sufficient. Its hunting instinct is so strong that it exercises the skill even when well-provided with food. The American shorthair is the only true "working cat" in the United States.

What controls the formation of the color points in a Siamese cat?

The color points are due to the presence of a recessive gene, which operates at cooler temperatures, limiting the color to well-defined areas—the mask, ears, tail, lower legs, and paws—the places at the far reaches of the cardiovascular system of the cat.

There are four classic varieties of Siamese cats. Seal-points have a pale fawn to cream colored coat with seal-brown markings. Blue-points are bluish-white with slate blue markings. Chocolate-points are ivory colored with milk-chocolate brown colored markings. Lilac-points have a white coat and pinkish-gray markings. There are also some newer varieties with red, cream, and tabby points.

The Siamese originated in Thailand (once called Siam) and arrived in England in the 1880s. They are medium-sized and have long, slender, lithe bodies, with long heads and long, tapering tails. Extroverted and affectionate, Siamese are known for their loud, distinctive voices, which are impossible to ignore.

How can pets be treated to remove skunk odor?

From a pet store, purchase one of the products specifically designed to counteract skunk odor. Most of these are of the enzyme or bacterial enzyme variety and can be used without washing the pet first. A dog may also be given a bath with tomato juice, diluted vinegar, or neuthroleum-alpha, or you could try mint mouthwash, aftershave, or soap and water.

Why do cats' eyes shine in the dark?

A cat's eyes contain a special light-conserving mechanism called the *tapetum lucidum*, which reflects any light not absorbed as it passes through the retina of each eye. The retina gets a second chance (so to speak) to receive the light, aiding the cat's vision even more. In dim light, when the pupils of the cat's eyes are opened the widest, this glowing or shining effect occurs when light hits them at certain angles. The *tapetum lucidum*, located behind the retina, is a membrane composed of 15 layers of special, glittering cells that all together act as a mirror. The color of the glow is usually greenish or golden, but the eyes of the Siamese cat reflect a luminous ruby red.

Which plants are poisonous to cats?

Certain common houseplants are poisonous to cats, which should not be allowed to eat the following:

Caladium (Elephant's ears)
Dieffenbachia (Dumb cane)
Euphorbia pulcherrima (Poinsettia)
Hedera (True ivy)
Mistletoe
Oleander
Philodendron
Prunus laurocerasus (Common or cherry laurel)
Rhododendron (Azalea)
Solanum capiscastrum (Winter or False Jerusalem cherry)

Why and how do cats purr?

Experts cannot agree on how or why cats purr, or on where the sound originates. Some think that the purr is produced by the vibration of blood in a large vein in the chest cavity. Where the vein passes through the diaphragm, the muscles around the vein contract, nipping the blood flow and setting up oscillations. These sounds are magnified by the air in the bronchial tubes and the windpipe. Others think that purring is the vibrations of membranes, called false vocal cords, located near the vocal cords. No one knows for sure why a cat purrs, but many people interpret the sound as one of contentment.

Why do cats have whiskers?

The function of a cat's whiskers is not fully understood. They are thought to have something to do with the sense of touch. Removing them can disturb a cat for some time. Some people believe that the whiskers act as antennae in the dark, enabling the cat to identify things it cannot see. The whiskers may help the cat to pinpoint the direction from which an odor is coming. In addition, the cat is thought to point some of its whiskers downwards to guide it when jumping or running over uneven terrain at night.

Which types of birds make the best pets?

There are several birds that make good house pets and have a reasonable life expectancy:

Bird	Life expectancy in years	Considerations
Finch	2-3	Easy care
Canary	8-10	Easy care; males sing
Budgerigar (parakeet)	8-15	Easy care
Cockatiel	15-20	Easy care; easy to train
Lovebird	15-20	Cute, but not easy to care for or train
Amazon parrot	50-60	Good talkers, but can be screamers
African grey parrot	50-60	Talkers; never scream

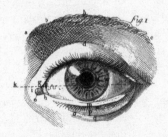

THE HUMAN BODY

BIOLOGICAL COMPOUNDS
AND THE HUMAN BODY

What are the major bioorganic molecules in humans?

The major bioorganic molecules are carbohydrates, lipids, proteins, and nucleic acids. These molecules are characteristic of life and have basic roles such as storing and producing energy, providing structural materials, or storing hereditary information.

What are carbohydrates?

Carbohydrates are organic compounds composed of carbon, hydrogen, and oxygen. The general chemical formula for carbohydrates is CH_2O, indicating there is twice as much hydrogen as oxygen. Carbohydrates are the major source of energy for cells and cellular activities.

How are carbohydrates classified?

Carbohydrates are classified in several ways. Monosaccharides (single unit sugars) are grouped by the number of carbon molecules they contain: triose has three, pentose has five, and hexose has six. Carbohydrates are also classified by their overall length (monosaccharide, disaccharide, and polysaccharide) or function. Examples of functional definitions are storage polysaccharides (glycogen and starch), which store energy, and structural polysaccharides (cellulose and chitin).

What are some of the uses of carbohydrates by the body?

Carbohydrates are mainly used as an energy source by the body, with the various carbohydrates having different functions. The following chart identifies some common carbohydrates and their uses in the human body:

Carbohydrate Name	Type	Use by the Body
Deoxyribose	Monosaccharide	DNA; constituent of hereditary material
Fructose	Monosaccharide	Important in cellular metabolism of carbohydrates
Galactose	Monosaccharide	Found in brain and nerve tissue
Glucose	Monosaccharide	Main energy source for the body
Ribose	Monosaccharide	Constituent of RNA
Lactose	Disaccharide	Milk sugar; aids the absorption of calcium
Sucrose	Disaccharide	Produces glucose and fructose upon hydrolysis
Cellulose	Polysaccharide	Not digestible by the body, but is an important fiber that provides bulk for the proper movement of food through the intestines
Glycogen	Polysaccharide	Stored in the liver and muscles until needed as energy source and is then converted to glucose
Heparin	Polysaccharide	Prevents excessive blood clotting
Starch	Polysaccharide	Chief food carbohydrate in human nutrition

What are lipids?

Lipids are organic compounds composed mainly of carbon, hydrogen, and oxygen, but they also may contain other elements, such as phosphorus and nitrogen. Lipids usually have more than twice as many hydrogen atoms as oxygen atoms. They are insoluble in water but can be dissolved in certain organic solvents such as ether, alcohol, and chloroform. Lipids include fats, oils, phospholipids, steroids, and prostaglandins.

What is the difference between fats and lipids?

Fats are one category of lipids. Each fat molecule is comprised of a glycerol (alcohol) molecule and at least one fatty acid (a hydrocarbon chain with an acid group attached). Fats are energy-rich molecules important as a source of reserve food for the body. They are stored in the body in the form of triacylglycerols, also known as triglycerides. Fats also provide the body with insulation, protection, and cushioning (especially of the body's organs).

What is cholesterol?

Cholesterol belongs to a category of lipids known as steroids. Steroids have a unique chemical structure. They are built from four carbon-laden ring structures that are fused together. The human body uses cholesterol to maintain the strength and flexibility of cell membranes. Cholesterol is also the molecule from which steroid hormones and bile acids are built.

What is an enzyme?

An enzyme is a protein that acts as a biological catalyst. It decreases the amount of energy needed (activation energy) to start a metabolic reaction. Different enzymes work in different environments due to changes in temperature and acidity. For example, the amylase that is active in the mouth cannot function in the acidic environment of the stomach; pepsin, which breaks down proteins in the stomach, cannot function in the mouth. In fact, without enzymes, the stomach would not be able to obtain energy and nutrients from food.

What are some enzyme deficiencies in humans?

Lactose intolerance, a condition that results from the inability to digest lactose—the sugar present in milk—is one of the most common enzyme deficiencies. According to the National Institutes of Health, it is estimated that around 90 percent of adults of East Asian descent have lactose intolerance, and overall, about 65 percent of the human population has a reduced ability to digest lactose after infancy.

Another less common but more serious enzyme deficiency is glucose–6-phosphate dehydrogenase deficiency, which is linked to the bursting of red blood cells (hemolysis). This deficiency is found in more than two hundred million people, mainly in Mediterranean, West African, Middle Eastern, and Southeast Asian populations.

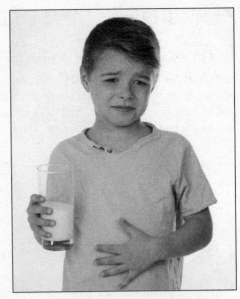

Lactose intolerance occurs when a person cannot digest the sugar lactose. Symptoms include cramping, gas, bloating, diarrhea, and sometimes vomiting.

What are proteins and what is their purpose?

Proteins are large, complex molecules composed of smaller structural subunits called amino acids. All proteins contain carbon, hydrogen, oxygen, and nitrogen, and sometimes sulfur, phosphorus, and iron. Human life could not exist without proteins.

The enzymes that are required for all metabolic reactions are proteins. These proteins also are important to structures like muscles, and they act as both transporters and signal receptors. The following lists the type of proteins and examples of their functions:

Type of Protein	Examples of Functions
Defensive	Antibodies that respond to invasion
Enzymatic	Increase the rate of reactions; build and break down molecules
Hormonal	Insulin and glucagon, which control blood sugar
Receptor	Cell surface molecules that cause cells to respond to signals
Storage	Store amino acids for use in metabolic processes
Structural	Major components of muscles, skin, hair
Transport	Hemoglobin carries oxygen from lungs to cells

BONE, MUSCLES, AND NERVES

How many bones are in the human body?

Babies are born with about 300 to 350 bones, but many of these fuse together between birth and maturity to produce an average adult total of 206. Bone counts vary according to the method used to count them, because a structure may be treated as either multiple bones or as a single bone with multiple parts.

Location of Bones	Number
Skull	22
Ears (pair)	6
Vertebrae	26
Sternum	3
Ribs	24
Throat	1
Pectoral girdle	4
Arms (pair)	60
Hip bones	2
Legs (pair)	58
TOTAL	206

What are the major types of bones?

There are four major types of bones: long bones, short bones, flat bones, and irregular bones. The name of each type of bone reflects the shape of the bone. Furthermore, the shape of the bone is indicative of its mechanical function. Bones that do not fall into any of these categories are sesamoid bones and accessory bones.

What are the characteristics of irregular bones?

Irregular bones have complex, irregular shapes and do not fit into any other category of bone. Many irregular bones are short, flat, notched, or ridged, with extensions that protrude from their many bone parts. Examples of irregular bones are the spinal vertebrae, many bones of the face and skull, and the hip bones.

What is unique about sesamoid bones?

Shaped similarly to sesame seeds, sesamoid bones develop inside tendons that pass over a long bone. They are most commonly found in the knees (the patella or kneecap is a sesamoid bone), hands, and feet. Sesamoid bones may form in 26 different locations in the body. However, the number of sesamoid bones varies from individual to individual.

Where are blood cells formed in the skeletal system?

Hematopoiesis (from the Greek *hemato*, meaning "blood" and *poiein*, meaning "to make"), or red blood formation, occurs in the red bone marrow in adults. Adult red marrow, found in the proximal epiphysis (the ends) of the femur and humerus, some short bones, and in the vertebrae, sternum, ribs, hip bones, and cranium, is the site of production of all red blood cells (erythrocytes), platelets, and certain white blood cells.

What are some specialized bone cells?

The four major types of specialized cells in bone are osteogenic cells, osteoblasts, osteocytes, and osteoclasts. The following defines each type:

Osteogenic cells: From the Greek osteo, meaning "bone," and *genes*, meaning "born," these are cells that are capable of becoming bone-forming cells (osteoblasts) or bone-destroying cells (osteoclasts).

Osteoblasts: From the Greek osteo and *blastos*, meaning "bud or growth," they are the cells that form and build bone. Osteoblasts secrete collagen and other organic components needed to build bone tissue. As they surround themselves with matrix materials, they become trapped in their secretions and become osteocytes.

Osteocytes: From the Greek *osteo* and *cyte*, meaning "cell," osteocytes are the main cells in mature bone tissue.

Osteoclasts: From the Greek *osteo* and *klastes*, meaning "break," these cells are multinuclear, huge cells that are usually found where bone is reabsorbed.

How does compact bone tissue differ from spongy bone tissue?

Bone tissue is classified as compact or spongy according to the size and distribution of the open spaces in the bone tissue. Compact bone tissue is hard or dense with few open spaces. Compact bone tissue provides protection and support. Most long bones consist of compact bone tissue. In contrast, spongy bone tissue is porous with many open spaces. Spongy bone tissue consists of an irregular latticework of thin needlelike threads of bone called trabeculae (from the Latin *trabs*, meaning "beam"). Most flat, short, and irregular-shaped bones are made up of spongy bone tissue.

How do bones grow?

Bones form and develop through a process called ossification. There are two types of ossification: intramembranous ossification and endochondral ossification. Intramembranous ossification is the formation of bone directly on or within the fibrous connective tissue. Examples of bone formed through intramembranous ossification are the flat bones of the skull, mandible (lower jaw), and clavicle (collarbone).

Endochondral ossification, from the Greek *endo*, meaning "within," and *khondros*, meaning "cartilage," is the transformation of the cartilage model into bone. Cartilage cells in the epiphyseal plate grow

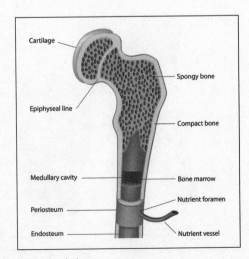

Anatomy of a bone

603

and move into the metaphysis where they are reabsorbed and replaced by bone tissue. Examples of bone formed through endochondral ossification are the long bones, such as the femur and humerus.

How serious is osteoporosis?

Osteoporosis (from the Greek *osteo*, meaning "bone," *por*, meaning "passageway," and *osis*, meaning "condition") is a condition that reduces bone mass because the rate of bone resorption is quicker than the rate of bone deposition. The bones become very thin and porous and are easily broken. Osteoporosis is most common in the elderly, who may experience a greater number of broken bones as a result of the mechanical stresses of daily living and not from accidents or other trauma. Generally, osteoporosis is more severe in women, since their bones are thinner and less massive than men's bones. In addition, estrogen helps to maintain bone mass, so the loss of estrogen in women after menopause contributes to more severe osteoporosis.

How does osteoporosis differ from osteomalacia?

In osteomalacia the bones are weakened and softened from a loss of calcium and phosphorous. The volume of the bone matrix does not change. In osteoporosis, the volume of the bone matrix is reduced, leaving holes in the bones.

What is a joint?

A joint is the place where two adjacent bones, adjacent cartilages, or adjacent bones and cartilages meet. Joints are also called articulations (from the Latin *articulus*, meaning "small joint"). Some joints are very flexible, allowing movement, while others are strong, providing protection of the internal tissues and organs, but do not permit movement.

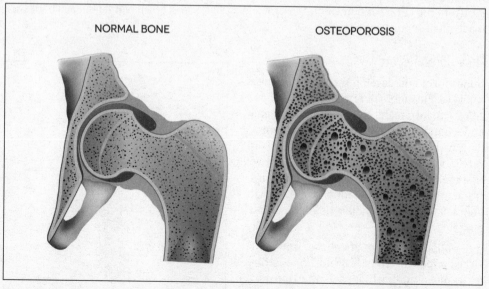

A normal bone versus one afflicted with osteoporosis in which the bone loses mass and becomes vulnerable to fracturing.

What are the structural classes of joints?

The two main criteria for the structural classification of joints are the presence or absence of a cavity known as the synovial cavity and the type of tissue that binds the bones together. The three types of structural categories are fibrous, cartilaginous, and synovial.

What are the functional classes of joints?

The functional classification of joints is determined by the degree and range of movement the joint allows. The three functional categories for joints are synarthrosis, amphiarthrosis,

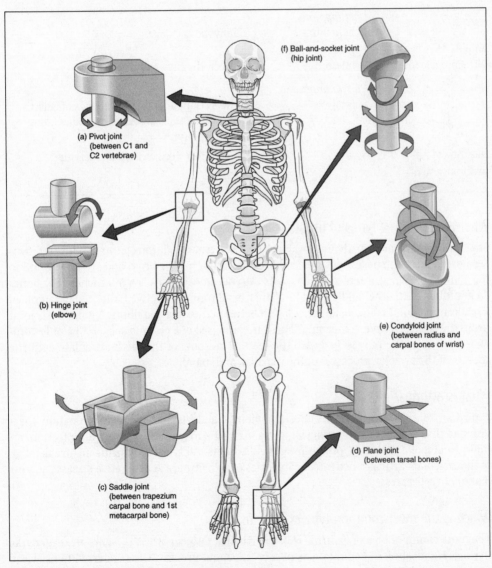

The six types of synovial joints, along with examples

and diarthrosis. A synarthrosis joint (from the Greek *syn*, meaning "together," and *arthrosis*, meaning "articulation") is immovable. An amphiarthrosis joint (from the Greek *amphi*, meaning "on both sides") is slightly movable. A diarthrosis joint (from the Greek *dia*, meaning "between") is a freely movable joint. The following shows the general classification of joints based on function:

Functional Category	Structural Category	Example
Synarthrosis (immovable joints)	*Fibrous* Suture	Between bones of adult skull
	Gomphosis	Between teeth and jaw
	Cartilaginous Synchondrosis	Epiphyseal cartilages
Amphiarthrosis (little movement)	*Fibrous* Syndesmosis	Between the tibia and fibula
	Cartilaginous Symphysis	Between right and left pubic bones of pelvis; and between adjacent vertebral bodies along vertebral column
Diarthrosis (free movement)	*Synovial*	Elbow, ankle, ribs, wrist, shoulder, hip

What are the three types of fibrous joints?

The fibrous joints are mostly immovable. The three types of fibrous joints are sutures, syndesmoses, and gomphoses. Sutures provide protection for the brain and are only found in the adult skull. They are immovable joints. A syndesmosis joint is a joint where the bones do not touch each other and are held together by fibrous connective tissue. One example of a syndesmosis joint is the distal articulation between the tibia and fibula. A gomphosis joint (from the Greek *gomphos*, meaning "bolt") is composed of a peg and socket. The only gomphosis joints in the human body are the teeth. The roots of the teeth articulate with the sockets of the alveolar processes of the maxillae and mandible.

What is arthritis?

Arthritis (from the Greek *arthro*, meaning "joint," and *itis*, meaning "inflammation") is a group of diseases that affects synovial joints. Arthritis may originate from an infection, an injury, metabolic problems, or autoimmune disorders. All types of arthritis involve damage to the articular cartilage. Two major categories of arthritis are degenerative diseases and inflammatory diseases.

Which is the most common type of arthritis?

The most common type of arthritis is osteoarthritis. Osteoarthritis is a chronic, degenerative disease most often beginning as part of the aging process. Often referred to as "wear and tear" arthritis because it is the result of life's everyday activities, it is a degradation of the

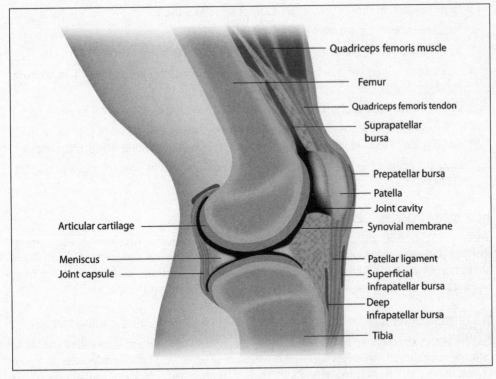

Quadriceps femoris muscle

Femur

Quadriceps femoris tendon

Suprapatellar bursa

Prepatellar bursa

Patella

Joint cavity

Articular cartilage

Synovial membrane

Meniscus

Joint capsule

Patellar ligament

Superficial infrapatellar bursa

Deep infrapatellar bursa

Tibia

Anatomy of the knee

articular cartilage that protects the bones as they move at a joint site. Osteoarthritis usually affects the larger, weight-bearing joints first, such as the hips, knees, and lumbar region of the vertebral column.

How does rheumatoid arthritis differ from osteoarthritis?

Rheumatoid arthritis is an inflammatory disease mainly characterized by inflammation of the synovial membrane of the joints. The disease may begin with general symptoms of malaise, such as fatigue, low-grade fever, and anemia, before affecting the joints. Unlike osteoarthritis, rheumatoid arthritis usually affects the small joints first, such as those in the fingers, hands, and feet. In the first stage of the disease there is swelling of the synovial lining, causing pain, warmth, stiffness, redness, and swelling around the joint. This is followed by the rapid division and growth of cells, or pannus, which causes the synovium to thicken. In the next stage of the disease, the inflamed cells release enzymes that may digest bone and cartilage, often causing the involved joint to lose its shape and alignment and leading to more pain and loss of movement. This condition is known as fibrous ankylosis (from the Greek *ankulos*, meaning "bent"). In the final stage of the disease, the fibrous tissue may become calcified and form a solid fusion of bone, making the joint completely nonfunctional (bony ankylosis).

What are the functions of the muscular system?

The major functions of the muscular system are as follows:

607

1. Body movement due to the contraction of skeletal muscles

2. Maintenance of posture also due to skeletal muscles

3. Respiration due to movements of the muscles of the thorax

4. Production of body heat, which is necessary for the maintenance of body temperature, as a byproduct of muscle contraction

5. Communication, such as speaking and writing, which involve skeletal muscles

6. Constriction of organs and vessels, especially smoother muscles that can move solids and liquids in the digestive tract and other secretions, including urine, from organs

7. Heartbeat caused by the contraction of cardiac muscle that propels blood to all parts of the body

How many muscles are in the human body?

There are about 650 muscles in the body, although some authorities believe there are as many as 850 muscles. No exact figure is available because experts disagree about which are separate muscles and which ones branch off larger ones. Also, there is some variability from one person to another, though the general musculature remains the same.

What is the difference between voluntary and involuntary muscle movements?

Muscle movements that an individual consciously controls are referred to as voluntary. Some examples of voluntary muscle movements would be when an individual walks or picks up an object. Involuntary muscle movements are those that occur without an individual's conscious control. An example of involuntary muscle movement is the pumping action of the heart.

What are the functions of the nervous system?

The nervous system is one of the major regulatory systems of the body maintaining homeostasis. Its functions are to: 1) monitor the body's internal and external environments; 2) integrate sensory information; and 3) direct or coordinate the responses of other organ systems to the sensory input.

What are the divisions of the autonomic nervous system?

The autonomic nervous system is divided into three parts: 1) the sympathetic nervous system; 2) the parasympathetic nervous system; and 3) the enteric nervous system. The parasympathetic and sympathetic nervous systems usually have opposing actions. For example, while the sympathetic nervous system controls the "fight or flight" responses, which increase the heart rate under stress, the parasympathetic nervous system will slow the heart rate. The enteric nervous system consists of nerve cells in the gastrointestinal tract.

What is a synapse?

A synapse is the location of intercellular communication. Every synapse has components associated with two cells: the presynaptic neuron and the postsynaptic neuron. The presynaptic neuron is the cell that sends the message, while the postsynaptic neuron is the cell that receives the message.

How large is the brain?

The brain weighs about 3 pounds (1.4 kilograms). The average brain has a volume of 71 cubic inches (1,200 cubic centimeters). In general, the brain of males averages about 10 percent larger than the brain of females due to overall differences in average body size. The brain contains approximately 100 billion neurons and 1 trillion neuroglia (or glial, types of cells that support neurons).

How is the weight of the brain reduced in cerebrospinal fluid?

Since the brain is buoyant and floats in the cerebrospinal fluid, its weight of approximately 3 pounds (1.4 kilograms) is reduced to about 14 percent of its unsupported weight, less than 2 ounces (50 grams).

Is brain size an indication of intelligence?

There is no correlation between brain size and intelligence. Individuals with the smallest brains (as small as 46 cubic inches [750 cubic centimeters]) and the largest brains (as large as 128 cubic inches [2,100 cubic centimeters]) have the same functional intelligence.

What are the major divisions of the brain and their function?

The brain has four major divisions: 1) brainstem, including the medulla oblongata, pons, and midbrain; 2) cerebellum; 3) cerebrum; and 4) diencephalon. The diencephalon is further divided into the thalamus, hypothalamus, epithalamus, and ventral thalamus or subthalamus. Each area of the brain has a specific function, as seen in the table below:

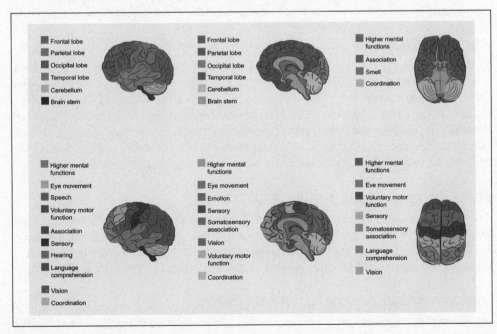

Areas of the brain and their functions

Brain Area	General Functions
Brainstem	
Medulla oblongata	Relays messages between spinal cord and brain and to cerebrum; center for control and regulation of cardiac, respiratory, and digestive activities
Pons	Relays information from medulla and other areas of the brain; controls certain respiratory functions
Midbrain	Involved with the processing of visual information, including visual reflexes, movement of eyes, focusing of lens, and dilation of pupils
Cerebellum	Processing center involved with coordination of movements, balance and equilibrium, and posture; processes sensory information used by motor systems
Cerebrum	Center for conscious thought processes and intellectual functions, memory, sensory perception, and emotions
Diencephalon	
Thalamus	Relay and processing center for sensory information
Hypothalamus	Regulates body temperature, water balance, sleep-wake cycles, appetite, emotions, and hormone production

What is intelligence?

There is no clear, standard definition of intelligence. Psychologists identify intelligence as an individual's adaptation to the environment as fundamental to understanding what intelligence is and what it does. Most researchers agree that intelligence is a person's ability to comprehend his or her environment, evaluate it rationally, and form appropriate responses.

How is IQ calculated?

IQ, or the intelligence quotient, was originally computed as the ratio of a person's mental age to his or her chronological age, multiplied by 100. Following this method, a child of ten years old who performed on the test at the level of an average twelve year old (mental age of twelve), was assigned an IQ of 12/10 x 100 = 120. More recently, the concept of "mental age" has fallen into disrepute and IQ is computed on the basis of the statistical percentage of people who are expected to have a certain IQ. An IQ of 100 is considered average. An IQ of 70 or below indicates mental retardation, and an IQ of 130 or above indicates gifted abilities.

What is the size and location of the heart?

Heart size varies with body size. The average adult's heart is about 5.5 inches (14 centimeters) long and 3.5 inches (9 centimeters) wide, or approximately the size of one's fist. The heart is located just above the diaphragm, between the right and left lungs. One-third of the heart is located on the right size of the chest, while two-thirds is located on the left side of the chest.

How much pressure does the human heart create?

The human heart creates enough pressure when it pumps blood out of the body to squirt blood about thirty feet (ten meters).

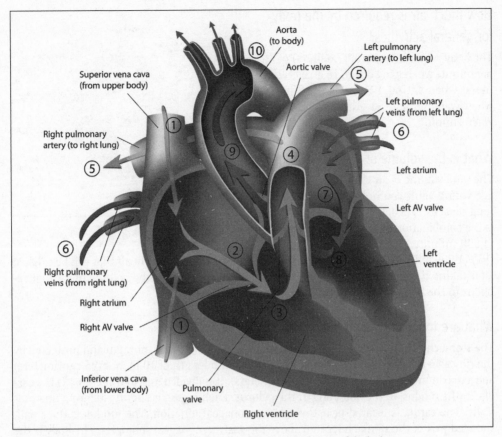

Aorta
(to body)

⑩

Aortic valve

Superior vena cava
(from upper body)

Left pulmonary
artery (to left lung)

⑤

①

Left pulmonary
veins (from left lung)

⑥

Right pulmonary
artery (to right lung)

⑨

④

⑤

Left atrium

⑦

Left AV valve

Right pulmonary
veins (from right lung)

⑥

②

⑧

Left
ventricle

Right atrium

③

Right AV valve

①

Inferior vena cava
(from lower body)

Pulmonary
valve

Right ventricle

The path of blood from the body, through the heart, and back out to the rest of the body

What are the various chambers of the heart?

The heart is divided into two upper chambers called atria (singular, atrium) and two lower chambers called ventricles. The atria are receiving chambers, where blood is delivered via large vessels, and the ventricles are pumping chambers, where blood is pumped out of the heart via large arteries.

How fast and how often does the human heart beat?

The human heart beats 130 times per minute in infants and slows to 90 times per minute in a ten-year-old. By the time adulthood is reached, the heart slows to an average of 70 times per minute in men and 78 times per minute in women. The heart will beat approximately 40 million times in one year, or about 3 billion times in an average lifetime.

What is a normal respiratory rate?

The average person breathes about 16 times each minute and takes in one pint of air (0.5 liters) with each breath. In an average lifetime, we breathe over 75 million gallons (2.85 trillion liters) of air.

611

How much air is required by the body for general activities?

The body requires 8 quarts (7.6 liters) of air per minute when lying down, 16 quarts (15.2 liters) when sitting, 24 quarts (22.8 liters) when walking, and 50 quarts (47.5 liters) when running.

What is the volume of air in the lungs?

The total volume of air the lungs of an average young adult can hold, also called total lung capacity (TLC), is 5,800 milliliters. This is the combination of the vital capacity (VC) (4,600 milliliters) and the residual volume (RV) (1,200 milliliters). The vital capacity is the maximum volume of air that can be exhaled after taking the deepest breath possible. The residual volume is the volume of air that remains in the lungs even after maximal expiration.

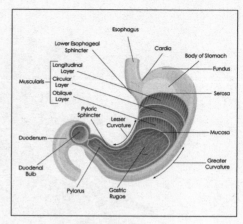

Anatomy of the stomach

What are the four regions of the stomach?

The stomach, which is located directly under the dome of the diaphragm and protected by the rib cage, is a J-shaped organ that has a maximum length of 10 inches (25 centimeters) and a maximum width of 6 inches (15 centimeters). It is divided into four regions: 1) the cardia, 2) the fundus, 3) the body, and 4) the pylorus. Each region is slightly different anatomically. The cardia is located near the gastroesophageal junction. The fundus is the small, rounded part of the stomach located above the gastroesophageal sphincter. The body is the main region of the stomach. It is the area between the fundus and the "J" shape of the stomach. Most food storage and mixing occur in the body. The pylorus is the bottom curve of the "J" shape. It is located at the junction between the stomach and the small intestine.

What are the major functions of the lower gastrointestinal tract?

The lower gastrointestinal tract, consisting of the small intestine and large intestine, is the main location where nutrient processing and absorption occurs. In general, a human's small intestine is about 22 feet (7 meters) long. The large intestine is about 5 feet (1.5 meters) long.

What are the functions of the large intestine?

The large intestine is mostly a storage site for undigested materials until they are eliminated from the body via defecation. Although digestion is complete by the time the chyme enters the large intestine and most absorption has occurred in the small intestine, water and electrolytes are still absorbed through the large intestine.

What is a unique feature of the liver?

The liver is the only organ that can regenerate itself. As much as 75 percent of the liver may be removed, and it will still grow back to the same shape and form within a few weeks.

What are the digestive functions of the liver?

The liver has more than five hundred vital functions. Its major function as a digestive organ is to produce and secrete bile. Other functions of the liver include separating and filtering waste products from nutrients, storing glucose, and producing many chemical substances, such as cholesterol and albumin.

What are the parts of the kidney?

The kidney has two layers: the outer layer, called the cortex, which is reddish brown and granular, and the inner zone, the medulla, which is darker and reddish brown in color. The medulla is subdivided into six to eighteen cone-shaped sections called the pyramids. The

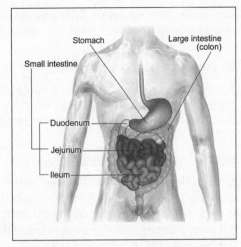

The small intestine is divided into the duodenum, jejunum, and ileum.

pyramids are inverted so that each base faces the cortex and the tops project toward the center of the kidney. Separating the pyramids are bands of tissue called renal columns. A renal lobe consists of a renal pyramid and its surrounding tissue.

What is a nephron and how many are found in the average kidney?

A nephron is the functional working unit of the kidney. Blood is filtered in the nephrons and toxic wastes are removed, while water and necessary nutrients are reabsorbed into the system. Each nephron produces a minute amount of urine, which then trickles into the renal pelvis. From there it goes into the ureter and eventually collects in the bladder. There are approximately one million nephrons in each kidney.

What are the functions of the endocrine system?

The endocrine system, together with the nervous system, controls and coordinates the functions of all of the human body systems. The endocrine system helps to maintain homeostasis and metabolic functions, allows the body to react to stress, and regulates growth and development, including sexual development.

What are hormones?

Hormones are chemical messengers that are secreted by the endocrine glands into the blood. Hormones are transported via the bloodstream to reach specific cells, called

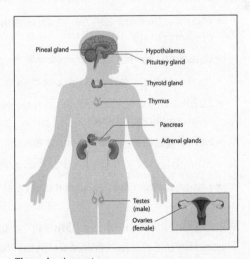

The endocrine system.

613

target cells, in other tissues. They produce a specific effect on the activity of cells that are remotely located from their point of origin.

Where is the pituitary gland located?

The pituitary gland is located at the base of the brain directly below the hypothalamus in the sella turcica ("Turkish saddle"), a depression in the sphenoid bone. It is protected on three sides by the bones of the skull and on the top by a tough membrane called the diaphragma sellae.

How many different hormones are secreted by the pituitary gland?

The pituitary gland is often called the "master gland," because it is responsible for the release of so many hormones. In all, there are nine different peptide hormones released by the pituitary gland. Seven are produced by the anterior pituitary gland and two are secreted by the posterior pituitary gland. The hormones of the anterior pituitary gland are thyroid-stimulating hormone (TSH), adrenocorticotropic hormone (ACTH), follicle-stimulating hormone (FSH), luteinizing hormone (LH), prolactin (PRL), growth hormone (GH), and melanocyte-stimulating hormone (MSH). The hormones of the posterior pituitary gland are antidiuretic hormone (ADH) and oxytocin.

What are the physical characteristics of the thyroid gland?

The thyroid gland is located in the neck, anterior to the trachea, just below the larynx (the voice box). It has two lobes connected by a slender bridge of tissue called the isthmus. The average weight of the thyroid gland is 1.2 ounces (34 grams). An extensive, complex blood supply gives the thyroid a deep red color.

What are the functions of the thyroid hormones?

Thyroid hormones affect almost every cell in the body. Some important effects of thyroid hormones on various cells and organ systems are as follows:

- Increases body metabolism by increasing the rate at which cells use oxygen and food to produce energy
- Causes the cardiovascular system to be more sensitive to sympathetic nervous activity
- Increases heart rate and force of contraction of heart muscle
- Maintains normal sensitivity of respiratory centers to changes in oxygen and carbon dioxide concentrations
- Stimulates the formation of red blood cells to enhance oxygen delivery
- Stimulates the activity of other endocrine tissues
- Ensures proper skeletal development in children

What is the function of the parathyroid glands?

The parathyroid glands secrete parathyroid hormone (PTH). The main function of PTH is to regulate the levels of calcium and phosphate in the blood.

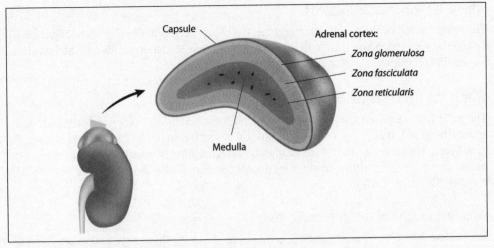

The adrenal glands are located atop the kidneys.

How many different types of hormones are secreted by the adrenal cortex?

The adrenal cortex secretes more than two dozen different steroid hormones called the adrenocortical steroids, or simply corticosteroids. The adrenal cortex is divided into three major zones or regions, each of which secretes a different type of corticosteroid. The outer region is the zona glomerulosa, which produces mineralocorticoids. The middle zone is the zona fasciculata, which accounts for the bulk of the cortical volume and produces glucocorticoids. The innermost, and smallest region, is the zona reticularis, which produces small quantities of the sex hormones.

What are the functions of the corticosteroids?

The corticosteroids are vital for life and well-being. Each of the corticosteroids serves a unique purpose. The following lists the corticosteroids and their functions:

Hormone	Target	Effects
Mineralocorticoids	Kidneys	Increases reabsorption of sodium ions and water from the urine; stimulates loss of potassium ions through excretion of urine
Glucocorticoids	Most cells	Releases amino acids from skeletal muscles, lipids from adipose tissues; promotes liver glycogen and glucose formation; promotes peripheral utilization of lipids; anti-inflammatory effects
Androgens		Promotes growth of pubic hair in boys and girls; in adult women, promotes muscle mass, blood cell formation, and supports the libido; in adult men, adrenal androgens are less significant because androgens are released primarily from the gonads

615

Where is the pancreas located?

The pancreas (from the Greek, meaning "all flesh") is located in the abdominopelvic cavity between the stomach and the small intestine. It is an elongated organ about 6 inches (12 to 15 centimeters) long.

Why is the pancreas called a mixed gland?

The pancreas is a mixed gland because it has both endocrine and exocrine functions. As an endocrine gland, it secretes hormones into the bloodstream. Only 1 percent of the weight of the pancreas serves as an endocrine gland. The remaining 99 percent of the gland has exocrine functions. (For more on the function of the pancreas as an exocrine gland, see the chapter "Digestive System.")

Who first described the pancreatic islets?

German pathologist and biologist Paul Langerhans (1847–1888) was the first to provide a detailed description of microscopic pancreatic structures in the late 1860s. He noticed unique polygonal cells in the pancreas. It was not until 1893 that French pathologist Gustave E. Laguesse (1861–1927) discovered that the polygon-shaped cells were the endocrine cells of the pancreas that secreted insulin.

What is the function of insulin?

Insulin is secreted when blood glucose levels rise above normal values. One of the most important effects of insulin is to facilitate the transport of glucose across plasma membranes,

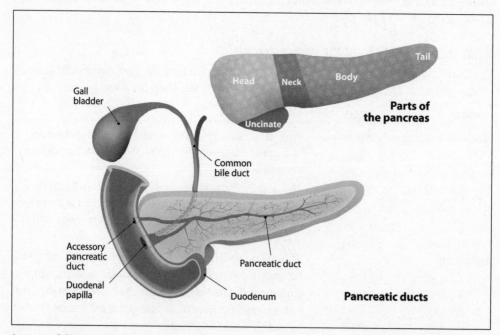

allowing the diffusion of glucose from blood into most body cells. It also stimulates the production of glycogen from glucose. The glucose is then stored in the liver to be released when blood glucose levels drop.

What is the difference between Type I and Type II diabetes?

Diabetes mellitus is a hormonal disease that occurs when the body's cells are unable to absorb glucose from the blood. Type I is insulin-dependent diabetes mellitus (IDDM), and Type II is noninsulin-dependent diabetes mellitus (NIDDM). Insulin is completely deficient in Type I diabetes. In Type II diabetes, insulin secretion may be normal, but the target cells for insulin are less responsive than normal.

What is the pineal gland?

The pineal gland (from the Latin *pinea*, meaning "pinecone") is a small gland located in the midbrain at the posterior end of the third ventricle. The physiological functions of the pineal are unclear. It secretes the hormone melatonin, which appears to be associated with circadian rhythms and setting the biological clock.

In Type I diabetes the pancreas does not make enough insulin, while in Type II it does, but the target cells can't receive the insulin as they are supposed to.

Which reproductive organs secrete hormones?

The gonads (from the Greek *gonos*, meaning "offspring") release hormones in both males and females. In males, the testes secrete hormones, while in females the ovaries are responsible for secreting hormones.

What are the functions of the sex hormones?

Testosterone is stimulated by luteinizing hormone (LH) from the pituitary gland. It regulates the production of sperm, as well as the growth and maintenance of the male sex organs. Testosterone also stimulates the development of the male secondary sex characteristics, including growth of facial and pubic hair. It causes the deepening of the male voice by enlarging the larynx.

The estrogens are stimulated by follicle-stimulating hormone (FSH) in the pituitary. They help regulate the menstrual cycle and the development of the mammary glands and female secondary sex characteristics. Luteinizing hormone (LH) stimulates the secretion of progestins. Progesterone prepares the uterus for the arrival of a developing embryo in case fertilization occurs. It also accelerates the movement of an embryo to the uterus. Relaxin helps enlarge and soften the cervix and birth canal at the time of delivery. It causes the ligaments of the pubic symphysis to be more flexible at the time of delivery.

What are anabolic steroids?

Properly called anabolic-androgenic steroids, anabolic steroids are hormones that work to increase synthesis reactions, particularly in muscle. They are synthetic versions of the primary male sex hormone testosterone. They promote the growth of skeletal muscle (anabolic effects) and the development of male sexual characteristics (androgenic effects).

Steroid abuse can lead to serious side effects, ranging from oily skin to disruption of sex hormones and the cardiovascular system, liver disease, and infections. Sometimes these problems can be lethal.

What is the thymus gland?

The thymus gland produces several hormones, called thymosins, which stimulate the production and development of T cells, which play an important role in immunity. (For more on this subject, see the chapter, "Lymphatic System.") The thymus gland is located in the mediastinum, generally posterior to the sternum and between the lungs. It is a double-lobed lymphoid organ well supplied with blood vessels but few nerve fibers. The outer cortex of the thymus has many lymphocytes, while the inner medulla contains fewer lymphocytes.

BODY FLUIDS

What is the normal pH of blood, urine, and saliva?

Normal pH of arterial blood is 7.4; pH of venous blood is about 7.35. Normal urine pH averages about 6.0. Saliva has a pH between 6.0 and 7.4.

How similar are seawater and blood?

Component	Seawater (grams/liter)	Blood (grams/liter)
Na (sodium)	10.7	3.2-3.4
K (potassium)	0.39	0.15-0.21
Ca (calcium)	0.42	0.09-0.11
Mg (magnesium)	1.34	0.012-0.036
Cl (chloride)	19.3	3.5-3.8
SO_4 (sulfate)	2.69	0.16-0.34
CO_3 (carbonate)	0.073	1.5-1.9
Protein		70.0

How does the body introduce oxygen to the blood and where does this happen?

Blood entering the right side of the heart (right auricle or atrium) contains carbon dioxide, a waste product of the body. The blood travels to the right ventricle, which pushes it through the pulmonary artery to the lungs. In the lungs, the carbon dioxide is removed and oxygen is added to the blood. Then the blood travels through the pulmonary vein carrying the fresh oxygen to the left side of the heart, first to the left auricle, where it goes through a one-way valve into the left ventricle, which must push the oxygenated blood to all portions of the body (except the lungs) through a network of arteries and capillaries. The left ventricle must contract with six times the force of the right ventricle, so its muscle wall is twice as thick as the right.

How much blood is in the average human body?

A man weighing 154 pounds (70 kilograms) would have about 5.5 quarts (5.2 liters) of blood. A woman weighing 110 pounds (50 kilograms) would have about 3.5 quarts (3.3 liters).

How many miles of blood vessels are contained in the body?

If they could be laid end to end, the blood vessels would span about 60,000 miles (96,500 kilometers).

What is the largest artery in the human body?

The aorta is the largest artery in the human body.

Why do various parts of the body fall asleep?

The sensation of "pins and needles" when an arm or leg "falls asleep" is caused by impaired blood circulation to that limb.

Which of the major blood types are the most common in the United States?

Blood type	Frequency in U.S.
O+	37.4%
O-	6.6%
A+	35.7%
A-	6.3%
B+	8.5%
B-	1.5%
AB+	3.4%
AB-	0.6%

In the world, the preponderance of one blood group varies greatly by locality. Group O is generally the most common (46 percent), but in some areas Group A predominates.

Who discovered the ABO system of typing blood?

The Austrian physician Karl Landsteiner (1868-1943) discovered the ABO system of blood types in 1909. Landsteiner had investigated why blood transfused from one individual was sometimes successful and other times resulted in the death of the patient. He theorized that there must be several different blood types. A person with one type of blood will have antibodies to the antigens in the blood type they do not have. If a transfusion occurs between two individuals with different blood types, the red blood cells will clump together, blocking the blood vessels.

How often can a person donate blood?

Blood is one of the most easily donated tissues. According to the American Red Cross, a person in good health who weights at least 110 pounds (50 kilograms) can donate a unit of blood every eight weeks.

What are apheresis and plateletpheresis?

Although most blood is donated as whole blood, it is also possible to donate only a portion of blood using a technique called apheresis. Blood is drawn from the vein of a donor into an apheresis instrument, which separates the blood into different portions by centrifugation. By appropriately adjusting the instrument, a selected portion of the blood, such as the platelets, can be recovered, while the rest of the blood is returned to the donor either into the same vein or into a vein in the other arm. This process takes more time than whole blood donation, but the yield of platelets is much greater. Platelets collected by apheresis are particularly useful for patients who require numerous platelet transfusions, for example cancer patients who have received chemotherapy.

Which blood type is the universal donor and which is the universal recipient?

Persons with blood type O are universal donors. They are able to donate blood to anyone. Persons with blood type AB are universal recipients. They are able to receive blood from any donor.

What is the Rh factor?

In addition to the ABO system of blood types, blood types can also be grouped by the Rhesus factor, or Rh factor, an inherited blood characteristic. Discovered independently in 1939 by Philip Levine (1900-1987) and R. E. Stetson and in 1940 by Karl Landsteiner (1868-1943) and A. S. Weiner, the Rh system classifies blood as either having the Rh factor or lacking it. Pregnant women are carefully screened for the Rh factor. If a mother is found to be Rh-negative, the father is also screened. Parents with incompatible Rh factors can lead to potentially fatal blood problems in newborn infants. The condition can be treated with a series of blood transfusions.

What is the amount of carbon dioxide found in normal blood?

Carbon dioxide normally ranges from 19 to 50 millimeters per liter in arterial blood and 22 to 30 millimeters per liter in venous blood.

Which blood type is the rarest?

The rarest blood type is Bombay blood (subtype h-h), found only in a Czechoslovakian nurse in 1961 and in a brother and sister named Jalbert living in Massachusetts in 1968.

What are the blood group combinations that can normally be used to prove that a man is not the father of a particular child?

If the mother is	and the child is	the father can be	but not
O	O	O, A, or B	AB
O	A	A or AB	O or B
O	B	B or AB	O or A
A	O	O, A, or B	AB
A	A	any group	
A	B	B or AB	O or A
A	AB	B or AB	O or A
B	O	O, A, or B	AB
B	B	any group	
B	A	A or AB	O or B
B	AB	A or AB	O or B
AB	AB	A, B, or AB	O

No child can acquire a gene, and consequently a blood grouping, if it is not possessed by either parent.

How do wounds heal?

Damage to tissue, such as a cut in the skin, begins to heal with the formation of a sticky lump known as a blood clot. Blood clots prevent blood and other fluids from leaking out. Microscopic sticky threads of the clotting protein fibrin make a tangled mesh that traps blood cells. Within a short time the clot begins to take shape, harden, and become more solid. The clot turns into a scab as it dries and hardens. Skin cells beneath the scab multiply to repair the damage. When the scab falls off the wound will be healed.

What percent of human body weight is water?

The human body is 61.8 percent water by weight. Protein accounts for 16.6 percent, fat 14.9 percent, and nitrogen 3.3 percent. Other elements are present in lesser amounts.

Why do eyes tear when we work with onions?

When an onion is cut, the pierced cells release a sulfur compound, thio-propanal-s-oxide, through a series of rapid chemical reactions. This substance is irritating to the eyes.

What causes people to sweat when they eat spicy foods?

The chemical capsaicin, a component of spicy foods, causes sweating by stimulating nerve endings in the mouth and tongue that, normally, only respond to a rise in body temperature. As a result, the brain receives a false signal that body temperature has risen, and in turn launches the chain of physiological events that leads to facial sweating.

Why do some people experience a runny nose while eating?

Called prandial rhinorrhea, this condition occurs when eating stimulates the autonomic nervous system to release the compound acetylcholine. This in turn prompts the increased production of saliva, stomach acid, and nasal mucus. Usually, the spicier the meal, the greater the reaction.

Does your heart stop beating when you sneeze?

The heart does not stop when you sneeze. Sneezing, however, does affect the cardiovascular system. It causes a change in pressure inside the chest. This change in pressure affects the blood flow to the heart, which in turn affects the heart's rhythm. Therefore, a sneeze does produce a harmless delay between one heartbeat and the next, often misinterpreted as a "skipped beat."

SKIN, HAIR, AND NAILS

How much skin does an average person have?

The average human body is covered with about 20 square feet (two square meters) of skin. Weighing six pounds (2.7 kilograms), the skin is composed of two main layers: the epidermis (outer layer) and the dermis (inner layer). The epidermis layer is replaced continually as new cells, produced in the stratum basale, mature, and are pushed to the surface by the newer cells beneath; the entire epidermis is replaced in about 27 days. The dermis, the lower layer, contains nerve endings, sweat glands, hair follicles, and blood vessels. The upper portion of the dermis has small, fingerlike projections called "papillae," which extend into the upper layer. The patterns of ridges and grooves visible on the skin of the soles, palms, and fingertips are formed from the tops of the dermal papillae. The capillaries in these papillae deliver oxygen and nutrients to the epidermis cells and also function in temperature regulation.

Who first used fingerprints as a means of identification?

It is generally acknowledged that Francis Galton (1822-1911) was the first to classify fingerprints. However, his basic ideas were further developed by Sir Edward Henry (1850-1931), who devised a system based on the pattern of the thumb print. In 1901 in England, Henry established the first fingerprint bureau with Scotland Yard called the Fingerprint Branch.

Do identical twins have the same fingerprints?

No. Even identical twins have differences in their fingerprints, which, though subtle, can be discerned by experts.

Are freckles dangerous?

Freckles, tan or brown spots on the skin, are small areas of increased skin pigment or melanin. Freckles are signs of sun damage to the skin. There is a genetic tendency to freckle, and often many members of the same family will have freckles. They are usually on the face, arms and other parts of the body that are exposed to the sun. Freckles appear in childhood, fade during the winter months, and reappear in the summer. Freckles themselves pose no health risks, but they are a marker of increased risk for all types of skin cancer.

What is the purpose of goose-bumps?

The puckering of the skin that takes place when goose-flesh is formed is the result of contraction of the muscle fibers in the skin. This muscular activity will produce more heat, and raise the temperature of the body.

How much does human hair grow in a year?

Each hair grows about nine inches (23 centimeters) every year.

Why does hair turn gray as part of the aging process?

The pigment in hair, as well as in the skin, is called melanin. There are two types of melanin: eumelanin, which is dark brown or black, and pheomelanin, which is reddish yellow. Both are made by a type of cell called a melanocyte that resides in the hair bulb and along the bottom of the outer layer of skin, or epidermis. The melanocytes pass this pigment to adjoining epidermal cells called keratinocytes, which produce the protein keratin—hair's chief component. When the keratinocytes undergo their scheduled death, they retain the melanin. Thus, the pigment that is visible in the hair and in the skin lies in these dead keratinocyte bodies. Gray hair is simply hair with less melanin, and white hair has no melanin at all. It remains unclear as to how hair loses its pigment. In the early stages of graying, the melanocytes are still present but inactive. Later they seem to decrease in number. Genes control this lack of deposition of melanin. In some families, many members' hair turns white they are still in their twenties. Generally speaking, among Caucasians 50 percent are gray by age 50. There is, however, wide variation.

Why is some hair curly while some hair is straight?

The shape of the hair follicle determines how wavy a hair will be. Round follicles produce straight hair. Oval follicles produce wavy hair. Flat follies produce curly hair.

What information can a forensic scientist determine from a human hair?

A single strand of human hair can identify the age and sex of the owner, drugs and narcotics the individual has taken, and, through DNA evaluation and sample comparisons, from whose head the hair came.

Do the nails and hair of a dead person continue to grow?

No. Between 12 and 18 hours after death, the body begins to dry out. That causes the tips of the fingers and the skin of the face to shrink, creating the illusion that the nails and hair have grown.

How fast do fingernails grow?

Healthy nails grow about 0.12 inch (3mm) each month or 1.4 inches (3.5 cm) each year. The middle fingernail grows the fastest, because the longer the finger the faster its nail growth.

What are sensory receptors?

Sensory receptors are structures in the skin and other tissues that detect changes in the internal or external environment. These receptors consist of specialized neuron endings or specialized cells in close contact with neurons that convert the energy of the stimulus (sound, color, odor, etc.) to electrical signals within the nervous system. Sensory receptors, together with other cells, compose the major sense organs, including eyes, ears, nose, and taste buds.

How many types of sensory receptors have been identified?

Five types of sensory receptors, each responding to a different type of stimulus, have been identified. They include the following receptor types:

- *Chemoreceptors*—Respond to chemical compounds such as odor molecules.
- *Photoreceptors*—Respond to light.
- *Thermoreceptors*—Respond to changes in temperature.
- *Mechanoreceptors*—Respond to changes in pressure or movement.
- *Pain receptors*—Respond to stimuli that result in the sensation of pain.

How does the sense of smell work?

The sense of smell is associated with sensory receptor cells in the upper nasal cavity. The smell, or olfactory, receptors are chemoreceptors. Chemicals that stimulate olfactory re-

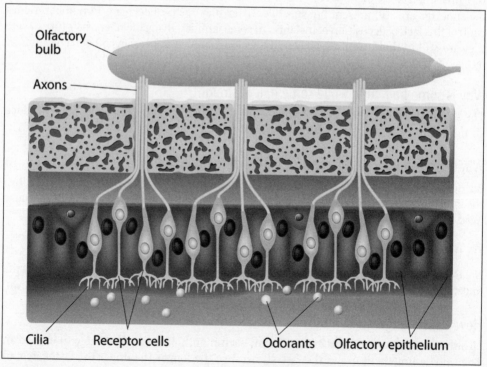

ceptors enter the nasal cavity as airborne molecules called gases. They must dissolve in the watery fluids that surround the cilia of the olfactory receptor cells before they can be detected. These specialized cells, the olfactory receptor neurons, are the only parts of the nervous system that are in direct contact with the outside environment. The odorous gases then waft up to the olfactory cells, where the chemicals bind to the cilia that line the nasal cavity. That action initiates a nerve impulse being sent through the olfactory cell, into the olfactory nerve fiber, to the olfactory bulb, and to the brain. The brain then knows what the chemical odors are.

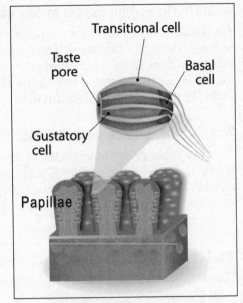

The taste buds (papillae) of the tongue are covered in cells that have pores to perceive salty, sweet, bitter, and sour flavors. Taste buds are also found on the inside of the cheeks, upper esophagus, soft palate, and epiglottis.

What are the special organs of taste?

The special organs of taste are the taste buds located primarily on the surface of the tongue, where they are associated with tiny elevations called papillae surrounded by deep folds. A taste bud is a cluster of approximately 100 taste cells representing all taste sensations and 100 supporting cells that separate the taste cells. Taste buds can also be found on the roof of the mouth and in the throat. An adult has approximately 9,000 to 10,000 taste buds; the average human taste bud lives for seven to ten days.

How do taste buds function?

The taste cells that comprise each taste bud act as receptors. Taste cells and adjacent epithelial cells comprise a spherical structure with small projections called taste hairs that protrude from the taste cells. The taste hairs are the sensitive part of each receptor cell. A network of nerve fibers surrounds and connects all of the taste cells. Stimulation of a receptor cell triggers an impulse on a nearby nerve fiber, and the impulse then travels to the brain via a cranial nerve for interpretation.

What two functions are performed by the ear?

The ear has three major parts: the external, middle, and inner ear. It also has two functions: hearing and maintaining equilibrium or balance (the eyes also often help assist the ears with balance). These two functions rely on certain special nerve receptors that respond to sound waves (hearing) or changes in movement of the body (balance).

What are the parts of the external ear?

The external ear is the visible part of the ear. It consists of an outer, funnel-shaped structure called the auricle (pinna) and a tube called the auditory canal that leads inward for about 1 inch (2.5 centimeters). It ends at the eardrum (tympanic membrane).

625

What structures comprise the middle ear?

The middle ear consists of the tympanic membrane, or the eardrum (it is about 0.00435 inches [about 0.11 millimeters] thick), tympanic cavity (an air-filled space in the temporal bone), and three small bones called auditory ossicles. The tympanic cavity is connected to the nasopharynx (the region linking the back of the nasal cavity and the back of the oral cavity) by the auditory (Eustachian) tube.

What are the three bones in the middle ear?

The three bones, or auditory ossicles, in the middle ear are the malleus (hammer), the incus (anvil), and stapes (stirrup). Tiny ligaments attach them to the wall of the tympanic cavity, and they are covered by mucous membranes. A special muscle, the stapedius, is attached to the stapes and can dampen its vibrations. These bones bridge the eardrum and the inner ear, transmitting vibrations.

What are the parts of the eye and their functions?

The major parts of the eye and their functions are summarized in the following chart:

Structure	Function
Sclera	Maintains shape of eye; protects eyeball; site of eye muscle attachment; it is also referred to as "the white of the eye"
Cornea	Refracts incoming light; focuses light on the retina
Pupil	Admits light
Iris	Regulates amount of incoming light
Lens	Refracts and focuses light rays
Aqueous humor	Helps maintain shape of eye; maintains introcular pressure; nourishes and cushions cornea and lens
Ciliary body	Holds lens in place; changes shape of lens
Vitreous humor	Maintains intraocular pressure; transmits light to retina; keeps retina firmly pressed against choroids
Retina	Absorbs light; stores vitamin A; forms impulses that are transmitted to brain
Optic nerve	Transmits impulses to the brain
Choroid	Absorbs stray light; nourishes retina

The accessory structures of the eye include the eyebrows, eyelids, eyelashes, conjunctiva, and lacrimal apparatus. These structures have several functions, including protecting the anterior portion of the eye, preventing the entry of foreign particles, and keeping the eyeball moist.

What determines eye color?

Variations in eye color range from light blue to dark brown and are inherited. Eye color is chiefly determined by the amount and distribution of melanin within the irises. If melanin

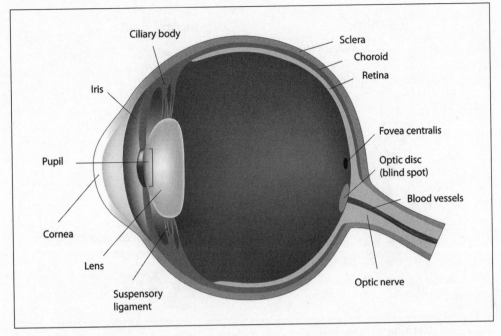

Anatomy of the human eye

is present only in the epithelial cells that cover the posterior surface of the iris, the iris appears blue. When this condition exists together with denser-than-usual tissue within the body of the iris, the eye color looks gray. When melanin is present within the body of the iris, as well as the epithelial covering, the iris appears brown.

What is the difference in the functions of the rods and cones found in the eyes?

Rods and cones are photoreceptor cells that convert light first into chemical energy and then into electrical energy for transmission to the vision centers of the brain via the optic nerve. Rods are specialized for vision in dim light; they cannot detect color, but they are the first receptors to detect movement and register shapes. There are about 125 million rods in a human eye. They contain a pigment called rhodopsin. Cones provide acute vision, functioning best in bright daylight. They allow us to see colors and fine detail. Cones are divided into three different types that contain cyanolabe, chlorolabe, or erythrolabe. These photopigments absorb wavelengths in the short (blue), middle (green), and long (red) ranges, respectively. There are about seven million cones in each eye.

What is nearsightedness?

Nearsightedness, or myopia, is the ability to see close objects but not distant ones. It is a defect of the eye in which the focal point is too near the lens and the image is focused in front of the retina when looking at distant objects. This condition is corrected by concave lenses (eyeglasses or contact lenses) that diffuse the light rays coming to the eyes so that when the light is focused by the eyes, it reaches the proper spot on the retinas.

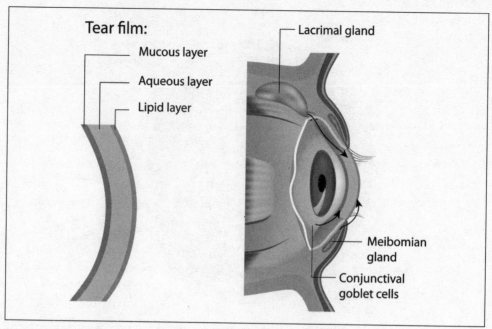

Tear film:

Mucous layer

Aqueous layer

Lipid layer

Lacrimal gland

Meibomian gland

Conjunctival goblet cells

The lacrimal gland in the eye produces tears to cleanse and lubricate the surface.

What is farsightedness?

Farsightedness, or hyperopia, is the ability to see distant objects but not close ones. It is a disorder in which the focal point is too far from the lens, and the image is focused "behind" the retina when looking at a close object. In this condition, the lens must thicken to bring somewhat distant objects into focus. Farsightedness is corrected by a convex lens that causes light rays to converge as they approach the eye to focus on the retina.

What is astigmatism?

Astigmatism is an irregularity in the curvature of the cornea or lens that causes light traveling in different planes to be focused differently. The normal cornea or lens has a spherical curvature like the inside of a ball. In astigmatism, the cornea or lens has an elliptical curvature, like the inside of a spoon. As a result, some portions of an image are in focus on the retina, while other portions are blurred and vision is distorted.

HUMAN GROWTH AND DEVELOPMENT

What is growth and development?

Growth is an increase in size. Human growth begins with a single fertilized ovum. As it grows, the number of cells increases as a result of mitosis, while at the same time the newly formed cells enlarge and grow in size. Development is the ongoing process of change in the anatomical structures and physiological functions from fertilization through each phase of life to death.

What are the two divisions of human development?

Human development is divided into the prenatal development phase and postnatal development phase. Prenatal development begins at the time of conception and continues until birth. Postnatal development begins at birth and continues to maturity, when the aging process begins and ultimately ends in death.

What is the gestation period of human development?

The gestation period is the time spent in prenatal development. Human gestation is conveniently divided into three trimesters of three months each. The first trimester is the period of embryological and early fetal development. During the second trimester, the organs and organ systems develop. The third trimester is characterized by a period of rapid growth prior to birth.

How do the terms zygote, embryo, and fetus differ?

All three terms refer to the individual developing within the uterus of a woman following conception. Fertilization between sperm and ovum produces a zygote, a single cell consisting of forty-six chromosomes. It is called a zygote during the first week of development. At the end of the first week of development, the zygote becomes an embryo. It is called an embryo from the second week of development through the eighth week of development. Beginning at the ninth week of development, it is called a fetus.

How large is a zygote at the time of conception?

The single cell that is formed at conception is the zygote. It is approximately 0.005 inches (0.135 millimeters) in diameter and weighs approximately 0.005 ounces (150 milligrams).

How many distinct stages of development are part of the prenatal period?

The prenatal period of development consists of two distinct stages of development: embryological development and fetal development. Embryological development begins with fertilization and continues until the end of the eighth week of development. Fetal development begins at the ninth week of development and continues until birth.

What four events follow fertilization?

The four events that occur immediately following fertilization are cleavage, implantation, placentation, and embryogenesis. Immediately after fertilization, the single cell divides into two cells. During cleavage, these cells continue to divide. Each division brings two new cells called blastomeres. Each blastomere is approximately half the size of the parent cell. Cleavage occurs as the cells move from the uterine tube to the uterine cavity.

629

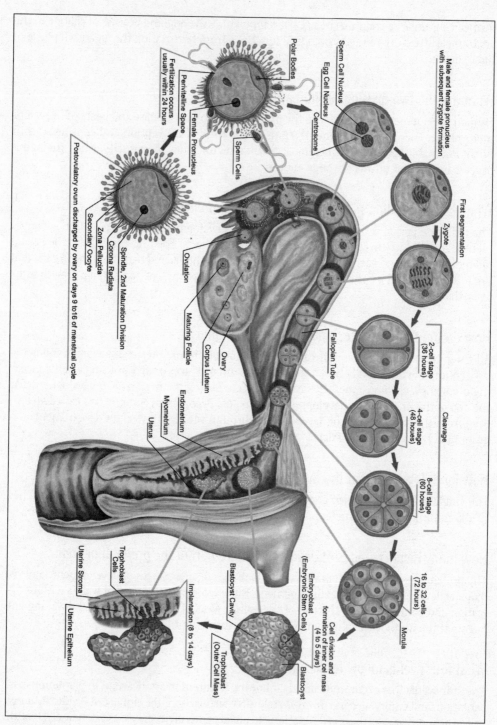

Early stages of embryo development

How long does the journey take from the uterine tube to the uterine cavity?

It takes about three days for the zygote to travel from the uterine tube to the uterine cavity. At the end of the journey, the solid mass of cells is called a morula (from the Latin *morum*, meaning "mulberry") because it resembles a mulberry.

When does the blastocyst form?

The morula hollows out into a fluid-filled sphere on day four or five following fertilization. It is now called a blastocyst. By the end of the first week, the blastocyst begins to implant in the uterus.

When does implantation occur?

Implantation, the attaching of the blastocyst to the endometrium of the uterus, begins about six to seven days following fertilization. By day nine, the blastocyst is completely enclosed by endometrial cells and is implanted in the uterus. Only after the blastocyst is implanted in the uterus can a pregnancy continue.

What is an ectopic pregnancy?

An ectopic pregnancy occurs when the fertilized ovum is implanted in an area other than the uterus. Most frequently, the fertilized ovum is implanted in the uterine tubes. A fetus in an ectopic pregnancy cannot survive because it does not receive nourishment from the uterus. An ectopic pregnancy must be terminated because it jeopardizes the health of the mother.

What are the functions of the placenta?

The placenta is a vascular structure that forms at the site of implantation between the cells that surround the embryo and the endometrium of the uterus. Its main functions are the exchange of gases, nutrients, and wastes between the maternal and fetal bloodstreams. In addition, the placenta secretes hormones. There is no actual blood flow between mother and fetus.

Does the placenta continue to grow throughout a pregnancy?

The placenta grows rapidly until the fifth month of a pregnancy, at which time it is nearly fully developed. At the end of a pregnancy, the placenta is about 1 inch (2.5 centimeters) thick and 8 inches (20.5 centimeters) in diameter. It weighs approximately 1 pound (0.45 kilograms).

How does the umbilical cord form?

The umbilical cord is formed from the extraembryonic or fetal membranes of the embryo during the fifth week of development. It contains two arteries and one vein. The arteries carry carbon dioxide and nitrogen wastes from the embryo to the placenta, and the vein carries oxygen and nutrients from the placenta to the embryo. The umbilical cord is usually 0.4 to 0.8 inches in diameter (1 to 2 centimeters) and 19 to 22 inches long (50 to 55 centimeters).

What is embryogenesis?

Embryogenesis is the process during which the embryo begins to separate from the embryonic disc. The body of the embryo and the internal organs begin to form at this point. The embryo becomes a distinct entity separate from the embryonic disc and the extraembryonic membranes. The left and right sides, as well as the dorsal and ventral surfaces, are now distinct.

How many embryonic layers are in the embryonic disc?

The embryonic disc contains three distinct embryonic layers: 1) the outer layer, called the ectoderm, which is exposed to the amniotic cavity; 2) the inner layer called the endoderm; and 3) the mesoderm. The mesoderm forms between the ectoderm and the endoderm. The following lists the organ and organ system formation from the three germ layers:

Organ System	Ectodermal Layer	Mesodermal Layer	Endodermal Layer
Integumentary system	follicles and hairs, nails, sweat glands, mammary glands, and sebaceous glands	Dermis	
Skeletal system	Pharyngeal cartilages, portion of thesphenoid bone, the auditory ossicles, the styloid processes of the temporal bone, neural crest (formation of the skull)	All components except some pharyngeal derivatives	
Muscular system		All components	
Nervous system	All neural tissue, including brain and spinal cord		
Endocrine system	Pituitary gland and adrenal medullae	Adrenal cortex, endocrine tissues of heart, kidneys, and gonads	Thymus, thyroid gland, and pancreas
Cardiovascular system		All components	
Respiratory system	Mucous epithelium of nasal passageways		Respiratory epithelium and associated mucous glands
Lymphatic system		All components	
Digestive system	Mucous epithelium of mouth and anus, salivary glands		Mucous epithelium (except mouth and anus), exocrine glands (except salivary glands), liver, and pancreas

Organ System	Ectodermal Layer	Mesodermal Layer	Endodermal Layer
Urinary system		Kidneys, including the nephrons and the initial portions of the collecting system	Urinary bladder and distal portions of the duct system
Reproductive system		Gonads and the adjacent portion of the duct systems	Distal portions of the duct system, stem cells that produce gametes
Miscellaneous		Lining of the body cavities (pleural, pericardial, and peritoneal) and the connective tissues that support all organ systems	

What is the amniotic cavity?

The amniotic cavity is a fluid-filled chamber. It contains amniotic fluid that surrounds and cushions the developing embryo. At week 10 there is approximately 1 ounce (30 milliliters) of fluid in the cavity. Towards the end of a pregnancy, between weeks 34 and 36, there is about 1 quart (1 liter) of fluid. The average temperature of the amniotic fluid is 99.7°F (37.6°C), slightly higher than the mother's body temperature.

When is amniocentesis usually performed and why?

Amniocentesis is usually done after the fifteenth week of pregnancy. It is a prenatal test used to screen for and identify genetic disorders or test for lung maturity. During the procedure, a thin needle is inserted into the amniotic cavity to remove some of the amniotic fluid, which contains fetal cells and various chemicals produced by the fetus.

When do significant changes occur during the early stages of prenatal development?

Several significant changes occur during the first two weeks of prenatal development, as shown in the accompanying table:

Time Period	Developmental Stage
12–24 hours following ovulation	Fertilized ovum
30 hours to third day	Cleavage
Third to fourth day	Morula (solid ball of cells is formed)
Fifth day through second week	Blastocyst
End of second week	Gastrula (germ layers form)

What are some major developmental events during the embryonic period?

At the end of the embryonic period (eighth week of development), all of the major external features (ears, eyes, mouth, upper and lower limbs, fingers, and toes) are formed and the major organ systems are nearing completion. The following lists the major developmental events during the embryonic period:

Time Period	Major Developments
Week 3	Neural tube, primitive body cavities and cardiovascular system form
Week 4	Heart is beating (it begins to beat by day twenty-five); upper limb buds and primitive ears visible; lower limb buds and primitive eye lenses appear shortly after ears
Week 5	Brain develops rapidly; head grows disproportionately; hand plates develop
Week 6	Limb buds differentiate noticeably; retinal pigment accentuates eyes
Week 7	Limbs differentiate rapidly
Week 8	Embryo appears human; external ears are visible; fingers, toes lengthen; external genitalia are visible, but are not distinctly male or female

How large is the embryo at the end of the embryonic period?

The embryo is about 0.75 inches (19 millimeters) in length at the end of the embryonic period (end of the eighth week).

How large is the fetus at the end of the first trimester?

At the end of the first three months of pregnancy, the fetus is nearly 3 inches (7.6 centimeters) long and weighs about 0.8 ounces (23 grams).

What is the purpose of the fetal stage of development?

During the fetal stage, beginning after the eighth week of development, the fetus increases in size. All organs formed during the embryonic stage mature to the point where they can function at birth.

What are some major developmental events during the second trimester of pregnancy?

The second trimester of a pregnancy lasts from weeks thirteen through twenty-seven. Each week brings changes and new developments in the fetus. The following lists the major developmental events during the second trimester:

Time Period	Major Developments
Week 13	Baby begins to move, although the movements are too weak to be felt by the mother; ossification of bones begins
Week 14	Prostate gland develops in boys; ovaries move from the abdomen to the pelvis in girls

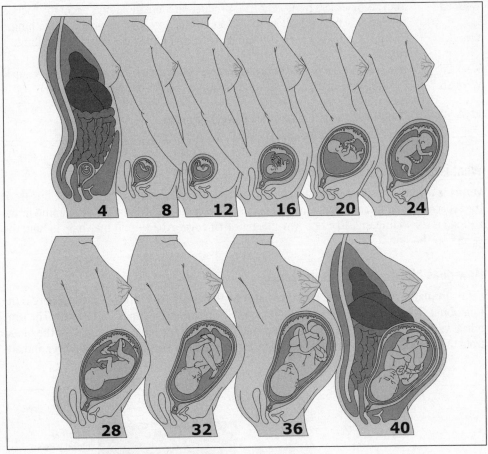

The stages of embryonic and fetal development (numbers indicate weeks)

Time Period	Major Developments
Week 15	Skin and hair (including eyebrows and eyelashes) begin to form; bone and marrow continue to develop; eyes and ears are nearly in their final location
Week 16	Facial muscles are developing allowing for facial expressions; hands can form a fist; eggs are forming in the ovaries in girls
Week 17	Brown fat tissue begins to develop under the skin
Week 18	Fetus is able to hear such things as the mother's heartbeat
Week 19	Lanugo and vernix cover the skin; fetal movement is usually felt by the mother
Week 20	Skin is thickening and developing layers; fetus has eyebrows, hair on the scalp, and well-developed limbs; fetus often assumes the fetal position of head bent and curved spine
Week 21	Bone marrow begins making blood cells
Week 22	Taste buds begin to form; brain and nerve endings can process the sensation of touch; testes begin to descend from the abdomen in boys; uterus and ovaries (with the lifetime supply of eggs) are in place in girls

Week 23	Skin becomes less transparent; fat production increases; lungs begin to produce surfactant, which will allow air sacs to inflate; may begin to practice breathing
Week 24	Footprints and fingerprints begin to form; inner ear is developed, controlling balance
Week 25	Hands are developed, although the nerve connections are not yet fully developed
Week 26	Eyes are developed; eyebrows and eyelashes are well-formed; hair on head becomes fuller and longer
Week 27	Lungs, liver, and immune system are developing

What is the purpose of vernix and lanugo?

Vernix is a white, pasty, cheese-like coating on the skin consisting of fatty secretions from the sebaceous glands and dead epidermal cells. It protects the skin of the developing fetus. Lanugo is a very fine, silk-like or down-like hair that covers the skin. It may help to hold the vernix on the skin.

How does blood circulate in the fetus?

Fetal circulation differs from circulation after birth because the lungs of the fetus are non-functional. Therefore, blood circulation essentially bypasses the lungs in the fetus. The umbilical vein carries oxygenated blood from the placenta to the fetus. About half of the blood from the umbilical vein enters the liver, while the rest of the blood bypasses the liver and en-

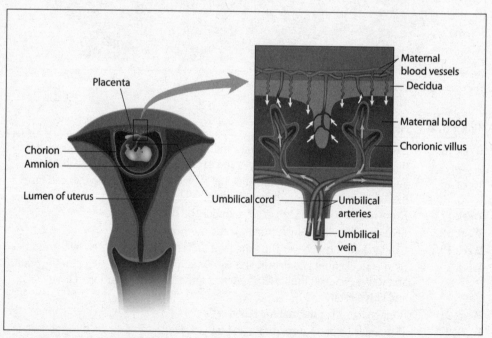

The umbilical cord connects the fetus to the placenta and is the lifeline for the growing baby, transporting nutrients and removing wastes.

ters the ductus venosus. The ductus venosus joins the inferior vena cava. Blood enters the right atrium of the heart and then flows through the foramen ovale to the left atrium. Blood then passes into the left ventricle (lower portion of the heart) and then to the aorta. From the aorta, blood is sent to the head and upper extremities. It returns to the right atrium of the heart through the superior vena cava. Some blood stays in the pulmonary trunk to reach the developing lung tissues.

How does fetal blood differ from adult blood?

Fetal blood has a greater oxygen-carrying capacity than adult blood. Fetal hemoglobin can carry 20 to 30 percent more oxygen than adult hemoglobin.

What is a normal fetal heart rate?

The fetal heart rate is much faster than an adult's (or even a child's) heart rate. The average resting heart rate is 60 to 80 beats per minute. The normal fetal heart rate is 110 to 160 beats per minute.

How does the fetal circulatory system change at birth?

Immediately after birth, an infant no longer relies on maternal blood to supply oxygen and nutrients. As soon as the baby begins to breathe air, blood is sent to the lungs to be oxygenated. The ductus arteriosus, the special fetal vessel connecting the aorta and pulmonary valve, is no longer needed and closes. A separate left pulmonary artery and aorta form after birth. In addition, the foramen ovale, the special opening between the left and right atria in the heart, closes and normal circulation begins.

What are some major developmental events during the third trimester of pregnancy?

During the third trimester of a pregnancy the fetus continues to grow, while the organ systems continue to develop to the point of being fully functional. Fetal movements become stronger and more frequent. The following lists the major developmental events during the third trimester:

Time Period	Major Developments
Week 28	Eyes begin to open and close; fetus has wake and sleep cycles
Week 29	Bones are fully developed, but still pliable; fetus begins to store iron, calcium, and phosphorus
Week 30	Rate of weight gain increases to 0.5 pounds (227 grams) per week; fetus practices breathing; hiccups are not uncommon
Week 31	Testes begin to descend into scrotum in boys; lungs continue to mature
Week 32	Lanugo begins to fall off
Week 33	Pupils in the eyes constrict, dilate, and detect light; lungs are nearly completely developed
Week 34	Vernix becomes thicker; lanugo has almost disappeared
Week 35	Fetus stores fat all over the body; weight gain continues

637

Time Period	Major Developments
Week 36	Sucking muscles are developed
Week 37	Fat continues to accumulate; the baby is considered to be at "full term"
Week 38	Brain and nervous system are ready for birth
Week 39	Placenta continues to supply nutrients and antibodies to fight infection
Week 40	Fetus is fully developed and ready for birth

How much does the fetus grow during each month of pregnancy?

During the early weeks of development there are great changes from the embryonic to the fetal stages, but the overall size of the embryo is very small. As the pregnancy continues, weight gain and overall size becomes much more significant. Until the twentieth week of pregnancy, length measurements are from the crown (or top) of the head to the rump. After the twentieth week, the fetus is less curled up, and measurements are from the head to the toes. The following lists the average size of a fetus during pregnancy:

Gestational Age (weeks)	Size	Weight
8	0.63 in (1.6 cm)	0.04 oz (1 g)
12	2.13 in (5.4 cm)	0.49 oz (14 g)
16	4.57 in (11.6 cm)	3.53 oz (100 g)
20	6.46 in (16.4 cm)	10.58 oz (300 g)
24	11.81 in (30 cm)	1.32 lb (600 g)
28	14.8 in (37.6 cm)	2.22 lb (1 kg)
32	16.69 in (42.4 cm)	3.75 lb (1.7 kg)
36	18.66 in (47.5 cm)	5.78 lb (2.62 kg)
40	20.16 in (51.2 cm)	7.63 lb (3.46 kg)

What are the complications of premature birth?

Babies born before the thirty-seventh week of gestation (preterm babies) are very small and fragile. Birth weights are often less than two pounds. Many of the organ systems are not fully developed, which leads to complications as these infants struggle to survive. Complications include:

- Inability to breathe or breathe regularly on their own due to underdeveloped lungs
- Difficulty in body temperature regulation; the baby cannot maintain his or her own body heat
- Feeding and growth problems because of an immature digestive system
- Jaundice due to a buildup of bilirubin
- Anemia due to not enough red blood cells to carry oxygen to tissues
- Bleeding into the brain

Although after a year or two most preterm babies are developmentally the same as full-term babies, some may still experience breathing difficulties, hearing or vision problems, and learning disabilities.

How common are premature births?

According to the Centers for Disease Control and Prevention, the preterm birth rate for 2012 in the United States was 450,000, or about one in nine infants born. Preterm refers to infants delivered at less than thirty-seven completed weeks of gestation. The number of preterm babies has risen 20 percent since 1990, when it was only 10.6 percent.

What are the maternal changes during pregnancy?

There are several physiological changes in a mother during pregnancy, in addition to changes in the size of the uterus and changes in the mammary glands. The mother must eat, breathe, and eliminate wastes for both herself and her developing fetus, which is totally dependent upon the mother. The mother's respiratory rate goes up so her lungs can deliver the extra oxygen and remove the excess carbon dioxide generated by the fetus. The maternal blood volume increases by nearly 50 percent by the end of a pregnancy, since blood flowing into the placenta reduces the volume of blood throughout the rest of the cardiovascular system. Because the mother must also nourish the fetus, she may feel hungry more often, and her nutritional requirements increase 10 to 30 percent. The maternal glomerular filtration rate increases by approximately 50 percent to excrete the fetus's waste. Consequently, the combination of increased weight and pressure on the mother's urinary bladder and the elimination of additional waste products lead to more frequent urination.

How do the mammary glands develop during pregnancy?

The mammary glands increase in size in response to placental hormones and maternal endocrine hormones. The areola darken in color. Clear secretions, such as colostrum, are stored in the duct system of the mammary glands. The secretions may be expressed from the nipple. (For more about breast feeding, see below.)

What are the stages of labor?

The goal of labor is the birth of a new baby. Labor is divided into three stages: 1) dilation, 2) expulsion, and 3) placental. Delivery of the fetus occurs during expulsion.

How is the onset of labor identified?

Different women will experience different symptoms at the onset of labor. Some women may experience lower back pain or cramping similar to menstrual cramps. In some women, the amniotic sac ruptures

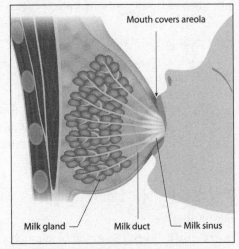

Mouth covers areola

Milk gland — Milk duct — Milk sinus

The infant receives milk from the milk ducts in the breast through the areolas.

early in labor with a sensation of fluid leaking either as a trickle or a large gush of fluid. Some women will lose the mucous plug that blocks the cervix with a brownish or red-tinged mucous discharge. Ultimately, as labor progresses, uterine contractions become more powerful and more frequent.

What events occur during dilation?

The purpose of dilation is to dilate (open) and thin (efface) the cervix to permit the fetus to move from the uterus into the vagina. Dilation is divided into three phases: 1) the early labor phase, 2) the active labor phase, and 3) transition. During the early phase, contractions last 30 to 60 seconds and occur every 5 to 20 minutes at regular intervals. As labor progresses, the frequency of the contractions will increase. The cervix dilates from 0 to 3 centimeters during the early phase of labor. During active labor, contractions become stronger, last longer (45 to 60 seconds or longer), and occur at more frequent intervals (as frequent as every 2 to 4 minutes). The cervix dilates from 3 to 7 centimeters. The final phase of dilation is transition. During transition, the cervix dilates from 7 to 10 centimeters. It is now fully dilated. Contractions during transition last 60 to 90 seconds with sometimes not even a minute between contractions.

What is the placental stage of labor?

During the placental stage of labor, uterine contractions separate the connections between the endometrium and the placenta. The placenta, along with the fetal membranes and any remaining uterine fluid, are ejected through the birth canal.

How does false labor differ from true labor?

Uterine contractions that are neither regular nor persistent are false labor. Oftentimes in false labor the contractions may stop when the mother walks or even shifts positions. The contractions in true labor become stronger, more frequent, and do not cease. Once true labor, begins it will continue until the fetus is delivered.

How long does labor last?

The length of labor differs with every woman. Even the same woman will experience labor differently with each pregnancy. In general, dilation is the longest stage of labor. It can last for several hours to several days, especially for the first-time mother. The early phase of labor is the longest. Active labor may last from three to eight hours, although it can be shorter or longer. Transition is the shortest part of dilation. It may last for only fifteen minutes. Expulsion (delivery) may take only a few minutes to several hours. Delivery of the placenta usually takes only five to ten minutes and is usually no longer than thirty minutes.

Why does the blood loss during labor not cause a problem for the mother?

In a normal delivery, there may be as much as 1 pint (0.473 liters) of blood loss during labor, most during the placental stage. Since the maternal blood volume increased during pregnancy, this blood loss is tolerated without difficulty.

What is the difference between fraternal and identical twins?

Fraternal, or dizygotic twins, develop when a woman ovulates two separate oocytes that are fertilized by two different sperm. Fraternal twins do not resemble each other any more than other brothers and sisters of the same parents resemble each other. They may be of the same sex or different sexes. Identical, or monozygotic twins, develop from the same fertilized ovum. The blastomeres may separate early in cleavage, or the inner cell mass may split prior to gastrulation. Identical twins have the same genetic makeup because they are formed from the same pair of gametes. They look alike and are the same sex.

Identical (maternal) twins originate from one egg and therefore share many physical traits, while fraternal twins are no more alike than other siblings; they merely come from two different eggs that happened to be fertilized at the same time.

Do twins share a placenta, umbilical cord, or amniotic sac?

Identical twins will often share the same placenta but usually have separate amniotic sacs. Each twin always has its own, separate umbilical cord. Nonidentical twins have separate placentas, amniotic sacs, and umbilical cords.

How do healthcare providers induce labor?

When labor does not begin on its own, healthcare providers may induce labor. The most common method of inducing labor is to give the hormone oxytocin. Oxytocin will start contractions and keep them strong and regular. Labor is generally induced when the pregnancy has lasted two weeks beyond the due date or if there is a concern the baby will be too large for safe delivery. Labor may also be induced if the health of the mother becomes endangered.

How does a multiple pregnancy affect the mother's health?

Multiple pregnancies (pregnancies with more than one fetus) pose special risks since the strains on the mother (for example, the need for oxygen and other nutrients for each fetus) are multiplied. Preeclampsia (high blood pressure and protein in the urine) and gestational diabetes are more common in multiple pregnancies.

What are some of the risks and complications associated with multiple pregnancies?

One of the most common risks of a multiple pregnancy is preterm birth. On average, most twin pregnancies last thirty-five weeks, while pregnancies with triplets last only thirty-three weeks. Pregnancies with quadruplets last only twenty-nine weeks on average. Low-birth weight (less than 5.5 pounds, or 2.5 kilograms) due to preterm birth or poor fetal development is also very

---

What is the origin of the term "Siamese twins"?

The term "Siamese twins" dates to 1811, when a pair of conjoined twins was born in Bangkok, the capital of Siam (now called Thailand). The twins Eng and Chang (which mean "left" and "right" in Siamese) were joined at the lower end of the sternum. They left Siam when they were eighteen, spending time in both the United States and England. In addition to becoming famous as part of the P. T. Barnum circus, they were farmers. They married sisters and each raised a family. The parents of Eng and Chang were Chinese, not Siamese. The Siamese called them "Chinese twins."

---

common in multiple pregnancies. Babies weighing less than 3.34 pounds (1.5 kilograms) at birth are at a greater risk for lasting disabilities, including mental retardation, cerebral palsy, and hearing and vision loss. Lung problems and breathing difficulties are common in babies born before thirty-four weeks.

What are some statistics about twins in the United States?

According to the Centers for Disease Control and Prevention, in 2009 (the latest data to date) one in every thirty babies born in the United States was a twin, compared with one in every fifty-three babies in 1980. The twin birth rate rose 76 percent from 1980 through 2009, from 18.9 to 33.3 per 1,000 births. Over the three decades, twin birth rates rose by nearly 100 percent among women aged thirty-five to thirty-nine and more than 200 percent among women aged forty and over. But the older age of women at childbirth in 2009 compared with three decades earlier accounts for only about one-third of the rise in twinning over the thirty years. And overall, twinning rates differed from state to state in 2009. The lowest was 22.3 percent per 1,000 births in New Mexico, while Connecticut had the highest percent of 45.9 per 1,000 births, or around 5 percent of all births that year.

How common are multiple births?

According to the Centers for Disease Control and Prevention, as reproductive technology—such as the use of fertility drugs and other methods of assisted reproduction—has become more refined, the number of triplets, quadruplets, and other multiple births dropped for the first time in more than ten years in 1999. The number of twins, however, continues to increase.

What are conjoined twins?

Conjoined twins are identical twins whose embryonic discs do not separate completely. They typically share some skin and an organ, often the liver, and perhaps other internal organs. If the fusion is minor, they may be separated surgically with relative ease. On rare occasions, conjoined twins are joined at the head or share so many organs that it is nearly impossible to separate them.

When does milk begin to be produced in a pregnant woman and how is it stimulated to be released?

By the end of the sixth month of a pregnancy, the mammary glands are developed in order to secrete milk. They begin to secrete colostrum. Once the placenta is delivered and the secretion of estrogen and progesterone drops, milk production increases. The hormones prolactin and oxytocin are involved in milk production and release. An infant's sucking stimulates the release of these two hormones.

What is the composition of human breast milk?

Human breast milk consists of mostly of water (88 percent), sugars (6.5 to 8 percent), lipids (3 to 5 percent), proteins (1 to 2 percent), amino acids, and salts. It also contains large quantities of lysozymes—enzymes with antibiotic properties. Human milk is bluish-white in color and sweet. The blue color comes from the protein and the white comes from the fat. There are approximately 750 calories per liter of breast milk.

How does colostrum differ from breast milk?

Colostrum is the first fluid secreted by the mother's breasts in the first several days after delivery. It is higher in proteins and has less fat than milk. It also contains a high concentration of antibodies that protect the baby from infections until his or her own immune system matures. A mother produces approximately three ounces of colostrum in a twenty-four-hour period.

After the colostrum, how much milk does a nursing mother produce?

A nursing mother produces 850 to 1,000 milliliters of milk each day. Mothers of multiples will naturally produce enough milk for each infant.

What are the benefits of breastfeeding?

Breastfeeding provides benefits to both the baby and the mother. A major benefit to the baby is that breast milk supplies the correct amount of nutrients as the baby grows from an infant to a healthy toddler. The nutrients in breast milk also protect the infant from certain childhood illnesses. Finally, recent research has shown that breast milk contains certain fatty acids (building blocks) that help the infant's brain develop. In the early days following childbirth, the mother's body releases a hormone that makes her uterus contract and get smaller in response to the baby's sucking. Breastfeeding also provides many emotional benefits between mother and child and encourages maternal-infant bonding.

What are the stages of postnatal development?

The five life stages of postnatal development are: 1) neonatal, 2) infancy, 3) childhood, 4) adolescence, and 5) maturity. The neonatal period extends from birth to one month. Infancy begins at one month and continues to two years of age. Childhood begins at two years of age and lasts until adolescence. Adolescence begins at around twelve or thirteen years of age and ends with the beginning of adulthood. Adulthood, or maturity, begins somewhere between the ages of eighteen and twenty-five and lasts into old age. The process of aging is called senescence.

What are some developmental changes that occur during the neonatal period?

The greatest change from birth to the neonatal period is that the neonate must begin to perform many functions that had previously been done by the mother, especially respiration, digestion, and excretion. With the first breath of air following delivery, the lungs fill with air and the neonate begins to breathe for himself or herself.

How do heart rate and the rate of respiration differ between a neonate and an adult?

The average neonate heart rate is 120 to 140 beats per minute, compared to a resting heart rate of 60 to 80 beats per minute in an adult. The average respiratory rate for a neonate is 30 breaths per minute, compared to 12 to 28 breaths per minute in an adult.

What are the major developmental milestones during infancy?

A normal infant will double his or her birth weight by five or six months of age and triple his or her birth weight during the first year of life. Major developmental milestones during infancy are summarized in the table below (note: there is considerable variation between individuals, but these are within the normal range):

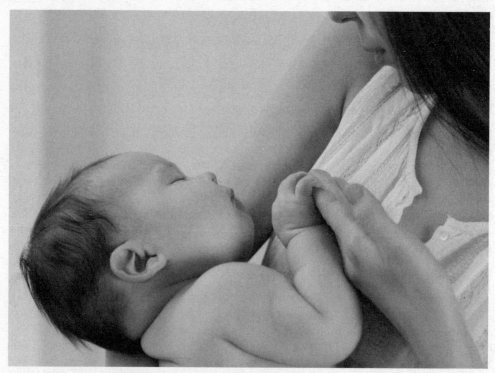

Newborns differ from older children in a number of ways. For example, a neonate's heart can be up to 140 times a minute, and that's okay; they also breathe more rapidly.

Age	Major Milestones in Average Infant
End of first month	Bring hands to face; move head from side to side while lying on stomach; hear very well and often recognize parents' voices
End of third month	Raise head and chest while lying on stomach; open and shut hands; bring hands to mouth; smile; recognize familiar objects and people
End of seventh month	Roll over stomach to back and back to stomach; sit up; reach for objects with hand; support whole weight on legs when supported and held up; enjoy playing peek-a-boo; begin to babble
End of first year	Sit up without assistance; get into the hands and knees position; crawl; walk while holding on; some babies are able to take a few steps without support; use the pincer grasp; use simple gestures, for example, nodding head, waving bye-bye
End of second year	Walk alone; begin to run; walk up and down stairs; pull a toy behind him or her; say single words (fifteen to eighteen months); use simple phrases and two-word sentences (eighteen to twenty-four months); scribble with a crayon; build a tower with blocks

What is the average age when puberty begins?

The average age when puberty begins in the United States today is around twelve years in boys and eleven years in girls. The normal range is ten to fifteen years in boys and nine to fourteen years in girls.

What are the major body changes at puberty?

In addition to general body changes that occur in both males and females at puberty, physical changes in the genitalia, skin, hair growth, and voice are collectively termed the secondary sex characteristics. The following lists the secondary sex characteristic changes in males and females during this time:

Area of Body	Males	Females
General body changes	Shoulders broaden, muscles thicken and height increases; body odor from armpits and genitals becomes apparent; skeletal growth ceases by about age twenty-one	Pelvis widens; fat distribution increases in hips, buttocks, breasts; skeletal growth ceases by about age eighteen
External genital organs	Penis increases in size; scrotum enlarges; penis and scrotum become more pigmented	Breasts enlarge; vagina enlarges and vaginal walls thicken

Area of Body	Males	Females
Internal genital organs	Testes enlarge; sperm production increases in testes; seminal vesicles, prostate gland, bulbourethral gland enlarge and begin to secrete	Uterus enlarges; ovaries secrete estrogens; ova in ovaries begin to mature; menstruation begins
Skin	Secretions of sebaceous gland thicken and increase, often causing acne; skin thickens	Estrogen secretions keep sebaceous secretions fluid, inhibit development of acne and blackheads
Hair growth	Hair appears on face, pubic area, armpits, chest, around anus; general body hair increases; hairline recedes in the lateral frontal regions	Hair appears on pubic area, armpits; scalp hair increases with childhood hairline retained
Voice	Voice becomes deeper as larynx enlarges and vocal cords become longer and thicker	Voice remains relatively high pitched as larynx grows only slightly

What hormonal events signal the onset of puberty?

Three different hormonal events occur that signal the onset of puberty (from the Latin *puber*, meaning "adult"). The hypothalamus increases production of gonadotropin-releasing hormone (GnRH). This stimulates the endocrine cells in the anterior lobe of the pituitary gland, causing circulating levels of follicle-stimulating hormone (FSH) and luteinizing hormone (LH) to rise rapidly. Finally, in response to increased levels of FSH and LH, the ovaries and testes secrete increased amounts of androgens and estrogens. The secondary sex characteristics appear, gamete production begins, and there is a sudden increase in the growth rate, culminating in the closure of the epiphyseal cartilages.

How does adolescence differ from puberty?

Adolescence (from the Latin *adolescere*, meaning "to grow up") begins at puberty and ends at adulthood when physical growth

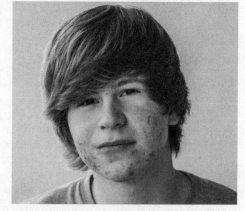

One of the more noticeable physical changes in pubescent youth is that the skin can be plagued with pimples or acne as sebaceous gland secretions thicken.

stops. Puberty is the point when an individual becomes physiologically capable of reproduction. Adulthood begins between ages eighteen and twenty-five.

How is senescence defined?

Senescence (from the Latin *senex*, meaning "old") is the process of aging. Physiological changes continue to occur even after complete physical growth is attained at maturity. As people age, the body is less able to and less efficient in adapting to environmental changes. Maintaining homeostasis becomes harder and harder, especially when the body is under stress. Ultimately, death occurs when the combination of stresses cannot be overcome by the body's existing homeostatic mechanisms.

What are some general effects of aging on the human body?

The aging process affects every organ system. Some changes begin as early as ages thirty to forty. The aging process becomes more rapid between ages fifty-five and sixty. The following lists some of the effects of aging:

Organ System	Effect of Aging
Integumentary	Loss of elasticity in the skin tissue, producing wrinkles and sagging skin; oil glands and sweat glands decrease their activity, causing dry skin; hair thins
Skeletal	Decline in the rate of bone deposition, causing weak and brittle bones; decrease in height
Muscular	Muscles begin to weaken; muscle reflexes become slower
Nervous	Brain size and weight decreases; fewer cortical neurons; rate of neurotransmitter production declines; short-term memory may be impaired; intellectual capabilities remain constant unless disturbed by a stroke; reaction times are slower
Sensory	Eyesight is impaired with most people becoming far-sighted; hearing, smell, and taste are reduced
Endocrine	Reduction in the production of circulating hormones; thyroid becomes smaller; production of insulin is reduced
Cardiovascular	Pumping efficiency of the heart is reduced; blood pressure is usually higher; reduction in peripheral blood flow; arteries tend to become more narrow
Lymphatic	Reduced sensitivity and responsiveness of the immune system; increased chances of infection and/or cancer
Respiratory	Breathing capacity and lung capacity are reduced due to less elasticity of the lungs; air sacs in lungs are replaced by fibrous tissue
Digestive	Decreased peristalsis and muscle tone; stomach produces less hydrochloric acid; intestines produce fewer digestive enzymes; intestinal walls are less able to absorb nutrients
Excretory	Glomerular filtration rate is reduced; decreased peristalsis and muscle tone; weakened muscle tone often leads to incontinence
Reproductive	Ovaries decrease in weight and begin to atrophy in women; reproductive capabilities cease with menopause in women; sperm count decreases in men

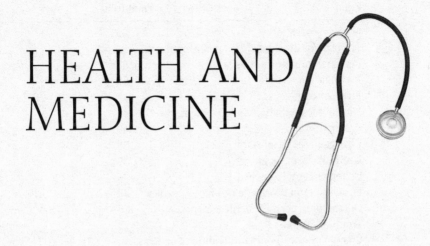

HEALTH AND MEDICINE

HEALTH HAZARDS, RISKS, ETC.

Which risk factors affect one's health?

Such characteristics as age, gender, work, family history, behavior, and body chemistry are some of the factors to consider when deciding whether one is at risk for various conditions. Some risk factors are statistical, describing trends among large groups of people but not giving information about what will happen to individuals. Other risk factors might be described as causative—exposure to them has a direct effect on whether or not the person will become sick.

What are the leading causes of stress?

In 1967, when they conducted a study of the correlation between significant life events and the onset of illness, Dr. Thomas H. Holmes and Dr. Richard H. Rahe from the University of Washington compiled a chart of the major causes of stress with assigned point values. They published their findings on stress effects as "The Social Readjustment Scale," printed in *The Journal of Psychosomatic Research*. The researchers calculated that a score of 150 points indicated a 50/50 chance of the respondent developing an illness or a "health change." A score of 300 would increase the risk to 90 percent. This type of rating scale continues to be used to help individuals determine their composite stress level within the last year. Since 1967 other researchers have adapted and modified the checklist, but the basic checklist has remained constant. Of course, many factors enter into an individual's response to a particular event, so this scale, partially represented below, can only be used as a guide.

Event	Point value
Death of spouse	100
Divorce	73

Event	Point value
Marital separation	65
Jail term or death of close family member	63
Personal injury or illness	53
Marriage	50
Fired at work	47
Marital reconciliation or retirement	45
Pregnancy	40
Change in financial state	38
Death of close friend	37
Change in employment	36
Foreclosure of mortgage or loan	30
Outstanding personal achievement	28
Trouble with boss	23
Change in work hours or conditions or change in residence or schools	20
Vacation	13
Christmas	12
Minor violations of the law	11

What are the leading causes of death in the United States?

In 2005, The U.S. Centers for Disease Control reported that heart disease continues to be the leading cause of death in America. Below are the ten major causes of death in the United States as of 2005.

Rank	Cause of Death	Number
1	Heart disease	652,091
2	Cancer	559,312
3	Stroke	143,579
4	Chronic lower respiratory disease	130,933
5	Accidents	117,809
6	Diabetes	75,119
7	Alzheimerís disease	71,599
8	Influenza/Pneumonia	63,001
9	Kidney disease	43,901
10	Septicemia	34,136

What are the odds against being struck by lightning?

The National Oceanic and Atmospheric Administration estimates the odds of being struck by lightning at one in 700,000. However, the odds drop to one in 240,000 based on the number of unreported lightning strikes. The odds of being struck by lightning in one's lifetime are 1 in 3,000.

What are the odds against being killed on a motorcycle?

1,250 to one against.

Can owning a pet be beneficial to your health?

As a result of several studies, researchers now believe that regular contact with pets can reduce heart rate, blood pressure, and levels of stress. In a study of 93 heart attack patients, only one of 18 pet owners died compared to one of three patients who did not have pets. Pets offer constancy, stability, comfort, security, affection, and intimacy.

Did raising the speed limit on rural interstate highways from 55 to 65 miles per hour have an effect on the accident and death rate?

There was an estimated 20 percent to 30 percent increase in deaths on those roads and a 40 percent increase in serious injuries when the speed limit was raised from 55 miles per hour (88.5 kilometers per hour) to 65 miles per hour (104.5 kilometers per hour) on rural interstate highways.

Which sport has the highest rate of injuries and what kind of injury is most common?

Football players suffer more injuries than other athletes, collectively. They have 12 times as many injuries as do basketball players, who have the next highest rate of injury. Knee problems are the most common type of injury, with two-thirds of basketball players' injuries and one-third of football players' injuries being knee-related.

Which direction of impact results in the greatest number of fatalities in automobile crashes?

Frontal crashes are responsible for the largest percentage of fatalities in passenger cars.

What are the most frequent sports-related injuries requiring visits to the emergency room for children and young adults?

Injuries associated with basketball and cycling are the most frequent sports-related injuries requiring visits to emergency rooms among children and young adults.

Approximate Number of Children's Sports Injuries per Year Requiring Visits to Emergency Rooms

Sport	Number of Emergency Room Visits
Basketball and cycling*	900,000*
Football	250,000
Baseball	250,000
Soccer	100,000
Ice or roller skating and skateboarding	150,000
Gymnastics and cheerleading	146,000

651

Sport	Number of Emergency Room Visits
Playground injuries	137,000
Water and snow sports	100,000

*These sports are not necessarily more dangerous; there are probably more children and young adults engaging in these activities than in other sports.

Sports-related injuries are more likely to be to the brain or skull and upper and lower extremities, more likely to be a fracture, strain or sprain, and more likely to have diagnostic and therapeutic services provided, especially orthopedic care.

Why is exposure to asbestos a health hazard?

Exposure to asbestos has long been known to cause asbestosis. This is a chronic, restrictive lung disease caused by the inhalation of tiny mineral asbestos fibers that scar lung tissues. Asbestos has also been linked with cancers of the larynx, pharynx, oral cavity, pancreas, kidneys, ovaries, and gastrointestinal tract. The American Lung Association reports that prolonged exposure doubles the likelihood that a smoker will develop lung cancer. It takes cancer 15 to 30 years to develop from asbestos. Mesothelioma is a rare cancer affecting the surface lining of the pleura (lung) or peritoneum (abdomen) that generally spreads rapidly over large surfaces of either the thoracic or abdominal cavities. No effective treatment exists for mesothelioma.

Asbestos fibers were used in building materials between 1900 and the early 1970s as insulation for walls and pipes, as fireproofing for walls and fireplaces, in soundproofing and acoustic ceiling tiles, as a strengthener for vinyl flooring and joint compounds, and as a paint texturizer. Asbestos poses a health hazard only if the tiny fibers are released into the air, but this can happen with any normal fraying or cracking. Asbestos removal aggravates this normal process and multiplies the danger level—it should only be handled by a contractor trained in handling asbestos. Once released, the particles can hang suspended in the air for more than 20 hours.

Can ozone be harmful to humans?

Ozone (O_3) in the lower atmosphere contributes to air pollution. It is formed by chemical reactions between sunlight and oxygen in the air in the presence of impurities, such as those found in automobile exhaust. Ozone can damage rubber, plastic, and plant and animal tissue. Exposure to certain concentrations can cause headaches, burning eyes, and irritation of the respiratory tract in many individuals. Asthmatics and others with impaired respiratory systems are particularly susceptible. Exposure to low concentrations for only a few hours can significantly affect normal persons while exercising. Symptoms include chest pain, coughing, sneezing, and pulmonary congestion.

Why is radon a health hazard?

Radon is a colorless, odorless, tasteless, radioactive gaseous element produced by the decay of radium. It has three naturally occurring isotopes found in many natural materials, such as soil, rocks, well water, and building materials. Because the gas is continually released into the air, it makes up the largest source of radiation that humans receive. A 1999 National Academy of Sciences (NAS) report noted that radon was the second leading cause of lung cancer. It has been estimated that it may cause as much as 12 percent, or about 15,000 to 22,000 cases, of lung cancer deaths annually. Smokers seem to be at a higher risk than non-smokers. The U.S. Environmental Protection Agency (EPA) recommends that in radon testing the level should not be more than four picocuries per liter. The estimated national average is 1.5 picocuries per liter. Because EPA's "safe level" is equivalent to 200 chest X-rays per year, some experts believe that lower levels are appropriate. The American Society of Heating, Refrigeration, and Air-Conditioning Engineers (ASHRAE) recommends two picocuries/liter. The EPA estimates that nationally 8 percent to 12 percent of all houses are above the four picocuries/liter limit; whereas in another survey in 1987 it was estimated that 21 percent of homes were above this level.

How is human exposure to radiation measured?

The radiation absorbed dose (rad) and the roentgen equivalent man (rem) were used for many years to measure the amount and effect of ionizing radiation absorbed by humans. While officially replaced by the gray and the sievert, both are still used in many reference sources. The rad equals the energy absorption of 100 ergs per gram of irradiated material (an erg is a unit of work or energy). The rem is the absorbed dose of ionizing radiation that produces the same biological effect as one rad of X-rays or gamma rays (which are equal). The rem of X-rays and gamma rays is therefore equal to the rad; for each type of radiation, the number of rads is multiplied by a specific factor to find the number of rems. The millirem, 0.001 rems, is also frequently used; the average radiation dose received by a person in the United States is about 360 millirems per year. Natural radiation accounts for about 82 percent of a person's yearly exposure, and manufactured sources for 18 percent. Indoor radon has only recently been recognized as a significant source of natural radiation, with 55 percent of the natural radiation coming from this source.

In the SI system (*Système International d'Unités*, or International System of Units), the gray and the sievert are used to measure radiation absorbed; these units have largely superseded the older rad and rem. The gray (Gy), equal to 100 rads, is now the base unit. It is also expressed as the energy absorption of one joule per kilogram of irradiated material. The sievert (Sv) is the absorbed dose of radiation that produces the same biological effect as one gray of X-rays or gamma rays. The sievert is equal to 100 rems, and has superseded the rem. The becquerel (Bq) measures the radioactive strength of a source, but does not consider ef-

What is the effect of radiation on humans?

When ionizing radiation penetrates living tissue, random collisions with atoms and molecules in its path cause the formation of ions and reactive radicals. These ions and reactive radicals break chemical bonds and cause other molecular changes that produce biological injury. At the cellular level, radiation exposure inhibits cell division, and produces chromosomal damage and gene mutations as well as various other changes. Large enough doses of ionizing radiation will kill any kind of living cell.

fects on tissue. One becquerel is defined as one disintegration (or other nuclear transformation) per second.

How much radiation does the average dental X-ray emit?

Dental examinations are estimated to contribute 0.15 millirems per year to the average genetically significant dose, a small amount when compared to other medical X-rays.

How does the United States Environmental Protection Agency (EPA) classify carcinogens?

A carcinogen is an agent that can produce cancer (a malignant growth or tumor that spreads throughout the body, destroying tissue). The EPA classifies chemical and physical substances according to their toxicity to humans.

EPA classification system for carcinogens

Group A. Human carcinogen

This classification indicates that there is sufficient evidence from epidemiological studies to support a cause-effect relationship between the substance and cancer.

Group B. Probable human carcinogen

B_1: Substances are classified as B_1 carcinogens on the basis of sufficient evidence from animal studies, and limited evidence from epidemiological studies.

B_2: Substances are classified as B_2 carcinogens on the basis of sufficient evidence from animal studies, with inadequate or nonexistent epidemiological data.

Group C. Possible human carcinogen

For this classification, there is limited evidence of carcinogenicity from animal studies and no epidemiological data.

Group D. Not classifiable as to human carcinogenicity

The data from human epidemiological and animal studies are inadequate or completely lacking, so no assessment as to the substance's cancer-causing hazard is possible.

Group E. Evidence of noncarcinogenicity for humans

Substances in this category have tested negative in at least two adequate (as defined by the EPA) animal cancer tests in different species and in adequate epidemiological and animal studies. Classification in group E is based on available evidence; substances may prove to be carcinogenic under certain conditions.

What is "good" and "bad" cholesterol?

Chemically a lipid, cholesterol is an important constituent of body cells. This fatty substance, produced mostly in the liver, is involved in bile salt and hormone formation, and in the transport of fats in the bloodstream to the tissues throughout the body. Both cholesterol and fats are transported as lipoproteins (units having a core of cholesterol and fats in varying proportions with an outer wrapping of carrier protein [phospholoids and apoproteins]). An overabundance of cholesterol in the bloodstream can be an inherited trait, can be triggered by dietary intake, or can be the result of a metabolic disease, such as diabetes mellitus. Fats (from meat, oil, and dairy products) strongly affect the cholesterol level. High cholesterol levels in the blood may lead to a narrowing of the inner lining of the coronary arteries from the build-up of a fatty tissue called atheroma. This increases the risk of coronary heart disease or stroke. However, if most cholesterol in the blood is in the form of high density lipoproteins (HDL), then it seems to protect against arterial disease. HDL picks up cholesterol in the arteries and brings it back to the liver for excretion or reprocessing. HDL is referred to as "good cholesterol." Conversely, if most cholesterol is in the form of low-density lipoproteins (LDL), or very-low-density lipoproteins (VLDL), then arteries can become clogged. "Bad cholesterol" is the term used to refer to LDL and VLDL.

How does blood alcohol level affect the body and behavior?

The effects of drinking alcoholic beverages depend on body weight and the amount of actual ethyl alcohol consumed. The level of alcohol in the blood is calculated in milligrams (one milligram equals 0.035 ounce) of pure (ethyl) alcohol per deciliter (3.5 fluid ounces), commonly expressed in percentages.

Number of drinks	Blood alcohol level	Effect of drinks
1	0.02-.03%	Changes in behavior, coordination, and ability to think clearly
2	0.05%	Sedation or tranquilized feeling
3	0.08-0.10%	Legal intoxication in many states
5	0.15-0.20%	Person is obviously intoxicated and may show signs of delirium
12	0.30-0.40%	Loss of consciousness
24	0.50%	Heart and respiration become so depressed that they cease to function and death follows

What is the composition of cigarette smoke?

Cigarette smoke contains about 4,000 chemicals. Carbon dioxide, carbon monoxide, methane, and nicotine are some of the major components, with lesser amounts of acetone, acetylene, formaldehyde, propane, hydrogen cyanide, toluene, and many others.

FIRST AID, POISONS, ETC.

Who discovered cardiopulmonary resuscitation (CPR) as a method to resuscitate an individual whose heart had stopped?

Cardiopulmonary resuscitation (CPR) is a first-aid technique that combines mouth-to-mouth resuscitation and rhythmic compression of the chest to a person whose heart has stopped. The Scottish surgeon William Tossach first performed mouth-to-mouth resuscitation in 1732. The technique was not further developed (or widely used) for many centuries until Dr. Edward Schafer developed a method of chest pressure to stimulate respiration. In 1910 the American Red Cross adopted and began to teach Schafer's method. A team of specialists at Johns Hopkins Medical School, O. R. Langworthy, R. D. Hooker, and William B. Kouwenhoven, attempted to improve on the technique. Kouwenhoven realized that chest compression could maintain blood flow in a person whose heart had stopped. In 1958 Kouwenhoven's method of chest compression was used on a two-year-old child whose heart had stopped. The American Red Cross endorsed the technique in 1963.

What is the "ABCD" survey first responders use to evaluate an emergency?

"A" stands for airway. It is important to be certain the airway from the mouth or nose to the lungs is clear. The airway can be opened by tilting the head back and lifting the chin.

"B" stands for breathing. Be certain the person is breathing or perform rescue breathing (CPR) to ensure a supply of oxygen.

"C" stands for circulation. If a pulse cannot be found, then there is no blood circulating. Emergency personnel can attempt to get the heart to resume breathing by performing rhythmic chest thrusts (CPR). Adults require 15 chest compressions for every two rescue breaths. It also means to check for profuse bleeding which must be controlled.

"D" stands for disability. It involves checking for consciousness and the likelihood of spinal cord or neck injury.

What is the Heimlich maneuver?

This effective first-aid technique to resuscitate choking and drowning victims was introduced by Dr. Henry J. Heimlich (b. 1920) of Xavier University in Cincinnati, Ohio. It is a technique for removing a foreign body from the trachea or pharynx where it is preventing flow of air to the lungs. When the victim is in the vertical position, the maneuver consists of applying subdiaphragmatic pressure by wrapping one's arms around the victim's waist from behind, making a fist with one hand and placing it against the victim's abdomen between the navel and the rib cage, clasping one's fist with the other hand, and pressing in with a quick, forceful thrust. Repeat several times if necessary. When the victim is in the horizontal position (which some experts recommend), the rescuer straddles the victim's thighs.

What safety rules should be observed during a thunderstorm?

These safety rules should be observed when lightning threatens:

1. Stay indoors. Seek shelter in buildings. If no buildings are available, the best protection is a cave, ditch, canyon, or under head-high clumps of trees in open forest glades. If there is no shelter, avoid the highest object in the area. Keep away from isolated trees.

2. Get out of the water and off small boats.

3. Do not use the telephone.

4. Do not use metal objects like fishing rods and golf clubs.

5. Stay in your automobile if you are traveling.

6. Do not use plug-in electrical equipment like hair dryers, electric razors, or electric toothbrushes during the storm.

What items should be included in a household first-aid kit?

According to the American Medical Association and National Safety Council, a first-aid kit should contain:

Allergy and medication information for each family member
Antiseptic cream
Antiseptic wipes
Aspirin or an aspirin substitute such as acetaminophen or ibuprofen
Adhesive bandages
Elastic bandages
Emergency telephone numbers
First-aid manual
Gauze bandages
Triangular bandage
Calamine lotion
Flashlight
Foil blanket
Hydrogen peroxide or rubbing alcohol
Medical exam gloves
Roll of sterile cotton
Round-ended tweezers
Safety pins
Snub-nosed scissors
Syrup of ipecac

What are some common causes of poisoning?

Poisoning is defined as the exposure to any substance in sufficient quantity to cause adverse health effects. Poisonings can be grouped into several different categories, including intentional, accidental, occupational and environmental, social and iatrogenic. Accidental poisonings are the most common, with more than 90 percent occurring in children at home. Intentional poisonings are usually suicide-related, with carbon monoxide being one of the most frequently used agents. Toxic chemical releases in industrial accidents are an occupational and environmental hazard.

How deadly is strychnine?

The fatal dose of strychnine or deadly nightshade (the plant from which it is obtained) is 0.0005 to 0.001 ounces (15 to 30 milligrams). It causes severe convulsions and respiratory failure. If the patient lives for 24 hours, recovery is probable.

Which part of mistletoe is poisonous?

The white berries contain toxic amines, which cause acute stomach and intestinal irritation with diarrhea and a slow pulse. Mistletoe should be considered a potentially dangerous Christmas decoration, especially if children are around.

What first-aid remedies may be used for bee stings?

If a person is allergic to bee stings, he or she should seek professional medical care immediately. For persons not allergic to bee stings, the following steps may be taken: The stinger should be removed by scraping with a knife, a long fingernail, or a credit card, rather than by trying to pull it out. A wet aspirin may be rubbed on the area of the sting to help neutralize some of the inflammatory agents in the venom (unless the person is allergic or sensitive to aspirin taken by mouth).

A paste made of meat tenderizer (or other product that contains papain) mixed with water will relieve the pain. Adults may take an antihistamine along with a mild pain reliever such as aspirin, ibuprofen, or acetaminophen.

Which first-aid measures can be used for a bite by a black widow spider?

The black widow spider (*Latrodectus mactans*) is common throughout the United States. Its bite is severely poisonous, but no first-aid measures are of value. Age, body size, and degree of sensitivity determine the severity of symptoms, which include an initial pinprick with a dull numbing pain, followed by swelling. An ice cube may be placed over the bite to relieve pain. Between 10 and 40 minutes after the bite, severe abdominal pain and rigidity of stomach muscles develop. Muscle spasms in the extremities, ascending paralysis, and difficulty in swallowing and breathing follow. The mortality rate is less than one percent, but anyone who has been bitten should see a doctor; the elderly, infants, and those with allergies are most at risk, and should be hospitalized.

How can the amount of lead in tap water be reduced in an older house having lead-containing pipes?

The easiest way is to let the tap run until the water becomes very cold before using it for human consumption. By letting the tap run, water that has been in the lead-containing pipes for awhile is flushed out. Also, cold water, being less corrosive than warm, contains less lead from the pipes. Lead (Pb) accumulates in the blood, bones, and soft tissues of the body as well as the kidneys, nervous system, and blood-forming organs. Excessive exposure to lead can cause seizures, mental retardation, and behavior disorders. Infants and children are particularly susceptible to low doses of lead and suffer from nervous system damage.

Another source of lead poisoning is old, flaking lead paint. Lead oxide and other lead compounds were added to paints before 1950 to make the paint shinier and more durable. Fourteen percent of the lead ingested by humans comes from the seam soldering of food cans, according to the United States Food and Drug Administration (FDA). The FDA has proposed a reduction in this lead to 50 percent over the next five years. Improperly glazed pottery can be a source of poisoning, too. Acidic liquids such as tea, coffee, wine, and juice can break down the glazes so that the lead can leak out of the pottery. The lead is ingested little by little over a period of time. People can also be exposed to lead in the air. Lead gasoline additives, nonferrous smelters, and battery plants are the most significant contributors of atmospheric lead emissions.

DISEASES, DISORDERS, AND OTHER HEALTH PROBLEMS

What is the difference between a virus and a retrovirus?

A virus is a rudimentary biosystem that has some of the aspects of a living system such as having a genome (genetic code) and the ability to adapt to its environment. A virus, however, cannot acquire and store energy and is therefore not functional outside of its hosts. Viruses and retroviruses infect cells by attaching themselves to the host cell and either entering themselves or injecting their genetic material into the cell and then reproducing its genetic material within the host cell. The reproduced virus then is released to find and attack more host cells. The difference between a virus and retrovirus is a function of how each replicates its genetic material. A virus has a single strand of genetic material—either DNA or RNA. A retrovirus consists of a single strand of RNA. Once a retrovirus enters a cell, it collects nucleotides and assembles itself as a double strand of DNA that splices itself into the host's genetic material. Retroviruses were first identified by David Baltimore (b. 1938) and Howard Temin (b. 1934). They were awarded the Nobel Prize in Medicine for their discovery.

What was the first retrovirus discovered?

Dr. Robert Gallo (b. 1937) discovered the first retrovirus, human T cell lymphoma virus (HTLV), in 1979. The second human retrovirus to be discovered was human immunodeficiency virus, HIV.

Which disease is the most common?

The most common noncontagious disease is periodontal disease, such as gingivitis or inflammation of the gums. Few people in their lifetime can avoid the effects of tooth decay. The most common contagious disease in the world is coryza or the common cold. There are nearly 62 million cases of the common cold in the United States annually.

Which disease is the deadliest?

The most deadly infectious disease was the pneumonic form of the plague, the so-called Black Death of 1347-1351, with a mortality rate of 100 percent. Today, the disease with the highest mortality (almost 100 percent) is rabies in humans when it prevents the victim from swallowing water. This disease is not to be confused with being bitten by a rabid animal. With immediate attention, the rabies virus can be prevented from invading the nervous system and the survival rate in this circumstance is 95 percent. AIDS (acquired immunodeficiency syndrome), first reported in 1981, is caused by HIV (the human immunodeficiency virus). In 1993, HIV infection was the most common cause of death among persons aged 25 to 44 years. In 1999 alone, 14,802 U.S. residents died from the AIDS/HIV infection, according to the National Center for Health Statistics. Although still a significant cause of death among persons aged 25 to 44, it is no longer the most common cause of death.

What is the difference between human immunodeficiency virus (HIV) and AIDS?

The term AIDS applies to the most advanced stages of HIV infection. The Center for Disease Control (CDC) definition of AIDS includes all HIV-infected people who have fewer than 200 CD4+ T cells per cubic millimeter of blood. (Healthy adults usually have CD4+ T cell counts of 1,000 or more.) The definition also includes 26 clinical conditions (mostly opportunistic infections) that affect people with advanced HIV disease.

How many individuals are infected with HIV/AIDS?

As of 2007, the estimate for the number of people worldwide who are either HIV positive or have AIDS is 32.9 million. This is down from 39.5 million in 2006, mostly because of more accurate reporting methods used in such places as India and sub-Saharan Africa.

What are the symptoms and signs of AIDS?

The early symptoms (AIDS-related complex, or ARC, symptoms) include night sweats, prolonged fevers, severe weight loss, persistent diarrhea, skin rash, persistent cough, and shortness of breath. The diagnosis changes to AIDS (acquired immunodeficiency syndrome) when the immune system is affected and the patient becomes susceptible to opportunistic infections and unusual cancers, such as herpes viruses (herpes simplex, herpes zoster, cytomegalovirus infection), *Candida albicans* (fungus) infection, *Cryptosporidium enterocolitis* (protozoan intestinal infection), *Pneumocystis carinii* pneumonia (PCP, a common AIDS lung infection), *toxoplasmosis* (protozoan brain infection), *progressive multifocal leukoencephalopathy* (PML, a central nervous system disease causing gradual brain degeneration), *Mycobacterium avium intracellulare* infection (MAI, a common generalized bacterial infection), and *Kaposi's sarcoma* (a malignant skin cancer characterized by blue-red nodules on limbs and body, and internally in the gastrointestinal and respiratory tracts, where the tumors cause severe internal bleeding).

The signs of AIDS are generalized swollen glands, emaciation, blue or purple-brown spots on the body, especially on the legs and arms, prolonged pneumonia, and oral thrush.

What is meant by vectors in medicine?

A vector is an animal that transmits a particular infectious disease. A vector picks up disease organisms from a source of infection, carries them within or on its body, and later deposits them where they infect a new host. Mosquitoes, fleas, lice, ticks, and flies are the most important vectors of disease to humans.

How is the term zoonosis defined?

A zoonosis is any infectious disease or parasitic disease of animals that can be transmitted to humans. Lyme disease and Rocky Mountain spotted fever, for example, are indirectly spread to humans from an animal through the bite of a tick. Common household pets also can directly transmit diseases to humans unless preventive measures are taken. Cat-scratch

What is "mad cow disease" and how does it affect humans?

Mad cow disease, bovine spongiform encephalopathy (BSE), is a cattle disease of the central nervous system. First identified in Britain in 1986, BSE is a transmissible spongiform encephalopathy (TSE), a disease characterized by the damage caused to the brain tissue. The tissue is pierced with small holes like a sponge. The disease is incurable, untreatable, and fatal. Researchers believe BSE is linked to Creutzfeldt-Jakob disease (CJD) in humans through the consumption of contaminated bovine products. CJD is a fatal illness marked by brain tissue deterioration and progressive degeneration of the central nervous system.

fever and toxoplasmosis may be contracted from cats. Wild animals and dogs can transmit rabies. However, most zoonosis diseases are relatively rare and can be treated once detected. Such sensible actions as regularly vaccinating pets and wearing long-sleeved shirts and pants when hiking can prevent the spread of most zoonoses.

Which species of mosquito causes malaria and yellow fever in humans?

The bite of the female mosquito of the genus *Anopheles* can contain the parasite of the genus *Plasmodium*, which causes malaria, a serious tropical infectious disease affecting 200 to 300 million people worldwide. More than one million African babies and children die from the disease annually. The *Aedes aegypti* mosquito transmits yellow fever, a serious infectious disease characterized by jaundice, giving the patient yellowish skin; 10 percent of the patients die.

How is Lyme disease carried?

The cause of Lyme disease is the spirochete Borrelia burgdorferi that is transmitted to humans by the small tick *Ixodes dammini* or other ticks in the Ixodidae family. The tick injects spirochete-laden saliva into the bloodstream or deposits fecal matter on the skin. This multisystemic disease usually begins in the summer with a skin lesion called erythema chronicum migrans (ECM), followed by more lesions, a malar rash, conjunctivitis, and urticaria. The lesions are eventually replaced by small red blotches. Other common symptoms in the first stage include fatigue, intermittent headache, fever, chills, and muscle aches.

In stage two, which can be weeks or months later, cardiac or neurologic abnormalities sometimes develop. In the last stage (weeks or years later) arthritis develops with marked swelling, especially in the large joints. If tetracycline, penicillin, or erythromycin is given in the early stages, the later complications can be minimized. High dosage of intravenously given penicillin can also be effective on the late stages.

When were the first cases of West Nile virus reported in the United States?

The first cases of West Nile virus were identified in 1999 in the New York City area. West Nile virus is primarily a disease of birds found in Africa, West Asia, and the Middle East. It is transmitted to humans mainly via mosquito bites (mainly from the species *Culex pipiens*). The female mosquito catches the virus when it bites an infected bird and then passes it on when it later bites a human. In humans it causes encephalitis, an infection of the brain that can be lethal.

Why is Legionnaire's disease known by that name?

Legionnaire's disease was first identified in 1976 when a sudden, virulent outbreak of pneumonia took place at a hotel in Philadelphia, Pennsylvania, where delegates to an American Legion convention were staying. The cause was eventually identified as a previously unknown bacterium that was given the name *Legionnella pneumophilia*. The bacterium probably was transmitted by an airborne route. It can spread through cooling tower or evaporation condensers in air-conditioning systems, and has been known to flourish in soil and excavation sites. Usually, the disease occurs in late summer or early fall, and its severity ranges from mild to life-threatening, with a mortality rate as high as 15 percent. Symptoms include diarrhea, anorexia, malaise, headache, generalized weakness, recurrent chills, and fever accompanied by cough, nausea, and chest pain. Antibiotics such as Erythroycin(tm) are administered along with other therapies (fluid replacement, oxygen, etc.) that treat the symptoms.

Which name is now used as a synonym for leprosy?

Hansen's disease is the name of this chronic, systemic infection characterized by progressive lesions. Caused by a bacterium, *Mycobacterium leprae*, that is transmitted through airborne respiratory droplets, the disease is not highly contagious. Continuous close contact is needed for transmittal. Antimicrobial agents, such as sulfones (dapsone in particular), are used to treat the disease.

How many types of herpes virus are there?

There are five human herpes viruses:

Herpes simplex type 1—causes recurrent cold sores and infections of the lips, mouth, and face. The virus is contagious and spreads by direct contact with the lesions or fluid from the lesions. Cold sores are usually recurrent at the same sites and reoccur where there is an elevated temperature at the affected site, such as with a fever or prolonged sun exposure. Occasionally this virus may occur on the fingers with a rash of blisters. If the virus gets into the eye, it could cause conjunctivitis, or even a corneal ulcer. On rare occasions, it can spread to the brain to cause encephalitis.

Herpes simplex type 2—causes genital herpes and infections acquired by babies at birth. The virus is contagious and can be transmitted by sexual intercourse. The virus produces small blisters in the genital area that burst to leave small painful ulcers, which heal within 10 days to three weeks. Headache, fever, enlarged lymph nodes, and painful urination are the other symptoms.

Varicella-zoster (Herpes zoster)—causes chicken pox and shingles. Shingles can be caused by the dormant virus in certain sensory nerves that re-emerge with the decline of the immune system (because of age, certain diseases, and the use of immunosuppressants), excessive stress, or use of corticosteroid drugs. The painful rash of small blisters dry and crust over, eventually leaving small pitted scars. The rash tends to occur over the rib area or a strip on one side of the neck or lower body. Sometimes it involves the lower half of the face and can affect the eyes. Pain that can be severe and long-lasting affects about half of the sufferers and is caused by nerve damage.

Epstein-Barr—causes infectious mononucleosis (acute infection having high fever, sore throat and swollen lymph glands, especially in the neck, which occurs mainly dur-

How are warts caused?

A wart is a lump on the skin produced when one of the 30 types of papillomavirus invades skin cells and causes them to multiply rapidly. There are several different types of warts: common warts, usually on injury sites; flat warts on hands, accompanied by itching; digitate warts having fingerlike projections; filiform warts on eyelids, armpits, and necks; plantar warts on the soles of the feet; and genital warts, pink cauliflower-like areas that, if occurring in a woman's cervix, could predispose her to cervical cancer. Each is produced by a specific virus, and most are usually symptomless. Wart viruses are spread by touch or by contact with the skin shed from a wart.

ing adolescence) and is associated with Burkitt's lymphoma (malignant tumors of the jaw or abdomen that occur mainly in African children and in tropical areas).

Cytomegalovirus—usually results in no symptoms but enlarges the cells it infects; it can cause birth defects when a pregnant mother infects her unborn child.

Three other human herpes viruses are also known: Human herpes virus 6 (HHV-6), commonly associated with roseola, and human herpes viruses 7 and 8 (HHV 7/8), whose disease association is not yet understood. Herpes gestationis is a rare skin-blister disorder occurring only in pregnancy and is not related to the herpes simplex virus.

What is necrotizing fasciitis?

This very rare infection is caused by strains of Group A streptococcus, close relatives of the bacteria that cause strep throat and scarlet fever. When this chain-linked bacteria enters the body through a small cut, bite, or scratch, the infected skin becomes discolored, then blisters and cracks, exposing the destroyed tissue below. Within hours, an infected person can lose inches of flesh, or, in extreme cases, his or her life. If the infection is diagnosed early, antibiotics are generally enough to stop the infection. However, amputation of an affected limb may be the only means of curing an advanced case. The bacteria are often called "flesh-eating bacteria" in sensational media accounts.

What is lactose intolerance?

Lactose, the principal sugar in cow's milk and found only in dairy products, requires the enzyme lactase for human digestion. Lactose intolerance occurs when the lining of the walls of a person's small intestine does not produce normal amounts of this enzyme. Lactose intolerance causes abdominal cramps, bloating, diarrhea, and excessive gas when more than a certain amount of milk is ingested. Most people are less able to tolerate lactose as they grow older.

A person having lactose intolerance need not eliminate dairy products totally from the diet. Decreasing the consumption of milk products, drinking milk only during meals, and getting calcium from cheese, yogurt, and other dairy products having lower lactose values are options. Another alternative is to buy a commercial lactose preparation that can be mixed into milk. These preparations convert lactose into simple sugars that can be easily digested.

What is the difference between Type I and Type II diabetes?

Type I is insulin-dependent diabetes mellitus (IDDM) and Type II is non-insulin-dependent diabetes mellitus (NIDDM). In Type I diabetes there is an absolute deficiency of insulin. It accounts for approximately 10 percent of all cases of diabetes and has a greater prevalence is children. In Type II diabetes, insulin secretion may be normal, but the target cells for insulin are less responsive than normal. The incidence of Type II diabetes increases greatly after age 40 and is normally associated with obesity and lack of exercise as well as genetic predisposition. The symptoms of Type II diabetes are usually less severe than Type I, but long-term complications are similar in both types.

What causes a stomach ulcer?

For decades, doctors thought that genetics or anxiety or even spicy foods caused stomach ulcers. Scientists now believe that stress and spicy foods only worsen the pain of an ulcer. The gastric ulcer itself is caused by a bacterium called *Helicobacter pylori*. Researcher Barry Marshall (1951-) of Australia observed that many ulcer patients had these bacteria present in their systems. So in 1984, to decide whether there was a link, he consumed a large amount of the bacteria. He developed ulcers 10 days later. Ulcers are now treated with antibiotics. In 1994, the *Helicobacter pylori* bacteria was classified as a carcinogen by the National Institutes of Health; ulcer sufferers would therefore do well to consult a doctor instead of ignoring or masking the pain with antacids.

What is carpal tunnel syndrome?

Carpal tunnel syndrome occurs when a branch of the median nerve in the forearm is compressed at the wrist as it passes through the tunnel formed by the wrist bones (or carpals), and a ligament that lies just under the skin. The syndrome occurs most often in middle age and more so in women than men. The symptoms are intermittent at first, then become constant. Numbness and tingling begin in the thumb and first two fingers; then the hand and sometimes the whole arm becomes painful. Treatment involves wrist splinting, weight loss, control of edema; treatments for arthritis may help also. If not, a surgical procedure in which the ligament at the wrist is cut can relieve pressure on the nerve. Those who work continuously with computer keyboards are particularly vulnerable to carpal tunnel syndrome. To minimize the risk of developing this problem, operators should keep their wrists straight as they type, rather than tilting the hands up. It is also best to place the keyboard at a lower position than a standard desktop.

What is the medical term for tennis elbow?

The technical term for tennis elbow is epicondylitis. A result of repeated strain on the forearm, it is a painful inflammation of the muscle and surrounding tissues of the elbow. A number of behaviors can cause its onset, ranging from playing tennis or golf to carrying a heavy load with the arm extended.

What is Lou Gehrig's disease?

Sometimes called Lou Gehrig's disease, amyotrophic lateral sclerosis (ALS) is a motor neuron disease of middle or late life. It results from a progressive degeneration of nerve cells controlling voluntary motor functions that ends in death three to 10 years after onset. There is no cure for it. At the beginning of the disease, the patient notices weakness in the hands and arms, with involuntary muscle quivering and possible muscle cramping or stiffness. Eventually all four extremities become involved. As nerve degeneration progresses, disability occurs and physical independence declines until the patient, while mentally and intellectually aware, can no longer swallow or move.

What is narcolepsy?

Although most people think of a narcoleptic as a person who falls asleep at inappropriate times, victims of narcolepsy also share other symptoms, including excessive daytime sleepiness, hallucinations, and cataplexy (a sudden loss of muscle strength following an emotional event). Persons with narcolepsy experience an uncontrollable desire to sleep, sometimes many times in one day. Episodes may last from a few minutes to several hours.

How does jet lag affect one's body?

The physiological and mental stress encountered by airplane travelers when crossing four or more time zones is commonly called jet lag. Patterns of hunger, sleep, and elimination, along with alertness, memory, and normal judgment, may all be affected. More than 100 biological functions that fluctuate during the 24-hour cycle (circadian rhythm) can become desynchronized. Most people's bodies adjust at a rate of about one hour per day. Thus after four time zone changes, the body will require about four days to return to its usual rhythms. Flying eastward is often more difficult than flying westward, which adds hours to the day.

What is factor VIII?

Factor VIII is one of the enzymes involved in the clotting of blood. Hemophiliacs lack this enzyme and are at high risk of bleeding to death unless they receive supplemental doses of factor VIII. The lack of factor VIII is due to a defective gene, which shows a sex-linked inherited pattern (it affects about one in 10 thousand males). Females can carry the gene. Hemorrhage into joints and muscles usually makes up the majority of bleeding episodes.

What is the medical term for a heart attack?

Myocardial infarction is the term used for a heart attack in which part of the heart muscle's cells die as a result of reduced blood flow through one of the main arteries (many times due to arteriosclerosis). The outlook for the patient is dependant on the size and location of the blockage and extent of damage, but 33 percent of patients die within 20 days after the attack;

What is the "Christmas factor"?

In the clotting of blood, factor IX, or the Christmas factor, is a coagulation factor present in normal plasma, but deficient in the blood of persons with hemophilia B or Christmas disease. It was named after a man named Christmas who, in 1952, was the first patient in whom this genetic disease was shown to be distinct from hemophilia (another genetic blood-clotting disease in which the blood does not have factor VIII).

it is a leading cause of death in the United States. Also, almost half of sudden deaths due to myocardial infarction occur before hospitalization. However, the possibility of recovery improves if vigorous treatment begins immediately.

What is the difference between heatstroke and heat exhaustion?

Heatstroke	Heat Exhaustion
Caused by: Body cannot regulate its own temperature due to intensive sweating under conditions of high heat and humidity. Advanced age can be a factor.	**Caused by:** Person doesn't get enough liquid and salt in very hot, humid weather.
Symptoms: Weakness, vertigo, nausea, headache, heat cramps, mild heat exhaustion, excessive sweating. Sweating stops just before heatstroke. Temperature rises rapidly, as high as 106°F (41°C); blood pressure is elevated. Skin is flushed at first, then turns ashen or purplish. Delirium or coma is common.	**Symptoms:** Excessive sweating, weakness, vertigo, and sometimes heat cramps. Skin is cold and pale, clammy with sweat; pulse is thready and blood pressure is low. Body temperature is normal or sub-normal. Vomiting may occur. Unconsciousness is rare.
First Aid: Heatstroke is a medical emergency. Call for medical assistance. Move person to a cool, indoor place. Loosen or remove clothing. Primary objective is to reduce body temperature, preferably by iced bath or sponging down with cool water until pulse lowers to below 110 per minute and body temperature is below 103°F (39.4°C). Caution is necessary.	**First Aid:** Lay person in cool place. Loosen clothing. Give water to drink with 1 tsp. salt to each quart of water. Fluid intake usually brings about full recovery. Seek medical assistance if severe.

How are the forms of cancer classified?

The over 150 different types of cancer are classified into four major groups:

1. Carcinomas—Nine in 10 cancers are carcinomas, which involve the skin and skin-like membranes of the internal organs.
2. Sarcomas—Involve the bones, muscles, cartilage, fat, and linings of the lungs, abdomen, heart, central nervous system, and blood vessels.
3. Leukemias—Develop in blood, bone marrow, and the spleen.
4. Lymphomas—Involve the lymphatic system.

What are HeLa cells?

HeLa cells, used in many biomedical experiments, were obtained from a cervical carcinoma in a woman named Henrietta Lacks. Epithelial tissue obtained by biopsy became the first continuously cultured human malignant cells.

If the sap of the poison ivy plant touches the skin, will a rash develop?

Studies show that 85 percent of the population will develop an allergic reaction if exposed to poison ivy, but this sensitivity varies with each individual according to circumstance, age, genetics, and previous exposure. The poison comes mainly from the leaves whose allergens touch the skin. A red rash with itching and burning will develop, and skin blisters will usually develop within six hours to several days after exposure. Washing the affected area thoroughly with mild soap within five minutes of exposure can be effective; sponging with alcohol and applying a soothing and drying lotion, such as calamine lotion, is the prescribed treatment for light cases. If the affected area is large, fever, headache, and generalized body weakness may develop. For severe reactions, a physician should be consulted to prescribe a corticosteroid drug. Clothing that touched the plants should also be washed.

What is dyslexia and what causes it?

Dyslexia covers a wide range of language difficulties. In general, a person with dyslexia cannot grasp the meaning of sequences of letters, words, or symbols or the concept of direction. The condition can affect people of otherwise normal intelligence. Dyslexic children may reverse letter and word order, make bizarre spelling errors, and may not be able to name colors or write from dictation. It may be caused by minor visual defects, emotional disturbance, or failure to train the brain. New evidence shows that a neurological disorder may be the underlying cause. Approximately 90 percent of dyslexics are male.

The term *dyslexia* (of Greek origin) was first suggested by Professor Rudolph Berlin of Stuttgart, Germany, in 1887. The earliest references to the condition date as far back as 30 C.E. when Valerius Maximus and Pliny described a man who lost his ability to read after being struck on the head by a stone.

What is anorexia?

Anorexia simply means a loss of appetite. Anorexia nervosa is a psychological disturbance that is characterized by an intense fear of being fat. It usually affects teenage or young adult women. This persistent "fat image," however untrue in reality, leads the patient to self-imposed starvation and emaciation (extreme thinness) to the point where one-third of the body weight is lost. There are many theories on the causes of this disease, which is difficult to treat and can be fatal. Between five and 10 percent of patients hospitalized for anorexia nervosa later die from starvation or suicide. Symptoms include a 25 percent or greater weight loss (for no organic reason) coupled with a morbid dread of being fat, an obsession with food, an avoidance of eating, compulsive exercising and restlessness, binge eating followed by induced vomiting, and/or use of laxatives or diuretics.

Why do deep-sea divers get the bends?

Bends is a painful condition in the limbs and abdomen. It is caused by the formation and enlargement of bubbles of nitrogen in blood and tissues as a result of rapid reduction of pressure. This condition can develop when a diver ascends too rapidly after being exposed to increased pressure. Severe pain will develop in the muscles and joints of the arms and legs. More severe symptoms include vertigo, nausea, vomiting, choking, shock, and sometimes death. Bends is also known as decompression sickness, caisson disease, tunnel disease, and diver's paralysis.

What is progeria?

Progeria is premature old age. There are two distinct forms of the condition, both of which are extremely rare. In Hutchinson-Gilford syndrome, aging starts around the age four, and by 10 or 12, the affected child has all the external features of old age, including gray hair, baldness, and loss of fat, resulting in thin limbs and sagging skin on the trunk and face. There are also internal degenerative changes, such as atherosclerosis (fatty deposits lining the artery walls). Death usually occurs at puberty. Werner's syndrome, or adult progeria, starts in early adult life and follows the same rapid progression as the juvenile form. The cause of progeria is unknown.

How many people in America are estimated to have Alzheimer's disease?

According to the Alzheimerís Association, as many as 5.2 million Americans are suffering from some degree of Alzheimerís disease. Alzheimer's disease is a progressive condition in which nerve cells in the brain degenerate and the brain substance shrinks. Although the cause is unknown, some theorize that it is toxic poisoning by a metal such as aluminum. Others believe it to be of genetic origin. There are three stages; in the first, the person becomes forgetful; in the second, the patient experiences severe memory loss and disorientation, lack of concentration, loss of ability to calculate and find the right word to use (dysphasia), anxiety, and sudden personality changes. In the third stage the patient is severely disoriented and confused, suffers from hallucinations and delusions, and has severe memory loss; the nervous system also declines, with regression into infantile behavior, violence, etc., often requiring hospital care.

What is pelvic inflammatory disease?

Pelvic inflammatory disease (PID) is a term used for a group of infections in the female organs, including inflammations of the Fallopian tubes, cervix, uterus, and ovaries. It is the most common cause of female infertility today. PID is most often found in sexually active women under the age of 25 and almost always results from gonorrhea or chlamydia, but women who use IUDs are also at risk. A variety of organisms have been shown to cause PID, including *Neisseria gonorrhoeae* and such common bacteria as staphylococci, chlamydiae, and coliforms (*Pseudomonas* and *Escherichia coli*). Signs and symptoms of PID vary with the site of the infection, but usually include profuse, purulent vaginal discharge, low-grade fever and malaise (especially with *N. gonorrhoeae* infections), and lower abdominal pain. PID is treated with antibiotics, and early diagnosis and treatment will prevent damage to the reproductive system. Severe, untreated PID can result in the development of a pelvic abscess that requires drainage. A ruptured pelvic abscess is a potentially fatal complication, and a patient who develops this complication may require a total hysterectomy.

What is the chemical composition of kidney stones?

About 80 percent are calcium, mainly calcium oxalate and/or phosphate; five percent are uric acid; two percent are amino acid cystine; the remainder are magnesium ammonium phosphate. About 20 percent of these stones are infective stones, linked to chronic urinary infections, and contain a combination of calcium, magnesium, and ammonium phosphate produced from the alkalinity of the urine and bacteria action on urea (a substance in urine).

How are burns classified?

Type	Causes and effects
First-degree	Sunburn; steam. Reddening and peeling. Affects epidermis (top layer of skin). Heals within a week.

Second-degree	Scalding; holding hot metal. Deeper burns causing blisters. Affects dermis (deep skin layer). Heals in two to three weeks.
Third-degree	Fire. A full layer of skin is destroyed. Requires a doctor's care and grafting.
Circumferential	Any burns (often electrical) that completely encircle a limb or body region (such as the chest), which can impair circulation or respiration; requires a doctor's care; fasciotomy (repair of connective tissues) is sometimes required.
Chemical	Acid, alkali. Can be neutralized with water (for up to half an hour). Doctor's evaluation recommended.
Electrical	Destruction of muscles, nerves, circulatory system, etc., below the skin. Doctor's evaluation and ECG monitoring required.

If more than 10 percent of body surface is affected in second-and third-degree burns, shock can develop when large quantities of fluid (and its protein) are lost. When skin is burned, it cannot protect the body from airborne bacteria.

What is the phobia of number 13 called?

Fear of the number 13 is known as tridecaphobia, tredecaphobia, or triskaidekaphobia. Persons may fear any situation involving this number, including a house number, the floor of a building, or the 13th day of the month. Many buildings omit labeling the 13th floor as such for this reason. A phobia can develop for a wide range of objects, situations, or organisms. The list below demonstrates the variety:

Phobia subject	Phobia term
Animals	Zoophobia
Beards	Pogonophobia
Books	Bibliophobia
Churches	Ecclesiaphobia
Dreams	Oneirophobia
Flowers	Anthophobia
Food	Sitophobia
Graves	Taphophobia
Infection	Nosemaphobia
Lakes	Limnophobia
Leaves	Phyllophobia
Lightning	Astraphobia
Men	Androphobia
Money	Chrometophobia
Music	Musicophobia
Sex	Genophobia
Shadows	Sciophobia
Spiders	Arachnophobia
Sun	Heliophobia
Touch	Haptophobia

Phobia subject	Phobia term
Trees	Dendrophobia
Walking	Basiphobia
Water	Hydrophobia
Women	Gynophobia
Work	Ergophobia
Writing	Graphophobia

ANATOMY AND IMAGING TECHNIQUES

What were some of the early ways to explore the inside of the body?

Until the end of the nineteenth century, there were no noninvasive techniques to explore the internal organs of the body. Medical practitioners relied on descriptions of symptoms as the basis for their diagnoses. X-rays, discovered at the very end of the nineteenth century, provided the earliest technique to explore the internal organs and tissues of the body. During the twentieth century, significant advances were made in the field of medical imaging to explore the internal organs.

What are X-rays and CAT (or CT) scans?

X-rays are electromagnetic radiation with short wavelengths and a great amount of energy. They were discovered in 1898 by Wilhelm Conrad Roentgen (1845–1923). X-rays are frequently used in medicine because they are able to pass through opaque, dense structures such as bone and form an image on a photographic plate. They are especially helpful in assessing damage to bones, identifying certain tumors, and examining the chest (heart and lungs, in particular) and abdomen.

CAT or CT scans (computer-assisted tomography, or simply computerized tomography) are specialized X-rays that produce cross-sectional images of the body. An X-ray-emitting device moves around the body region being examined. At the same time, an X-ray detecting device moves in the opposite direction on the other side of the body. As these two devices move, an X-ray beam passes through the body from hundreds of different angles. Since tissues and organs absorb X-rays differently, the intensity of X-rays reaching the detector varies from position to position. A computer records the measurements made by the X-ray detector and combines them mathematically. The result is a sectional image of the body that is viewed on a screen.

Who discovered and pioneered the use of CT scans?

Allan M. Cormack (1924–1998) and Godfrey N. Hounsfield (1919–2004) independently discovered and developed computer assisted tomography in the early 1970s. They shared the 1979 Nobel Prize in Physiology or Medicine for their research. The earliest computer-assisted tomography was used to examine the skull and diseases of the brain.

How are CT scans used in the study of the human body?

CT scans are used to study many parts of the body, including the chest, belly and pelvis, extremities (arms and legs), and internal organs, such as pancreas, liver, gall bladder, and kidneys. CT scans of the head and brain may detect an abnormal mass or growth, stroke damage, area of bleeding, or blood vessel abnormality. Patients complaining of pain may have a CT scan to determine the source of the pain. Sometimes a CT scan will be used to further investigate an abnormality found on a regular X-ray.

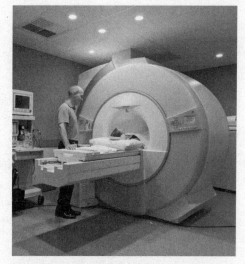

A computerized tomography (CT) scan machine helps doctors look inside patients's bodies without performing surgery.

What is an advantage of positron emission tomography (PET imaging) over CT scans and X-rays?

Unlike traditional X-rays and CT scans, which reveal information about the structure of internal organs, positron emission tomography (PET imaging) is an excellent technique for observing metabolic processes. Developed during the 1970s, PET imaging uses radioactive isotopes to detect biochemical activity in a specific body part.

What is the procedure for a PET scan?

A patient is injected with a radioisotope, which travels through the body and is transported to the organ and tissue to be studied. As the radioisotopes are absorbed by the cells, high-energy gamma rays are produced. A computer collects and analyzes the gamma-ray emission, producing an image of the organ's activity.

How are PET scans used to detect and treat cancer?

PET scans of the whole body may detect cancers. While the PET scans do not provide cancer therapy, they are very useful in examining the effects of cancer therapies and treatments on a tumor. Since it is possible to observe biochemical activities of cells and tumors using PET scans, biochemical changes to tumors following treatment may be observed.

Is it possible to study blood flow to the heart or brain?

PET scans provide information about blood flow to the heart muscle and brain. They may help evaluate signs of coronary heart disease and reasons for decreased function in certain areas of the heart. PET scans of the brain may detect tumors or other neurological disorders, including certain behavioral health disorders. Studies of the brain using PET scans have identified parts of the brain that are affected by epilepsy and seizures, Alzheimer's disease, Parkinson's disease, and stroke. In addition, they have been used to identify specific regions of the healthy brain that are active during certain tasks.

> ## What are the disadvantages of X-rays as a diagnostic tool?
>
> **A** major disadvantage of X-rays as a diagnostic tool is that they provide little information about the soft tissues. Since they only show a flat, two-dimensional picture, they cannot distinguish between the various layers of an organ, some of which may be healthy while others may be diseased.

What is nuclear magnetic resonance (NMR)?

Nuclear magnetic resonance (NMR) is a process in which the nuclei of certain atoms absorb energy from an external magnetic field. Scientists use NMR spectroscopy to identify unknown compounds, check for impurities, and study the shapes of molecules. This technology takes advantage of the fact that different atoms will absorb electromagnetic energy at slightly different frequencies.

What is nuclear magnetic resonance imaging?

Magnetic resonance imaging (MRI), sometimes called nuclear magnetic resonance imaging (NMR), is a noninvasive, nonionizing diagnostic technique. It is useful in detecting small tumors, blocked blood vessels, or damaged vertebral discs. Because it does not involve the use of radiation, it can often be used in cases where X-rays would be dangerous. Large magnets beam energy through the body, causing hydrogen atoms in the body to resonate. This produces energy in the form of tiny electrical signals. A computer detects these signals, which vary in different parts of the body and show the contrast between a healthy and diseased organ. The variation enables a picture to be produced on a screen and interpreted by a medical specialist.

What distinguishes MRI from computerized X-ray scanners is that most X-ray studies cannot distinguish between a living body and a cadaver, while MRI "sees" the difference between life and death in great detail. More specifically, it can discriminate between healthy and diseased tissues with more sensitivity than conventional radiographic instruments like X-rays or CAT scans.

Who proposed using MRI for diagnostic purposes?

The concept of using MRI to detect tumors in patients was proposed by American medical researcher, biophysicist, and inventor Raymond Damadian (1936–) in a 1972 patent application. The fundamental MRI concept used in all present-day MRI instruments was proposed by American chemist Paul Lauterbur (1929–2007) in an article published in *Nature* in 1973. Lauterbur and English physicist Peter Mansfield (1933–) were awarded the Nobel Prize in Physiology or Medicine in 2003 for their discoveries concerning MRI. The main advantages of MRI are that it not only gives superior images of soft tissues (like organs), but it can also measure dynamic physiological changes in a noninvasive manner (without penetrating the body in any way). A disadvantage of MRI is that it cannot be used for every patient. For example, patients with implants, pacemakers, or cerebral aneurysm clips made of metal cannot be examined using MRI because the machine's magnet could potentially move these objects within the body, causing damage.

What is ultrasound?

Ultrasound, also called sonography, is another type of 3-D computerized imaging. Using brief pulses of ultrahigh frequency acoustic waves (lasting 0.01 seconds), it can produce a sonar map of the imaged object. The technique is similar to the echolocation used by bats, whales, and dolphins. By measuring the echo waves, it is possible to determine the size, shape, location, and consistency (whether it is solid, fluid-filled, or both) of an object.

Why is ultrasound used frequently in obstetrics?

Ultrasound is a very safe, noninvasive imaging technique. Unlike X-rays, sonography does not use ionizing radiation to produce an image. It gives a clear picture of soft tissues, which do not show up in X-rays. Ultrasound causes no health problems (for a mother or unborn fetus) and may be repeated as often as necessary.

What imaging techniques are used to examine breast tissue and diagnose certain breast diseases?

Mammography is the specific imaging technique used to examine breast tissue and diagnose breast diseases. It has become a very important tool in diagnosing early breast cancer, as small tumors may be visible on a mammogram years before they may be felt physically by a woman or her healthcare provider. A small dose of radiation is passed through the breast tissue, producing an image of the interior of the breast tissue.

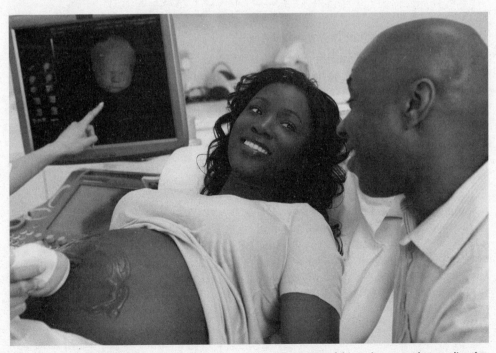

Ultrasound machines use sound much like a bat does to create a 3-D image of things that cannot be seen directly.

One improvement to the mammogram is the digital breast tomosynthesis, or three-dimensional (3-D) mammography. A study in 2014 showed that this method of mammography found significantly more invasive, and potentially lethal, cancers than the traditional mammograms that would often yield false positive results. The 3-D reconstruction of breast tissue has been shown to give radiologists a clearer view of the overlapping slices of breast tissue, thus resulting in less false positives—and often reducing the number of unnecessary breast biopsies.

What is a barium test used to determine in the upper gastrointestinal tract?

Barium tests (called barium swallow) are used to examine the upper gastrointestinal tract, especially the pharynx (back of the mouth and throat) and esophagus (the tube of muscle from below the tongue to the stomach). A liquid suspension called barium sulfate is ingested by the patient, essentially coating the inside wall linings of the gastrointestinal tract. Because barium is an "X-ray absorber," the size, shape, and sometimes conditions of the upper gastrointestinal tract can be seen on the X-rays. For example, such conditions as tumors, ulcers, hernias, diverticula (pouches in the intestines), and inflammations can often be detected from a barium swallow.

DIAGNOSTIC TECHNIQUES FOR VARIOUS SYSTEMS

What are some common hearing tests?

There are many diagnostic techniques to determine a person's hearing ability and if there is hearing loss. For example, the basic audiogram determines the patient's ability to hear relative to what is considered a normal adult hearing level. Tymphanometry examines the middle ear for blockages or malfunctions to determine if they can be treated medically or surgically. And testing the stapedial reflexes will determine if the auditory nerve is efficiently transmitting hearing signals to the brain.

What is echocardiography?

Echocardiography is a noninvasive method for studying the motion and internal vessels of the heart. This method uses ultrasound beams, which are directed into the patient's chest by a transducer. The transducer uses the ultrasonic waves, which are directed back from the heart to form an image. An echocardiogram can show internal dimensions of the chambers, valve motion, blood flow, and the presence of increased pericardial fluid, blood clots, or tumors.

Modern pacemakers are smaller than a matchbox and weigh between 20 and 50 grams (1 to 2 ounces).

When was the first successful pacemaker invented?

The first successful pacemaker was developed in 1952 by American cardiologist Paul Zoll (1911–1999) in Boston, in collaboration with the Electrodyne Company. The device was worn externally on the patient's belt. It relied on an electrical wall socket to stimulate the patient's heart through two metal electrodes attached to the patient's chest. American engineer and inventor Wilson Greatbatch (1919–2011) developed an internal pacemaker. It was first implanted by surgeons William Chardack (1915–2006) and Andrew Gage (1922–) in 1960. According to the American Heart Association, more than a half million pacemakers are transplanted each year.

How can electrical activity of the heart be monitored?

The electrical activity of the heart can be monitored by an electrocardiogram. Electrodes are placed at different locations on the chest, and each time the heart beats, there is a wave of electrical activity through the heart muscle. This test can detect very slight changes in the heart's electrical activity through deflections on a monitor. An electrocardiogram can be used to detect and diagnose cardiac arrhythmias, which are abnormalities in the heart's conduction system.

What is a circulatory assist device?

A circulatory assist device, also known as a ventricular assist device, is a mechanical circulatory machine. These pumps are used on a short-term basis to allow the patient's heart to rest while it is healing. However, they have also been used on a long-term basis to support the hearts of patients awaiting a heart transplant. There are three major types of devices: counterpulsation devices, cardiopulmonary assist devices, and left ventricular assist devices.

What is a defibrillator?

A defibrillator is an electronic device—called an automated external defibrillator (AED)—that gives an electric shock through the chest to the heart. This is to reestablish the normal contractions that a heart experiences, especially when the organ is having dangerous arrhythmia (irregular heart rhythm) or is in cardiac arrest. According to the American Heart Association, most sudden cardiac arrests result from ventricular fibrillation. When this rapid and unsynchronized heart rhythm starts, the heart must be "defibrillated" quickly (the chance of surviving drops by 7 to 10 percent each minute the heart is not beating normally). The newest AED models are lightweight, portable, and can be used not only by medical and emer-

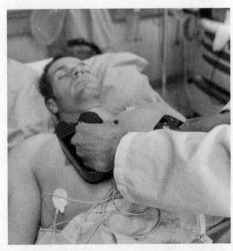

Defibrillators—you might have heard them referred to as paddles—provide a shock to the chest that stimulates a non-beating heart to start beating again.

gency medical technicians (EMTs), but also by non-medical personnel who have been trained in the use of the AED.

Why do physicians perform a spinal tap?

A spinal tap, also called a lumbar puncture, is the withdrawal of a small amount of cerebrospinal fluid from the subarachnoid space in the lumbar region of the vertebral column. Since the spinal cord ends at the level of the first or second lumbar vertebra, a needle can be inserted into the subarachnoid space at the fourth lumbar vertebra with little risk of injuring the spinal cord. The cerebrospinal fluid may be tested and examined for infection. Cerebrospinal fluid is also withdrawn to reduce pressure caused by swelling of the brain or spinal cord following injury or disease.

What is a bronchoscopy?

A bronchoscopy is a direct visual examination of the larynx and airways through a long, flexible viewing tube. A bronchoscope can be inserted through the mouth or nose and extended into the lungs. It can also be used to collect tissue and fluid samples. Bronchoscopy can help a physician make a diagnosis and treat certain medical conditions.

What are some diagnostic procedures used to examine the digestive tract?

Several diagnostic tests are available to examine organs of the digestive tract and to determine causes of abdominal pain and disorders that affect the digestive system. Some of the commonly performed screening tests are colonoscopy, flexible sigmoidoscopy, endoscopy, upper GI series and lower GI series X-rays, ERCP (endoscopic retrograde cholangiopancreatography), and liver biopsy. The following briefly describes each procedure:

Colonoscopy allows a physician to look inside the entire large intestine. It is used to detect early signs of cancer in the colon and rectum.

Flexible sigmoidoscopy allows a physician to examine part of the large intestines—or the inside of the large intestine from the rectum through the sigmoid or descending colon (the last part of the colon). It is used to detect the early signs of cancer in the descending colon and rectum.

Upper endoscopy allows a physician to look inside the esophagus, stomach, and duodenum (the first part of the small intestine). This procedure is used to discover the reason for swallowing difficulties, nausea, vomiting, reflux, bleeding, indigestion, abdominal pain, or chest pain.

The upper GI series uses X-rays to diagnose problems in the esophagus, stomach, and duodenum. Ulcers, scar tissue, abnormal growths, hernias, or areas where something is blocking the normal path of food through the digestive system are visible with the upper GI series.

The lower GI series uses X-rays to diagnose problems in the large intestine, including the colon and rectum. Problems such as abnormal growths, ulcers, polyps, diverticuli, and colon cancer may be diagnosed through a lower GI series.

ERCP (endoscopic retrograde cholangiopancreatography) enables a physician to diagnose and treat problems in the liver, gall bladder, bile ducts, and pancreas.

Liver biopsy is performed when other liver function tests reveal the liver is not working properly. It allows a physician to examine a small sample of liver tissue for signs of damage or disease.

Why is screening for colorectal cancer important?

Colorectal cancer is the most common cancer of the digestive system. Screening tests are important to diagnose a disease prior to developing symptoms. When detected in the early stage, the five-year survival rate for colorectal cancer is greater than 90 percent. In addition, polyps, which are not malignant, may be removed during a screening procedure, thus avoiding cancer. The screening guidelines suggested by the American Cancer Society for both men and women over the age of fifty with average risk for colorectal cancer include:

1. A fecal occult blood test (FOBT) or fecal immunochemical test (FIT) every year, or
2. Flexible sigmoidoscopy every five years, or
3. An FOBT or FIT every year, plus flexible sigmoidoscopy every five years, or
4. Double-contrast barium enema every five years, or
5. Colonoscopy every ten years (the time can vary if high-risk polyps are discovered in a previous colonoscopy or if there is a history of polyps or colon cancer in a person's family)

Of the first three options, the combination of FOBT or FIT every year, plus flexible sigmoidoscopy every five years, is preferable.

What is assisted reproductive technology (ART) in fertility treatments?

According to the Centers for Disease Control and Prevention (CDC), assisted reproductive technology (ART) includes all fertility treatments in which both the sperm and eggs are handled during the treatment. Most ART procedures involve surgically removing eggs from a woman's ovaries, combining them with sperm in the laboratory, and returning them to the woman's body or donating them to another woman. One of the most successful and effective ART methods is in vitro fertilization (IVF). It may be used when the woman's fallopian tubes are blocked or when the man produces too few sperm. The woman takes a drug that causes the ovaries to produce multiple eggs. Once mature, the eggs are removed and put in a dish in the lab along with the man's sperm for fertilization. After three to five days, healthy embryos are implanted in the woman's uterus.

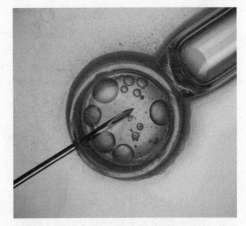

There are several other methods. For example, zygote intrafallopian transfer (ZIFT), also called tubal embryo transfer, is similar to IVF. Fertilization occurs in the laboratory.

With in vitro fertilization a woman's eggs are removed, fertilized in a petri dish, allowed to mature for three to five days, and then re-implanted in the uterus.

Then the very young embryo is transferred to the fallopian tube instead of the uterus. Gamete intrafallopian transfer (GIFT) involves transferring eggs and sperm into the woman's fallopian tube. Fertilization occurs in the woman's body. It is not as common a procedure as either IVF or ZIFT. Couples in which there are serious problems with the sperm or who have been unsuccessful with IVF may try intracytoplasmic sperm injection (ICSI). In ICSI, a single sperm is injected into a mature egg. Then the embryo is transferred to the uterus or fallopian tube.

Are there fertility treatments other than assisted reproductive technology?

Fertility treatments may also include artificial (or intrauterine) insemination in which sperm (from the woman's husband, partner, or a donor) are injected into the woman's uterus, leading to conception. Women may also take medications to stimulate egg production. They may then be able to conceive without further medical intervention.

What are some other prenatal diagnostic techniques used during pregnancy?

Ultrasonography, chorionic villi sampling, and alpha-fetoprotein screening are other prenatal diagnostic screening techniques besides amniocentesis. Fetal ultrasound is often done early in a pregnancy to determine whether it is an ectopic pregnancy. Fetal ultrasound is an accurate way to determine fetal age and predict a due date. Placental abnormalities, fetal growth and development (including heart rate), and congenital abnormalities may be detected with fetal ultrasound. It is a noninvasive test and relatively safe for the mother and fetus.

Chorionic villi sampling is another technique used to detect birth defects, such as Down syndrome or Tay-Sachs disease. It is usually done early in a pregnancy, between the ninth and fourteenth weeks. A sample of cells, called the chorionic villi, is taken from the placenta where it attaches to the wall of the uterus. The chorionic villi are tiny projections from the placenta that have the same genetic material as the fetus. The tissue sample is taken either through the cervix or through the abdominal wall.

The alpha-fetoprotein (AFP) test is a screening test to determine whether a woman is at risk for carrying a fetus with birth defects. AFP is produced by the fetus and appears in the mother's blood during a pregnancy. Abnormally high amounts of this protein may indicate a problem with the fetus. It is usually done between weeks sixteen to eighteen in the pregnancy.

When did the Pap test become accepted as a diagnostic tool to detect cancer?

During the 1920s American physician George Papanicolaou (1883–1962) did research that showed a microscopic smear of vaginal fluid could detect the presence of cancer cells in the uterus. These findings were not generally accepted at the time by the medical community. Several years later, in 1943, he published *Diagnosis of Uterine Cancer by the Vaginal Smear* with Herbert F. Traut (1894–1963), a clinical gynecologist. This time, following publication of his findings, the medical community began to use the Pap smear as a diagnostic tool for cancer. The Pap smear is more than 90 percent reliable in detecting cancer, decreasing dramatically the mortality rate for cancer of the uterus and cervix.

What tests are available to screen for possible prostate cancer?

The two tests often mentioned by doctors to screen for possible prostate cancer are the prostate-specific antigen (PSA) blood test and digital rectal exam (DRE). Prostate-specific antigen (PSA) is a protein produced by the cells of the prostate gland. The PSA test measures the level of PSA in the blood. The use of this test is currently debated by the medical community for several reasons. For example, there are many false positives, and thus unnecessary prostate biopsies. Often times a high PSA could be indicative of an infection or benign prostate enlargement, not cancer. In fact, there is no PSA level known that truly indicates prostate cancer. But to date, most doctors agree that the PSA test, although not perfect, is still one way to possibly detect early signs of prostate cancer, especially for certain age groups and for those who have a family history of the disease. (If a person is concerned about his or her PSA, it is best to consult his or her physician for information.)

A DRE involves a physician inserting a gloved, lubricated finger into the rectum to feel the prostate for any irregularities or firm areas. The DRE is sometimes recommended in conjunction with an abnormal PSA (or if a man is a candidate for prostate cancer—for example, there is a family history of the disease) to detect abnormalities in the prostate.

How do doctors test for osteoporosis?

There are several ways that doctors watch for osteoporosis in patients. One of the simplest ways is by height measurements over time. In most cases, as a person ages, and if he or she has osteoporosis, he or she usually loses height of a half inch or more over a few years. And although many times osteoporosis is found by accident after an X-ray is taken (usually after a fall or an illness), X-rays cannot give the entire picture of osteoporosis. Thus if a doctor suspects osteoporosis, he or she will often suggest an ultrasound, usually of a person's heel, to detect early stages of osteoporosis. For a greater understanding of a patient's fracture risk, doctors usually suggest the dual X-ray absorptiometry, or DXA or DEXA test. Most DEXA tests measure the spine and hip, while others cover the total body bone density. Overall, the test offers the statistical chances a person has of fracturing his or her spine or hip over a certain time.

OPERATIONS, PROCEDURES, AND TRANSPLANTS

Why is it necessary to keep operating rooms clean?

In the mid-1800s, many patients would undergo operations successfully, only to die later from a postoperative infection (at that time, called "ward fever"). This led to the discovery that medical instruments and other apparatus should be disinfected and/or sterilized to ward off microorganisms that cause infection.

What are some common heart procedures?

There are several common procedures to help a patient's heart perform more efficiently. For example, the angioplasty (also called percutaneous coronary intervention, balloon angioplasty, or coronary artery balloon dilation) includes a special tube with an attached deflated balloon. The tube is threaded into the coronary arteries and the balloon inflated to expand the areas blocked with plaque. This causes an increase in blood flow through the artery, reducing the risk of a heart attack. Laser angioplasty is also used to increase the flow of blood in the arteries; the tube has a laser tip that opens the blockage; while an atherectomy uses a tube with a rotating shaver at the end that cuts away plaque from the artery.

What is the most common heart surgery?

According to the National Heart, Lung, and Blood Institute of the National Institutes of Health, coronary artery bypass grafting (CABG) is the most common type of heart surgery. This operation is most often used to treat patients with severe coronary heart disease, or when plaque (a waxy substance) builds up inside the coronary arteries. The buildup narrows the coronary arteries, reducing the flow of blood to the heart, and can cause chest pain or angina. If the plaque ruptures, it can form a blood clot; if large enough, it can completely block the flow of blood through a coronary artery, which most often causes a heart attack.

How are kidney stones dissolved?

There are several procedures to dissolve kidney stones. Most smaller stones usually pass through a person's urinary tract on their own (around 85 percent are less than 5 millimeters), but larger stones usually need certain treatments. The following lists three major procedures:

Ureteroscopy—An ureteroscopy is usually used for stones in the middle and lower ureter. After a small incision is made, a small fiber-optic instrument called an ureteroscope is passed through the urethra and bladder into the ureter. A laser is then often used to break up the stones, which are grabbed or sucked out by a special tool.

Percutaneous nephrolithotomy (PCNL)—A PCNL is often used for larger stones in the upper tract. It also includes a small incision; from there, an instrument called a nephroscope is inserted in a channel directly into the kidney where it locates and removes the stones (if necessary for removal, they are broken into small pieces using ultrasound, laser, or other techniques).

Extracorporeal shockwave lithotripsy (SWL)—A SWL is used for smaller stones that are in the upper part of the ureter and don't pass on their own. SWL uses sound waves (ultrasound) to break up simple stones. The ultrasound generates shock waves that travel through the skin and tissues until it hits the denser kidney stones, crushing them into small, sand-like pieces that can pass easily through the urinary tract.

What is the difference between a tracheotomy and a tracheostomy?

A tracheotomy is the surgical opening of the trachea, or windpipe. This may be necessary if the trachea becomes occluded through inflammation, excessive secretion, trauma, or aspiration of a foreign object. This procedure may be performed to create an emergency opening into the trachea so that ventilation can still occur. A tracheostomy involves the insertion of a tube into the trachea to permit breathing and to keep the passageway open.

Who was the first person to suggest using a disinfectant in surgery?

In 1865, after learning about Louis Pasteur's theory that microorganisms cause infection, British surgeon Joseph Lister (1827–1912) introduced the use of disinfectants in surgery. He used phenol (also known as carbolic acid) to clean surgical instruments and to clean open wounds. Because of his use of the disinfectant at the Glasgow Royal Infirmary's surgery, it is estimated surgical death rates were reduced from 45 to 15 percent in just four years.

Why is a hysterectomy recommended?

Hysterectomy is the surgical removal of the uterus. The most frequent reasons for a woman undergoing a hysterectomy are uterine fibroids, endometriosis, and uterine prolapse. Cancers of the pelvic organs account for only about 10 percent of all hysterectomies.

How does a complete hysterectomy differ from a partial or radical hysterectomy?

The most common type of hysterectomy is a complete or total hysterectomy. Both the cervix and uterus are removed in this procedure. A partial or subtotal hysterectomy removes only the upper part of the uterus and leaves the cervix in place. The most extensive hysterectomy is a radical hysterectomy, which removes the uterus, the cervix, the upper part of the vagina, and supporting tissues. A radical hysterectomy is usually only performed in some cases of cancer.

Which human organ was the first to be transplanted?

The first human organ to be successfully transplanted was the kidney. American plastic surgeon Joseph Murray (1919–2012) performed the transplant in 1954 in Boston, Massachusetts. The patient, Richard Herrick (1931–1963), lived for eight years after receiving the new kidney from his identical twin brother, Ronald Herrick (1931–2010).

How successful are kidney transplants and what are the risks?

The one-year success rate for kidney transplants is 85 to 95 percent. As with any transplant, rejection of the foreign body is the major cause of transplant failure. Recipients of kidney transplants have to take immunosuppressants for the rest of their lives.

Why are cartilage transplants successful?

Cartilage does not contain blood vessels. Oxygen, nutrients, and cellular wastes diffuse through the selectively permeable matrix. Cartilage transplants are successful because foreign proteins in the transplanted cells do not have a way to enter the host body's circulation and cause an immune response. However, since there are no blood vessels in cartilage, the healing process is slower than for other tissues.

What is an artificial joint?

Artificial joints are joints designed by engineers to replace diseased or injured joints. Most artificial joints consist of a steel component and a plastic component. For example, an artificial knee joint has three components: the femoral component (made of a highly polished strong metal), the tibial component (made of a durable plastic often held in a metal tray), and the patellar component (also plastic). Artificial joints may be used to replace finger joints, hip joints, or knee joints.

Is it possible to keep organs alive outside the human body?

Yes, it is possible to keep human organs alive outside the body, but only for short periods of time and under certain conditions. Depending on the organ, most can stay alive outside the human body between five to twenty-four hours before they begin to deteriorate.

Why can't organs be frozen before transplanting?

There is a major reason why organs cannot be frozen and thus preserved for transplant: ice crystals. The sharp crystals can rip though the cell walls, destroying the cells and rendering the organ useless.

As of 2015, how many people are waiting for organ transplants in the United States?

It is estimated that 120,000 people are waiting for certain types of organs for transplant. The most needed organ is the kidney, and it is also the most commonly transplanted.

Can lungs be transplanted?

Lung transplantation is surgery used to replace one or both diseased lungs with a healthy lung or lungs. It is only recommended if the patient has end-stage pulmonary disease that cannot be treated any other way. Examples of end-stage pulmonary diseases include emphysema, cystic fibrosis, sarcoidosis, and pulmonary fibrosis. Survival rates for lung transplants are as high as 80 percent at one year and 60 percent at four years after surgery.

What part of the eye was the first to be successfully transplanted?

The cornea was the first tissue from the eye that was successfully transplanted. On December 7, 1905, Eduard Konrad Zirm (1863–1944), who was head of medicine at Olomouc Hospital in Moravia (now part of the Czech Republic), performed the first corneal transplant. It was the first successful human-to-human tissue transplant. Interestingly, the cornea is the only tissue in the body that can be transplanted from one person to another with little or no possibility of rejection.

Who performed the first heart transplant?

The world's first heart transplant was performed in South Africa in 1967 by cardiac surgeon Christiaan N. Barnard (1922–2001). The first heart transplant in the United States was performed in 1968 by American surgeon Norman Shumway (1923–2006) at Stanford University.

When was the first artificial heart implanted?

The first artificial heart, the Jarvik 7, was made by heart surgeon Robert K. Jarvik (1946–) in 1981. It was implanted in 1982 into Barney Clark (1921–1983), who lived for 112 days after the surgery.

As of 2015, how many heart transplants are performed annually?

Worldwide, about 3,500 heart transplants are performed annually. The vast majority of these are performed in the United States (2,000–2,300 annually). Cedars-Sinai Medical Center in Los Angeles, California, currently is the largest heart transplant center in the world, having performed 119 adult transplants in 2013 alone.

Index

Note: (ill.) indicates photos and illustrations.

687

condensed matter physics, 370
cones, 627
Confucius, 224, 224 (ill.)
Congress of Racial Equality (CORE), 192
Congressional salary increases, 56
conifer, 562
conjoined twins, 642
Conrad, Charles P., 433
conservation, 497–98
Constantine I, 33, 34–35
constellations, 427
Constitution, U.S., 53 (ill.), 53–56
consumerism, 208–9
Consumers' Research Inc., 209
Consumers Union, 209
container gardening, 559
container-grown plants, 558
Continental Congress, First, 50–51
Continental Congress, Second, 51
Continental Divide, 455
continentality, 484
continents, 450, 450 (ill.)
convective zone, 407
Convention for the Pacific Settlement of International Disputes, 79
convergent evolution, 530
Cook, James, 451
Cooke, Jay, 299
Coolidge, Calvin, 88
Cooper, Gary, 274
Cooper, Leon N., 371
Cooper, Martin, 351
copepods, 581
copper, 386
Coppola, Francis Ford, 264
Coptic calendar, 329
coral reefs, 571
Corbusier, Le, 257
Cordelia, 419
Cormack, Allan M., 670
Cornwallis, Charles, 111
coronary artery bypass grafting, 680
corrosive materials, 504
Cortés, Hernán, 31, 32, 39
cortex, 613
corticosteroids, 615
Corwin, Jonathan, 83 (ill.)
Cosby, William, 83–84
cosmic microwave background radiation, 399
cosmological constant, 401
cosmology, 394
cosmonauts, 432
Coubertin, Baron Pierre de, 277
Council for Mutual Economic Assistance (COMECON), 24
Counter Reformation, 221–22
counterculture, 207–8
counting, 309
country music, 267

countryside, 486
Court, Margaret, 285
court-martials, 88
Crabbe, Buster, 274 (ill.)
Crassus, 33
craters, 454
Crazy Horse, 125
Creek War, 117
Creutzfeldt-Jakob disease, 661
Crimean War, 120, 128
Croatia, 158–59
Crockett, Davy, 118
Cromwell, Oliver, 41, 46 (ill.), 46–47
Cromwell, Richard, 47
cross-pollination, 546–47
crucifixion, 260
Crusades, 17, 18, 218–19
crust, 441, 442 (ill.), 443
crustaceans, 582
crystallography, 381
Cuba, 24–25
Cuban Missile Crisis, 25, 149, 149 (ill.)
cubic zirconium, 466–67
culinary herbs, 554–55
Cullinan, Thomas M., 466
Cullinan Diamond, 466
cumuliform clouds, 482
Cunningham, Merce, 270
Cunningham, Ward, 364
curbside recycling program, 514
Curie, Jacques, 381
Curie, Marie, 377, 384, 465
Curie, Pierre, 377, 381, 384, 465
curium, 384
curly hair, 623
currents, 444
Cushing, William, 79, 80
Custer, George A., 125–26
Custer's Last Stand, 125–26
cut of diamonds, 466
cybernetics, 367
cytokinesis, 523
cytology, 519
cytomegalovirus, 663
cytoplasmic organelles, 521–22
cytoskeleton, 522
Czechoslovakia, 25
Czolgosz, Leon F., 63

D

Dactyl, 424
daddy longlegs, 585
daffodils, 561
dairy products, 663
Daladier, Edouard, 139
Dalai Lama, 211, 212 (ill.)
Dalton, John, 382
Damadian, Raymond, 672
damp, 472

dance, 268–71
Dance Theater of Harlem, 270–71
Danes, 15
Dante Alighieri, 11, 238
Darfur, Sudan, 164 (ill.), 165
Dark Ages, 5–6
dark energy, 401–2
dark matter, 400 (ill.), 400–401
Darnley, Lord, 44
Darrow, Clarence, 86, 87
Darwin, Charles, 87, 525, 525 (ill.), 526–27, 573, 579
Darwin-Wallace theory, 526
David (Michelangelo), 248
Davis, Jan, 436
Davis, John, 451
Davis, Miles, 266
Dawes, William, 112
dawn, 328
daybreak, 328
Daylight Savings Time, 334–35
days of the week, 332
D-Day, 144
de Klerk, F. W., 186
De La Beckwith, Byron, 193
Dead Sea, 443, 447
Dead Sea Scrolls, 213
Dean, John, 64, 91
death, 650, 651
death penalty, 98
Death Valley, California, 443
Debs, Eugene, 205
Debussy, Claude, 269
December, 333
Declaration of Independence, 51, 52
deep-sea divers, 667
deer, 563
defibrillator, 675 (ill.), 675–76
deforestation, 496
Degas, Edgar, 249
Deimos, 414, 421
Democratic Party, 58
Democratic Republic of the Congo, 181
Democratic-Republicans, 56
Democritus, 8
demosponge, 570
Demosthenes, 7
Dempsey, Jack, 280
Denali, Alaska, 443
density, 386
dental X-ray, 654
department stores, 297
Derain, André, 269
dermis, 622
Descartes, René, 20, 21, 228–29, 316
desert, 485
Desert Fox, 142–43
desert locust, 584
desertification, 485
deserts, 453–54

installation art, 253
insulin, 595, 616–17, 617 (ill.)
insulin-dependent diabetes mellitus, 664
integration in baseball, 280–81
intelligence, 609, 610
interest, 320
interior of Earth, 441, 442 (ill.)
Internal Revenue Service (IRS), 306
International Astronomical Union, 428
International Date Line, 335
International Fixed calendar, 330
International Humanitarian Law, 78
International Labor Organization (ILO), 69
international law, 77–79
International Military Tribunal, 89
International Monetary Fund (IMF), 69
International Space Station, 438
Internet, 360–61, 362–66
Internet Protocol (IP), 363
interphase, 523
Interstate Commerce Commission, 299, 306–7
intestines, 612, 612 (ill.)
Intifada uprisings, 154
Intolerable Acts, 49–50
intracytoplasmic sperm injection, 678
intrauterine insemination, 678
invertebrate, 566–68
involuntary muscle movements, 608
Io, 416, 421
Ionian War, 100
ionosphere, 440
IQ (intelligence quotient), 610
Iran-Contra affair, 64–65
Iraq, 158, 169, 175, 178, 179
Iraq war, 175–76
Iredell, James, 79, 80
iridium, 386, 468
iron, 442
Iron Age, 1, 3
iron curtain, 72
ironwood, 473–74
ironworks, 469–70
irrational number, 312
irregular bones, 602
Irwin, James B., 433
Isabella, Queen of Spain, 39, 256
ISIL (Islamic State of Iraq and the Levant), 180
isinglass, 475
ISIS (Islamic State of Iraq and Syria), 180
Islam, 215–18, 226
Ismaili Khoja Muslims, 216
Isocrates, 7
isomers, 387

isotopes, 386, 534
Israel, 71, 154–55, 155
Italy, 23, 143–44
Ivan the Terrible, 40
ivory, 502
Iwo Jima, 146

J

Jackson, Andrew, 57, 59–60, 64, 117, 118, 120, 305
Jackson, Robert, 89, 143
Jacquel-Droz, Henri-Louis, 366
Jacquel-Droz, Pierre, 366
James (apostle), 214–15
James, the son of Alphaeus (apostle), 214–15
James I, King of England, 43, 108, 260
James V, King of Scotland, 43
Jannings, Emil, 272
Janssen, Zacharias, 429
January, 333
January 1, 328
Janus, 333
Japan, 23, 130, 138, 146, 212, 559–60, 562
Japanese calendar, 330
Japanese kabuki, 259 (ill.), 259–60
Japanese-American internment, 143
Jarvik, Robert K., 683
Jarvis, Richard, 352
Jay, John, 50, 53, 79, 80, 128
jazz, 265–67
The Jazz Singer, 272, 273
Jeanneret, Charles-Édouard, 257
Jefferson, Thomas, 51, 52, 53, 58, 304
Jefferson Airplane, 208
jellyfish, 570–71
Jemison, Mae Carol, 435, 436
Jenner, Edward, 538
Jenney, William Le Baron, 257, 258
Jerusalem, 154
Jesuits, 222
Jesus Christ, 12, 214–15, 218, 260
jet lag, 665
jet stream, 488
Jewish calendar, 329
Jews, 217–18
Jiang Qing, 94–95
Jim Crow laws, 81
Joan of Arc, 106–7
Joan of Castile, 39
Johanson, Donald C., 2
John (apostle), 214–15
John, King of England, 45
John XII, Pope, 10, 18
John XIX, Pope, 261
John Paul II, Pope, 185
Johns, Jasper, 251–52

Johnson, Andrew, 58–59, 63, 66, 122–23
Johnson, Ben, 259
Johnson, Lyndon Baines, 63, 152, 153
Johnson, Robert Underwood, 498
Johnson Wax Company Research Tower, 258
joint, 604–6, 605 (ill.)
joints, 682
Jolson, Al, 261, 272, 273
Jones, Allen, 251
Jones, Edward Davis, 300
Jones, Mary "Mother," 204
Jones, Meredith, 579
Jones, Robert Edmond, 269
Jones, William, 312
Jonson, Ben, 239–40
Joplin, Scott, 266
Jordan, Michael, 282
Jordan Marsh, 297
Joshua, 313
Joyce, James, 242–43, 379
Juan Carlos I, King of Spain, 139
Juarez, Benito, 120–21
Judas Iscariot (apostle), 214–15
Judd, Donald, 253
Julian calendar, 330
Julian Day calendar, 330
Julian Day count, 330–31
Julius Caesar, 9, 10, 13, 32–33, 103, 328, 330, 333
July, 333
June, 333
Juno, 333
Jupiter, 412, 413, 413 (ill.), 415, 416, 416 (ill.), 421, 422, 424, 432
Jupiter, 434
Justinian I, 35, 75, 76
Justinian Code, 9

K

Ka Le, Hawaii, 451
kabuki, 259 (ill.), 259–60
Kadyrov, Ramzan, 162
Kagan, Elena, 80 (ill.)
Kamerlingh Onnes, Heike, 371
Kanada, Yasumasa, 312
Kant, Immanuel, 229–30
Kaplan, Justin, 243
Kapp, Robert, 143
Karadzic, Radovan, 159 (ill.), 159–60
karat, 469
Karsavina, Tamara, 269
Karzai, Hamid, 174, 175
Kasner, Edward, 312
katabatic wind, 488
Kaufman, Irving, 91

696

rings of Uranus, 419
rip tides, 448
Ripuarians, 13
risk factors, 649
Rite of Spring (Stravinsky), 265
rivers, 448–49
Rizzio, David, 44
Roadmap for Peace, 156
Roaring Twenties, 22
robber barons, 298 (ill.), 298–99
Roberson, Willie, 88
Roberts, John G., 80 (ill.)
Roberts, Owen J., 143
Robertson, Howard Percy, 394
Robertson, Lord, 172
Robespierre, Maximilien, 113–14, 232
Robespierre's Terror, 49
Robie House, 258
Robinson, Jackie, 280–81
Robinson-Patman Act (1936), 296
robots, 366–67
Rochambeau, Jean-Baptiste Dona-tien de Vimeur, Comte de, 111
Roche, Martin, 257
rock and roll, 267–68
rock fossils, 529
Rockefeller, John D., 298 (ill.), 299, 307
Rockefeller Center, 258
rockets, 431
rocks, 462–63, 464
Roderick, 12
rods, 627
Roe v. Wade (1973), 93–94
Roebling, John Augustus, 256
Roebling, Washington Augustus, 256
Roebuck, Alvah C., 297
Roentgen, Wilhelm Conrad, 670
roentgen equivalent man (rem), 653
Rogers, Ginger, 261
Rogers, Will, 261
Roman calendar, 329
Roman Catholic Church, 17, 108, 220, 221–22
Roman Conquest, 101–2
Roman Empire, 8, 9–11, 33–34, 102–3
Roman law, 75
Roman numerals, 309–10
Roman Republic, 8, 32–33
Romania, 25, 95–96
Romanov, Michael, 40
Romanov Dynasty, 40–41
Rome, 9, 101–2, 102–3
Rommel, Edwin, 142–43
Roosa, Stuart A., 433
Roosevelt, Eleanor, 60–61, 62, 62 (ill.)

Roosevelt, Franklin D., 59, 61–62, 62 (ill.), 64, 66, 67, 140, 141, 142, 288, 302–3, 308
Roosevelt, Theodore, 60–61, 63, 64, 66, 127, 127 (ill.), 130, 209, 307–8
Root, John Wellborn, 257
root system, 544
Roper v. Simmons (2005), 98
Rose, Pete, 281 (ill.), 281–82
Rosecrans, William, 122
Rosenberg, Ethel, 91, 91 (ill.), 97
Rosenberg, Julian, 91, 91 (ill.), 97
Rosenthal, Joe, 146
rosin, 474
Ross, James Clark, 451
rotational time, 327
Rough Riders, 127 (ill.), 127–28
roundworms, 579
Rousseau, Jean-Jacques, 20, 113
royal houses, 41–45
Rubin, Vera C., 401
Rubinstein, Ida, 269
ruby, 467
Ruby, Jack, 63
Rudolf I, King of Germany, 39
Rumsfeld, Donald, 177
runny nose, 622
Russell, Bill, 282
Russia, 120, 161–62
Russian Revolution, 131–34
Russo-Japanese War, 130
Ruth, George Herman "Babe," 280, 280 (ill.)
ruthenium, 468
Rutherford, Ernest, 377, 378
Rutledge, John, 79, 80
Rwandan genocide, 163–65

S

Sacco, Nicola, 96–97
Sachs, Julius von, 558
Sadat, Anwar, 154, 155
saguaro cactus forest, 492 (ill.)
Sahara Desert, 454, 485
salamander, 576
Salameh, Mohammed A., 166
Salem witch trials, 82–83, 83 (ill.)
Salians, 13
Salinas de Gortari, Carlos, 308
saliva, 618
salt, 388
Saluki, 593
San Andreas Fault, 460, 461
San Francisco earthquake, 460, 460 (ill.)
San Juan Hill, Battle at, 127 (ill.), 127–28
sand, 453–54
sand cat, 589–90
sand dunes, 453, 453 (ill.)

Sanders, Barry, 283
sandy soils, 556
Sanford, John F. A., 85
Sanger, Margaret Higgins, 200–201
Santa Anna, Antonio López de, 118, 119, 120
Santorio, Santorio, 389
Sanzio, Raphael, 246–47
Sappho, 7
Sarabi, Habiba, 174
sarcomas, 666
Sardinia, 120
Sargent, Charles Sprague, 498
Sartre, Jean-Paul, 230–31
satellite digital radio, 341
satellite photographs, 477
satellites, 436, 440
Saturday, 332
Saturn (god), 332
Saturn (planet), 412, 413, 413 (ill.), 415, 416–18, 417 (ill.), 418, 418 (ill.), 422, 429, 432
Saud, Ibn, 179
Saudi Arabia, 180
Saul, King, 71
Savitskaya, Svetlana, 434
Saxe-Coburg, House of, 42
Saxons, 14
scab, 621
Scalia, Antonin, 80 (ill.), 172
Scaliger, Joseph Justus, 330
Scaliger, Julius Caesar, 330
Schade, Otto, 344
Schafer, Edward, 656
Scheuchzer, Johann, 576
Schmitt, Harrison H., 433
Schoenberg, Arnold, 264
Scholasticism, 226–27
School of American Ballet, 269
school of fish, 574
Schrieffer, John Robert, 371
Schultz, Dutch, 89
Schwermer, Michael, 193
science fiction movies, 275
scientific revolution, 21
Scopes, John T., 87, 87 (ill.), 528
Scopes (monkey) trial, 528–29
Scotch pine, 550
Scott, David R., 433
Scott, Dred, 84–85
Scott, Robert Falcon, 451
Scott, Winfield, 57
Scott v. Sandford, 85
Scottsboro Boys, 88, 97
Screen Actors Guild (SAG), 272
scrubbing of flue gases, 507
sea, 446–47
sea monkeys, 582
sea time, 336
Seagram Building, 258
search engine, 364